THE EARTH
AS A PLANET

The Solar System

(IN FOUR VOLUMES)

I

THE SUN
1953

II

THE EARTH AS A PLANET
1954

III

PLANETS AND COMETS · PART I

IV

PLANETS AND COMETS · PART II

THE EARTH
AS A PLANET

EDITED BY GERARD P. KUIPER

THE UNIVERSITY OF CHICAGO PRESS

CHICAGO · ILLINOIS

This publication has been supported in part by the Geophysics Research Directorate of the Air Force Cambridge Research Center, Air Research and Development Command

Library of Congress Catalog Number: 54-7183

THE UNIVERSITY OF CHICAGO PRESS, CHICAGO 37
Cambridge University Press, London, N.W. 1, England
The University of Toronto Press, Toronto 5, Canada

Preface

As the title implies, Volume 2 intends to cover those aspects of geophysics, geochemistry, and atmospheric physics as pertain to the earth as a whole and which, incidentally, are able to assist and guide the astrophysical studies of the other planets. The latter studies, to be described in Volume 3, are still extremely fragmentary, hampered as they are by the remoteness of the objects. The interpretation of the fragmentary data must lean heavily on the much fuller development of the earth sciences.

The contents and arrangement of the subject matter, then, reflect the astronomical setting. The dynamical properties are treated first (chaps. 1 and 2); they are in some respects the simplest and most basic, while the methods of investigation do not differ in principle from those used for the other planets. Next come the bulk properties of the earth, from the point of view of both the physicist (chap. 3) and the chemist (chap. 6). These chapters, too, have their counterparts in planetary studies, though the planetary data are scant and the physics of matter under high pressures is incompletely developed.

When the surface features of the earth are considered, however, the planetary astronomer can only marvel at the incredible richness of the data. The great problems of the formation of mountains and whole continents (chap. 4); the formation, composition, and circulation of the oceans (chap. 5); and the infinitely complex and beautiful problems of the biosphere and its effects on the inorganic surroundings (chap. 8) have, at best, only the dimmest counterparts in planetary astronomy. But they are vital for an understanding of the problems of planetary evolution, and related studies of other planets may even become possible.

The study of planetary atmospheres is at present one of the most hopeful approaches toward fuller understanding of the planets and their evolutions. For this reason, half the book is devoted to our atmosphere, although its fractional mass is only a millionth. Even so, space requirements dictated severe economy. The recent appearance of the *Compendium of Meteorology* made it unnecessary to include many meteorological topics of great potential interest to the planetary astronomer: climatology, cloud physics, atmospheric turbulence, diffusion, meteorological optics, etc. Chapter 7 gives a general summary of the global aspects of meteorology, while chapter 10 collects the density and temperature measurements above the level covered by meteorological observation. The remaining chapters use methods that are at least partially transferable to the analogous problems of the other planets. The full development which these terrestrial problems allow, owing to the numerous control measures possible, will in time be of the greatest benefit to planetary studies.

The benefits of a closer integration between the geosciences and planetary astronomy may seem to lack reciprocity. The generous response which the authors of this volume have accorded the editor's invitation may reflect their hope that such reciprocity will develop. And, indeed, it may. The planets, though members of a family of eight or nine, are individuals; no two are quite alike. No complete understanding of one member will be possible without reference to the family. This holds for problems of composition and development as well as for problems of origin.

The editor is greatly indebted to the authors for their collaboration on this series. The production of Volume 2 has taken more time than originally anticipated, and the editor is deeply grateful for the willingness of authors who submitted their manuscripts early to bring them up to date just before printing (early 1954) or during the galley-proof stage (June–August, 1954). Special thanks are due to Professor Hutchinson for editorial advice. The editor wishes to record his thanks also to the Geophysical Research Directorate of the Air Force for their continued interest in this publication and to the University of Chicago Press for unfailing courtesy and help.

GERARD P. KUIPER, *Editor*

YERKES OBSERVATORY
October 1953

Table of Contents

13. DYNAMIC EFFECTS IN THE HIGH ATMOSPHERE 644
   M. Nicolet

CHAPTER 1

Dimensions and Rotation

By SIR HAROLD SPENCER JONES
Astronomer Royal of England

1. HISTORICAL

THE belief that the Earth was spherical in shape was held long before any observational proof was obtained. As early as the sixth century B.C., Pythagoras taught that the Earth was a sphere. He interpreted the phases of the Moon as being due to the changing aspect of a dark body, one half of which was illuminated by the Sun; the curved shape of the terminator—the boundary between the bright and the dark portions of the Moon—was an indication that the Moon was not flat, but a sphere. By analogy, it was natural to suppose that the Earth was also a sphere.

Aristotle in the fourth century B.C. advanced arguments from observation in support of the belief that the Earth was spherical, such as the circular form of the boundary of the shadow of the Earth as seen on the face of the Moon during an eclipse and the changes in the positions of stars with respect to the horizon when traveling in a north or south direction. The first reasonably good estimate of the size of the Earth was made by Eratosthenes in the third century B.C. From the length of the shadow cast by a vertical rod it was found that the Sun was vertically overhead at Syene in Upper Egypt at noon at the summer solstice, whereas at Alexandria at the same time the Sun was about 7° south of the zenith. Syene was estimated to be due south of Alexandria and at a distance from it of 5000 stadia. It was concluded that the circumference of the Earth was 252,000 stadia. It is uncertain how accurate this estimate was, because different values of the stadium were in use. If Eratosthenes used the Olympic stadium, his estimate was about 20 per cent too great; but if another value in common use is adopted, the estimate is within 1 per cent of the correct value.

Not until the seventeenth century, however, was any estimate of the size of the Earth made that could be accepted with some confidence. In 1617 Willebrord Snell made measurements in Holland from which he concluded that the length of a degree of a meridian was 69 miles. In 1636 Richard Norwood in England measured the distance from London to York and obtained the length of a degree with an error less than a half-mile. Then in 1671 Picard made some measurements near Paris which gave a still more accurate value of the length of a degree.

In 1671 G. D. Cassini, the director of the Paris Observatory, sent an expedition to Cayenne (in latitude 5° N.) to make observations of Mars at its favorable opposition, so that, in conjunction with observations at Paris, the distance of Mars from the Earth and thence the distance of the Earth from the Sun could be determined. Richer, who was in charge of this expedition, found that his pendulum beat more slowly at Cayenne than at Paris, which suggested to him that the Earth was not a perfect sphere.

The first estimate of the departure of the Earth from the spherical shape was made by Newton in the *Principia*. On the assumption that the Earth was originally in a fluid state, he conjectured that the effect of the mutual gravitation of its particles, combined with the effect of its rotation, would be to cause it to assume the shape of an oblate spheroid. By an ingenious argument, based on the assumption that the Earth was of uniform density, he made an estimate of the amount of the flattening. He imagined a canal of water to pass from the pole to the center of the Earth and then from the center to a point on the equator, and he considered the equilibrium of the water in this canal, each of the two columns being attracted toward the center of the Earth by its gravitation. He concluded that the equatorial radius would exceed the polar radius by about 1/230 of its value. This result is correct on the assumption of uniform density; the ellipticity of figure of the Earth is not so great, however, as Newton estimated, because the density increases toward the center. Newton also showed that the ellipticity of figure of the Earth, combined with the effect of its rotation, would cause the value of gravity to increase with latitude from the equator to the poles, thereby accounting for Richer's observation that his pendulum beat more slowly in Cayenne than in Paris.

Newton's conclusion that the Earth is spheroidal in shape enabled him to give the first satisfactory explanation of the phenomenon of the precession of the equinoxes, which had been discovered by Hipparchus about 130 B.C. If the Earth were a perfect sphere, the attraction of the Sun or of the Moon on it would be equivalent to a single force passing through its center; this is no longer true for a body of spheroidal shape. Such a body can be considered as a spherical body on which are superimposed two equatorial protuberances. The attraction of the Sun or Moon on these two protuberances will not be exactly in the same direction, nor will they be exactly equal: except when the attracting body is in the equatorial plane, there will be a couple tending to turn the Earth until the attracting body is in its equatorial plane. Since the Earth is rotating, this couple will produce a precessional motion of the axis of the Earth around the pole of the ecliptic. The rate of the precessional motion does, in fact, provide information about the dynamical flattening of the Earth.

The shape of the Earth can be determined by measurements in different latitudes of the length of an arc of the meridian corresponding to a difference in latitude of 1°. Such measurements determine, in effect, the radius of curvature in different latitudes. If the Earth is an oblate spheroid, flattened at the poles, the radius of curvature will increase progressively from the equator to the poles. The first measures of this type that were made supported the conclusion that the Earth was not flattened toward the poles, but was elongated; these measures were, however, not of very high accuracy, nor was their range in latitude adequate. In 1735 the French Academy sent an expedition under Bouguer to Peru and in 1736 another under De Maupertuis to Lapland, to determine the lengths of meridional arcs of 1°, for comparison with the length of a degree of the meridian in France. The three separate determinations proved conclusively that the length of a 1° arc increased with the latitude, so that the Earth was therefore oblate in shape.

Though Newton had conjectured that a rotating body like the Earth would assume the form of an oblate spheroid, he was not able to prove it. A proof that a homogeneous fluid mass in slow rotation would be in equilibrium if it had the form of an oblate spheroid whose shortest axis coincided with the axis of rotation was first given by Maclaurin in 1740; he also proved that the rate of increase in gravity from the equator to the pole would be proportional to the square of the sine of the latitude. Then in 1743 Clairaut, who had taken part in the expedition under De Maupertuis to Lapland, published his classical memoir on the figure of the Earth. In this important work the general equations of the equilibrium of fluids were given, independently of any hypotheses about the law of attraction or about the density. He used the equations to investigate the figure of the Earth under the inverse-square law of attraction, and he proved that the figure of an oblate spheroid would satisfy the equations of equilibrium, provided that the mass was disposed in concentric strata of similar form and each of uniform density. His results enabled the ellipticity of the Earth to be determined from observations of gravity in different latitudes, without any assumption about the internal constitution of the Earth, so long as the reasonable condition just stipulated was satisfied. Clairaut's memoir was so complete in its treatment of the problem that it practically closed the subject, except for later extensions of it to the second and higher orders of small quantities.

Thus by the middle of the eighteenth century fairly accurate information about the size and shape of the Earth and about the variation of gravity over its surface had been obtained. But when more detailed and more precise knowledge is sought, considerable complications ensue.

2. GEODETIC DATA

Information about the size and shape of the Earth is obtained directly in the process of geodetic triangulation, which provides the framework for the construction of topographical maps. The process starts with the determination, with all possible accuracy, of the lengths and azimuths of suitably selected base lines; the triangulation is then commenced by observations of a distant point or points from the two ends of each measured base and is progressively extended over the area to be surveyed by a continuous net or by a series of chains. In the course of the triangulation, the scale and azimuth of each side of a triangle depend upon the scale and azimuth of the preceding side; the errors in scale and azimuth will therefore be cumulative in their effect unless suitable controls are provided. Controls are obtained both by having more than one measured base, each of which is made to form a side in the triangulation, and also by astronomical observations for azimuth and longitude at suitable places in the triangulation, which are known as "Laplace stations." When the network of observation has been completed, a general adjustment of the whole triangulation has to be made by the method of least squares in order to average out the errors of observation.

There is the complication, however, in the fact that the actual surface of the Earth, though it approximates to an oblate spheroid, is very irregular in its structure and may in places deviate from a true spheroid by as much as several miles. For the computation of a triangulated chain or network, it is necessary to adopt a suitable spheroid of reference to which the observations must be referred. The minor axis of this spheroid is chosen to be parallel to the axis of rotation of the Earth; to the length of its major axis and to its ellipticity are assigned values that approximate those of the Earth itself. But as the direction to the center of the Earth is not precisely known, it is not possible to make the center of the spheroid of reference coincide with the center of the Earth. It is necessary here to bring in the conception of the geoid.

The *geoid* is the equipotential surface that, on the average, coincides with the mean sea-level surface over the oceans. At any point on the geoid the direction of gravity is normal to its surface, so that the process of leveling over a land area with a spirit level determines heights of that area above the geoid. The geoid more nearly approximates to a spheroid than does the Earth itself; but the attractions of the land masses of the continents cause the figure of the geoid to become somewhat irregular. Because of the partial compensation of the effect of the surface irregularities, as indicated in the "roots of mountains" of isostatic theory, the irregularities of the geoid are less than might have been expected; its deviations from a true spheroidal shape are normally not more than a few hundred feet.

For the computation of a triangulation, the height of the reference spheroid above or below the geoid can be defined arbitrarily for a selected station, which is adopted as the origin. The spheroidal or *geodetic* latitude (defined by the normal to the spheroid) and longitude of the origin are also defined arbitrarily. The *astronomical* latitude and longitude of the origin are determined in the usual way by star observations. The difference between the geodetic and astronomical values determines the direction of the normal to the spheroid relative to the direction of the vertical at the origin. The direction of the normal to the spheroid is thus obtained. By spirit leveling from a mean sea-level datum, the height of the origin above the geoid is obtained and hence its height above the spheroid. Thus it becomes possible to define the position of the center of the geoid.

It may be remarked that the deviation of the vertical at any point, which is the angle between the vertical (the direction of gravity) and the normal to the spheroid, has no meaning except in relation to a particular spheroid of reference. Different triangulations may be computed with different spheroids of reference; if the triangulations of adjacent countries are not computed with the same spheroid of reference, there will be discontinuities where they meet. It is possible, however, to adjust the computation of a triangulation from the initial spheroid of reference to a different spheroid; this may be desirable if the initial spheroid deviated considerably from the geoid.

In order to determine as accurately as possible the size and shape of the geoid, it is desirable that triangulation chains should be extended over the longest possible arcs. The triangulations of countries that cannot be directly connected, because they are separated by oceans or for other reasons, can in theory be connected by using the Moon as an intermediary, either by suitable observations at total eclipses of the Sun or by means of occultations; at present, however, the horizontal parallax of the Moon and the precise figure of the limb of the Moon for all its librations are not known with quite sufficient accuracy to enable such connection to be possible with the precision that is required.

Various figures of the Earth, derived from the measurement of astro-geodetic arcs, are given in Table 1.

TABLE 1

FIGURE OF THE EARTH

Author	Date	Equatorial Semiaxis (Meters)	Polar Semiaxis (Meters)	Flattening	Notes
Everest.........	1830	6,377,276	6,356,075	300.80	1
Bessel.........	1841	6,377,482	6,356,163	299.15	2
Clarke.........	1866	6,378,298	6,356,676	294.98	3
Clarke.........	1880	6,378,341	6,356,607	293.47	
Hayford.......	1909	6,378,388	6,356,909	297.00	
Heiskanen......	1929	6,378,400	6,357,010	298.2	4
Jeffreys........	1948	6,378,099	6,356,631	297.10	5

NOTES TO TABLE 1

1. Everest's values were given in Indian feet. The meter values are as given by G. Bomford, *Geodesy* (Oxford: Clarendon Press, 1952), p. 307.

2. Converted from legal meters (1799) to international meters by the ratio legal meter = 1.000013255 international meters.

3. Converted from feet by the ratio 1 international meter = 39.370113 inches.

4. Heiskanen concluded that the equatorial section is not circular and found a difference between maximum and minimum axes of 165 meters. The mean equatorial radius is given.

5. The ellipticity is based on information from gravity and astronomy, in addition to geodesy.

The Hayford figure, with polar semiaxis of 6,356,912 meters corresponding exactly with the flattening of 297.00, has been adopted by the Association of Geodesy of the International Union of Geodesy and Geophysics as the *International Spheroid*. It is urged that this spheroid should be used for the computation of all triangulations, so that it can form a spheroid with reference to which the actual form of the geoid can be represented as it becomes known.

3. CLAIRAUT'S FORMULA FOR GRAVITY

Further information about the figure of the Earth can be obtained from measurements of gravity, the constant of precession, and the motion of the Moon. We will consider, first, Clairaut's formula, which enables the ellipticity of the Earth's figure to be calculated independently of trigo-nometrical determinations, if the variation of gravity over a wide range of latitude is known.

The Earth is assumed to be a spheroid of equilibrium of mass M and ellipticity ϵ. If V is the potential of the mass and ω the angular-velocity of rotation, then, because the surface is a surface of equilibrium, the quantity Ψ, defined by

$$\Psi \equiv V + \tfrac{1}{2}\omega^2 r^2 \cos^2 \phi , \tag{1}$$

is constant over the surface, where r is the radius vector and ϕ the angle which it makes with the major axis.

If the square of the ellipticity is neglected, we can write

$$r = a(1 - \epsilon \sin^2 \phi) , \tag{2}$$

where a is the semimajor axis.

To this degree of approximation, V will have the form

$$\frac{fM}{r} + \frac{2k}{r^3} P_2 (\sin \phi) = \frac{fM}{r} + \frac{k}{r^3} (3 \sin^2 \phi - 1) ,$$

in which f denotes the gravitational constant, k is a numerical constant, and P_2 is the Legendre function of the second order. Therefore, the expression

$$\Psi = \frac{fM}{r} + \frac{k}{r^3} (3 \sin^2 \phi - 1) + \tfrac{1}{2}\omega^2 r^2 \cos^2 \phi \tag{3}$$

is constant over the surface. Substituting in equation (3) the value of r from equation (2) and equating to zero the coefficient of $\sin^2 \phi$, we obtain

$$\frac{k}{a^3} = \frac{1}{6} a^2\omega^2 - \frac{1}{3} \frac{\epsilon fM}{a} .$$

The acceleration of gravity is given by $-d\Psi/dr$. Hence, from equation (3), on substituting the expression for k just obtained, we have

$$g = \frac{fM}{a^2} (1 + \epsilon - \tfrac{3}{2} m) + \left(\tfrac{5}{2} a\omega^2 - \frac{\epsilon fM}{a^2} \right) \sin^2 \phi$$

$$= g_0 [1 + (\tfrac{5}{2} m - \epsilon) \sin^2 \phi] , \tag{4}$$

where $m = a^3\omega^2/fM$, the ratio of the centrifugal force at the equator to gravity at the equator (g_0).

This is Clairaut's equation (Clairaut, 1743). It shows that, to a first approximation, the value of gravity increases proportionally to the square of the sine of the latitude. It will be noted that in deriving this formula no assumption about the interior constitution of the Earth is made. The value of the coefficient of $\sin^2 \phi$ from gravity determinations is 0.005286, while the value of m is 0.003461. It follows from this formula that $\epsilon = 1/297.0$. To this degree of approximation, however, the decimal place is uncertain. For a more precise determination, the theory must be developed to the second order.

4. THE THEORY OF CLAIRAUT DEVELOPED TO THE SECOND ORDER

The development of Clairaut's theory to the second order has been done by Airy (1826), Callandreau (1889), Darwin (1899), and others. De Sitter (1924) showed that the formulae become somewhat simpler if they are expressed in terms of the mean radius instead of the equatorial radius. His derivation is followed here.

The outer potential of any body, symmetrical with reference both to an equatorial plane and to an axis perpendicular to this plane, can be expressed to the order of accuracy here required as

$$V = \frac{fM_1}{r}\left[1 - \frac{2}{3}\frac{Ja^2}{r^2}P_2(\sin\phi) + \frac{4}{15}\frac{Ka^4}{r^4}P_4(\sin\phi)\right], \qquad (5)$$

where f is the constant of gravitation, M_1 is the mass, ϕ is the angle between the radius vector and the equatorial plane, P_2 and P_4 are the Legendre functions of the second and fourth orders, J and K are constants characteristic of the body, and

$$J = \frac{3}{2}\frac{C - A}{M_1 a^2}, \qquad (6)$$

where C and A are moments of inertia with respect to the polar and equatorial diameters, respectively.

If the surface of the body is an equipotential surface, its equation to the same order can be written as that of a spheroid,

$$r = a[1 - \epsilon \sin^2 \phi' - (\tfrac{3}{8}\epsilon^2 + \kappa) \sin^2 2\phi'], \qquad (7)$$

where ϕ' is the geocentric latitude and ϵ is the ellipticity. This surface deviates from an ellipsoid by the amount $-\kappa a \sin^2 2\phi'$, which has its maximum value at latitude 45°. The value of κ will be considered later.

If the body rotates with angular velocity ω, the potential at the surface is given by

$$\Psi = V + \tfrac{1}{2}\omega^2 r^2 \cos^2 \phi' ; \qquad (8)$$

substituting for V and r from equations (5) and (7) and equating to zero the coefficients of the second and fourth harmonics, it is found that

$$\epsilon - J = \tfrac{1}{2}\rho_1 + \tfrac{1}{2}\epsilon^2 - \tfrac{1}{7}\epsilon\rho_1 - \tfrac{4}{7}\kappa, \tag{9}$$

$$K = \tfrac{24}{7}\kappa + 3\epsilon^2 - \tfrac{15}{7}\epsilon\rho, \tag{10}$$

where

$$\rho_1 = \frac{\omega^2 r_1^3}{fM_1}; \tag{11}$$

r_1 is the mean radius (at which $\sin^2 \phi' = \tfrac{1}{3}$), so that

$$r_1 = a(1 - \tfrac{1}{3}\epsilon - \tfrac{1}{3}\epsilon^2 - \tfrac{8}{9}\kappa) .$$

The acceleration of gravity at the surface is given by

$$g^2 = \left(\frac{\partial \Psi}{\partial r}\right)^2 + \frac{1}{r^2}\left(\frac{\partial \Psi}{\partial \phi}\right)^2 ;$$

and on development it is found that

$$g = g_0 \left(1 + \beta \sin^2 \phi' + \gamma \sin^2 2\phi'\right) , \tag{12}$$

where

$$g_0 = \frac{fM_1}{a^2} [1 + J + \tfrac{1}{2} K - \rho_1 (1 + \epsilon)]$$

$$= \frac{fM_1}{a^2} (1 + \epsilon - \tfrac{3}{2}\rho_1 + \epsilon^2 - \tfrac{27}{14}\epsilon\rho_1 + \tfrac{16}{7}\kappa) \tag{13}$$

$$\beta = -\epsilon + \tfrac{5}{2}\rho_1 + \tfrac{15}{4}\rho_1^2 - \tfrac{17}{14}\epsilon\rho_1 + \tfrac{8}{7}\kappa, \tag{14}$$

and

$$\gamma = \tfrac{15}{8}\epsilon\rho - \tfrac{7}{8}\epsilon^2 - 3\kappa. \tag{15}$$

It should be noted that ϵ, J, β, and ρ_1 are quantities of the first order; K, γ, and κ are of the second order.

Further development proceeds on the assumption that the body is in hydrostatic equilibrium, so that the surfaces of equal density are equipotential surfaces. If β is the mean radius of any one of these surfaces, expressed in terms of the mean radius of the outer surface as unity (not to be confused with β in eqs. [12] and [14]), the equation of this surface can be written in the form

$$r = \beta[1 - \tfrac{2}{3}(\epsilon' + \tfrac{2}{3}\epsilon^2)P_2(\sin \phi') + \tfrac{4}{35}(3\epsilon^2 + 8\kappa)P_4(\sin \phi')], \tag{16}$$

where

$$\epsilon' = \epsilon - \tfrac{5}{42}\epsilon^2 + \tfrac{4}{7}\kappa. \tag{17}$$

The introduction of ϵ', due to De Sitter, simplifies the subsequent analysis. In the second-order terms the distinction between ϵ' and ϵ can be dropped.

The potential Ψ at any point (r, ϕ') within the Earth is then given by

$$\frac{\Psi}{fW} = D\left(\frac{1}{r} + \frac{1}{2}\,\rho\,\frac{r^2}{\beta^3}\cos^2\phi'\right) - \frac{2}{5}\left(S\frac{\beta^2}{r^3} + T\frac{r^2}{\beta^2}\right)P_2$$
$$+ \frac{12}{35}\left(P\frac{\beta^4}{r^5} + \frac{128}{105}Q\frac{r^4}{\beta^5}\right)P_4,$$

(18)

where

$$\rho = \frac{\omega^2\beta^3}{fM} = \frac{\rho_1}{D},$$

(19)

in which W is the volume, M the mass within the surface whose mean radius is β, while D, S, T, P, and Q are given by the following expressions:

$$D = \frac{3}{\beta^3}\int_0^\beta \delta\,\beta^2 d\beta,$$

$$S = \frac{1}{\beta^5}\int_0^\beta \delta\,\frac{d}{d\beta}[\,(\epsilon' + \tfrac{2}{7}\epsilon^2)\,\beta^5]\,d\beta,$$

$$T = \int_\beta^1 \delta\,\frac{d}{d\beta}[\epsilon' + \tfrac{16}{21}\epsilon^2]\,d\beta,$$

(20)

$$P = \frac{1}{\beta^7}\int_0^\beta \delta\,\frac{d}{d\beta}[\,(\epsilon^2 + \tfrac{8}{9}\kappa)\,\beta^7]\,d\beta,$$

$$Q = \beta^2\int_\beta^1 \delta\,\frac{d}{d\beta}[\kappa\beta^{-2}]\,d\beta,$$

δ being the density, expressed in terms of the mean density as a unit, and D the mean density within the surface β in terms of the same unit. For the outer surface $D_1 = 1$; $S_1 = \tfrac{5}{3}J$; $P_1 = \tfrac{7}{9}K$; $T_1 = 0$; $Q_1 = 0$.

The conditions that the surface β is an equipotential surface are found, after simplification, to be

$$D(\epsilon' + \tfrac{2}{7}\epsilon^2 - \tfrac{1}{2}\rho) - \tfrac{3}{5}(S + T) = \tfrac{4}{21}\epsilon(\rho_1 - 3T)$$

(21)

and

$$D(3\epsilon^2 - 8\kappa) + 3P + \tfrac{32}{3}Q - 6\epsilon S = 0.$$

(22)

Radau (1885) introduced a new dependent variable, η', defined by

$$\eta' = \frac{d\log\epsilon'}{d\log\beta} = \frac{\beta}{\epsilon'}\frac{d\epsilon'}{d\beta}.$$

(23)

By differentiating equation (21) and introducing η', the following equation is obtained, after reduction:

$$\eta'\,[D\,(1 + \tfrac{4}{7}\epsilon) - \tfrac{4}{21}\rho_1 + \tfrac{4}{7}T] = 3\,D\,(1 + \tfrac{2}{7}\epsilon) - \frac{3S}{\epsilon'};$$

(24)

and, by differentiating again,

$$\beta \frac{d\eta'}{d\beta} + \eta'^2 + 5\eta' - 2\zeta(1+\eta') - \tfrac{4}{21}\zeta\xi = 0,\qquad(25)$$

in which

$$\zeta = -\frac{\beta}{D}\frac{dD}{d\beta} = \frac{\beta}{\rho}\frac{d\rho}{d\beta} = 3\left(1 - \frac{\delta}{D}\right)\qquad(26)$$

and

$$\xi = 7\rho(1+\eta') - 3\epsilon(1+\eta')^2 - 4\epsilon.\qquad(27)$$

Following Radau's procedure, equation (25) can be transformed into

$$\frac{d}{d\beta}[D\beta^5\sqrt{(1+\eta')}] = 5D\beta^4 F(\eta'),\qquad(28)$$

where

$$F(\eta') = \frac{1 + \tfrac{1}{2}\eta' - \tfrac{1}{10}\eta'^2 + \tfrac{2}{105}\zeta\xi}{\sqrt{(1+\eta')}},\qquad(29)$$

which, if the small term in ξ is omitted, is Radau's equation. The importance of the transformation lies in the property of the function $F(\eta')$, which is always very near to unity, its maximum departure being 0.0007. If $(1+\lambda)$ denotes an average value of this function over the range of integration, we can write

$$\int_0^\beta D\beta^4 d\beta = \frac{D}{5}\frac{\sqrt{(1+\eta')}}{1+\lambda}\beta^5\qquad(30)$$

and

$$\int_0^1 D\beta^4 d\beta = \frac{1}{5}\frac{\sqrt{(1+\eta'_1)}}{1+\lambda_1}.\qquad(30a)$$

The moment of inertia, C, can be expressed, to the order of accuracy required, in the form

$$C = \tfrac{8}{15}\pi \int_0^1 \delta \frac{d}{d\beta}[\beta^5(1+\tfrac{2}{3}\epsilon)]\,d\beta$$

$$= \tfrac{8}{3}\pi \int_0^1 \delta\beta^4 d\beta + \tfrac{2}{3}(C-A).\qquad(31)$$

If we now write

$$H = \frac{C-A}{C},\qquad q = \frac{3}{2}\frac{C}{M_1 a^2},\qquad(32)$$

we have, from equation (6),

$$J = \frac{3}{2}\frac{C-A}{M_1 a^2} = qH;\qquad(33)$$

also in our units

$$M_1 a^2 = \tfrac{4}{3}\pi(1+\tfrac{2}{3}\epsilon),\qquad(34)$$

so that

$$q = 3 \left(1 - \tfrac{2}{3}\epsilon\right) \int_0^1 \delta \beta^4 d\beta + \tfrac{2}{3} J \, ,$$

which can be transformed into

$$q = 1 - \tfrac{1}{3}\rho_1 - 2 \left(1 - \tfrac{2}{3}\epsilon\right) \int_0^1 D\beta^4 d\beta \, , \tag{35}$$

or, from equation (30a),

$$q = 1 - \tfrac{1}{3}\rho_1 - \tfrac{2}{5} \left(1 - \tfrac{2}{3}\epsilon\right) \frac{\surd(1 + \eta_1')}{1 + \lambda_1} \, . \tag{36}$$

For the outer surface, from equation (24), we obtain

$$\epsilon'\eta_1' = \tfrac{5}{2}\rho_1 - 2\epsilon' + \tfrac{10}{21}\rho_1^2 + \tfrac{4}{7}\epsilon^2 - \tfrac{6}{7}\epsilon\rho_1 \tag{37}$$

an equation which gives η_1' (the value of η' at the surface) when ϵ is known, or ϵ when η'_1 is known.

5. DISTRIBUTION OF DENSITY WITHIN THE EARTH

The values of the small quantities λ_1 and κ depend upon the distribution of density within the Earth. De Sitter derived values from two hypotheses about the distribution, in accordance (a) with Clairaut's theory and (b) with Wiechert's hypothesis. The values he obtained were

  (a) $0.00000063 < \kappa < 0.00000072$, $\lambda_1 = 0.00031$;

  (b) $0.00000047 < \kappa < 0.00000052$, $\lambda_1 = 0.00039$.

Bullard (1948) has derived more reliable values, using Bullen's estimate of the variation of density with depth, based mainly on seismological evidence, which is the best assumption that can be made at present. This estimate gives the density as a function of β, from which the mean density, D, within a radius β is obtained. It is assumed, as a first approximation, that the function $F(\eta')$ has the value unity: equation (28) can then be integrated to give a first approximation to η'. The value of ϵ' corresponding to this value of η' is obtained from equation (37). These first approximations are then used to give an improved value of F, and so on. Bullard found that the second approximation was all that was necessary. The value of λ_1 is obtained from equation (30a), when η_1' is known.

The value of κ as a function of β was derived by Bullard from Darwin's equation,

$$\beta^2 \frac{d^2\kappa}{d\beta^2} + 6 \frac{\delta}{D} \beta \frac{d\kappa}{d\beta} - \left(20 - 6 \frac{\delta}{D}\right) \kappa = \epsilon'^2 \left[3 \left(1 - \frac{\delta}{D}\right)\right.$$

$$\left. + \left(1 - \frac{9}{2} \frac{\delta}{D}\right) \eta' - \frac{1}{4}\left(1 + 9 \frac{\delta}{D}\right) \eta'^2\right].$$

The variation with depth from the surface to the center of the density δ, the mean density D, the ellipticity ϵ, and the quantities η' and κ, as derived by Bullard, are shown in Figures 1 and 2. The surface values are $\eta_1' = 0.565$ (corresponding to $\epsilon = 0.003364$), $\kappa = 68 \times 10^{-8}$, and $\lambda_1 = 0.00016$.

The value of the ellipticity of the outer surface $(1/297.3)$ merely reproduces one of the assumptions made in the calculations for the purpose of

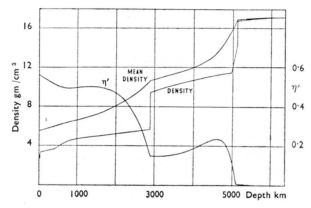

FIG. 1.—Density, mean density, and η' as functions of the depth (in kilometers)

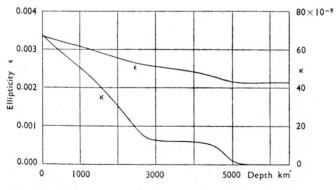

FIG. 2.—The ellipticity ϵ and quantity κ as functions of the depth (in kilometers)

deriving values of κ and λ_1. Any reasonable change in ϵ would have given a compensating change in η'_1 but would not have altered the derived values of the small quantities κ and λ_1; these quantities are required to take account of the internal density distribution for the purpose of calculating the ellipticity from the precessional constant.

6. THE DERIVATION OF THE ELLIPTICITY OF THE EARTH

Relation (33), $J = qH$, can now be used to derive the value of the ellipticity. J is given in terms of ϵ by equation (9), and q by equation (36) in association with equation (37); H can be derived with high accuracy from the constant of precession by the relationship

$$P = \left(A + B \, \frac{\mu}{1+\mu} \right) H \,, \tag{38}$$

in which μ denotes the ratio of the masses of the Moon and Earth and A and B are determined in the theory of the Moon's motion. According to De Sitter (1938), their values are

$$A = 530977''.04 \, (1 - 2.0839 \cdot 10^{-6} T) \,,$$

$$B = 94419319'' \, (1 - 1.69 \cdot 10^{-8} T) \,,$$

in which T denotes tropical centuries counted from 1900.0.

Expression (36) for q has been derived on the assumption that the Earth is in hydrostatic equilibrium, so that the surfaces of equal density are also equipotential surfaces. The surface of the Earth is, however, neither a surface of equal density nor an equipotential surface. The question therefore arises as to whether the theory of Clairaut, developed as above to the second order, is applicable to the actual Earth. De Sitter has discussed this question in some detail (De Sitter, 1924). The geoid, determined by geodetic measurements on the continents and by gravity measurements on land and over the oceans, deviates only slightly from an ellipsoid. The spheroid which best fits the geoid is called the *normal surface, S,* and the differences between the geoid and this normal surface never exceed a few tens of meters: it is not an equipotential surface. The upper surface that would result if the conditions of the theory of Clairaut were satisfied throughout is called by De Sitter the *ideal surface, S_1*. The relationship $J = qH$ can be applied to the ideal surface, but not necessarily to the normal surface.

The process of fitting the normal surface to the geoid is accomplished by making, in the development of both surfaces by spherical harmonics, the coefficients of orders 0, 2, and 4 the same. Equation (9) therefore holds if, for ϵ, we take the ellipticity of the normal surface and for J its actual value for the real Earth.

If the Earth were constituted throughout by the theory of Clairaut, it would be covered by an ocean of average depth 2.4 km, whose upper surface would be the ideal surface S and whose bottom would be an equipotential surface. The true distribution of mass does not differ greatly from this ideal one, because of the isostatic compensation of excesses and deficiencies of mass, which, though not exact, appears to hold approximately. De Sitter has computed for the various land and ocean masses the effects of excesses and deficiencies in H and C. He concludes that the correction to q is negligible and that it would still be negligible, even if there were no isostatic compensation. The difference in the ellipticities of the ideal and normal surfaces is such that $\epsilon^{-1} - \epsilon_1^{-1} = +0.04$, which is negligible. It implies that the polar semidiameter of the ideal surface is 1.8 meters shorter, and the equatorial radius 0.9 meters longer, than that of the normal surface. If there were no isostatic compensation, the difference in the values of ϵ^{-1} would have been about two units.

A convenient basis for a numerical adjustment of the relevant data, when the second-order terms are included, is provided by the important paper "On the System of Astronomical Constants" by De Sitter (1938, edited and completed by D. Brouwer). In this investigation a selection of fundamental constants was adopted, a correcting factor for each of these quantities was introduced, and the derived constants, including these factors as undetermined quantities, were obtained. For the present purpose, the following adopted quantities, as used by De Sitter, are required:

Mean radius of the Earth: $\qquad R_1 = 6371260(1 + u)$ meters,

Acceleration of gravity in mean latitude: $\qquad g_1 = 979.770(1 + v)$ cm/sec²,

Dynamical flattening $(C - A)/C$: $\qquad H = 0.003279423(1 + w)$,

Constants depending on the inner constitution of the Earth $\left.\begin{array}{l}\\ \\ \end{array}\right\}$ $\kappa = 0.00000050 + 10^{-3}\chi$
$\lambda_1 = 0.00040 + \psi$,

Reciprocal of Moon's mass: $\qquad \mu^{-1} = 81.53(1 + z)$.

The following derived quantities are used:

Equatorial radius: $a = 6378387(1 + 1.00021u - 0.00021v + 0.00090w$
$$+ 0.00070\chi + 0.00090\psi),$$

Acceleration of gravity: $g = g_0(1 + \beta \sin^2 \phi + \gamma \sin^2 2\phi)$,

with

$g_0 = 978.0530[1 - 0.00267u + 1.00267v + 0.00092w + 0.00209\chi$
$$+ 0.00092\psi],$$
$\beta = 0.00528612[1 + 1.5221(u - v) - 0.5209w + 0.324\chi - 0.518\psi]$,
$\gamma = -0.00000734[1 + 1.100(u - v) + 0.491w + 0.488\psi] - 0.00299\chi$;

Constant of precession: $P = 5493''157[1 - 0.6747z + w]$;

Constant of sine lunar parallax: $\pi_{\text{C}} = 3422''526[1 + 0.00404z$

$$+ 0.33277(u - v) + 0.00091w + 0.00011\chi + 0.00091\psi].$$

The values of these various quantities derived directly or indirectly from observation will now be considered.

The mean radius of the Earth used by De Sitter was derived from isostatic reductions (Heiskanen, 1926) of different geodetic surveys. Jeffreys (1948) has remarked that the use of isostatic reductions is unsuitable for this problem; they make nonrandom changes in the external field, which can contribute to the estimates of a and ϵ and, in particular, instead of removing a systematic difference between land and sea, they create one. Jeffreys discussed the available determinations of a and ϵ, based on free-air solutions, and obtained the value for a of 6,378,118 ± 119 (s.e.) meters, this value being practically independent of the precise value of the flattening. This value differs somewhat from the value in the table above, the determination of which is tied up with the determination of the flattening.

The absolute value of gravity has been based on the determination of gravity at Potsdam, but that value is known to be appreciably too high, because of the application of a correction for the effect of the bending of the knife-edges of the pendulums, which is unwarranted. The absolute determinations have been discussed by Jeffreys (1948), who concludes that the Potsdam value needs a reduction of 13.4 ± 1.0 mgal. The distribution of gravity with latitude has been investigated by Jeffreys (1941, 1943), who has given a detailed discussion of all the relevant data.

The result obtained by Jeffreys, if the terms depending on longitude, which are uncertain, are neglected, can be given in the form

$$978.0384\,(1 + 0.0052860 \sin^2 \phi - 0.0000059 \sin^2 2\phi).$$
$$\pm\quad 21 \qquad\qquad\qquad \pm 75$$

Newcomb's determination of the constant of precession assumed that the average of the stars had no appreciable rotational motion. The recognition that the Galaxy is in rotation has required a correction to Newcomb's value. Morgan (1950) obtains a correction of $+0''74$ to Newcomb's value of the general precession; this correction has been closely confirmed by Oort and others. The value of the general precession in longitude at epoch 1900 is thus $5026''38$ per century; the corresponding value of the lunisolar precession constant, according to Newcomb's definition, is $5493''553 \pm 0''145$. The assigned probable error is an estimated value;

the several determinations quoted by Morgan would suggest a much smaller value, but other uncertainties require an increase in the probable error.

The Greenwich-Cape determination of the constant of the sine of the lunar parallax, referred to De Sitter's basic value of the ellipticity of the Earth's figure, is $3422''.414 \pm 0''.060$.

The quantity J is involved in the theoretical values of the motions of the Moon's perigee and node and in the monthly terms in the Moon's latitude. The derivation of J in this way has been made by Spencer Jones (1932, 1937) and by Jeffreys (1937, 1941). The value $J = +0.00164146 \pm 0.00000360$ is adopted.

The mass of the Moon determined by Spencer Jones (1941) from the observation of Eros at the opposition of 1931 is used, viz., $\mu^{-1} = 81.27 \pm 0.025$.

The values of χ and ψ follow from the values of κ and λ, obtained by Bullard (1948); $\chi = +0.00018$, $\psi = -0.00024 \pm 0.00018$.

On equating these values to the expressions given above and solving by least squares, the following values for the correcting factors are obtained:

$$u = -0.0000456 \pm 0.0000122 \,,$$

$$v = -0.0000183 \pm 0.0000014 \,,$$

$$w = -0.0019845 \pm 0.000204 \,.$$

The derived value of the flattening is

$$\epsilon^{-1} = 297.300 \pm 0.065 \,.$$

The value of the mean radius is $6{,}370{,}969 \pm 78$ meters, and for the equatorial radius it is $6{,}378{,}084 \pm 78$ meters. This value of the equatorial radius is necessarily in close agreement with that obtained by Jeffreys, which is smaller than the other values in Table 1, because isostatic compensation is discarded. The ellipticity is derived more accurately in this way than in any other, because the constant of precession is known with high accuracy.

Jeffreys (1948) has made an adjustment of the data without making the assumption that the Earth is in hydrostatic equilibrium. The determination of the ellipticity is based on survey and gravity data, the Moon's parallax, the constant of precession, and the value of J derived from the lunar data. The value of the flattening obtained by him in this way is 297.10 ± 0.36 (s.e.). There is agreement with the value obtained above on the hydrostatic equilibrium hypothesis within the indicated probable errors. Including the data obtained from H (which involves the assumption of hydrostatic equilibrium), he obtains 297.324 ± 0.065, in close agreement with the value derived above. The indication is, therefore, that there is no serious departure from hydrostatic equilibrium. It is satisfactory that there is close accordance between the values obtained with and without the assumption of hydrostatic equilibrium. The assumption of hydrostatic equilibrium may somewhat underestimate the real uncertainty in the determination of the flattening, but De Sitter's discussion suggests that the underestimation is not serious.

7. THE MASS OF THE EARTH

The first attempt to determine the mass of the Earth (or, which is equivalent, its mean density) was made by Maskelyne. When measuring an arc of the meridian in South America, Bouguer had found that the plumb line was deviated toward the mountain of Chimborazo by about $7''.5$. Maskelyne proposed to the Royal Society in 1772 that the attraction of a mountain mass should be used for an experiment to determine the mean density of the Earth. The mountain of Schiehallien in Perthshire was selected as being particularly suitable for the purpose, since it was in the form of a narrow ridge running nearly east and west, with an elevation of about 2000 feet above the surrounding country. Two stations were selected to the north and south of the ridge; the difference in their astronomical latitudes was determined from observations of the zenith distances of stars made at each station, while the difference in their geodetic latitudes was determined by geodetic measurement, reduced with an assumed figure of the Earth. The vertical is deviated toward the mountain on each side; the difference in astronomical latitudes of the two stations therefore exceeds that of their geodetic latitudes by an amount equal to the sum of the attraction of the mountain at the two stations. The astronomical difference in latitude was $54''.6$, while the geodetic difference was $42''.9$, giving $11''.7$ as the amount attributable to the attraction of the mountain. On the assumption that the mean density of Schiehallien was 2.5, the mean density of the earth was found to be 4.7 (Playfair, 1811).

Shortly after the Schiehallien observations, the Rev. John Michell contrived a method of determining the mean density by direct measurement of the gravitational attraction between two known masses of lead. The apparatus was completed by Michell, but he died before he could make any experiments with it. The apparatus came, after his death, into the possession of Henry Cavendish and was used for the now famous "Cavendish experiment." The apparatus consisted of a wooden arm, braced for rigidity, 6 feet in length and suspended by a slender wire, from each of whose two ends a lead ball about 2 inches in diameter was attached. Two large lead spheres, about 8 inches in diameter, were brought near the small ones on opposite sides of the arm, so as to rotate it slightly against the torsion of the wire. The spheres were then brought to the other side of the arm, so as to deflect it in the contrary direction. The effect of the torsion of the wire was determined by removing the large lead spheres, twisting the arm through a small angle, and observing its time of swing. The attracting force between the large and small masses could then be calculated, and the constant of gravitation deduced. When the constant of gravitation is known, the mass of the Earth and its mean density can be readily determined.

The experiments with this apparatus were made by Cavendish in 1797–1798. Special care was taken to exclude disturbances from draughts and from air currents arising from differences of temperature in different parts of the apparatus. In the reduction of the observations, allowance was made for the attraction of each weight on the arm and on the farther ball, for the attraction of the case, and for other small effects. From the results of 17 experiments, Cavendish derived for the mean density of the Earth a value of 5.48 and concluded that it was very unlikely that the true mean density should differ from this value by as much as $\frac{1}{14}$ of the whole (Cavendish, 1798).

An improved form of this experiment was performed in 1895 by Boys, who made the apparatus very much smaller, thereby enabling uniformity of temperature to be much more easily attained. The arm was only 2.4 cm in length and was suspended by a fine quartz fiber. The attracted masses were gold balls, 5 mm in diameter, suspended by quartz fibers, but one was suspended much lower than the other so that the attractions of the lead spheres, 10 cm in diameter, should not neutralize each other. A mirror was attached to the arm, and the deflections were read on a distant scale. The mean density of the Earth derived by Boys was 5.527. This is probably the most accurate determination yet made (Boys, 1895).

The torsion balance was used in a different manner by Braun, who determined the time of swing of the arm carrying the small masses, first when the attracting masses were in line with the arm and, second, when the line joining them was at right angles to the arm. The arm was 20 cm in length, the small masses weighed 54 gm each, and the spherical attracting masses 9 kg each. The mean density derived by Braun was 5.527, in exact agreement with the value obtained by Boys (Braun, 1897).

The same method has been used by Heyl, the principal difference being that the attracting masses were much larger, weighing 66 kg each, and were made in the form of cylinders, which avoided the practical difficulty in accurately shaping large spheres. In the first series of experiments the cylindrical attracting masses were mounted with their axes vertical. The mean density of the Earth obtained was 5.517 (Heyl, 1930). In a later series of experiments, in which the cylinders were placed with their axes horizontal, the value obtained was 5.514 (Heyl and Chrzanowski, 1942).

A different method, in which the common balance was used instead of a torsion balance, was employed by Poynting in a careful series of experiments in 1890. In this method the attraction between two known masses is compared directly with the weight of one of the masses, i.e., with the attraction of the Earth on it. A spherical mass is hung from one arm of an accurate and sensitive balance and counterpoised by a similar mass at the end of the other arm. A heavy mass is introduced directly beneath each of the suspended masses in turn; its attraction on the mass causes a slight apparent increase in weight, which can be determined by adding a small weight to the other pan. In the actual experiments the suspended masses were lead spheres, each weighing 20 kg, while the attracting mass weighed 150 kg; this mass was supported on a turntable and was balanced by a smaller mass on the other side of the turntable and at a greater distance, so as to prevent tilting of the ground. The mean result of a number of experiments gave the value 5.493 for the mean density of the Earth (Poynting, 1892).

From these experiments it can be concluded that the mean density of the Earth is not greatly different from 5.52. It is of interest to recall that Newton conjectured that the mean density is about five or six times that of water. In Book III, proposition 10, of the *Principia* he states: "Verisimile est quod copia materiae totius in Terra quasi quintuplo vel sextuplo major sit tota ex aqua constaret."

8. THE RATIO OF THE MASS OF THE EARTH TO THE MASS OF THE SUN

A knowledge of the mean density of the Earth and of its size and shape determines its actual mass, in kilograms or tons. In astronomy, however, it is the ratio of the mass of the Earth to the mass of the Sun that is usually required. The mass of the Earth in terms of that of the Sun as unity is connected with the mean equatorial horizontal parallax of the Sun by a numerical relationship, which can be derived as follows:

If R and r denote, respectively, the semimajor axes of the orbits of the

Earth around the Sun and of the Moon around the Earth; T and T' denote the length of the sidereal year and of the sidereal revolution of the Moon, respectively; and M, m_1, and m_2 denote the masses of the Sun, Earth, and Moon, then, by Kepler's third law, we have

$$4\pi^2 R^3 = f(M + m_1 + m_2)T^2$$

and

$$4\pi^2 r^3 = f(m_1 + m_2)T'^2 .$$

Also, from equation (4),

$$g_0 = \frac{f m_1}{a^2}(1 + \epsilon - \tfrac{3}{2} m) .$$

From these equations we derive

$$\frac{M}{m_1} = \frac{4\pi^2}{g_0 a^2}\left[\frac{R^3}{T^2} - \frac{r^3}{T'^2}\right](1 + \epsilon - \tfrac{3}{2} m)$$

$$= \frac{4\pi^2 R^3}{g_0 a^2 T^2}(1 + \epsilon - \tfrac{3}{2} m)\left[1 - \left(\frac{r}{R}\right)^3\left(\frac{T}{T'}\right)^2\right].$$

Using the approximate values $r = 3.84 \times 10^5$ km, $R = 1.50 \times 10^8$ km, $T = 365.256$ days, and $T' = 27.3216$ days, the second term in the last bracket has the value 3×10^{-6}.

Writing $a = R\varpi \sin 1''$, where ϖ denotes the Sun's horizontal parallax in seconds of arc, and using the values of a, ϵ, and m obtained above, and with the value for T of 365.25635442 days, we have

$$\boldsymbol{M}\varpi^3 = 2.26444 \times 10^8 ,$$

where $\boldsymbol{M}$ denotes the ratio of the masses of the Sun and Earth, and ϖ is expressed in seconds of arc. From this relationship $\boldsymbol{M}$ can be deduced when ϖ is determined. Table 2 gives the value of $\boldsymbol{M}$ corresponding to values of ϖ within its probable range.

TABLE 2

ϖ	$\boldsymbol{M}$	ϖ	$\boldsymbol{M}$
8″790..........	333,422	8″796..........	332,740
8.792..........	333,194	8.798..........	332,513
8.794..........	332,967	8.800..........	332,286

The most precise direct determination of the solar parallax is that based on the observations of the minor planet Eros around its favorable opposition in 1931 (Spencer Jones, 1941), viz., $8″790 \pm 0″001$. The corresponding value for $\boldsymbol{M}$ is $333,422 \pm 114$.

The mass of the Earth + Moon can also be found directly from its perturbing effect on other bodies in the solar system. The most accurate determination by this method is that deduced by Rabe (1950) from the perturbations of Eros from 1926 to 1945. In this investigation Rabe took into account the perturbations of Eros by Mercury, Venus, the Earth-Moon system, Mars, Jupiter, Saturn, and Neptune; he also allowed for the differences between astronomical time and uniform time. The largest residuals from his final solution for 37 normal places of Eros were 0.072 sec in right ascension and 0".66 in declination. For the 21 normal places based on the observations between October, 1930, and April, 1931, the largest residuals were 0.029 sec in right ascension and 0".32 in declination.

Rabe derived the value 328,452 ± 43 for the reciprocal of the mass of the Earth + Moon. Using the value 81.271 for the ratio of the mass of the Earth to the mass of the Moon, this gives, for the reciprocal of the mass of the Earth, the value 332,493. To this mass there corresponds a value of the solar parallax of 8".798 ± 0".0004.

The discordance between the values of the solar parallax derived by Rabe from the determination of the mass of the Earth and by Spencer Jones by the trigonometric method is several times the combined probable error. The reason for the discordance is not yet known: in the trigonometric determination the effects of atmospheric dispersion, which might conceivably introduce systematic error, were carefully controlled in several different ways, while the perturbation method does not appear to be liable to any serious systematic error.

The mass of the Earth can also be derived from the analysis of the secular variations of the orbital elements of the four inner planets. This method was used by Newcomb (1895). The mass found by Newcomb by this method corresponded to the abnormally low value for the solar parallax of 8".759 ± 0".010. The determination depends mainly on the motion of the node of Venus, and the difference between the observed and the theoretical values of this motion exceeds its probable error several fold; this difference remains as the most outstanding discordance in the motions of the solar system. It may be mentioned that the meridian observations and observations of the transits of Venus give concordant values for the motion of the node. Newcomb commented as follows on this result:

"What adds to the embarrassment and prevents us from wholly discarding the suspicion that some disturbing cause has acted on the motion of Venus, or that some theoretical error has crept into the work, is that, of all the determinations of the solar parallax, this is the one which seems the most free from doubt arising from possible undiscovered sources of error."

This comment was written nearly sixty years ago. The last sentence can equally well be applied to Rabe's determination from the motion of Eros. Newcomb's discussion was revised by Spencer Jones (1932), taking account of relativity corrections to the motions of the perihelia of the planets, but Newcomb's result was not appreciably altered. Adopting the value 81.27 for the ratio of the mass of the Earth to the mass of the Moon, the mass of the Earth is found to be 1/336,370, corresponding to a solar parallax of 8″.764 ± 0″.007. Many meridian observations of Venus have become available since Newcomb's investigation was made, and further light on this discordance will have to await a new discussion of all the available observations.

Meanwhile, a value of 1/333,000 can be given as closely representing the true mass of the Earth. The corresponding value for the combined mass of the Earth and Moon is 1/328,950.

9. THE ROTATION OF THE EARTH

The rotation of the Earth on its axis provides the standard unit of time. The sidereal day is the time taken by the Earth to make a complete rotation of 360°. For civil purposes it is necessary to employ a unit which is related to the Sun; the apparent or true solar day is the time taken by the Earth to complete one rotation with respect to the Sun. As the apparent solar day is variable in length, the mean solar day is adopted as the unit of time for civil purposes: its length is equal to the average length of the apparent solar day throughout the year. The relationship between the mean solar day and the sidereal day can be expressed in the following forms:

365.24220 solar days = 366.24220 sidereal days ;

The solar day = 1.0027379 sidereal days

= 24 hours 3 minutes 56.556 seconds sidereal time ;

The sidereal day = 0.9972696 mean solar days

= 23 hours 56 minutes 4.090 seconds mean solar time .

It is assumed in the computation of astronomical ephemerides that the length of the day is invariable or, in other words, that the Earth by its rotation provides us with a perfect clock. Common experience tells us that any irregularities in the rotation cannot be large, or they would be revealed by any reasonably good clock. It has nevertheless been well established that the length of the day is slightly variable in three different ways and that the variations, though small, are sufficiently large to require to be taken into account in various astronomical investigations. The three types of variation in the length of the day are (i) a slow secular increase; (ii) irregular fluctuations; and (iii) seasonal variations. These three types of variation in length will be considered in turn.

9.1. SLOW SECULAR INCREASE IN THE LENGTH OF THE DAY

In 1695 Halley was led to suspect, from comparison between ancient and modern observations of eclipses, that the mean motion of the Moon was becoming increasingly more rapid. He could not be certain of this because at that time the longitudes of the places at which the ancient observations had been made were not sufficiently well known. His conjecture was confirmed in 1749 by Dunthorne, who discussed the early observations and found that they could be respresented if a term $10''\ T^2$ (where T is expressed in centuries) were included in the mean longitude of the Moon; Mayer in 1753 fixed the coefficient of T^2 at $7''$, but in 1770 revised the value to $9''$; Lalande in 1757 obtained a value of $10''$, in agreement with Dunthorne. The term in the mean longitude depending upon the square of the time corresponds to a term in the mean motion proportional to the time; the mean motion is being accelerated.

The problem of accounting for this acceleration of the mean motion of the Moon attracted much attention; among others, Euler, Lagrange, and Laplace all attempted to account for it. At length, in 1787, Laplace announced that the acceleration was a consequence of the gradual decrease in the eccentricity of the Earth's orbit arising from the action of the planets on the Earth; the mean action of the Sun on the Moon depends upon the square of the eccentricity of the orbit of the Earth, and the slow decrease in this action results in a slow increase in the Moon's mean motion. Laplace computed the acceleration (as the coefficient of the T^2 term is usually called) and obtained the value $10''.18$, agreeing closely with the best observational determinations.

In 1853, however, J. C. Adams found that the calculations of Laplace were incomplete; on revising them, he obtained a value of $5''.70$ for the secular acceleration due to gravitational action, which is little more than half the observed value.

The explanation of the difference between the observed value and the value computed by Adams had therefore to be found. In 1754 Kant had published an essay, entitled "Untersuchung der Frage, ob die Erde in ihrer Umdrehung um die Achse, wodurch sie die Abwechselung des Tages und der Nacht hervorbringt, eine Veränderung seit den ersten Zeiten ihres Ursprunges erlitten nahe, und woraus man sich ihrer versichern könne," in which he pointed out that the action of the Moon in raising tides in the oceans on the Earth must have a secondary effect in a slight retardation of the rotation of the Earth; such a retardation would produce an acceleration in the observed motion of the Moon. He explained by the same cause the fact that the Moon always turned the same face to the Earth.

If the observed acceleration of the Moon's motion were due to a gradual retardation in the Earth's rotation or, in other words, to a secular increase in the unit of time, accelerations of the mean motions of the planets should also have been observed, as Laplace pointed out. No such accelerations had been observed; it was not until 1905 that an acceleration of the mean motion of the Sun was found (Cowell, 1905).

The ancient observations of solar and lunar eclipses and of occultations, together with the ancient equinox determinations, were discussed very thoroughly in a series of papers by Fotheringham (1909, 1915, 1918, 1920). De Sitter (1927) co-ordinated and discussed all the data obtained by Fotheringham and deduced by a least-squares analysis a secular acceleration of the Sun of $+1''.80 \pm 0''.16$, and of the Moon of $+5''.22 \pm 0''.30$.

The rate of increase in the length of day needed to account for the secular acceleration of the Moon requires a dissipation of energy by tidal friction at a rate of about 2×10^9 h.p. Neither viscosity nor turbulence in the open oceans can cause sufficient friction to account for the acceleration. In 1920 G. I. Taylor pointed out that since the rate of dissipation of energy by tidal friction is proportional to the cube of the tidal current, the open oceans and all seas where the currents are very small contribute practically nothing to the total dissipation of energy. The regions where the greatest dissipation occurs are long bays and channels in which the waters are comparatively shallow and in which there is a large rise and fall of tide. Taylor found that the dissipation of energy by tidal currents in the Irish Sea accounted for about 2 per cent of the total dissipation concerned in the retardation of the Earth's rotation. Following on this suggestion, Jeffreys (1920) discussed the dissipation in the shallow seas of the globe. The Bering Sea proved to be of particular importance. The total dissipation of energy as calculated by Jeffreys amounted to about 80 per cent of what is required to account for the unexplained secular acceleration of the Moon's motion. Considering the uncertainty of the data, little doubt can remain that tidal friction in narrow seas is quantitatively adequate to account for the acceleration.

The length of the day is increasing as the result of tidal friction by slightly more than 1 millisecond in the course of a century. The effect on the mean longitude of the Moon increases proportionally to the square of the time and hence becomes very noticeable in the course of centuries, though the increase in the length of the day is far too small to be detected by any clocks developed up to the present time.

The angular momentum of the Earth-Moon system must remain constant. The decrease in the angular momentum of the rotation of the Earth must be compensated by a corresponding increase in the angular momentum of the Moon's orbital motion; this will be effected primarily by a slow increase in the mean distance of the Moon, though there will also be an increase in the eccentricity of its orbit. But without a detailed knowledge of the forces that are acting, it is not possible to calculate what the precise effect on the Moon will be.

The retardation of the Earth's rotation will produce an apparent acceleration of the mean motions of the Sun and planets; the effects on their mean longitudes will be the same when expressed in time, so that, when expressed in arcs, they will be proportional to the respective mean motions. As Mercury is the planet with the largest mean motion, the effect will most readily be detectable for this planet. The actual values will be referred to later, after discussing the irregular fluctuations in the Earth's rotation.

Jeffreys (1952) derives the following expression for the ratio of the secular acceleration of the Moon, ν, to that of the Sun, ν_1:

$$\frac{\nu}{\nu_1} = \frac{[(\kappa - 3)/\kappa] N + N_1}{N + N_1} \frac{n}{n_1},$$

in which κ denotes the ratio of the orbital angular momentum of the Moon to the rotational angular momentum of the Earth (the present value being 4.82); N and N_1 denote the magnitudes of the retarding couples acting on the Earth due to the lunar and solar tides, respectively; and n and n_1 are the mean motions in longitude of the Moon and Sun, respectively.

The ratio N/N_1 cannot be determined theoretically with certainty. Assuming that the friction follows a linear law, one obtains the value of 4.7. But tidal friction is mainly a skin effect, proportional to the square of the velocity of the tidal current. For this case, on certain simplifying assumptions, Jeffreys finds the value 3.4. If N/N_1 tends to infinity, so that all the friction is in the lunar tides, ν/ν_1 tends to $(\kappa - 3)n/\kappa n_1$ and so to the value 5.0. This is the smallest possible value of the ratio of ν/ν_1.

The ratio of the secular acceleration of the Moon to that of the Sun, deduced by De Sitter from Fotheringham's data, as given above, is 2.90, which is much smaller than the smallest possible theoretical value on the basis of the assumptions made by Jeffreys. Spencer Jones (1939), assuming De Sitter's value for the secular acceleration of the Moon, derived the secular acceleration of the Sun from observations of Mercury, Venus, and the Sun, and obtained a value of $1.''23$, which gives a ratio of 4.24, a value also smaller than the theoretical minimum value of 5.0. If De Sitter's values are substituted in the formula found by Jeffreys, given above, a negative value is obtained for the ratio of N/N_1. This would imply that the solar and lunar tidal torques are of opposite sign, which is absurd.

Urey (1951) avoids this difficulty by abandoning the assumption that the moment of inertia of the Earth is constant. If Ω is the angular velocity and C the moment of inertia about the axis of rotation, he obtains the following formula for the ratio of the secular accelerations:

$$\frac{\nu}{\nu_1} = \frac{[(\kappa - 3)/\kappa] \, N + N_1 + \Omega dC/dt}{N + N_1 + \Omega dC/dt} \frac{n}{n_1}.$$

It is then found that $\Omega dC/dt$ has a negative value for any likely values of ν/ν_1 and of N/N_1. With this interpretation, it is concluded that the moment of inertia of the Earth is decreasing at such a rate that the consequent decrease in the length of the day is about half its observed rate of increase during the last 25 centuries. Urey interprets the decrease in the moment of inertia as the consequence of the continuous formation of an iron-nickel core, which sinks toward the center as it is formed.

A secular change in the moment of inertia of the Earth could also be caused by a secular change in sea-level, caused by a melting or growth of the icecaps over Greenland and Antarctica. W. H. Munk and R. R. Revelle (1952a) have discussed the magnitude of this effect. The secular decrease in the moment of inertia required by Urey could be caused by a lowering of sea-level at a rate of 10 cm per century or 3 meters in 3000 years. Associated with the change in sea-level, there will be a tilting of the instantaneous axis of rotation, because of the asymmetrical distribution of land and sea. The amount of tilt will depend upon whether the growth of the icecap is mainly over Antarctica or over Greenland or equally over both; it is greatest when the effect is confined to Greenland. The astronomical evidence of the movements of the poles is not inconsistent with the required changes. During the past century, however, there has been a shrinkage of glaciers and a *rise* in sea-level, estimated to be at least 5 cm. Other causes may contribute to bring about changes in sea-level, such as movement of the sea bottom or a slight change in temperature of the oceans. An increase in temperature of all the water in the oceans of $1°$ C would raise the sea-level by 40 cm.

9.2. IRREGULAR FLUCTUATIONS IN THE LENGTH OF THE DAY

In 1870 Newcomb first called attention to fluctuations in the motion of the Moon, which were either of long period or of an irregular nature and which were not accounted for by Hansen's tables of the Moon, which had been published in 1857. This matter was further investigated in a large memoir (Newcomb, 1878) in which all available observations of the Moon before 1750 were compared with Hansen's *Tables*. Newcomb concluded that either Hansen's theory of the motion of the Moon had omitted some important terms of long period or the rotation of the Earth on its axis was subject to fluctuations of an irregular character. In a later memoir (Newcomb, 1912) the available observations of the Moon were compared with the "provisionally accepted theory," in which corrections were made to Hansen's *Tables*. The reality of the fluctuations was confirmed, but the question of whether they were to be attributed to defects in the gravitational theory of the Moon's motion or to fluctuations in the Earth's rate of rotation remained unanswered.

The completion by E. W. Brown of his theory of the motion of the Moon and the publication of his *Tables of the Motion of the Moon* provided a firm theoretical basis for the further examination of the cause of the fluctuations. Various investigations (Brown, 1926; De Sitter, 1927; Spencer Jones, 1932, 1939) established that the fluctuations were due to irregularities in the rate of rotation of the Earth and that fluctuations of a character similar to those shown by the Moon were present in the observed motions of Mercury, Venus, and the Sun.

In Brown's *Tables* the term in the mean longitude depending upon the square of the time is the theoretical term arising from planetary action. The secular acceleration due to the tidal retardation of the Earth's rotation is not included. Brown did include in his tables, however, the "Great Empirical Term" of approximately 260-year period which had been introduced by Newcomb to represent approximately the unexplained fluctuations.

Spencer Jones defined a quantity B as the fluctuation in the Moon's longitude, defined by

$$B = \text{Observed longitude} - C ,$$
$$C = \text{Brown's } Tables - 10''.71 \sin (140°.0T + 240°.7)$$
$$+5''.22T^2 + 12''.96T + 4''.65 ,$$

where T is expressed in centuries from 1900.0. He showed that the corrections required by the longitude of the Sun (ΔL), of Mercury (Δl_1), and of Venus (Δl_2) could be represented in the following form:

$$\Delta L = a + bT + cT^2 + \frac{n_0}{n} B ,$$

$$\Delta l_1 = a_1 + b_1 T + c \frac{n_1}{n_0} T^2 + \frac{n_1}{n} B ,$$

$$\Delta l_2 = a_2 + b_2 T + c \frac{n_2}{n_0} T^2 + \frac{n_2}{n} B ,$$

where n, n_0, n_1, and n_2 denote the mean motions of the Moon, the Sun, Mercury, and Venus, respectively.

These expressions imply that the fluctuations in the motions of the Moon, Sun, Mercury, and Venus are proportional to their mean motions; also that the secular accelerations of the Sun, Mercury, and Venus are proportional to their respective mean motions. The secular accelerations of the Moon and Sun are not proportional to their respective mean motions, however. Since the secular accelerations are caused by tidal friction, there is interaction between the Earth and the Moon; the total angular momentum of the Earth-Moon system remains constant, but a detailed knowledge of the forces acting would be needed before the exact quantitative effect produced on the motion of the Moon could be calculated. The approximate estimates made by Jeffreys are referred to above.

The corrections to the tabular mean longitudes of the Sun, Mercury, and Venus found in this investigation are as follows:

$$\Delta L = +1''\!.00 + 2''\!.97T + 1''\!.23T^2 + 0.0748B ,$$

$$\Delta l_1 = +4''\!.96 + 13''\!.08T + 5''\!.10T^2 + 0.310B ,$$

$$\Delta l_2 = +2''\!.26 + 5''\!.39T + 2''\!.00T^2 + 0.112B .$$

The secular acceleration of the Sun, $+1''\!.23 \pm 0''\!.04$ (that of the Moon having been assumed to be $+5''\!.22$), is not in good agreement with the value derived by De Sitter from Fotheringham's discussion of the ancient eclipses, viz., $+1''\!.80 \pm 0''\!.16$. There was close agreement between the values inferred from the observations of the Sun ($+1''\!.14 \pm 0''\!.11$) and from the observations of Mercury ($+1''\!.24 \pm 0''\!.04$). These values are derived solely from observations from 1675 onward, whereas De Sitter's value was based on comparison between ancient and modern observations. The correction to the mean longitude of Mercury has been confirmed by Clemence (1943).

It is not possible to make a unique separation between the secular-acceleration terms and the fluctuation terms. The fluctuations have been defined in such a way that their extreme positive and negative values since 1675 are about equal; this is an arbitrary definition, and it is conceivable that throughout this period they may have had either a large negative or a large positive value.

The fluctuations can be interpreted as changes in the length of the day occurring at irregular intervals. The excesses of the length of the day over its average value during this period are approximately as given in Table 3.

The changes appear to occur rather suddenly, but the precision of the observations is not sufficient to decide whether any of the changes is more or less instantaneous or whether it is spread over a few weeks, a few months, or a few years. It is to be expected that the precision of modern quartz-crystal clocks will in due course give some more detailed information about the nature of the changes. Much more certain information would follow the development of an atomic clock.

TABLE 3

Period	Excess (Sec.)	Period	Excess (Sec.)
1682–1740.	+0.0018	1860–1870.	−0.0028
1740–1786.	+ .0010	1870–1876.	− .0056
1786–1822.	− .0008	1876–1900.	− .0016
1822–1838.	− .0019	1900–1918.	+ .0020
1838–1848.	− .0002	1918–1936.	−0.0023
1848–1860.	−0.0009		

The irregular curve representing the fluctuations is very similar in character to the curve representing the errors of a precision pendulum clock, such as the Shortt free-pendulum clock. From comparisons between the free-pendulum clocks and quartz-crystal clocks (which have a very high short-term stability) at the Royal Observatory, Greenwich, it has been concluded (Greaves and Symms, 1943) that free-pendulum clocks are liable to frequent small erratic changes of rate; the integrated effect of such changes produces an irregular wandering of the clock error. By analogy, it appears likely that the rate of rotation of the Earth is subject not to somewhat infrequent and large changes of rate but to frequent small changes and that it is the integrated effect of these small changes that is observed (Spencer Jones, 1950).

Brouwer (1952a, b) has independently postulated random cumulative changes in the rate of rotation of the Earth. On this assumption, the mean error of the fluctuation in the Earth's rotation should increase with time proportionally to $T^{3/2}$, measured from the present epoch. The principal uncertainty in old observations of the Moon's position would then be due to the accumulation of the random process rather than to errors of observation. The rather large errors of early observations, therefore, become relatively of less effect. It is consequently desirable that all available observations, well distributed in time, should be used for the investigation of the changes in the Earth's rotation. A new discussion on this basis is to be made by Brouwer. From a preliminary investigation, the values for the secular accelerations of the Moon and Sun are found to be $+2\overset{''}{.}2 \pm 3\overset{''}{.}8$ and $+1\overset{''}{.}01 \pm 0\overset{''}{.}28$ (mean errors), respectively. The errors of these values are necessarily much larger than in previous determinations.

The general statistical properties of cumulative series of random numbers have been discussed by A. J. J. van Woerkom (1953). Applying the methods of variate analysis to the annual values of the observed fluctuations in the Moon's mean longitude for the period 1820–1950, Van Woerkom confirms the hypothesis that the observed changes in the rate of rotation of the Earth are due primarily to cumulative random changes. He concludes, however, that Brouwer's assigned mean errors should be increased by a factor of 2.5; the values for the secular accelerations of the Moon and Sun thus become $+2\overset{''}{.}2 \pm 9\overset{''}{.}5$ and $+1\overset{''}{.}01 \pm 0\overset{''}{.}70$ (mean errors), respectively.

There is a close agreement between the period of rotation of the Earth and a natural period of vibration of the atmosphere. Attention was first drawn to this coincidence by Lord Kelvin (1882), who used it to explain the large amplitude of the semidiurnal barometric variation. More recently it has been called upon to account for the magnitude of the diurnal variation of the Earth's magnetic field, which requires the period of rotation to agree with the natural vibrational period within a few minutes. Holmberg (1952) has suggested that the coincidence between the two periods is not fortuitous. Kelvin pointed out that the phase of the semidiurnal atmospheric tide is such that the attraction of the Sun exerts an accelerating couple on the Earth. This couple can be calculated with considerable accuracy and corresponds to a rate of working of 2.7×10^{18} ergs/sec; the rate of working for the oceanic tides calculated by Jeffreys is 1.1×10^{19} ergs/sec, but is admittedly very uncertain. It thus seems possible that the Earth's rotation has been slowed down by tidal friction in the oceans until it has become equal to the natural period of vibration of the atmosphere and that the resulting atmospheric accelerating couple balances the effect of the oceanic retarding couple. If Jeffreys' estimate of the latter is not grossly in error, it is inferred that the oceanic couple is at present the larger. But changes of level in the shallow seas, where the tidal dissipation of energy mainly occurs, may be appreciable; it is possible that the oceanic couple may fluctuate widely within times that are short geologically and astronomically, though statistical equilibrium is maintained between the oceanic and atmospheric couples.

If the solar atmospheric accelerating couple is denoted by N_2, the formula obtained by Jeffreys (see Sec. 9.1) for the ratio of the secular accelerations of the Moon and Sun becomes

$$\frac{\nu}{\nu_1} = \frac{[(\kappa - 3)/\kappa] N + N_1 - N_2}{N + N_1 - N_2} \frac{n}{n_1}.$$

Agreement between the observed ratio and the ratio provided by this formula can be obtained without introducing Urey's assumption that the moment of inertia of the Earth is decreasing. If we adopt the value of 3.4 for the ratio N/N_1 and for N_2 the value computed by Holmberg, the value of N_1 required to give zero value for the secular acceleration of the Moon is within the limits of uncertainty of the value computed by Jeffreys. The formula can, in fact, be brought into agreement with any of the determinations of the secular accelerations without straining the data. A more precise determination of the oceanic retarding couple is needed before more definite conclusions can be drawn.

The cause of the irregular changes in the length of the day is not as yet known. The effect of the changes is sometimes to increase and sometimes to decrease the length of the day. Whatever the cause may be, it would seem to be of a world-wide nature rather than localized. It is easily shown that if there were an expansion of the Earth as a whole, so that its radius increased by 6 inches, the day would increase by 5 milliseconds.

Possible causes of the irregularities in the rate of rotation have been discussed by Munk and Revelle (1952b). During the last 60 years the length of the day has fluctuated by as much as 5 milliseconds, but the pole of rotation has not moved by more than 15 feet. Thus only disturbances that are nearly symmetrical about the axis of rotation need be considered. The possible causes considered fall into two categories: those due to changes in the moment of inertia caused by changes in the distribution of matter and those due to a variable motion relative to the Earth's crust. It is found that variations in the distribution of air mass or in oceanic circulation are quite inadequate to account for the observed fluctuations. Random changes in the elevation of continental blocks of the Earth's crust, large enough to account for the fluctuations, would cause displacements in the pole of rotation much greater than have been observed. The most probable cause appears to be electromagnetic coupling of the mantle to a turbulent core, by which means the observed fluctuations can be accounted for, provided that the conductivity of the mantle is about 10^{-9} e.m.u. This value, though it appears high, cannot be considered to be outside possible limits. There is some evidence of general agreement between fluctuation in the length of the day and variations in the westward drift of the Earth's magnetic field, which gives some support to this explanation.

9.3. SEASONAL CHANGES IN THE LENGTH OF THE DAY

The first suggestion of an annual fluctuation in the rotation of the Earth was made by Pavel and Uhink (1935) from the investigation of the performance of two quartz-crystal clocks at the Geodetic Institute, Potsdam, from May, 1934, to June, 1935. Both clocks showed similar fluctuations in the residuals from a parabolic ephemeris; but these fluctuations were probably due largely to systematic errors in the time determinations and not to a fluctuation in the Earth's rotation; the supposed range in the length of the day during the year amounted to about 9 milliseconds, which is much too large to be real.

The first discussions to indicate with some confidence that there was a seasonal fluctuation in the Earth's rotation were made by Stoyko (1936, 1937) at the Bureau de l'Heure, Paris, based on the performance of clocks at Paris, Washington, and Berlin during the three years 1934–1937.

The results obtained by Stoyko have been closely confirmed by analyses of the performance of the clocks at the Physikalisch-Technischen Reichsanstalt from 1934 to 1944 (Böhme, 1949; Scheibe and Adelsberger, 1950); of the clocks at the Geodetic Institute, Potsdam, from 1938 to 1944 (Uhink, 1949); and of the clocks at the Royal Greenwich Observatory from 1943 to 1951 (Finch, 1950; Smith, 1952).

The method used by Finch was to assume that the observed clock corrections can be fitted to an ephemeris of the form

$$E = a + bt + ct^2 + f,$$

where f is a hypothetical fluctuation with a period of 1 year. By forming the third differences of a series of clock corrections determined at equal intervals of time, a, b, and c are eliminated, and the third differences of the function f are obtained. These third differences should be the same, accidental errors apart, for all the clocks. The values from different clocks can therefore be combined, thus reducing the accidental errors; then, by successive integration, the second and first differences and the function itself are obtained.

From the mean of the investigations of the performance of the clocks at the Physikalisch-Technischen Reichsanstalt, Berlin; the Deutsches Seewarte, Hamburg; the Geodetic Institute, Potsdam; the Bureau de l'Heure, Paris; the Naval Observatory, Washington; and the Royal Greenwich Observatory, for various periods between 1934 and 1949, Smith (1952) finds that the amount f in milliseconds by which the Earth is slow can be represented by

$$f = 55.1 \sin n(d - 58) + 5.8 \sin 2n(d - 117) ,$$

where n is the diurnal motion of the mean Sun in degrees of arc (0.986) and d is the day of the year reckoned from January 0. The Earth gets slow in the spring and fast in the autumn.

For 1950–1951, Smith finds, from the Greenwich clocks,

$$f = 33.0 \sin n(d - 14) + 5.8 \sin 2n(d - 76) ,$$

the annual term being appreciably smaller than for the earlier period. Pavel and Uhink (1951), from the Potsdam clocks during 1949–1950, remark that there was a decrease in the amplitude of the yearly term and an increase in amplitude of the half-yearly term. The latter is not confirmed by the Greenwich clocks.

These determinations of the annual fluctuations were based on the star places of the FK3 catalogue. The new *Catalog of 5268 Standard Stars, 1950.0, Based on the Normal System N30*, prepared by H. R. Morgan (1953), shows that there are periodic errors in right ascension, which depend also on declination, in the FK3 system. These periodic errors enter into the determination of the annual fluctuation. Comparisons between the N30 and FK3 systems were communicated privately to the Astronomer Royal by Dr. Morgan and have been used by H. M. Smith and R. H. Tucker (1953) to revise the determination of the annual fluctuation. Expressing this in the form

$$f = a_1 \sin n(d - d_1) + a_2 \sin 2n(d - d_2) ,$$

they obtain the results shown in Table 4. The results for Mount Stromlo, Washington, and Richmond are based on the time determinations at those observatories, referred to the Greenwich quartz-crystal clocks through the link provided by radio time signals.

The total variation in the length of the day during the year is about $2\frac{1}{2}$ milliseconds. The fluctuations in the time error of the Earth relative to a uniform time and in the length of the day are variable from year to year, both in amplitude and in phase, though the general effect is for the

Earth to be slow in the spring and fast in the autumn relative to a uniform time.

Seasonal fluctuations in the length of the day are to be expected from such meteorological causes as the seasonal shifts in air masses, the melting of polar icecaps, seasonal variations in the angular momentum of the atmosphere, etc. The question is whether such causes can account for the magnitude and phase of the observed fluctuations.

Van den Dungen, Cox, and Van Mieghem (1949) have considered the effects of seasonal shifts in air mass. Comparing atmospheric pressures in February and in August (for the Northern Hemisphere only), they con-cluded that 20 per cent of the observed effect could be accounted for and thought that the uncertainty of the data was such that the whole effect

TABLE 4

COEFFICIENTS OF THE ANNUAL FLUCTUATION

Observatory	Period	a_1	d_1	a_2	d_2
Greenwich............	Jan., 1951—Sept., 1952	18.5	26	10.5	87
Mount Stromlo.......	Jan., 1951—June, 1952	23.9	364	8.5	84
Washington..........	Jan., 1951—June, 1952	22.3	35	11.0	119
Richmond............	Jan., 1951—June, 1952	23.0	36	10.5	111

might be explained in this way. Data for all the months in the year were used by Laurent (1950), who obtained a rather smaller effect. The inclu-sion of data from the Southern Hemisphere appreciably reduces the total effect, however (Munk and Miller, 1950).

The effect of fluctuations in atmospheric and oceanic circulation on the angular velocity of the Earth has been more fully discussed by Munk and Miller (1950), who take into account transfer of angular momentum as well as transfer of mass. If I_e, I_a, and I_o denote the moments of inertia of the solid Earth, atmosphere, and oceans, respectively, and if Ω_e is the Earth's angular velocity, ω_a and ω_o the components along the Earth's axis of the *relative* angular velocities of atmosphere and ocean, then

$$I_e\Omega_e + I_a(\Omega_e + \omega_a) + I_o(\Omega_e + \omega_o) = \text{Constant} .$$

Differentiating, we have

$$-\frac{\Delta\Omega_e}{\Omega_e} = \frac{\Delta(I_a\omega_a)}{I\Omega_e} + \frac{\Delta(I_o\omega_o)}{I\Omega_e} + \frac{\Delta I}{I} ,$$

where $I = I_e + I_a + I_o$ is the total angular momentum.

The various terms in this equation for January and July were estimated for both Northern and Southern Hemispheres, and the differences (January *minus* July) were formed. The results obtained were as follows:

$$\frac{\Delta\,(I_a\omega_a)}{I\Omega_e} \sim +1.6\times 10^{-8},$$

$$\frac{\Delta\,(I_o\omega_o)}{I\Omega_e} \sim 0.15\times 10^{-8}\,(\text{plus or minus})\,,$$

$$\frac{\Delta I}{I} \quad \sim 0.12\times 10^{-8}\,(\text{plus or minus})\,.$$

The mean value of $-\Delta\Omega_e/\Omega_e$ obtained from observation is about 2×10^{-8}, in satisfactory agreement. It appeared, therefore, that seasonal fluctuation in the transfer of angular momentum by the atmosphere could by itself account for the whole of the observed seasonal fluctuation in the Earth's rate of rotation. The ocean currents and seasonal displacements in air and water masses play only a minor role. A similar conclusion about the part played by the transfer of angular momentum has been reached by Van den Dungen, Fox, and Van Mieghem (1950).

In a later paper, however, Mintz and Munk (1951) have modified these conclusions. Using new information about zonal winds, the effect of the transfer of angular momentum by the atmosphere is found to give only one-third the effect computed by Miller and Munk, i.e., about 0.5 millisecond. This new investigation covers data for all longitudes, whereas previously the data for longitudes 100° E. and 80° W. had been used; the variations in the zonal winds are, it appears, larger for these longitudes than for all other longitudes. The revised estimate may be considerably in error because of uncertainties concerning the tropical Southern Hemisphere winds. The circulation in the ocean, changes in sea-level, and shifts in air masses may possibly contribute another 0.5 millisecond, but Mintz and Munk do not consider that this has been established.

Their investigation was based on a comparison between January and July, representing winter and summer in the Northern Hemisphere and summer and winter in the Southern, which might be expected to be the seasons when meteorological phenomena would have their extreme values. The recent Greenwich determinations of the annual fluctuation suggest, however, that the extreme values are in March and July; comparing January and July, the Greenwich values agree pretty well with the effect computed by Mintz and Munk.

While this chapter was in proof, the same authors (1954) re-examined the problem, computing the effects month by month and including the effects of bodily tides. They found good agreement between the annual terms derived from meteorological data and from astronomical observation; for the semiannual term the astronomical observations are uncertain and suggest a somewhat larger amplitude than that computed from the bodily tide.

10. ASTRONOMICAL TIME AND UNIFORM TIME

In the computation of the ephemerides of the Sun, Moon, and planets it is necessarily assumed that the unit of time is constant. Because of the nonuniformity of the rotation of the Earth, astronomical time, determined by the observations of transits of stars, is not uniform; there will, in consequence, be varying divergences between the observed positions of bodies in the solar system and the positions interpolated from the ephemerides. These divergences are most readily revealed by the observations of the Moon. For many purposes in dynamical astronomy it is necessary to convert from astronomical time to a uniform time system.

The Conference on the Fundamental Constants of Astronomy held in Paris in 1950 adopted the following resolutions bearing on this question:

a) In order to bring the lunar ephemeris into accordance with the solar ephemeris, the Conference recommends that Brown's "Tables of the Motion of the Moon" should be amended by removing the empirical term and by applying to the mean longitude the correction:

$$-8''.72 - 26''.75T - 11''.22T^2$$

where T is measured in Julian centuries from 1900 January 0 Greenwich Mean Noon.

b) The Conference recommends that, in all cases where the mean solar second is unsatisfactory as a unit of time by reason of its variability, the unit adopted should be the sidereal year at 1900; that the time reckoned in this unit be designated *Ephemeris Time;* that the change of mean solar time to ephemeris time be accomplished by the following correction

$$\Delta T = +24^s.349 + 72^s.3165T + 29^s.949T^2 + 1.821B$$

where T is reckoned in Julian centuries from 1900.0 January 0 Greenwich Mean Noon and B has the meaning given by Spencer Jones in *M.N., R.A.S.* **99**, 541, 1939, and that the above formula define also the second.

The first of these recommendations is based on the following considerations. The correction required by the Moon's tabular mean longitude from Brown's *Tables* is given (Spencer Jones, 1939) by

$$+4''.65 + 12''.96T + 5''.22T^2 + B - \text{empirical term}, \qquad (39)$$

where T is reckoned as in resolution *b*, and B is defined as the fluctuation in the Moon's longitude which is to be determined observationally. The correction to the Sun's mean longitude, as given by Newcomb's tables, is found to be

$$+1''\!.00 + 2''\!.97T + 1''\!.23T^2 + 0.0748B. \qquad (40)$$

This represents the increase in the Sun's mean longitude in the interval ΔT between mean solar time and the time (defined in resolution b as "Ephemeris Time") relative to which the solar ephemeris will agree with observation. In this time, ΔT, the Moon's mean longitude increases by

$$+13''\!.37 + 39''\!.71T + 16''\!.44T^2 + B. \qquad (41)$$

Hence the correction required to the mean longitude in Brown's *Tables* so that the tabular position of the Moon will agree with observation in ephemeris time is obtained by subtracting expression (41) from (39) and thus is

$$-8''\!.72 - 26''\!.75T - 11''\!.22T^2 - \text{empirical term}. \qquad (42)$$

The correction (39) to the Moon's mean longitude is thus interpreted as the combination of a correction to the mean longitude, given by expression (42), together with a time correction ΔT to bring the amended lunar ephemeris into accord with observation. This facilitates the future calculation of B.

ΔT is obtained by multiplying the correction to the Sun's mean longitude (40) by the time required for the mean longitude of the Sun to increase by $1''$, i.e.,

$$\Delta T = +24^s\!.349 + 72^s\!.3165T + 29^s\!.949T^2 + 1.8214B,$$

which is the basis of resolution b.

The distinction between astronomical time and ephemeris time should be kept clearly in mind. Astronomical time (as either sidereal time or universal time) is a measure of the rotation of the Earth. Ephemeris time is the independent variable in the solar, lunar, and planetary theories. It is a uniform time which has been defined so that the length of the day in ephemeris time is equal to the average length of the day in universal time over the last 3 centuries. The tables of the Sun and the Moon will agree with observation (accidental errors of observation apart) in ephemeris time, which is related to universal time by the correction ΔT.

Ephemeris time provides a uniform time system to which the motions of bodies in the solar system can be referred. It enables the ephemerides of the Sun, Moon, and planets to be based on pure gravitational theory, except for the secular accelerations, whose values are determined observationally. As previously explained, it is not possible to make a unique separation between the fluctuations and the secular accelerations. The time difference, ΔT, is theoretically defined by the Sun alone but is necessarily determined from observations of the Moon. Hence there is the possibility that inconsistencies may arise in the future. Judging from the agreement with observation for the last 3 centuries, it does not seem likely that the inconsistencies will be serious for several centuries. On the other hand, continuation of the present basis of tabulation would inevitably have resulted sooner or later in considerable discordances between observed and tabulated positions. The comparison between observation and theory will be greatly facilitated by the introduction of ephemeris time.

REFERENCES

ADAMS, J. C.	1853	*Phil. Trans. A.*, **143**, 397.
AIRY, G. B.	1826	*Phil. Trans. A.*, Part III, p. 548.
BÖHME, S.	1949	*A.N.*, **278**, 41.
BOYS, C. V.	1895	*Phil. Trans. A.*, **186**, 1.
BRAUN, C.	1897	*Denkschriften k. Akad. Wiss. Wien*, **64**, 187.
BROUWER, D.	1952a	*Proc. Nat. Acad. Sci., Washington*, **38**, 1.
	1952b	*A.J.*, **57**, 125.
BROWN, E. W.	1926	*Trans. Yale U. Obs.*, Vol. **3**, Part 6.
BULLARD, E. C.	1948	*M.N.*, Geophys. Suppl., **5**, 186.
CALLANDREAU, O.	1889	*Ann. Obs. Paris*, **19**, E1.
CAVENDISH, H.	1798	*Phil. Trans.*, **88**, 469.
CLAIRAUT, A. C.	1743	*Théorie de la figure de la terre* (Paris: Durand).
CLEMENCE, G. M.	1943	*Astr. Papers, Amer. Ephem.*, Vol. **11**, Part 1.
COWELL, P. H.	1905	*M.N.*, **66**, 3.
DARWIN, G.	1899	*M.N.*, **60**, 82.
DUNGEN, F. H. VAN DEN; FOX, F. J. and VAN MIEGHEM, J.	1949	*Bull. Acad. r. belg. sci.*, **35**, 642.
	1950	*Ibid.*, **36**, 388.
DUNTHORNE, R.	1749	*Phil. Trans.*, **46**, 162.
FINCH, H. F.	1950	*M.N.*, **110**, 3.
FOTHERINGHAM, J. K.	1909	*M.N.*, **69**, 204 and 666.
	1915	*Ibid.*, **75**, 395.
	1918	*Ibid.*, **78**, 406.
	1920	*Ibid.*, **80**, 578; **81**, 104.
GREAVES, W. M. H., and SYMMS, L. S.	1943	*M.N.*, **103**, 196.
HALLEY, E.	1695	*Phil. Trans.*, **19**, 174.
HEISKANEN, W.	1926	*Veröff. Finn. Geod. Inst.*, Vol. **6**.

HEYL, P. R.   1930   *J. Res. Bur. Standards*, **5**, 1243.
HEYL, P. R., and
   CHRZANOWSKI, P.   1942   *Ibid.*, **29**, 1.
HOLMBERG, E. R. R.   1952   *M.N.*, Geophys. Suppl., **6**, 325.
HUTTON, C.   1778   *Phil. Trans.*, **68**, 689.
JEFFREYS, H.   1920   *Phil. Trans. A.*, **221**, 239.
                    1937   *M.N.*, Geophys. Suppl., **4**, 1.
                    1941   *Ibid.*, **5**, 1.
                    1943   *Ibid.*, p. 55.
                    1948   *Ibid.*, p. 219.
                    1952   *The Earth* (3d ed.; Cambridge: At the University Press), chap. viii.
JONES, H. SPENCER   1932   *Cape Ann.*, **13**, Part 3, 47.
                    1937   *M.N.*, **97**, 406.
                    1939   *Ibid.*, **99**, 541.
                    1941   *Mem. R.A.S.*, Vol. **66**, Part 2.
                    1950   *Smithsonian Inst. Ann. Rept., 1948–49*, p. 201.
KANT, I.   1754   *Sämmtliche Werke, herausgegeben von G. Hartenstein* (Leipzig, 1867), Vol. **1.**
KELVIN, LORD   1882   *Proc. Roy. Soc. Edinburgh*, **11**, 325.
LAPLACE, P. S. DE   1788   *Mém. Acad. Sci.* (year, 1786), p. 235; see also *Mécanique céleste*, Book 7, chap. i, §16, and chap. iv, §23.
MASKELYNE, N.   1775   *Phil. Trans.*, **65**, 500.
MINTZ, Y., and MUNK,
   W. H.   1951   *Tellus*, **3**, 117.
                    1954   *M.N.*, Geophys. Suppl. (in press).
MORGAN, H. R.   1950   *Constantes fondamentales de l'astronomie* (Paris: Centre Nat. de la Recherche Scientifique), p. 47.
                    1953   *Astr. Papers Amer. Ephem.*, Vol. **13**, Part III.
MUNK, W. H., and MIL-
   LER, R. L.   1950   *Tellus*, **2**, 93.
MUNK, W. H., and RE-
   VELLE, R. R.   1952*a*   *Am. J. Sci.*, **250**, 829.
                   1952*b*   *M.N.*, Geophys. Suppl., **6**, 331.
NEWCOMB, S.   1878   *Researches on the Motion of the Moon* (Washington: Government Printing Office), Part I.
                    1895   *The Elements of the Four Inner Planets and the Fundamental Constants of Astronomy* (Washington: Government Printing Office).
                    1912   *Researches on the Motion of the Moon* (Washington: Government Printing Office), Part II.
PAVEL, F., and UHINK,
   W.   1935   *A.N.*, **257**, 365.
                    1951   *Ibid.*, **279**, 267.
PLAYFAIR, J.   1811   *Phil. Trans A.*, **101**, 347.
POYNTING, J. H.   1892   *Phil. Trans. A.*, **182**, 565.

RABE, E.	1950	*A.J.*, **55**, 112.
RADAU, R.	1885	*C.R. Acad. Sci. Paris*, **100**, 972.
SCHEIBE, A., and ADELS- BERGER, U.	1950	*Zs. f. Phys.*, **127**, 416.
SITTER, W. DE	1924	*B.A.N.*, **2**, 97.
	1927	*Ibid.*, **4**, 21.
	1938	*Ibid.*, **8**, 213 (revised and edited by D. Brouwer).
SMITH, H. M.	1952	*I.E.E. Monograph*, No. 39.
SMITH, H. M., and TUCKER, R. H.	1953	*M.N.* **113**, 251.
STOYKO, N.	1936	*C.R. Acad. Sci. Paris*, **203**, 39.
	1937	*Ibid.*, **205**, 79.
	1949	*Bull. Acad. r. belg. sci.*, **35**, 669.
	1951	*Ibid.*, **37**, 378.
TAYLOR, G. I.	1919	*Phil. Trans. A.*, **220**, 1.
UHINK, W.	1949	*A.N.*, **278**, 97.
UREY, H. C.	1951	*Geochim. et Cosmochim. Acta*, **1**, 209.
WOERKOM, A. J. J. VAN	1953	*A.J.*, 58, 10.

CHAPTER 2

Dynamics of the Earth-Moon System

By SIR HAROLD JEFFREYS
St. John's College, Cambridge

THIS chapter will be concerned mainly with changes in the rotations of the Earth and Moon. These will include (1) changes in the directions of the axes of rotation and (2) changes, especially secular changes, in the rates of rotation.

1. PRECESSION AND NUTATION

Of these phenomena, the first to be discovered was the precession of the equinoxes, usually attributed to Hipparchus. The Sun, in its annual motion relative to the Earth, crosses the plane of the equator from south to north at the "first point of Aries." This point was found not to be fixed with regard to the stars but to have a secular motion from east to west. In other words, in the interval between two occasions when the Sun crosses the equator from south to north, the Sun's longitude increases by somewhat less than 360°. The difference is about 50″, so that the complete revolution of the equinoxes would take about 25,000 years. It is called the *constant of precession*. The Earth's axis moves approximately in a cone about an axis normal to the plane of the ecliptic. The average motion is now called the *precession;* the small harmonic motions superposed on it the *nutations*. All are due to the attractions of the Sun and Moon on the Earth's equatorial bulge. The attraction of the Sun tends to draw the equator toward the plane of the ecliptic. But, on account of the rotation of the Earth, this is converted into a secular motion of the axis of figure about the normal to the ecliptic, just as a slightly inclined top, instead of falling, precesses in a cone about the vertical. The explanation is due to Newton, but an elegant treatment had to wait for Euler. The effect of the Moon is more complicated, because its orbit is itself somewhat inclined to the ecliptic and rotates on the ecliptic in about 18.6 years. The result is that the average effect of the Moon is similar to that of the Sun (and about twice as large), but, in addition, the inclination of the Moon's orbit produces an oscillation in the rate and direction of the movement, which has a period of 18.6 years. This affects both the longitude and the obliquity of the axis with reference to inertial axes at the Sun.

Even without this complication, the motion would not be quite uniform, because the Sun and Moon have no tendency to turn the Earth at the moments when they are crossing the equatorial plane. The rate due to the Sun, therefore, while always in the same direction, vanishes twice a year, and that due to the Moon twice a month. There are also various minor disturbances due to the fact that the orbits are not quite circular.

The principal nutation (18.6 yearly) was discovered by Bradley in 1747, who also gave the foregoing explanation; the associated variation in the obliquity was estimated by Newcomb to have an amplitude of $9''.210$, and this value is used in astronomical prediction. The values adopted for the minor nutations are taken to be in the theoretical ratios to the principal nutation.

For a long time the precession and the 18.6-yearly nutation gave the best available evidence on the mass of the Moon. Both contain a factor $(C - A)/C$, in which C and A are the moments of inertia of the Earth about the polar and equatorial axes. (If a possible departure of the equator from a circle is taken into account, A must be replaced by the mean of the greatest and least moments of inertia for axes in the equator.) The nutation contains a factor which depends on the mass of the Moon, and this factor appears also in the part of the precession due to the Moon. Hence the precession and the nutation together give two equations to determine $(C - A)/C$ and the mass of the Moon.

A more direct and accurate method is to make use of the perturbations of the Earth's center by the Moon. Apart from the complicating effect of the Sun, the Earth's center would move monthly in an ellipse about the center of mass of the Earth and Moon together. This is about 5000 km from the center of the Earth. The consequence is that the direction of an external body as seen from the Earth suffers a perturbation with a period of a month, with an amplitude depending on the mass of the Moon. Observations of the Sun and various asteroids have been used for this purpose. The amplitude for the Sun is about $6''$; but, for a close approach of an asteroid, it can exceed this several times. Such approaches are studied to determine the solar parallax; and analysis of the same observations gives the mass of the Moon. Newcomb employed direct observations of the Sun. The first use of the method for an asteroid was by Gill on Victoria.

Hinks's study was based on the 1900–1901 opposition of Eros; H. Spencer Jones's (1942) study of the 1930–1931 opposition of Eros gives the best value to date. The mass of the Moon found from the Eros opposition of 1931, according to his solution (slightly modified by me [1942]), was Earth/(81.278 ± 0.025); with the rate of precession, this gives

$$\frac{C-A}{C} = 0.00327260 \pm 0.00000069,$$

and the constant of nutation should be $9''\!.2272 \pm 0''\!.0012$. The observed value (a summary of several determinations) is $9''\!.2109 \pm 0''\!.0023$. The determinations of the mass of the Moon from the precession and nutation agree roughly with those from the lunar inequality. It was J. Jackson (1930) who first insisted that the difference, though small, is too large to be due to accidental error. Later discussions and observations have reinforced his conclusion. There is now some prospect of an explanation, which we shall consider later.

A complication in the analysis of observations for the nutation is that tidal deformation of the Earth leads to deflections of the vertical and will affect the amplitude found; this disturbance will vary with the latitude of the observatory. The effect is small but possibly not negligible. No departure of the Earth from symmetry about an axis of figure leads to motions of astronomical interest, though irregularities of the gravitational field lead to constant deflections of the vertical, which complicate the reduction of observations, notably those used in determining the lunar parallax. The fullest set of theoretical values of the various terms in the nutation is due to E. W. Woolard (1953).

2. THE VARIATION OF LATITUDE

Besides the precession and nutations, which are essentially forced motions, a free vibration was predicted theoretically by Euler. It consists of a motion of the instantaneous axis of rotation in a circular cone of arbitrary angle about the axis of figure; referred to axes rotating with the Earth, it should complete its revolution in $A/(C-A)$ rotation periods. With the value of $(C-A)/C$ derived from the precession, this would be about 305 days. The most easily observable consequence is that the latitude of an observatory should show an oscillation with this period. This motion was sought for many years without success; but Küstner in 1888 announced that latitudes did vary, and S. C. Chandler in 1892 tested observations of latitude for periodicities in general and found that most of the variation could be represented by motions of the pole in two periods, of 14 and 12 months, respectively, with amplitudes of the order of

0".1. The annual part might be a meteorological effect. Newcomb pointed out immediately that the 14-monthly part could be the Eulerian motion, after all. Euler's theory treated the Earth as a perfectly rigid body; but the actual Earth has some elasticity. The effect of this can be seen qualitatively as follows: The Eulerian motion is a consequence of displacement of the instantaneous axis from the axis of figure. In an elastic Earth, part of the equatorial bulge can be regarded as an elastic deformation due to the rotation, and this part is necessarily symmetrical about the instantaneous axis. It is therefore only the remainder that can do anything to displace the instantaneous axis; the motion would therefore have a longer period than in a rigid Earth with the same values of A and C, and the difference gives an estimate of the elastic deformation and therefore of the rigidity. A mean rigidity about equal to that of steel would give the correct period.

A detailed program for observations of the variations of latitude was begun in 1895. Six observatories about 39° N. co-operated, namely Mizusawa, Tchardjui, Carloforte, Ukiah, Gaithersburg, and Cincinnati. There have been some changes since in the co-operating observatories. Other stations, notably Greenwich and Washington, also carry out variations-of-latitude observations as part of their regular activity.

Elasticity has a negligible effect on the precession and all forced nutations, as was shown by Kelvin; in an elastic Earth the amounts of these are practically the same as for a rigid Earth with the same total A and C.

3. EFFECTS OF A LIQUID CORE

The distribution of elasticity within the Earth is now known in some detail from a combination of data from seismology and the theory of the figure of the Earth. The rigidity 50 km below the surface is already about two-thirds that of steel and increases to about 3 times that of steel halfway to the center. No transverse elastic waves have been traced at greater depths, and this has led to the suggestion that the central core is liquid. Enough geophysical information is now available to determine the theoretical period of the variation of latitude and to compare it with observation. There are great mathematical difficulties, however; and until recently it has been necessary to use a rough approximation on the assumption that the shell and core are homogeneous and incompressible. This is known as the "Herglotz model." A complete numerical solution has, however, now been made by H. Takeuchi (1950), who finds that the free period would be inconsistent with any rigidity in the core exceeding a tenth of the bulk modulus; a smaller rigidity would be most exceptional in a solid.

There is, however, a further complication if the core is liquid. In the elastic theory the inertia associated with internal distortions had always been neglected, on the ground that the free periods of elastic vibrations are all short compared with the astronomical periods. With a liquid core, this does not follow, because distortions in the core are not controlled by rigidity and some of them have long periods. The theory of a "liquid gyrostat," consisting of an ellipsoidal shell and a liquid core, had, in fact, been worked out by Kelvin, Poincaré, and others, but its geophysical application had been overlooked. The inertia of the core cannot, in fact, be neglected. In some of the nutations the transverse motion in the core is many times what it would be on a statical theory; and in the free period, if the core boundary was a sphere, changes in rotation of the shell would not communicate themselves to the core at all. With a rigid shell and a liquid core, the free period would be shorter, not longer, than for a completely rigid Earth; it would be about 270 days (Jeffreys, 1948). It was also found that the amplitude of the 18.6-yearly nutation would be reduced by about 1 part in 160, that is, in the right direction to explain the discrepancy found by Jackson, but three times too large. H. R. Morgan (1952) has studied the fortnightly nutation and found that its amplitude agrees with the theory for a rigid Earth. A liquid core would make this component about 10 per cent larger. With a liquid core, also, the amplitudes of the 18.6-yearly nutation in obliquity and longitude would not be in quite the same ratio as for a rigid Earth. So far they have not been determined separately by observation, but this could be done from the material available.

Allowance for elasticity of the shell, with a Herglotz model, reduces the discrepancies (Jeffreys, 1949). Takeuchi's calculation for the actual distribution of elasticity in the shell is sufficiently general to be used in combination with a hydrodynamic theory of the core; but the detailed theory for a liquid core of variable density has not yet been worked out. So far as present information goes, it looks as if the theoretical and observed values are approaching agreement, but much remains to be done.

4. OBSERVATIONS OF THE FREE PERIOD

Any free period in physics proposes the question: How is it maintained in spite of damping? There are two types of answer, one based on nonlinearity of the equations, the other on random disturbances. The first applies to many musical instruments; but most natural periodicities seem to arise in the second way. A model proposed by G. U. Yule (1927) is informative. A heavy pendulum of long natural period is bombarded by boys with peashooters. At irregular intervals they make hits and generally build up an oscillation. The amplitude of this oscillation is limited essentially by damping. There is an interval T such that most of the motion at time t will have been damped out by time $t + T$; any motion surviving at time $t + T$ is a consequence of hits in the interval t to $t + T$. Since the hits occur at random intervals, it follows that the motions, at times differing by more than T, are practically uncorrelated. Yule gave a method for estimating the natural period and the damping in such a system and also showed that the usual methods of analysis for periodicities would fail utterly. M. G. Kendall has studied systems of Yule's type much further and has shown that methods adapted to determine persistent vibrations (as in the tides) usually lead to spurious periods and may fail to detect real periods, owing to change of phase during the interval of observation. The phenomena have an extensive literature under the names of "serial correlation" and "stochastic processes."

Every known type of complication occurs in the variation of latitude. There is an underlying annual period, which presumably is fixed. Its components can be estimated by considering intervals of 6 or 7 years, during which the 14-monthly motion will occur in all possible phases relative to the annual one. Comparison of amplitudes over such intervals will presumably give the annual motion and estimates of the uncertainty of its terms. Subtracting this leaves the free motion and the random disturbance. In an ideal case this could be treated by Yule's methods. Unfortunately, there are three further complications. The random disturbance and the observational error appear to be comparable in magnitude, say $0''03$, on an average. Either could be treated separately without much difficulty, but the two together are very intractable. The random disturbances themselves appear to depart widely from the normal law of error; in one case the amplitude increased by the full amount of the annual term within a few months, while over one interval of several years the motion appeared to be substantially undisturbed. Finally, owing to the proper motions of the stars observed, it is frequently necessary to choose other stars, and the observations therefore do not form a homogeneous series. I made two solutions for the interval 1892–1938 (Jeffreys, 1940). In one of these I used an adaptation of Yule's methods, with a correction for observational error. This gave a period of 446.7 ± 6.9 mean solar days, with a time of relaxation of 17 ± 7 years. In the other I used the interval 1908–1921, which seemed nearly undisturbed, and treated irregularities as observational error. This gave a period of 439.0 ± 5.8 mean solar days and time of relaxation of 15.1 ± 1.8 years. I think the second pair of estimates the better.

5. THE ANNUAL MOTION AND THE RANDOM DISTURBANCE

The annual motion and random disturbance are generally supposed to be of meteorological origin. Any change that would lead to changes in the products of inertia with respect to the polar axis and a pair of axes in the equator would imply shifts of the axis of rotation with respect to that of figure. Such a change is provided by the seasonal accumulation of air in special regions, especially Central Asia, which produces the Indian monsoons as a by-product. The changes of mass per unit area can be estimated from the variation of atmospheric pressure at the surface. (The motion is not due directly to changes of pressure, as is sometimes stated, but to the fact that the rotating Earth has to carry the extra air with it; the angular momentum needed has components about axes in the equator.) The effect was first estimated by R. Spitaler, whose result was several times too large. I applied certain corrections and made some allowance for accumulation of snow and ice, which has an appreciable effect. The effect of vegetation is negligible. A more accurate treatment was given by L. Rosenhead. Independently of mine, a solution was given by W. Schweydar. The agreement between theory and observation is quite good.

As meteorological phenomena contain a considerable random part, a random disturbance was to be expected. Its amount is, however, surprising. The associated changes in the products of inertia are comparable with those that give the annual terms, and these are among the most outstanding phenomena of meteorology. It is difficult to see how any meteorological cause could account for the random disturbance without having been noticed directly.

6. DYNAMICAL ELLIPTICITIES OF THE MOON

The Moon is definitely triaxial; the axis of least moment of inertia (A) points approximately toward the Earth, and that of greatest moment (C) is nearly normal to the plane of the orbit. Its rotation is much slower than that of the Earth, and the Earth's attraction on the protuberance toward the Earth has a dominating effect on its rotation. The counterpart of the precession is that the plane of the Moon's equator, the plane of the orbit, and that of the ecliptic always meet in one line; in other words, the axis of greatest moment of inertia moves about the normal to the ecliptic in 18.6 years. The fact was observed by Cassini, and the explanation was given by Lagrange and Laplace. The inclination gives a determination of the ratio $(C - A)/B$. The difference $B - A$ must be positive, from considerations of stability, but is still poorly determined. There should be a free vibration in the plane of the orbit, but its amplitude is too small to be measured. However, the variations of the Moon's angular velocity about the Earth lead to deflections, the largest of which has an annual period. Many attempts have been made to measure this, but there are troublesome systematic errors. What has to be observed is the distance between a small crater near the center of the disk and a given point on the limb. It is necessary always to measure from the bright limb; thus opposite limbs must be used, according to whether the Moon is waxing or waning; and the fact that the motion sought is annual leads to a possibility that seasonal variations in illumination may lead to systematic errors. The limb is not an accurate circle, and detailed corrections for its form are needed. The amplitude of the vibration as seen from the Earth is about $1''$, which could be measured fairly accurately apart from the extra complications. But, in fact, $B - A$ remains uncertain by a considerable fraction of its whole amount.

The ellipticities of the Earth and Moon lead to disturbances of the relative orbit. The chief of these are secular motions of the node and perigee and a monthly variation in latitude. The two former are combined with much larger effects due to the Sun and can be estimated only when these have been calculated and subtracted. The difficulty of the theory is such that, in spite of the enormous amount of skill and labor devoted to it, the theoretical values are still less accurately known than the observed ones, though probable limits of accuracy can be stated. The accuracy is sufficient for these motions to give useful supplementary information. The monthly inequality of latitude is less useful because it is combined observationally with the obliquity of the ecliptic, which has a secular variation and possibly a systematic error.

The best values of the Moon's dynamical ellipticities to date are probably

$$\frac{C - A}{C} = 0.0006269 \pm 0.0000027 , \qquad \frac{B - A}{C} = 0.000118 \pm 0.000057 .$$

They lead to a difficulty noticed by Laplace. If the Moon was fluid, rotation and the Earth's tidal action would lead to positive values of these quantities, which would persist when it became solid. If solidification took place at the present distance, the theoretical values would be near

$$\frac{C - A}{C} = 0.0000375 , \qquad \frac{B - A}{C} = 0.0000281 ;$$

and at whatever distance it occurred, the ratio would be 4 to 3, so long as the Moon had already come to present a constant face to the Earth. The actual values are in complete disagreement. The immediate conclusion is that the Moon is at present far from being in a hydrostatic state, even in its deep interior; a strength comparable with that of brick is needed to prevent the ellipticities from subsiding. The second conclusion is that we can explain one of the ellipticities by supposing the Moon to have solidified when much closer to the Earth than it is now, but not both at once. If the Moon was in free rotation at solidification, A and B would be equal. The differences must be the result of tectonic processes. Incidentally, they offer a serious objection to any theory that supposes the lunar craters or maria to have originated from a fluid layer near the surface within geological time; for the first effect of such a layer would be that the surface would sink into it in such a way as to remove the excess ellipticities.

It should be noticed that an elastic tide would lie exactly under the Earth; the value found for $B - A$ is really the excess of the true value over the elastic value.

7. FIGURE OF THE EARTH

Clairaut and his successors, mainly in France, studied the theory of the figure of the Earth and its gravitational field; this was taken to the second order in the ellipticity by Helmert, Callandreau, G. H. Darwin, and De Sitter. Two important results of the first-order theory, due to Clairaut, are that if e is the ellipticity, g_0 and g_{90} gravity at the equator and the poles, M the mass of the Earth, C and A its moments of inertia, and a its radius, then

$$\frac{3}{2}\frac{C - A}{Ma^2} = e - \tfrac{1}{2}m \; ; \qquad \frac{g_{90} - g_0}{g_0} = \tfrac{5}{2}m - e \; ,$$

where $m = \omega^2 a/g_0$, ω being the Earth's rate of rotation. Survey leads to a determination of e; the perturbations of the Moon to one of $(C - A)/Ma^2$; and the distribution of gravity is also studied directly. The three sets of data are consistent. The theory of the internal field supposes that the stress everywhere in the interior is hydrostatic and studies the ellipticities of surfaces of equal density. The hypothesis is certainly wrong for the Moon, and there is also fairly good evidence against its accuracy for the Earth (if it was wrong only near the surface, the main results of the theory would not be much affected). It is nevertheless interesting. It is shown that, to a high degree of accuracy, $(C - A)/C$ on this theory suffices to determine e; in fact, e could be found with an uncertainty of the order of one-tenth of that given by all the other data together. Even when allowance is made for the probable inaccuracy of the fundamental hypothesis, this remains the most accurate single equation for the ellipticity.

Even without this hypothesis, the external-field theory determines $(C - A)/Ma^2$; and the precession, combined with the mass of the Moon, gives $(C - A)/C$. By division we find

$$\frac{C}{Ma^2} = 0.334 \pm 0.002 .$$

For a homogeneous body this ratio would be 0.4, so that we have decisive evidence that the density increases strongly toward the center. Further consequences have been worked out in much detail by K. E. Bullen. The main conclusions are that the mean density of the core is about 10 gm/ cm³; at a depth of 50 km the density is that of olivine, 3.3 or so; but at about 500 km it increases by about 0.5. This has been explained by J. D. Bernal as possibly due to a change of olivine under pressure from a rhombic to a cubic form; if so, since the pressure concerned is not reached in the Moon and Mercury, these bodies should be nearly homogeneous. This conclusion is, in any case, very difficult to avoid for the Moon, because its mean density is almost exactly that of an olivine body of the same size; there is no room for an appreciable amount of a denser constituent.

A recent thorough discussion of the motions of Eros over about 35 years by E. Rabe (1950) has led to two difficulties. There is a theoretical relation between the solar parallax and the ratio of the masses of the Earth and the Sun. Rabe's determination of the perturbations of Eros by the Earth and the Moon led to a solar parallax of 8″.798, against Spencer Jones's 8″.790; and there is a discrepancy of about six times the standard error. Several other methods, mainly dynamical, agree better with Rabe's estimate than with Spencer Jones's. The mass of the Moon, as found from the lunar inequality, is nearly inversely proportional to the solar parallax, and the dynamical ellipticity to the mass of the Moon. If, then, Rabe is right, the dynamical ellipticity needs an increase of about 1 part in 1000, and a similar increase is needed by the surface ellipticity. My solution, with Spencer Jones's parallax, gave

$$e^{-1} = 297.10 \pm 0.36 ,$$

after allowing for the known uncertainties; but Rabe's value would reduce this to about 296.8 ± 0.4.

The other difficulty concerns Mercury. The best previous determination of its mass had a probable error of 35 per cent. Rabe reduces this to about 1 in 140, and his estimate, combined with the diameter, leads to a density of 5.0 gm/cm³, which much exceeds that of Mars and is about that of Venus. It is hard to reconcile this density with any theory of a common origin for the planets. On the other hand, the diameter may be somewhat uncertain.

8. TIDAL FRICTION

Study of ancient observations, chiefly of eclipses and occultations, has shown that they occurred systematically earlier than would be inferred from the mean motions of the Moon and Sun at present. Such a result was, in fact, predicted by Laplace, but a serious correction was made by J. C. Adams. Planetary theory shows that at present the eccentricity of the Earth's orbit is slowly diminishing; an effect of this change is a systematic change in the Moon's orbit, which results in a secular acceleration of its mean motion. The first term of this was calculated by Laplace; but Adams found that some later terms had very large coefficients and that the total effect was only about half what Laplace had found. E. W. Brown's lunar theory has given the theoretical value as accurately as we need. The observed secular acceleration of the Moon is about twice the theoretical value. Again, occultations give the secular acceleration of the Moon directly, eclipses the difference of those of the Moon and Sun; and it appears that there must also be a secular acceleration of the Sun, for which purely gravitational theory provides no explanation.

An explanation was given by Kelvin and developed by G. H. Darwin. If the ocean has any viscosity or if the solid parts of the Earth are not perfectly elastic, the tides will be shifted in phase, and the attractions of the Sun and Moon on the tides raised by them separately will tend to retard the Earth's rotation and transfer angular momentum to the orbital motions, thus increasing the mean distances and decreasing the mean angular motions. The largest effect on times of ancient observations comes from the retardation of the Earth's rotation, since this provides the practical standard of time.

Darwin developed the theory in detail and showed how the Earth-Moon system could have developed from a state where the bodies were close together, revolving in about 4 hours, to the present state; if all changes took place at the greatest possible rate, this could have been achieved in about 50,000,000 years. The system will proceed to a further state when each body keeps a constant face to the other and the period of revolution will be about 50 days.

Darwin's discussion virtually assumed tidal friction to be due to viscosity in the body of the Earth; to make it occur as fast as possible, it was necessary to have a varying viscosity so as to produce the maximum dissipation of energy at every instant. In various places, however, he hinted that viscosity in the ocean was likely to be more important, and he clearly did not insist on his time scale.

I found a serious difficulty in 1915. If the Earth is elasticoviscous,[1] it is possible to estimate the viscosity needed to account for the secular acceleration of the Moon; but it was found that the viscosity needed would suffice to damp out the free variation of latitude in a few days. It was necessary to abandon either the elasticoviscous law, the hypothesis that tidal friction is bodily, or the hypothesis that the 14-monthly motion is the Eulerian nutation. Alterations of the elasticoviscous law led only to new contradictions, and it seemed that tidal friction could not be mainly bodily.

The orders of magnitude of the dissipations in the deep ocean by viscosity and turbulence were estimated from tidal theory, but these were found inadequate; thus there was no apparent place where there could be enough tidal friction.

A way out of the difficulty was found in 1919 by G. I. Taylor in studying the tides in the Irish Sea. The tidal currents are much faster in shallow coastal seas than in the deep ocean, and, since the dissipation by turbulence varies as the cube of the velocity, the greater velocities much more than compensate for the restricted area. Taylor found that 50 Irish Seas would do all that was needed. I extended his methods to other shallow seas, using information prepared by the Admiralty for navigators, and found that the available dissipation agreed as closely as could be expected with that required. It appeared, therefore, that the secular accelerations were explained. The time needed for the system to reach its present state from the minimum possible separation would be about 4,000,000,000 years.

The minimum possible distance from the Moon to the Earth suggested that they had previously formed one body, and much attention has been given to possible modes of disruption. It has appeared, however, that the angular momentum of the system is too small for it to have originated by rotational fission, and there are serious objections to the resonance theory, which Darwin himself favored. The Earth and Moon have therefore probably always been separate bodies, and the original distance between them is unknown.

Darwin also traced the variation with time of the inclinations and the

[1] Elasticoviscosity is the simplest possible form of imperfect elasticity at low stress; under it, the sudden application of a stress, which is thereafter kept constant, gives an immediate elastic strain; but the strain continues to increase uniformly with the time, as for a viscous liquid.

eccentricity of the Moon's orbit. His results depend, however, on the hypothesis that tidal friction is bodily; the corresponding theory for tidal friction in seas has not been investigated.

More recent work has disclosed several new anomalies. If the whole of the secular accelerations of the Moon and Sun were due to changes in the Earth's rotation, such as might be produced by variations of the Earth's moment of inertia, their ratio should be 13.3 to 1. If they are due to tidal friction according to a linear law of resistance, the ratio would be 6.3 to 1; a square law of resistance would give 7.2 to 1. The actual ratio is about 2.9 to 1; the secular acceleration of the Sun relative to that of the Moon is larger than we should expect.[2] Further, modern observations show anomalies not only in the Moon's motion but also in the motions of the terrestrial planets and the satellites, which are in such ratios that they could be explained by irregularities in the Earth's rotation and therefore by fluctuations in the moment of inertia about the polar axis; but no geophysical explanation is available for such fluctuations. They would have to be of the same order of magnitude as the random variation of the products of inertia needed to account for the maintenance of the variation of latitude; but their time scales are totally different, being of the order of years to centuries in the one case and months in the other. It seems unlikely that any one explanation can be sufficient. These irregular changes affect the present mean motions and introduce an uncertainty into the observed secular accelerations. The fullest discussion is by Munk and Revelle (1952); see also Young (1953). Spencer Jones (1939) considers it possible that when the irregular changes are eliminated, the secular accelerations are in the theoretical ratio, after all.

D. Brouwer (1952), assisted by A. J. J. van Woerkom, has reanalyzed the data on the assumption that the Sun and Moon have secular accelerations with random disturbances in rate superposed. They find that the random disturbance in the interval t is proportional to $t^{3/2}$, and by the method of least squares they derive nongravitational perturbations in mean longitude:

$$\text{Moon } (+2''.2 \pm 5''.5) \ (T/\text{century})^2,$$
$$\text{Sun } (+1''.01 \pm 0''.41) \ (T/\text{century})^2.$$

These have been claimed to contradict the theoretical ratio of about 7; but 7″ for the Moon and 1″ for the Sun would agree with both results

[2] Kelvin showed in 1882 that the semidiurnal variation of atmospheric pressure corresponded to a semidiurnal redistribution of mass and that the attraction of the Sun on this would tend to accelerate the Earth's rotation. Allowance for this effect would reduce the discrepancy. Further consequences are discussed in a paper by E. R. R. Holmberg (1953); cf. also chap. 1.

within the uncertainties. However, I mistrust the method of least squares in this problem, since it assumes independence of the errors of consecutive observations, which cannot be right for a cumulative error.

The existence of the changes, as distinct from their explanation, is sufficiently established for dynamical astronomers to have introduced a correction to convert ordinary time, determined from the Earth's rotation, to Newtonian or dynamical time. An interesting result found by N. Stoyko (1937) was an annual variation, which invited a meteorological explanation. Van den Dungen, Cox, and Van Mieghem considered annual changes of the moment of inertia of the atmosphere about the axis of rotation; Munk and Miller considered seasonal changes of angular momentum. Reference is made to chapter 1.

Besides the Moon, every other satellite whose rotation is known keeps a constant face toward its primary; Mercury also keeps a constant face to the Sun. This is explained qualitatively by tidal friction, and no other explanation is known. But none of these bodies has shallow seas, and probably none of them every had; so tidal friction in them must be bodily. It would be of the greatest interest to have some idea of its nature and amount.

A possible clue is provided by the damping of the 14-monthly variation of latitude. This must give a long-period oceanic tide, which must be affected by tidal friction; but, since long-period tides should satisfy an equilibrium theory closely, they are unlikely to be subject to great magnification in shallow seas. Rough treatment indicates that tidal friction in seas cannot account for an appreciable amount of the damping. Viscosity in the core could do it if the kinematic viscosity was about 10^6 cm^2/sec. Extrapolations from laboratory conditions, however, suggest that, at the temperatures and pressures in the core, 1 cm^2/sec is likely to be an overestimate. If so, the only available explanation would be imperfections of elasticity in the shell. There is no satisfactory evidence for the viscous type, and the excess ellipticities of the Moon appear to be decisive evidence against it. But elastic afterworking would be possible. This is a well-known property of some solids; a sudden change in stress may give an instant elastic strain, but maintained stress gives an increasing strain, which tends to a finite limit. Such a material would behave almost as if perfectly elastic (with different effective rigidities) for very short and very long periods, but there would be damping at intermediate periods.

Viscosity in a central core would hardly arise for any satellite, though it might for Mercury and Venus. Elastic afterworking would be possible for all, and study of its effects is needed.

The slow rotation of Venus (apparently in about 20 days) presents a difficult problem. In comparison with the Earth, tidal friction due to the Sun would be larger; on the other hand, there is no satellite, and the effect of the Moon on the Earth is about five times that of the Sun at present and may have been much more in the past. If Mercury was once a satellite of Venus, this difficulty might be met. A satellite, if it became sufficiently remote, would grow unstable and would become an independent planet. The suggestion would, however, require an explanation of how the aphelion distance of Mercury has come to be much less than the perihelion distance of Venus, and there may be other difficulties.

Fuller discussions of many of the problems considered in this chapter, with references, are found in a recent book (Jeffreys, 1952).

REFERENCES

Brouwer, D.	1952	*Proc. Nat. Acad. Sci., Washington*, **38**, 1.
Holmberg, E. R. R.	1953	*M.N.*, Geophys. Suppl., **6**, 325.
Jackson, J.	1930	*M.N.*, **90**, 733.
Jeffreys, H.	1940	*M.N.*, **100**, 139.
	1942	*Ibid.*, **102**, 194.
	1948	*Ibid.*, **108**, 206.
	1949	*Ibid.*, **109**, 670.
	1952	*The Earth* (3d ed.; Cambridge: At the University Press).
Jones, H. Spencer	1939	*M.N.*, **99**, 541.
	1942	*Mem. R. Astr. Soc.*, **66**, 11.
Morgan, H. R.	1952	*A.J.*, **57**, 232.
Munk, W., and Revelle, R.	1952	*M.N.*, Geophys. Suppl., **6**, 331.
Rabe, E.	1950	*A.J.*, **55**, 112.
Stoyko, N.	1937	*C.R. Acad. Sci., Paris*, **205**, 79.
Takeuchi, H.	1950	*Trans. Amer. Geophys. Union*, **31**, 651.
Woolard, E. W.	1953	*Astr. Papers Amer. Ephemeris*, **15**, 1.
Young, A.	1953	*M.N.*, Geophys. Suppl., **6**, 453.
Yule, G. U.	1927	*Phil. Trans. R. Soc. London, A*, **226**, 267.

CHAPTER 3

The Interior of the Earth

By SIR EDWARD BULLARD

Director, National Physical Laboratory, Teddington, England

1. INTRODUCTION

THE earth is unique among the planets, in that we can examine in detail the materials of which its outer parts are made. We can also perform experiments at its surface which give more complete information about the interior than is available for any other planet. The earth is the only planet for which we have gravity or magnetic surveys or seismological observations or measurements of bodily tides or of heat flow. Our views about the constitution of all the inner planets are therefore greatly influenced by our knowledge of the earth.

In this chapter we are primarily concerned with the interior of the earth below the levels at which the geologist, the mineralogist, and the petrologist ordinarily work. The structure, history, and composition of the outer parts are discussed in chapters 4 and 6, which are concerned with those parts of the earth of which we have direct, or nearly direct, knowledge.

2. SEISMOLOGY

2.1. INSTRUMENTS

When an earthquake or an explosion occurs in the earth, elastic waves spread out in all directions from the point of origin and can be recorded by seismographs. A seismograph is an instrument for recording the motion of the ground. The motion recorded is always complex, and the appearance of the record depends markedly on the characteristics of the instrument employed. The main characteristics are (1) the component of the motion recorded (usually north-south, east-west, or vertical); (2) the quantity recorded (usually displacement, velocity, acceleration, or strain); (3) the variation of the magnification as a function of frequency, and, in particular, the high- and low-frequency limits for effective recording; and (4) the variation of the phase distortion with frequency. These characteristics are not all independent; in fact, 2 is really only another aspect of 3 and 4; for example, a seismograph recording the amplitude of the ground motion with a magnification proportional to the frequency and with a $90°$ phase change at all frequencies is, in fact, faithfully recording the velocity of the ground motion.

No actual instrument will record faithfully over an indefinitely wide range of frequencies, and such an instrument would not be very useful if it existed, for its magnification would have to be kept so low, to avoid the record's being disturbed by microseisms with periods of a few seconds, that it would not effectively record the small displacements at higher frequencies. In practice, a well-equipped seismological observatory has a number of instruments, each recording one component over a restricted range of frequency with a magnification just sufficient to show the microseismic background. The useful magnification generally increases with the frequency at which the maximum magnification occurs. It is highest in the instruments used for the reflection method of seismic prospecting, where it may exceed 10^6 at periods near 0.02 second. For the study of explosions, rock bursts in mines, and small earthquakes within a distance of 10–20 km, the most important components have a period of a few tenths of a second, and a magnification of about 10^5 is suitable. At greater distances, certain phases, particularly the compressional waves, are best shown by instruments with a maximum magnification at periods near 1 second and a magnification of 10^4–10^5. The distortional waves have longer periods and need instruments that will record with a magnification of a few thousand at periods of 3–10 seconds. For recording surface waves, instruments recording up to periods of 60 seconds have been used. The longest period that could occur in a seismogram is that of the lowest mode of oscillation of the earth as an elastic body, which is about 60 minutes.

In many places, particularly in towns, the unsteadiness of the ground much exceeds that occurring under the best conditions, and the magnification that can usually be employed is much less than has been suggested above. Further, at many observatories the magnification used is not so great as is desirable, and the frequency range is often not the best for recording the important phases; this does not affect the value of good records when they are obtained, but it does prevent usable records from being obtained from many earthquakes that would be satisfactorily recorded by better instruments.

Details of particular instruments are given by Leet (1938), Sohon (1932),

Willmore (1950), Volk and Robertson (1950), and Gane (1948). There are about 600 seismological stations in the world; a map indicating most of them is shown in Figure 1, and a list is given by Jeffreys (1951).

The interpretation of a seismogram depends on the possibility of regarding it as the record of pulses that have traveled over different paths from the earthquake to the recording point and which therefore arrive at different times. In fact, the record is not that of a set of sharp, perfectly distinct pulses, but of a complicated oscillatory motion with many changes of period and amplitude, some of which are sudden enough to be regarded as the onsets of distinct "phases." Examples are given in Figures 2 and 3. Clearly, much depends on the experience and skill of the reader of the records, and certainty of interpretation can be obtained only by combining the information from many stations and interpreting it in the light of the theory of the propagation of elastic waves.

2.2. Propagation of Elastic Waves

We shall not enter into the details of the theory of the propagation of elastic waves, as this has been admirably summarized by Bullen (1947); only the main results of importance for seismology will be indicated.

In an isotropic elastic solid of indefinite extent, two types of elastic waves are possible, a *compressional* or P wave, in which the displacement is in the direction of propagation, and a *distortional* or S wave, in which the displacement is transverse to the direction of propagation. These waves are propagated without change of form and with velocities which depend only on the properties of the medium. The velocities v_P and v_S of the P and S waves are

$$v_P = \sqrt{\left(\frac{k + 4\mu/3}{\rho}\right)}, \qquad v_S = \sqrt{\frac{\mu}{\rho}}, \tag{1}$$

where k is the bulk modulus, the reciprocal of the compressibility, μ is the rigidity, and ρ is the density. The ratio of the two velocities is

$$\frac{v_P}{v_S} = \sqrt{\left(\frac{k}{\mu} + \frac{4}{3}\right)} = \sqrt{\left(\frac{2(1-\sigma)}{1-2\sigma}\right)},$$

where σ is Poisson's ratio. For most solids, σ is about a quarter and

$$\frac{v_P}{v_S} = \sqrt{3} \cong 1.7.$$

In a liquid, the rigidity, μ, is zero, σ is $\frac{1}{2}$, and shear waves cannot be propagated. The velocity of P waves, then, is

$$v_P = \sqrt{\frac{k}{\rho}}.$$

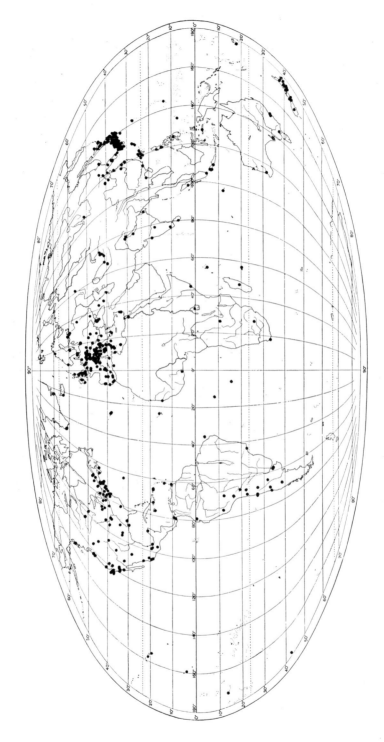

Fig. 1.—Distribution of seismological stations (Bellamy, 1936). The figure does not give the present distribution exactly but gives a good general idea of which areas are well covered and which are without stations.

If an elastic wave meets a surface at which the properties of the medium change discontinuously, it is partly transmitted and partly reflected, but the reflected and transmitted parts usually do not retain their original character; that is, a P or an S wave approaching a discontinuity will be reflected and transmitted partly as a P wave and partly as an S wave. The original type of motion is preserved only if symmetry makes conversion impossible, as it does at normal incidence or when the displacement in an S wave is normal to the plane of incidence. The theory and some numerical examples are given by Bullen (1947).

The P and S waves can be propagated anywhere in a solid medium. Near the surface of a body a type of wave is also possible which travels along the surface with a speed rather below that of the S waves and in which the motion falls off exponentially on going into the body. This wave is called a *Rayleigh wave*, after J. W. Strutt, third Baron Rayleigh (1842–1919), its discoverer. During the passage of a Rayleigh wave the motion of every particle is in an ellipse in the plane of propagation. Such waves bear a certain analogy to waves on the surface of the sea but are controlled by rigidity and not by gravity.

If the velocity of distortional waves increases with depth, a type of surface wave is possible in which the displacement is at right angles to the plane containing the direction of propagation and the normal to the surface. Such waves are called *Love waves*, after A. E. H. Love (1863–1940), who was for many years professor of mathematics at the University of Oxford. Their wave velocity, which always lies between the greatest and the least velocity for S waves in the medium, depends on the period; the waves therefore show dispersion, the longer waves preceding the shorter ones.

The P and S waves were first recognized in seismograms by R. D. Oldham. They are sometimes very clear; as in Figure 2, a single P and S followed by surface waves may be almost the only feature of the records. At greater distances the complexity of the records increases, and the surface waves separate clearly from S, as in Figure 3. Excellent reproductions of typical records from various distances have been published by Miss Lehmann (1954). The problems of interpretation are rather different for "near earthquakes," that is, earthquakes recorded within a few hundred kilometers of their point of origin, and for more distant ones. The two will therefore be considered separately.

2.3. Near-Earthquakes and Explosions

The velocity of elastic waves near the surface of the earth varies widely with the nature of the rock exposed. Some typical velocities for P

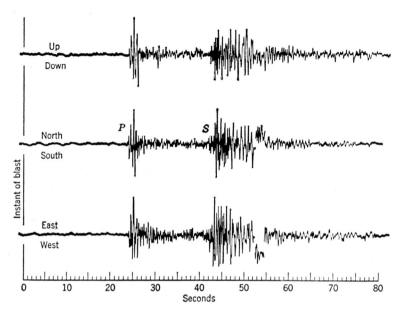

FIG. 2.—Record obtained from a seismograph at Harvard at a distance of 152.5 km from an explosion (Leet, 1938). The *P* wave arrives at about 24 seconds and the *S* wave at about 43 seconds (reproduced from *Practical Seismology and Seismic Prospecting*, by L. D. Leet [New York: Appleton-Century-Crofts, Inc., 1938]).

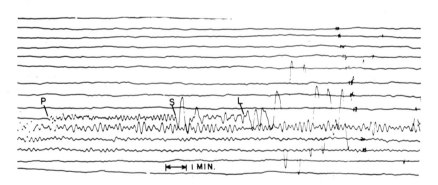

FIG. 3.—Portion of a record obtained from a seismograph at Pasadena at a distance of 4600 km from an earthquake in Panama (Gutenberg, 1948*b*). The record shows clear *P* and *S* and very conspicuous surface waves starting at the point marked *L* on the record. These are also numerous ill-defined phases both before and after *L*.

are given in Table 1. The ranges for each rock type are intended to give an idea of what is usually found and do not necessarily cover the extremes that are possible. The velocities have ordinarily been determined by observations of the waves from small buried charges which give no distinct S wave; the S velocities given have been calculated by assuming Poisson's ratio to be $\frac{1}{4}$ and are $1/\sqrt{3}$ times the P velocities. Further values will be found in tables of constants (e.g., Birch *et al.*, 1942; Landolt-Börnstein, 1952), and in accounts of particular investigations and regional summaries (e.g., Bullard *et al.*, 1940; Faust, 1951). Laboratory experiments show that the velocities vary rapidly with pressure between 0 and 1000 kg/cm². The figures in Table 1 can therefore be used only for rocks within a kilometer or two of the surface.

TABLE 1

VELOCITIES OF P AND S WAVES AT NORMAL
PRESSURE AND TEMPERATURE

Material	P (km/sec)	S (km/sec)	Material	P (km/sec)	S (km/sec)
Sand............	0.2–2	....	Shale and slate...	2.3–4.7	1.3–2.7
Alluvium.........	0.5–2	....	Limestone.......	1.7–6.4	1.0–3.7
Sea water.........	1.5	....	Gneiss and schist.	3.1–5.4	1.8–3.1
Clay.............	1.0–2.8	....	Granite.........	5.2–5.6	3.0–3.2
Sandstone.......	1.4–4.3	0.8–2.5	Basalt..........	5.1–6.2	2.9–3.6

From the results of Table 1 it is clear that the times for P and S waves over short distances will depend greatly on the local geology, and it is only when the greater part of the path is in rocks below the sediments that any regularity can be expected. The study of seismic waves in sediments is of great importance to economic geology but is largely irrelevant to the purpose of this book.

Observations at distances of up to 1000 km are used for the determination of the *structure of the crust* of the earth. Typical time-distance plots are shown in Figures 4 and 5, which give Willmore's (1949) results from the Heligoland explosion. The first arrivals shown in these figures can be represented by straight lines. These are interpreted as being due to the propagation of P waves through horizontal layers, as shown in Figure 6; the theory of the propagation of waves over such paths is discussed by Bullen (1947, chap. 12). In Figure 4 the first arrivals up to a distance of 24 km give a velocity of 4.4 km/sec; these waves travel in the Mesozoic and Paleozoic sediments which overlie the basement rocks of northern Germany. Between 24 and 115 km, the first arrivals give a velocity of

5.95 km/sec. We call these waves P_1; they travel in the material immediately underlying the sedimentary rocks, whose calculated thickness is 6.7 km. Beyond 115 km the first arrivals give a velocity of 8.18 km/sec. The material with this velocity is calculated to lie at a depth of 27 km.

There is a large and confusing literature concerning the observations of earthquakes at distances of up to a few hundred kilometers and the interpretation of the results in terms of the structure of the crust. In many

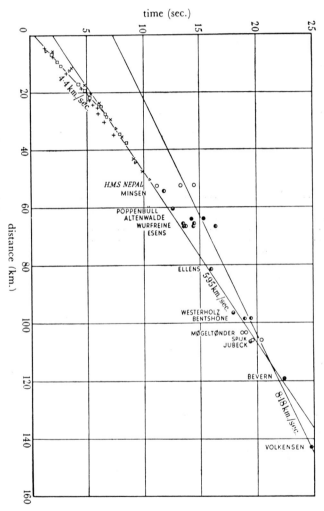

FIG. 4.—Time-distance curves for explosions at Heligoland (*circles*) and Soltau (*crosses*, *squares*, and *triangles*) at distances up to 150 km (Willmore, 1949). The 4.4-km/sec line is given by *P* waves that have traveled through sediments, the 5.95-km/sec line by *P* waves in the basement rocks beneath the sediments.

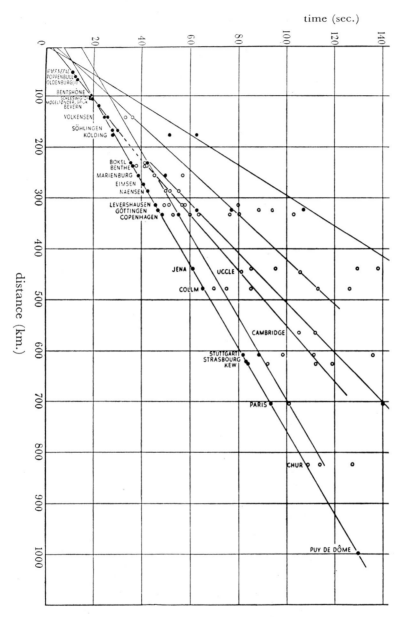

FIG. 5.—Time-distance curves for the Heligoland explosion (Willmore, 1949). The line join-ing the first arrivals at distances between 120 and 1000 km is P_n. It travels below the Mohoro-vičić discontinuity and gives a velocity of 8.18 km/sec.

such studies the number of observations is small, and much of the information goes into fixing the focus and time of origin of the earthquake. We
shall make no attempt to discuss all this material, since during the last
10 years a considerable body of data of much higher quality has been
obtained. Table 2 gives a summary of the results obtained in the principal
recent studies of near earthquakes and explosions. In this table the first
wave to arrive in the range of distance immediately beyond that where
the wave through the sediments arrives first has been called P_1. Waves
with a velocity near 8.2 km/sec have been called P_n, and anything between P_1 and P_n has been called P^*. The corresponding S waves have been
assigned in accordance with the choice made by the authorities quoted,

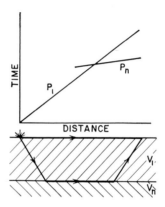

FIG. 6.—Time-distance relation produced by two layers, giving velocities V_1 and V_n
$(V_n > V_1)$. The slopes of the lines give the velocities in the two layers. These combined with
the intercept on the time axis give the depth of the interface.

which usually means that the P's and S's have been correlated in such a
way that the ratio of their velocities is about 1.7.

The results for P_n and S_n are very concordant and indicate the widespread presence of material giving velocities for P and S of about 8.2 and
4.6 km/sec at a depth of 30–40 km. Over the range of distance for which
it arrives first, P_n gives remarkably consistent results, the standard error
of the observed times being only 0.1–0.2 second. Jeffreys (1952a) has
found velocities of about 7.8 km/sec for P_n in Japan (see also Research
Group for Explosion Seismology, 1953); this is the only area in which the
velocity of P_n is less than 8 km/sec.

The velocities of P_1 and S_1 are much more variable than P_n and S_n,
though the observations in a given region are usually fairly concordant.
The observations of P^* and S^* are much less satisfactory. In many series

TABLE 2

RESULTS OF STUDIES OF NEAR EARTHQUAKES AND EXPLOSIONS ON LAND

SOURCE	VELOCITY (km/sec)						DEPTH (km)	NOTES AND REFERENCES
	P_1	S_1	$P*$	$S*$	P_n	S_n		
Western and central European earthquakes	5.60 ±0.03	3.40 ±0.20			8.09 ±0.08	4.33 ±0.04	34	Jeffreys (1947)
Heligoland explosion	{ 5.95, 5.57		6.50		8.18, 8.18		27, 30	Willmore (1949); S not identified; alternative solutions with and without $P*$
Heligoland explosion	5.40	2.94	6.18, 6.60	3.67, 3.87	8.19	4.38	27	Schulze and Förtsch (1950); Reich (1950); Reich, Foertsch, and Schulze (1951)
Haslach explosion	6.0		6.5		8.2		31	Reich, Schulze, and Förtsch (1948)
Haslach explosion	5.97		6.54		8.15		30	Rothé and Peterschmitt (1950)
Transvaal mine bursts	{ 6.09, 6.09	3.68, 3.68	6.83	3.89	8.27	4.83, 4.83	34, 38	Willmore, Hales, and Gane (1952); alternative solutions with and without $S*$ and $P*$
Ontario rock bursts	6.25	3.54			8.18	4.85	35	Hodgson (1953)
New England earthquakes and explosions	6.13	3.45	6.77, 7.17	3.93, 4.27	8.43	4.62	36	Leet (1941)
Corona (Calif.) explosions	5.9	3.6	6½–7		8.1–8.2		40	Gutenberg (1952)
Earthquakes in southern California	6.35	3.67			8.1	4.5	35	Gutenberg (1951a); some evidence for lower velocity at depths between 20 and 28 km
Maryland and Virginia explosions	6.1				8.1		32	Tatel et al. (1953 and unpublished); velocity probably increases gradually or by several steps to about 7.1 km/sec just above the jump to 8.1
Appalachian explosions	6.0				8.1		47	
Minnesota explosions	6.1				8.1		44	Slichter (unpublished); velocity probably increases gradually to 6.9 km/sec just above the jump to 8.2
Wisconsin explosions	6.0				8.2		41	
Means					8.18	4.63		

of observations P^* is never the first wave to arrive; this is particularly
clear in the South African work (Willmore et al., 1952), where 450 readings
of P are used and the P time-distance curve bends over sharply at a distance of 170 km from P_1 at 6.09 km/sec to P_n at 8.27. In some investigations there is a small range of distance over which the first arrival is believed to be P^* (e.g., Schulze and Förtsch, 1950), but in the main the
existence of P^* and S^* and of the corresponding "intermediate layer" depends on readings of motions following P_n and S_n. Such readings are difficult to interpret, for it frequently happens that individual records give
clear phases that cannot be correlated with anything on the records of
neighboring stations. When there are several such readings, it becomes to
some extent a matter of choice whether they shall be joined by a line on
the time-distance plot and whether doubtful features on other records
shall also be read because they are near the proposed line. It is only too
possible for an observer who is determined to get all the information that
can be extracted from the records to be imperceptibly led to accept points
that lie near the line and to reject ones that do not and to finish with apparently convincing evidence for the existence of a phase that is entirely
spurious. Examples of this danger can be seen in the lines of Figures 4
and 5. The lines through the first arrivals are obviously well established.
Some of the later ones in Figure 5 have a number of points lying near
them, and it is difficult to say whether they represent real travel-time
curves or not; Willmore rejects some and arrives at no certain conclusion
about the rest. Tuve et al. (1953) have taken records at closely spaced
stations which clearly show the spurious phases that can occur in individual records.

   Another possible source of uncertainty is the doubt as to how many
lines should be drawn through a set of observations that lie near a single
line. For example, the observations near 60 km in Figure 4 lie above the
5.95-km/sec line, and those near 105 km lie below it. Should a line with
a velocity somewhat below 5.95 km/sec be fitted between 24 and 60 km,
and one giving a higher velocity between 60 and 110 km? Is such a line
to be regarded as evidence for a separate layer underlying the 5.95-km/sec
one, or are the departures from the 5.95-km line due to some other cause,
such as horizontal changes in the basement rocks? It is on delicate points
like this that the existence or absence of P^* and an "intermediate layer"
depends. Willmore (1949) gives two solutions, one with and one without
the intermediate layer. Schulze and Förtsch (1950) and Reich (1950),
discussing the same data, accept the existence of the layer.

   In judging this important question, it must be remembered that the concept of universal horizontal layers beneath the continents is an arbitrary one. The observations show conclusively that there is a rapid and perhaps discontinuous increase in velocity at a depth which is usually about 35 km and that below this we have nearly everywhere a P velocity close to 8.2 km/sec. This discontinuity, which was discovered by Mohorovičić, is firmly established. It does not, however, follow that the material above this is disposed in horizontal layers; indeed, the facts of geology make this most unlikely (see chap. 4).

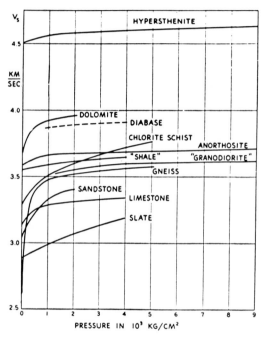

FIG. 7.—Effect of pressure on the velocity of shear waves in rocks (Birch and Bancroft, 1940).

In the work in the Transvaal, Ontario, and New England quoted in Table 2, the basement rocks are exposed at the surface, and there can be no doubt that P_1 and S_1 travel through them. The basement is made up of a great variety of rocks, but the bulk are granites, granite gneisses, and other acidic rocks.

Many laboratory investigations have been made on the elastic constants and densities of granites, from which the seismic velocities can be calculated. The values obtained increase rapidly with increasing pressure in the first 1000 kg/cm² and decrease slowly with rise of temperature (Zisman, 1933; Birch et al., 1942; Hughes and Jones, 1950, 1951; Hughes and Cross, 1951); for example Zisman found the bulk modulus of Quincy granite to be 1.1×10^{11} dynes/cm² at atmospheric pressure; 2.0×10^{11} at a pressure of 120 kg/cm²; and 4.0×10^{11} dynes/cm² at 600 kg/cm². Results obtained by Birch and Bancroft (1940) and Birch (1941) for the velocity of S waves are shown in Figures 7 and 8. From these, Birch (1938) has deduced travel times for S waves in a layer of granite which give a ve-

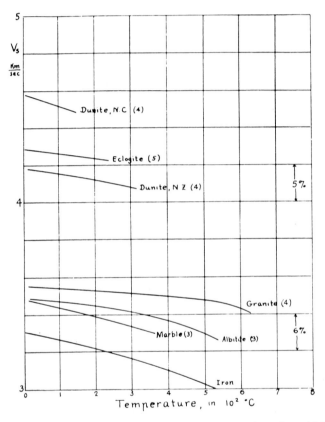

Fig. 8.—Effect of temperature on the velocity of shear waves in rocks at high pressure. The figures beside the curves give the pressure in thousands of kilograms per square centimeter (Birch, 1941).

locity increasing from 2.6 km/sec at short distances to 3.5 km/sec at distances of over 100 km, as shown in Figure 9. The variations due to temperature and pressure and those due to variation of rock type are more than sufficient to cover the variability in the velocities of P_1 and S_1 shown in Table 2; and there seems no difficulty in accepting the natural view that the velocities found for these waves are averages over the varied types of rocks which make up the basement beneath the continents and which are exposed in the pre-Cambrian shields.

The P_1 velocities in Table 2 are mostly in the neighborhood of 6 km/sec and are considerably higher than those found in the earlier near-earthquake studies, which gave about 5.6 km/sec (Jeffreys, 1937b, 1947). The latter are obtained largely from distances beyond 100 km, where P_1 is not the first wave to arrive. It seems likely that the phase then observed is usually not a continuation of the line giving first arrivals at short distances and is therefore not the wave in the basement rocks. What it is, is obscure; Gutenberg (1951b, 1954) suggests the possibility of a reduction in the velocity in granite at depths between 15 and 25 km, due to the transformation of quartz to the β-form by the elevated temperature. Since energy from a surface source could not travel in such a low-velocity layer, the

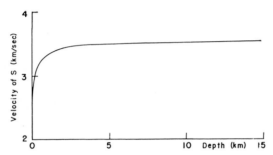

Fig. 9.—Velocity of S as a function of depth in granite

hypothesis would account for the frequent observation of the 5.6-km/sec velocity in records of earthquakes and its absence from those of explosions.

Some of the velocities found for the intermediate layer are not beyond the possible range for granite at high pressures (Birch et al., 1942; Hughes and Cross, 1951). It is therefore possible that in some places the intermediate layer may be merely the lower part of the granitic layer. If the higher velocities, near 6.8 km/sec, found in New England and California are genuine, it would be necessary to assume the presence there of basalt or some similar rock. So far as the seismic results go, there is no certainty as to whether such a rock occurs above the Mohorovičić discontinuity only in some places or everywhere. In view of the uncertainty as to the existence of an intermediate layer; the possibility that, if it exists, it has no sharp upper boundary; and the nonuniformity of the standards used by different workers in dealing with it, we have not given any estimates in Table 2 of the separate thicknesses of the granitic and intermediate layer but merely the total depth, h, of the Mohorovičić discontinuity. The latter is only slightly affected by the doubts about the intermediate layer.

There is some seismological evidence that h sometimes varies in the way required by the theory of isostasy (Gutenberg, 1943). The thickness given for the intermediate layer is usually between 10 and 25 km.

The material immediately *below* the Mohorovičić discontinuity is usually identified as dunite, a rock consisting largely of olivine $(Mg,Fe)_2SiO_4$. The observed velocity of S is a little higher than would be expected from Birch's experiments (1940b, 1941, 1943) and about the same as that found by Hughes and Cross (1951). The velocity of P is a little below that found by Hughes and Cross in dunite. The transition from the material above

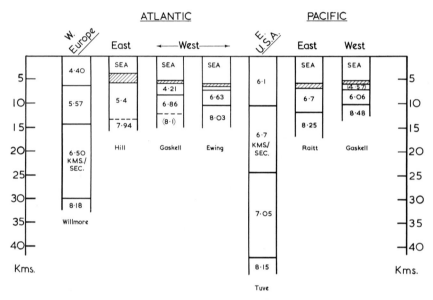

FIG. 9A.—Oceanic and continental coast

the Mohorovičić discontinuity to that below is probably discontinuous, as reflections have been observed from it by Gutenberg (1944b, 1951a) and by Tuve and Tatel (1953).

Investigations similar to those on the continents have been made at sea by Ewing, Gaskell, Hill, Raitt, and their collaborators (Ewing *et al.*, 1950, 1954; Officer *et al.*, 1952; Tolstoy *et al.*, 1953; Gaskell, 1954; Gaskell and Swallow, 1951, 1952, 1953a, b; Hill and Swallow, 1950; Hill, 1952; Hill and Laughton, 1954; Raitt, 1949). The results are compared with those on the continents in Figure 9A. In the deep ocean a material with a velocity similar to that below the Mohorovičić discontinuity occurs at a depth of about 10 km below sea-level. The thickness of sediment is variable but does not usually exceed 1 km. Below the sediment is material giv-

ing a velocity of about $6\frac{1}{2}$ km/sec; this is presumably basalt. Some relatively shallow areas have structures resembling that of the continents. Investigations on the continental shelf have been made by Ewing and his
collaborators (Press and Beckmann, 1954, with references to earlier work),
by Bullard and Gaskell (1941), and by Hill and King (1953).

The conclusions drawn from work on near earthquakes and explosions
have been confirmed to some extent by the study of surface waves. In particular, the difference between the structures of the continents and of the
oceans is well shown by this method (Gutenberg and Richter, 1936;

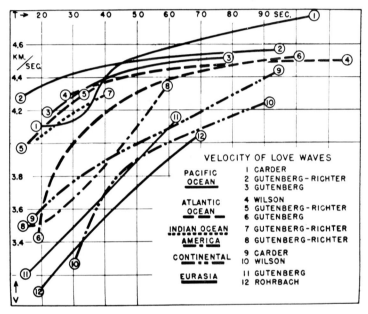

FIG. 10.—Group velocity of Love waves as a function of period (reprinted from *Internal
Constitution of the Earth*, by B. Gutenberg [New York: Dover Publications, Inc., 1951]).

Baykal and Wilson, 1948; Stoneley, 1948; Ewing and Press, 1950, 1952,
1954; Gutenberg, 1951*b;* Evernden, 1954). Figure 10 shows the variation
of the observed velocity of Love waves with period in continental and
oceanic areas; Figure 11 shows a comparison of the observed and expected
dispersion of Rayleigh waves over oceanic paths.

The structure derived from the seismic results is consistent with the results of gravity observations (Hess, 1954; Browne, 1954). In general, the
acceleration of gravity at sea-level is about the same over the continents
and oceans (see chap. 4). This implies that the ocean basins are isostati-

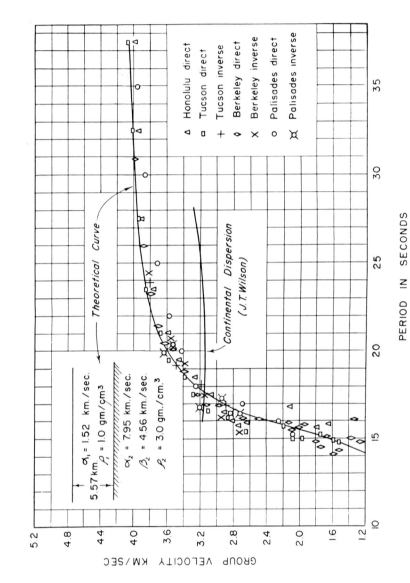

FIG. 11.—Group velocity of Rayleigh waves over oceanic paths (Ewing and Press, unpublished). "Direct" refers to waves traveling by the shortest path and "inverse" to waves passing through the antipodes of the station; α is the velocity of P, and β that of S.

cally compensated and that there is the same mass per unit area under the continents and under the oceans. The average density of the basement rocks of the continents is about 2.65 gm/cm³; it may reasonably be supposed to increase with depth, owing to the increasing proportion of the more basic rocks. The mean for the 35 km above the continental Mohorovičić discontinuity is probably about 2.8 gm/cm³. A column of this density, 1 square centimeter in area and 35 km high, would weigh 9800 kg. This would be closely balanced by a 35-km oceanic column consisting

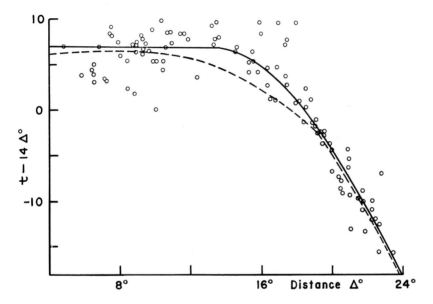

FIG. 12.—Travel times of P; 14 Δ has been subtracted from the times, where Δ is the distance in degrees. This allows a larger scale to be used and enables the change of slope to be more easily seen (adapted from Gutenberg, 1948a). ————, Gutenberg's tables; .... Jeffreys-Bullen tables.

of 6 km of water, 1 km of sediment of density 1.7 gm/cm³, 4 km of basalt of density 2.9 gm/cm³, and 24 km of dunite of density 3.3 gm/cm³.

2.4. The 20° Discontinuity

The velocities of 8.1 km/sec for P and 4.5 for S, found from the study of near earthquakes and explosions, persist with little change to distances of about 10° (1100 km). Between 15° and 22° there is a striking increase in the velocity of P to 9.1 km/sec, and of S to 5.3 km/sec; this is shown in Figure 12, where a number of California earthquakes are compared with the tables of Jeffreys and Gutenberg based on a much larger body of data. This phenomenon of a sharp curvature in the travel-time curve near 20°

was first observed by Byerly (1926). Its interpretation has been repeatedly discussed (Lehmann, 1934; Jeffreys, 1939a, 1952a; Gutenberg, 1948a, 1954). Jeffreys considers it to be due to a sudden increase in the rate of change of velocity with depth at a depth of 413 km, as shown in Figure 20, below. Gutenberg has found that the amplitudes of both P and S are unusually small at distances between 8° and 15°. He interprets this as indicating a decrease in velocity at a depth of about 80 km (from 8.1 to about 7.8 km/sec for P) followed by an increase. Such a layer causes a discontinuity in the time-curve and a "shadow zone." At short distances the waves travel above the low-velocity layer, while at greater distances they penetrate it. If the decrease is such that $(r/v)dv/dr > 1$, no ray returns to the surface after having had its deepest point in the layer. The velocity in the layer cannot then be found from the time-distance curve, though it can be inferred from the small amplitudes observed in the shadow zone.

It is difficult to distinguish between the hypotheses of Jeffreys and Gutenberg by a study of the travel times of the waves from earthquakes with shallow foci, but a clear distinction should be possible with an earthquake having its focus at a depth of about 250 km. Jeffreys requires such an earthquake to give a travel-time curve with a strong curvature at distances near 16°; Guternberg requires no such curvature. Miss Lehmann (1954) has studied such an earthquake and finds a marked curvature. It therefore seems likely that Jeffreys is correct in supposing that there is a rapid increase in velocity with depth just below 400 km; this is not necessarily inconsistent with an explanation of the small amplitudes of P and S between 8° and 15° by a low-velocity layer at a depth of about 80 km, as required by Gutenberg. Miss Lehmann and others have found that the decrease in amplitude of S is much more marked than for P—in fact, there may be no real S in this range of distance. This suggests that the cause of the low-velocity layer might be a softening of the material which would affect S more than P (see Sec. 5.3, below).

2.5. THE CORE

Beyond 20°, the velocities of P and S increase steadily, without any perceptible discontinuities; then at about 103° the amplitudes of both decrease, and in most earthquakes neither can be observed reliably beyond this distance, (Lehmann 1953b). The decrease in amplitude is illustrated in Figure 13, which shows some seismograms taken near the critical distance. At a distance of 98°.6, P is quite clear; at 124°.8 and 138°.2 it is very small. Beyond 143° large amplitudes are again observed in the first

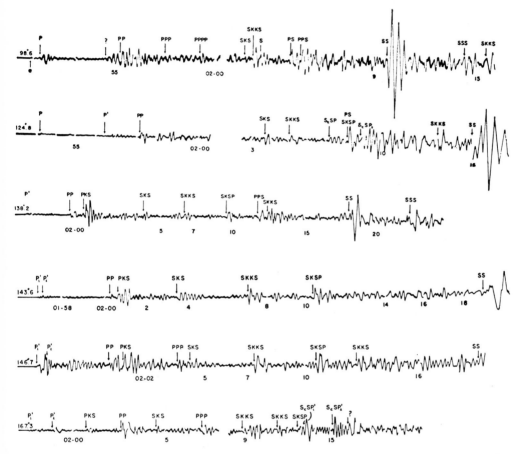

FIG. 13.—Seismograms showing small amplitude of P in the shadow zone between 103° and 142° and the large amplitude just beyond 142°. The seismograms are from an earthquake in South America on June 26, 1924; they are not all on the same scale, the time in hours and minutes is given beneath each (reproduced from *Practical Seismology and Seismic Prospecting*, by L. D. Leet [New York: Appleton-Century-Crofts, Inc., 1938]).

waves to arrive. From there to 180° the amplitudes decrease. This behavior was interpreted by Oldham, Wiechert, and Gutenberg as indicating the existence of a central core to the earth in which the velocity of P waves is less than that in the material nearer the surface. The radius of the core is 2900 km and is known with an accuracy of a few kilometers (see Sec. 2.8). Refraction by the core produces wave fronts and rays, as shown in

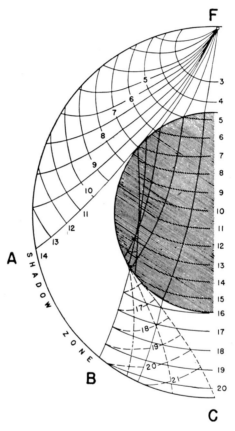

FIG. 14.—Seismic wave fronts and rays for P. The wave fronts are shown at intervals of 1 minute. The inner core has been omitted from this figure (adapted from Gutenberg).

Figure 14. In the region between F and A the waves can travel direct from the focus F to the point of observation. Rays more steeply inclined than $\overline{FA}$ will be refracted at the outer boundary of the core and will emerge between B and C. Between A and B there will be a "shadow zone" which cannot be reached either by the direct wave from F or by that refracted at the outer boundary of the core. At B there will be what in the corresponding optical problem would be called a *caustic;* energy will be concentrated in this region, and the observed large amplitudes would be expected. The region $\overline{BC}$ can be reached by two paths, as is shown in the figure; these paths will take different times to traverse, and two separate arrivals would be expected and are observed.

S waves through the core are not observed; it is therefore supposed that the material of the core is liquid. The same result would be obtained if the core had rigidity but absorbed or scattered S waves. Such behavior is not uncommon in solids but would not explain the observations of earth tides (see Sec. 3.4). There seems no doubt that the core of the earth is truly fluid.

The material between the base of the continental layers and the core is called the *mantle.*

2.6. The Inner Core

At points within the shadow zone, some motion is observable at times, corresponding to a reasonable extrapolation of the observations at distances below 103° and beyond 142°. That near 103° can be ascribed to diffraction around the outside of the core, but that near 142° cannot. Waves with periods of a few seconds are sometimes observed as much as 30° from the caustic, and it is quite impossible that so much energy can be diffracted through such large angles (Jeffreys, 1939c). Miss Lehmann (1936) suggested that this was due to the existence of a small inner core, giving a higher velocity than the rest. This suggestion has been investigated by Gutenberg and Richter (1938), by Jeffreys (1939c, d), by Gutenberg (1951c), and by Denson (1952). The velocity distributions obtained are shown in Figure 15. All agree that the radius of the inner core is about 1300 km, but the variations of velocity near its outside differ. Gutenberg supposes the increase of velocity with depth to be continuous, while Jeffreys suggests a sharp decrease and then a discontinuous increase. No S waves through the inner core are known, though they might exist and have escaped observation; it is not impossible that the inner core is solid (Bullen, 1950a, b). The ray paths and wave fronts associated with the inner core are shown in Figure 16.

2.7. Other Phases

The picture of a solid mantle surrounding a fluid core is beautifully confirmed by the observation of waves reflected at the outer surface of the earth and internally and externally at the boundary of the core. On reflection, a P wave may be converted into an S wave or vice versa. The number of possible waves is therefore very great. Some of them are shown in Figures 17 and 18, which also illustrate the usual notation by which they are designated. The segments of the path are taken in turn, starting from the focus, and are called P or S if in the mantle and K if in the core. Reflection at the outside of the core is denoted by c. Thus PP is a wave reflected once at the surface of the earth; PcP is a wave reflected once at the surface of the core; PKS is a wave starting as P, traversing the core (necessarily as a compressional wave), and converted into S on emergence into the mantle. The two waves PKP arriving at any point are called PKP_1 and PKP_2 or sometimes P_1' and P_2'. If the focus is not at the surface, there

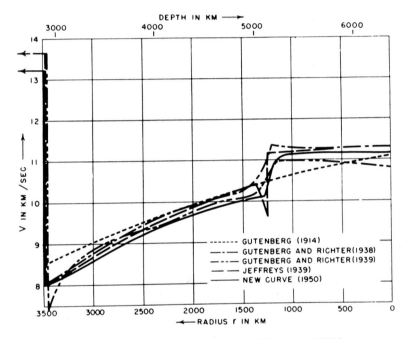

Fig. 15.—Velocity of P waves in the core (Gutenberg, 1951c)

are three paths by which a wave can travel to a given point with one reflection at the outer surface. The one involving a reflection near the epicenter is called pP, sS, sP, or pS, and the one reflected halfway between the focus and the point of observation PP or SS, etc.; the third possibility involving reflection at the antipodes of the point of reflection of PP is $PKPPKP$ or $P'P'$ and needs no special notation. Paths in the inner core are called I, but the notation is not free from ambiguity and has not been universally adopted.

Observations of PcP and the other waves reflected from the outside of the core are of special interest. The existence in them of components with periods as short as 1 second shows that the transition from mantle to core

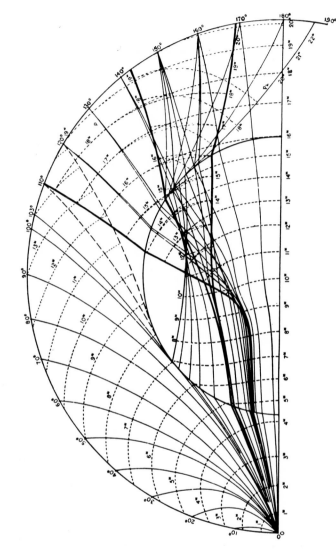

Fig. 16.—Seismic wave fronts and rays with central core. The wave fronts are shown at intervals of 1 minute (Gutenberg, 1948b).

must take place within a few kilometers. They also provide the most accurate method for determining the radius of the core.

2.8. VARIATION OF VELOCITY WITH DEPTH

The travel times of P and S have been worked out by a process of successive approximation. The epicenter and time of occurrence of an earthquake are found from the observed times of arrival of P and S at a number of stations by the use of the best timetables available. The results from

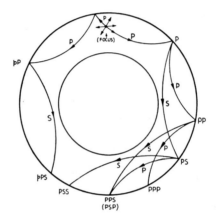

FIG. 17.—Paths of seismic rays in the mantle (Bullen, 1947)

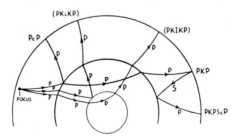

FIG. 18.—Paths of seismic waves reflected or refracted by the core (Bullen, 1947)

a number of earthquakes are then combined to improve the tables, which are then used to improve the epicenters. Thus both the tables and the positions and times of the earthquakes are gradually perfected. In order to use the full accuracy of the observations, it is necessary to allow for the ellipticity of the earth. The work has been done independently by Jeffreys and Bullen (1940) and by Gutenberg and Richter (1939), whose results agree within 1 or 2 seconds. Numerous checks are possible by comparing the results from P and S with those of other phases; for example, the time for PP must be twice the time for P to half the distance. An abstract of the Jeffreys-Bullen tables is given in Table 3 and a plot of a number of phases in Figure 19; phases involving the central core have been omitted from this figure. Gutenberg (1953) has obtained a valuable check on the tables from the records obtained from "known surface sources" in the Pacific.

TABLE 3

SUMMARY OF THE JEFFREYS-BULLEN SEISMOLOGICAL TABLES FOR A SURFACE FOCUS

Distance	Time (sec.)					
	P	PP	PcP	PKP_1	S	SKS_1
5°......	78	85	515	....	138	....
10......	148	156	519	....	262	....
15......	215	227	525	....	383	....
20......	277	296	533	....	497	....
25......	327	364	543	....	589	....
30......	372	430	555	....	670	....
40......	458	554	584	....	824	....
50......	538	654	618	....	969	....
60......	611	745	657	....	1103	....
70......	675	832	698	....	1226	1273
80......	733	916	741	....	1336	1346
90......	783	998	784	....	1434	1413
100......	828	1076	828	....	1520	1467
110......	....	1151	....	....	....	1512
120......	....	1221	....	....	....	1550
130......	....	1288	....	....	....	1580
140......	....	1351	....	1170	....	1599
150......	....	1410	....	1187	....	1614
160......	....	1465	....	1201	....	1625
170......	....	1517	....	1209	....	1632
180......	....	1565	....	1212	....	1634

If the velocity of elastic waves in a sphere is a function of the radius only and if the times of travel of P or S are known as a function of distance, the variation of velocity with depth may be found by a method due to Herglotz and improved by Wiechert, Bateman, and Slichter (Bullen, 1947, p. 118). This method is difficult to apply if there is a rapid increase in velocity with depth over a small range of depth. There is then a loop in the time-distance curve, and parts of it may be unobservable in practice, owing to their being represented by small motions closely following large ones. The velocity in a region in which it decreases with depth may

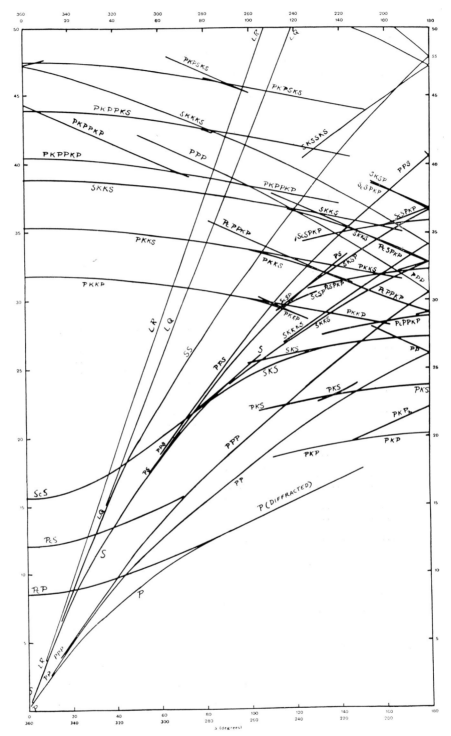

FIG. 19.—The Jeffreys-Bullen travel times for seismic waves from a surface focus (Jeffreys, 1939d).

also be unobservable. These things complicate the determination of velocities in the immediate neighborhood of the "20° discontinuity" and near the outer boundary of the inner core. With these exceptions, the method can be applied at all depths between the base of the continental layers and the center.

The results according to Jeffreys (1939a) are given in Table 4 and Figure 20 (cf. also Fig. 15). The calculations provide further stringent checks on the consistency and correctness of the *P* and *S* tables; for example, the velocities in the core determined from *PKP* and from *SKS* must agree.

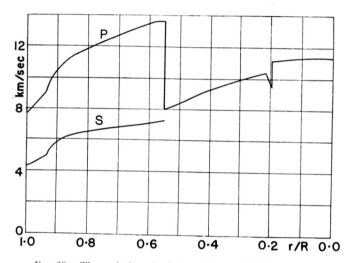

FIG. 20.—The variation of velocity with depth (Jeffreys, 1939d)

The mean radius of the core is best determined from the times of *PcP*. It is found to be (Jeffreys, 1939b) 3473 ± 2.5 km, which agrees with the result from *P;* the depth below the surface is 2898 km.

It is remarkable that in the whole investigation there is little indication of nonuniformity in the earth below the crustal layers. It seems that below a depth of about 35 km the complications of geology are left behind and the earth is a body in which the properties are very closely a function of the radius only; the surfaces on which any property is constant are presumably nearer to spheroids than to spheres, but inside the earth the distinction is of little practical importance; the depths in Table 4 refer to spheres having the same volume as the actual spheroids. There are small departures from the average timetables in the arrival of waves at particular stations, but most of these are due to variations in the crustal layers near the stations. Systematic differences between the times of *P* over continental and oceanic paths have been claimed, but it appears doubtful whether they are genuine, and it is certain that they do not exceed 2 seconds.

2.9. Deep-Focus Earthquakes

The foci of most earthquakes are within 60 km of the surface, but about 30 per cent have deeper foci. The distribution in depth is given in Figure 21. The deepest known earthquake was at a depth of 720 km and had its epicenter south of the Celebes (Gutenberg and Richter, 1949).

Deep-focus earthquakes are detected by the late arrival of P at near stations, when the origin time has been adjusted to suit the more distant stations, by the presence of phases, such as pP, which involve reflection

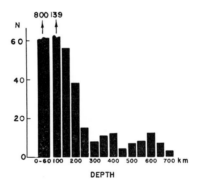

Fig. 21.—Distribution of earthquakes in depth. The figure gives the numbers in 50-km ranges of depth (except for the first range, which is 0–60, and the second, which is 60–125). For details of time and magnitude limits see Gutenberg and Richter (1949).

at the surface near the epicenter, and by the weakness of the surface waves. The depth is best determined by the observation of pP or of PKP near the antipodes of the shock.

Deep-focus earthquakes occur only in a belt surrounding the Pacific and at a few places on the Alpine-Himalayan chain. This distribution is discussed in chapter 4; much further information on the distribution of both deep and shallow earthquakes is given by Gutenberg and Richter (1949).

2.10 The Absorption of Energy

A study of the amplitudes of P and S waves over a range of distance from an earthquake shows that they suffer little attenuation by absorption. Gutenberg (1944a, 1945) suggests that the falling-off in the amplitude of P due to absorption is as exp $(-x/8300)$, where x is the distance in kilometers. This means that the waves will travel 5800 km before absorption halves their amplitude.

The amplitude of waves reflected at the inside and outside of the core has been studied by Gutenberg (1951c), Dana (1944, 1945), Martner (1950), and Ergin (1953). Such studies could give evidence on the discontinuity in density and elastic constants between the mantle and the core. In practice, it is difficult to get useful information, as the results from different earthquakes show a scatter of about 10 to 1 and there are inconsistencies of the same order which cannot be explained by any combination of properties; in particular, the amplitude of the horizontal motion in PcP is much larger than is predicted.

2.11. ENERGY OF EARTHQUAKES

The energy traveling out from an earthquake in the form of seismic waves can be roughly estimated from the amplitude of the movement on the seismograph records. The results are usually quoted in terms of magnitude, M, which is related to the energy, E, by (Gutenberg and Richter, 1949)

$$\log_{10} E = 12 + 1.8M .$$

Several other systems of assigning magnitude are also in use. The largest earthquake for which there are instrumental records was that of January 31, 1906, off the coast of Ecuador; this was of magnitude 8.6 and released about 3×10^{27} ergs. The Lisbon earthquake of 1755 may have released rather more energy than this. The San Francisco earthquake of 1906 was of magnitude $8\frac{1}{4}$ and released 10^{27} ergs. All these energies are those radiated as seismic waves; presumably, a considerable additional amount of energy is used up in nonelastic deformation near the focus and appears as heat.

The numbers of earthquakes in different magnitude ranges are shown in Figure 22. The figure suggests that there is an upper limit to the magnitude of an earthquake, which is about 8.6 for shallow earthquakes and 8.0 for those with foci below 300 km. This would mean that the maximum energy stored in a shallow earthquake is about ten times that stored in a deep one. In view of the high temperature of the interior of the earth, it is perhaps surprising that the ratio is not larger.

The total energy released varies greatly from year to year; the highest recorded was 6×10^{27} ergs in 1906, and the lowest, 1.5×10^{26} in 1930. The mean for 1904–1945 is 1.2×10^{27} ergs/year. Nearly all the energy comes from the large shallow shocks, and it is the fluctuation in the number of these from year to year that causes the large variation; there were eight shocks of magnitude $7\frac{3}{4}$ or greater in 1906 and none in 1930. The release of energy in particular regions has been studied by Benioff (1951*a*, *b*, *c*; 1954); it appears that energy may accumulate for some years and then be released in a series of earthquakes.

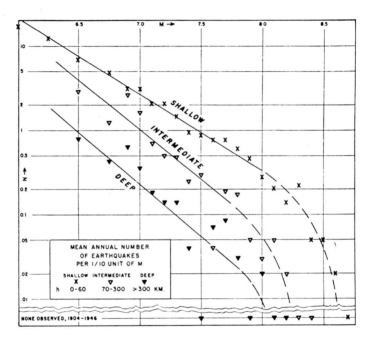

FIG. 22.—Mean annual number of earthquakes per tenth unit of magnitude (reproduced from *Seismicity of the Earth*, by B. Gutenberg and C. F. Richter [Princeton: Princeton University Press, 1949]).

3. PROPERTIES OF THE INTERIOR

Seismology gives the velocities of P and S waves as a function of depth. Equation (1) then gives k/ρ and μ/ρ, from which Poisson's ratio σ can be found. These results are given in Table 4. The seismological results alone cannot give k, μ, and ρ separately as a function of depth; but, by combining them with other data, reasonable estimates can be made.

3.1. DENSITY DISTRIBUTION

It was shown in chapter 1 that the earth is very closely a spheroid of revolution rotating about its axis and that its mean density is about 5.52 gm/cm³. This density is substantially greater than that of the rocks occurring at the surface. The basement rocks underlying the continents have a mean density of about 2.8, and the heaviest of the common igneous rocks have a density not exceeding 3.3. The greater density of the interior must be due in part to the compression of the material by the superincumbent load, but it could also be due to the concentration of denser material inward.

The mean density alone gives only a vague idea of the extent of the concentration toward the center. Some further information is provided by the moment of inertia, C. It is shown in chapter 2 that if M is the mass of the earth and a its equatorial radius,

$$C = 0.3335 \, Ma^2 \, .$$

For a homogeneous earth we should have

$$C = 0.4 \, Ma^2 \, .$$

The moment of inertia is therefore less than that of a homogeneous sphere of the same density, which is again evidence for an inward concentration of mass.

The known values of the mean density and the moment of inertia considerably restrict the possible density laws. In fact, they enable two constants in any proposed law to be found. If, in addition, we assume that the density at the base of the continental layers is known, we can determine three constants. On petrological and other grounds the density at the base of the continental layers cannot be far from 3.3 gm/cm³. To find the general trend of the possible density distributions, we take the density ρ at radius r to be given by

$$\rho = a + br^2 + cr^4 \, .$$

When the constants are chosen to give the three experimental quantities, this gives

$$\rho = 12.19 - 16.71r^2 + 7.82r^4 \, , \tag{2}$$

where r is taken as 0 at the center and 1 at the base of the continental layers. The densities found from this expression (see also curve a of Fig. 23) are given in the accompanying table. Clearly, an expression such

r	0.0	0.1	0.2	0.3	0.4	0.5	0.6	0.7	0.8	0.9	1.0
ρ (gm/cm³).	12.2	12.0	11.5	10.7	9.7	8.5	7.2	5.9	4.7	3.8	3.3

as equation (2) is to a large extent arbitrary and cannot be expected to give an accurate idea of the density at a particular depth. Departures from it at one point must, however, be compensated by departures in the other direction such that both the density and the moment of inertia keep their known values. Equation (2) therefore, in a sense, represents a smoothed version of any possible density distribution. It is independent of any assumption about the nature or state of the material within the earth (except for the density assumed at the base of the continents); in particular, the deduction of the mean density and the moment of inertia from the experimentally determined quantities does not involve the assumption that the interior of the earth is in hydrostatic equilibrium. In fact, the close agreement of the ellipticity found from the precessional constant and the mass of the moon on the assumption of hydrostatic equilibrium with that found by methods not depending on this assumption (chaps. 1 and 2) indicates a close approach to hydrostatic equilibrium throughout the bulk of the earth (Bullard, 1948a; Jeffreys, 1948, 1950).

Hydrostatic equilibrium requires the surfaces of equal density to be approximately spheroids of revolution and to have an ellipticity less than that of the surface (Jeffreys, 1952b, p. 140; Bullard, 1948a). Since the surface ellipticity is small, this implies that the density can be taken as a function of r only, as in equation (2). This does not follow from the approximate spherical symmetry of the external field without the hydrostatic assumption, though it would be an odd coincidence if an asymmetrical mass distribution were of the very special form needed to produce a symmetrical field.

The existence of topographic features and gravity anomalies shows that hydrostatic equilibrium cannot be exact throughout the earth. Most of the smaller-scale irregularity is doubtless to be accounted for by irregularities of density within the crust (chap. 4) and does not imply deep-seated departures from hydrostatic stress. The lower harmonics in the gravity field do, however, imply stresses extending to depths of many hundreds and perhaps thousands of kilometers. The harmonics up to the fourth degree and the rather smaller-scale variations between 30° and 10° squares have been discussed by Jeffreys (1941, 1943a). The ellipticity of the equator has been discussed by many authors (e.g., Niskanen, 1945) and the variation between 5° squares by Tanni (1948). If these irregularities in the gravity field have their source within a few hundred kilometers of the surface, they imply stress differences of the order of 10^8 dynes/cm² (Jeffreys, 1932, 1943b, 1948, p. 243, 1950).

On the hydrostatic assumption, equation (2) could be used to calculate the radial variation of quantities, such as gravity, pressure, and the ellipticity of the level surfaces within the earth. For example, the pressure, p_0, at the center is given by

$$p_0 = 4\pi G a^2 \int_0^1 \rho r^{-2} \int_0^r \rho r^2 dr\, dr = 3.31 \times 10^{12}\, \text{dynes/cm}^2,$$

where G is the Newtonian constant of gravitation. The results of such calculations are necessarily approximate, and better values can be obtained by using, in addition, the results of seismology.

The seismological results show that there is a major discontinuity at a depth of 2900 km. As a very crude assumption, it might be supposed that both the mantle and the core have a constant density. The known radius of the core and the mean density and moment of inertia then enable the densities to be found. The results are shown in curve b, Figure 23. This curve and curve a, which is that given by equation (2), represent extreme assumptions. Curve a assumes that there is no discontinuity in density at the core, while curve b assumes that all the increase in density is concentrated in a single discontinuity. Owing to the finite compressibility of all materials, there is certain to be some increase in density with depth both in the mantle and in the core. On the other hand, it is natural to suppose that there is some discontinuity of density at the boundary of the core. The truth would therefore be expected to lie between the two extreme hypotheses, and the density-curve to lie largely between curves a and b of Figure 23.

More detailed information can be obtained only if some further hypothesis is made. Suppose that there is a range of depth in the interior of the earth over which the material is chemically homogeneous and where no change of phase takes place. Suppose, further, that the only stress in this region is a hydrostatic pressure, p. Then the pressure gradient and the density, ρ, are connected by

$$\frac{dp}{dr} = -\rho g , \qquad (3)$$

where g is the gravitational acceleration at radius r. From equation (1) the bulk modulus is $\rho(v_P^2 - 4v_S^2/3)$ and therefore

$$\frac{dp}{d\rho} = v_P^2 - \frac{4}{3}\frac{v_S^2}{3} = F(r) , \qquad (4)$$

where F is a function of r known from the seismological results. If m is the mass inside radius r, then

$$g = \frac{Gm}{r^2} \qquad (5)$$

$$\frac{dm}{dr} = 4\pi r^2 \rho , \qquad (6)$$

where G is the Newtonian constant of gravitation. For a homogeneous material the only cause of change of density with depth is the increase in pressure and temperature. The effect of temperature is small (Sec. 5), and therefore

$$\frac{d\rho}{dr} = \frac{dp/dr}{dp/d\rho}. \tag{7}$$

From equations (3)–(7) we obtain

$$\frac{d\rho}{dr} = -\frac{G\rho m}{F r^2}. \tag{8}$$

If m and ρ are known at the outside of the homogeneous layer, equations (6) and (8) can be integrated inward and ρ found as a function of r.

If the layer is not homogeneous, it is likely that the materials which are denser at the prevailing pressures will be found below those that are lighter, that equation (7) will underestimate the density gradient, and that its integration will give too low densities at depth.

If the whole earth were of uniform chemical composition, the integration of equations (5) and (7) could be carried to the center. Unless the hypothesis of homogeneity were true, m would not be found to vanish there, and the correct moment of inertia would not be obtained. This follows formally from equations (6) and (8), which give

$$r^2 \frac{d^2 m}{d r^2} - 2 r \frac{d m}{d r} + \frac{G m}{F} \frac{d m}{d r} = 0. \tag{9}$$

The solution of this equation, which is zero at $r = 0$, has a single constant of integration. This can be used to fix the total mass, the moment of inertia, or the surface density, but not two or three of these.

Since the earth is known to possess a core, it cannot be homogeneous, and there is no point in integrating equations (6) and (8) on the hypothesis that it is. The next simplest assumption is to suppose the mantle and the core to constitute two separate homogeneous regions. It is convenient to start the integration below the crustal layers at a depth of about 33 km. The mass of the crust can be calculated to a sufficient approximation and deducted from the whole, to give a starting value of m; as the mass of the crust constitutes less than $\frac{1}{2}$ per cent of the whole mass, this introduces no appreciable error. The density just below the crust will be that of the material in which the P_n and S_n waves travel. If this is olivine, the density would be 3.32 gm/cm^3. Other possible materials would not lead to very different results. This value is confirmed by the density of the moon, which is 3.34. The downward integration has been performed by Bullen (1949); on reaching the outer surface of the core at $r = r_c$, values are found for its mass M_c and moment of inertia C_c that lead to

$$C_c = 0.57 M_c r_c^2.$$

This is greater than the moment of inertia of a homogeneous body of the same mass and radius and would require the density to decrease inward, which is impossible in a liquid core.

The explanation of this difficulty must lie in the lack of homogeneity of the mantle. One type of departure from homogeneity has been extensively investigated by Bullen (1940, 1942, 1947, 1949). He assumes a rapid change of material and increase in density between 413 and 984 km, which, according to Jeffreys, is the region of rapid increase in velocity below the "20° discontinuity." For purposes of exposition it is convenient to replace this by a sudden discontinuity, δ, in the density. Corresponding to any particular value of δ, a mass and moment of inertia of the core will be obtained. If a new integration of equations (6) and (8) is now started inside the core with a density ρ_c at its outer boundary, it will not, in general, be found that the mass vanishes at the center or that the right moment of inertia is obtained. By choosing suitable values of δ and ρ_c, it may be possible to obtain an acceptable solution. Allowance for the inner core introduces a complication; but since, with a density of 12, it would give only 2 per cent of the mass and 0.1 per cent of the moment of inertia of the whole earth, its effect is not very serious. Bullen has given two solutions, one assuming that the density within the core varies continuously, and one assuming that it is 10 gm/cm^3 greater in the inner core than on the previous hypothesis. The solutions are not very different; their mean is given in Figure 23 and Table 4. Bullen (1949, 1950a) has also considered a model in which, following Gutenberg, the 20° discontinuity is assumed to be at a depth of 80 km. He has further assumed that the bulk modulus and its rate of increase with pressure are continuous at the boundary of the core. No solution of equations (6) and (8) exists that satisfies these conditions; but one can be found if the requirement of homogeneity is dropped between depths of 2700 and 2900 km. The assumptions about the bulk modulus have no experimental or theoretical basis except that they were found to be roughly true in Bullen's previous solutions. There seems no reason for requiring them to be exact or to suppose that doing so will improve the calculated density variation.

The assumption of chemical homogeneity in the core seems reasonable in view of the evidence for motion in it given by terrestrial magnetism (Sec. 6.2), but in the mantle it is much less convincing. The density in the mantle must increase at least as steeply as in Bullen's solution for depths between 1000 and 2900 km, but there is little to show how much steeper it might be. Ramsey (1949) and Shimazu (1952) have given solutions allowing for a reasonable inhomogeneity. It would be worth while to work out some more solutions with arbitrary density laws in the mantle and the law derived from equations (5) and (7) in the core. It is possible that the range of admissible solutions is not very great. If the density jump at the outer surface of the core could be found independently, the range of uncertainty would be greatly restricted. In principle, this can be found from the amplitudes of waves reflected at the surface of the core, but the results are somewhat indefinite (Sec. 2.11, above). An important paper by Birch (1952) was received too late for its results to be included in this section.

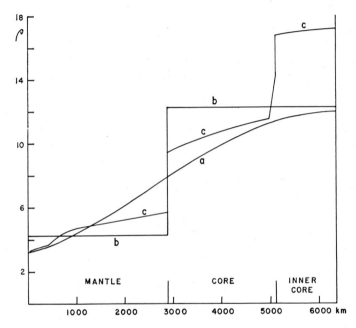

FIG. 23.—Variation of density with depth. Curve a from equation 2; curve b, density in core and mantle constant; curve c, mean of Bullen's solutions.

He refines the argument of equations (3)–(8) by the use of thermodynamic relations. He concludes that the lower part of the mantle, the core, and the inner core are each homogeneous but that there is a transition layer at depths between 300 and 900 km which is not homogeneous. It is not clear whether the change in the transition layer is a change in chemical composition or a phase change. The matter has been further discussed by Birch (1953, 1954a) and by Verhoogen (1953, 1954).

For the purposes of this chapter we take the mean of Bullen's two solutions (1940, 1942). We do this because many properties of the interior of the earth have been calculated on this assumption (Bullen, 1947). It is, in principle, an unsatisfactory basis, as equations (6) and (8) are not homogeneous in ρ and m, and a linear combination of two solutions is therefore not itself a solution. It is probable that little error is introduced, but further investigation is desirable.

3.2. ELLIPTICITY

The form of the surfaces of constant density can be calculated if the radial variation of density is known and the stress is hydrostatic, that is, if the surfaces of constant density are also equipotentials.

The surfaces are very nearly spheroids. Their ellipticity has been calculated from Bullen's densities by Bullard (1948a), whose results are given in Table 4. He has also calculated the departure of the surfaces from a spheroidal form. These results are of little importance, as the form of internal surfaces is not observable. The work is, however, a necessary preliminary to the accurate calculation of the ellipticity of the geoid from the precessional constant (see chap. 1).

3.3. ELASTIC CONSTANTS, PRESSURE, AND GRAVITY

The distribution of density can be combined with the seismic velocities to give the bulk modulus and rigidity, and from these the other elastic constants can be calculated. The results are given in Table 4 and Figure 24. As has been remarked earlier, the bulk modulus is approximately the same inside and outside the core. By integration of the density distribution, the gravitational acceleration can be found. The results are given in Table 4. It is remarkable that g is constant within 5 per cent throughout the mantle. By a further integration, the pressure can be found (Fig. 25 and Table 4). The pressure is relatively insensitive to the details of the density distribution, the results for the central pressure derived from curves a, b, and c of Figure 23 being as shown in the accompanying table.

Continuous density distribution, curve a........ 3.31×10^{12} dynes/cm^2
Uniform density in mantle and core, curve b..... 3.59×10^{12}
Bullen's curve, c. .... 3.64×10^{12}

The calculated pressures can be used to express the densities and elastic constants as functions of the pressure instead of the density, which is a form more useful for comparison with laboratory observations than is the correlation with depth. The results are given in Figures 26 and 27.

3.4. EARTH TIDES AND THE RIGIDITY OF THE CORE

Since no S waves have been observed to traverse the core of the earth, it is natural to suppose that it cannot sustain a shear stress and is a liquid. It is, however, conceivable that the absence of S waves is due to absorp-

TABLE 4*

INTERIOR OF EARTH ACCORDING TO JEFFREYS AND BULLEN

Depth (km)	Velocity (km/sec) P	S	Dens- ity (gm/cm²)	Elastic Constants (10¹² dyne/cm²) σ	k	μ	Pres- sure (dyne/ cm² $\times 10^{12}$)	g (cm/ sec²)	Ellip- ticity $\times 10^{-3}$
33.........	7.75	4.35	3.32	0.269	1.16	0.63	0.009	985	3.354
100.........	7.95	4.45	3.38	.272	1.24	0.67	0.031	989	3.334
200.........	8.26	4.60	3.47	.275	1.38	0.74	0.065	992	3.305
300.........	8.58	4.76	3.55	.277	1.54	0.81	0.100	995	3.276
400.........	8.93	4.94	3.63	.280	1.71	0.89	0.136	998	3.248
413.........	20° discontinuity								
500.........	9.66	5.32	3.89	.283	2.15	1.10	0.174	1000	3.220
600.........	10.24	5.66	4.13	.282	2.57	1.32	0.213	1001	3.192
700.........	10.67	5.93	4.33	.278	2.90	1.52	0.256	1000	3.165
800.........	11.01	6.13	4.49	.275	3.19	1.69	0.30	999	3.137
900.........	11.25	6.27	4.60	.276	3.41	1.81	0.35	997	3.109
1000.........	11.43	6.36	4.68	.276	3.59	1.89	0.39	995	3.081
1200.........	11.71	6.50	4.80	.278	3.88	2.03	0.49	991	3.023
1400.........	11.99	6.62	4.91	.281	4.20	2.15	0.58	988	2.963
1600.........	12.26	6.73	5.03	.284	4.52	2.28	0.68	986	2.903
1800....	12.53	6.83	5.13	.288	4.87	2.39	0.78	985	2.842
2000.........	12.79	6.92	5.24	.292	5.23	2.51	0.88	986	2.782
2200.........	13.03	7.02	5.34	.295	5.57	2.63	0.99	990	2.723
2400.........	13.27	7.12	5.44	.298	5.90	2.76	1.09	998	2.667
2600.........	13.50	7.21	5.54	.300	6.23	2.88	1.20	1009	2.618
2800.........	13.64	7.30	5.63	.300	6.47	3.00	1.32	1026	2.580
2898.........	13.64	7.30	5.68	0.300	6.51	3.03	1.37	1037	2.567
	Boundary of core								
	8.10	....	9.43	....	6.2	....	1.37	1037	2.567
3000.........	8.22	....	9.57	....	6.5	....	1.47	1020	2.556
3200.........	8.47	....	9.85	....	7.1	....	1.67	980	2.532
3400.........	8.76	....	10.11	....	7.8	....	1.85	930	2.508
3600.........	9.04	....	10.35	....	8.5	....	2.04	890	2.480
3800.........	9.28	....	10.56	....	9.1	....	2.22	840	2.450
4000.........	9.51	....	10.76	....	9.7	....	2.40	800	2.414
4200.........	9.70	....	10.94	....	10.3	....	2.57	750	2.372
4400.........	9.88	....	11.11	....	10.8	....	2.73	710	2.322
4600.........	10.06	....	11.27	....	11.4	....	2.88	670	2.265
4800.........	10.26	....	11.41	....	12.0	....	3.03	640	2.203
4982.........	10.44	....	11.54	....	12.6	....	3.17	620	2.155
5121.........	9.7†	....	14.20	....	....	....	3.27	590	2.141
5121.........	11.16	....	16.80	....	....	....	3.27	590	2.141
5200.........	11.18	....	16.85	....	....	....	3.32	560	2.139
5400.........	11.21	....	16.96	....	....	....	3.42	460	2.138
5600.........	11.25	....	17.05	....	....	....	3.50	370	2.136
5800.........	11.27	....	17.12	....	....	....	3.56	270	2.134
6000.........	11.29	....	17.16	....	....	....	3.61	180	2.133
6200.........	11.30	....	17.19	....	....	....	3.63	80	2.132
6371‡.........	11.31	....	17.20	....	....	....	3.64	0	2.132

* The quantities in this table are mutually consistent, but not all are known to the accuracy given; in particular, there is great uncertainty in the quantities for the inner core.

† Velocity of P decreases from 4982 km to boundary of inner core at 5121 km.

‡ Center of earth.

96

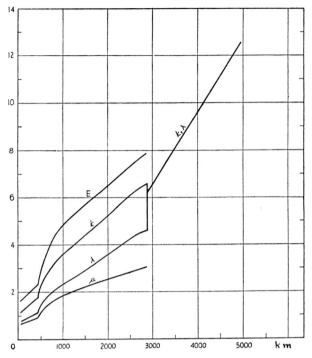

F̄ɪɢ.24.—Variation of elastic constants (in 10^{12} dynes/cm²) with depth in kilometers (Bullen, 1947).

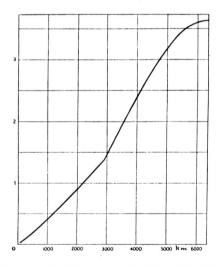

Fɪɢ. 25.—Variation of pressure (in 10^{12} dynes/cm²) with depth in kilometers (Bullen, 1947)

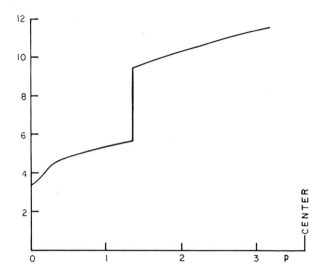

FIG. 26.—Density within the earth as a function of pressure (in 10^{12} dynes/cm^2)

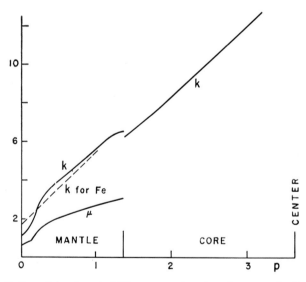

FIG. 27.—Bulk modulus, k, and rigidity, μ, as a function of pressure (in 10^{12} dynes/cm^2). The line for iron gives an extrapolation of Bridgman's (1940) results at pressures up to 3×10^{10} dynes/cm^2.

98

tion and not to lack of rigidity. Evidence that this is not so and that the core is a true liquid is given by observations of earth tides.

Suppose that S_2 is a second harmonic term in the tide-generating potential due to the sun and moon. On a rigid earth S_2 will be the potential observed at the surface, and S_2/g will be the height of the equilibrium oceanic tide. If the earth yields, there will be an additional potential, kS_2, in its external field, where k is a constant depending on the extent of the yielding; k will be zero for a rigid earth. Let the distortion of the surface be hS_2/g, where h is a constant giving the ratio of the tide in the solid earth to the equilibrium tide. The equilibrium oceanic tide relative to the surface of the earth is then $(1 + k - h)$ times what it would be on a rigid earth. Unfortunately, the natural periods of the ocean are of the same order as the periods of the diurnal and semidiurnal tides, and their amplitudes cannot be expected to agree with those predicted on an equilibrium theory. The tides of longer period, such as the fortnightly tide, should agree with the equilibrium theory. Tides in pipes and small bodies of water and the deflection of the vertical relative to the adjacent ground also yield $(1 + k - h)$. Values ranging from 0.60 to 0.84 have been obtained by these methods (Lambert, 1940; Takeuchi, 1950). The best value is probably about 0.69. 75650

The tidal variation of gravity is due to the combined effect of the tide-generating potential, the distortion of the surface hS_2, and the potential kS_2 due to distortion. The effect of the three together is a variation $1 + h - 3k/2$ times what would be observed on a rigid earth. The observed value of this quantity derived from observations at 26 stations is 1.22 (Baars, 1951, 1952; Tomaschek, 1952; Pettit et al., 1953).

The tide-generating forces produce a horizontal, as well as a vertical, displacement of the earth's surface. This introduces a third observable constant l, defined as the ratio of meridional horizontal displacement to $\partial S_2/\partial\theta \cdot g$, where θ is the latitude. This constant is involved in tidal fluctuations of latitude and longitude; these give $1 + k - l$ as about 1.22 (Nishimura, 1950).

The period of the Eulerian nutation of the earth's axis of figure relative to its axis of rotation is determined by k. The value derived from the observations is about 0.28 but is subject to some uncertainties (see chap. 2).

The quantities h, k, and l, which are known as *Love's numbers*, can be calculated if the radial variation of density and elastic constants is known. They therefore provide a method of checking the distribution of these quantities derived from seismology; in particular, they provide a check on the lack of rigidity in the core. The calculation has been carried out by

Takeuchi (1950) with Bullen's densities and elastic constants. The results are given in the accompanying table.

	k	h	l	$1+k-h$	$1+h-3k/2$	$1+k-l$
Obs.........	0.28	....	....	0.69	1.22	1.22
Calc.........	0.281	0.606	0.082	0.675	1.184	1.199

The comparison between theory and observation is subject to some uncertainty, since the observed values are disturbed by the attraction of the oceanic tides and by the yielding of the crust under tidal loads and other forces. The agreement is within the limits of uncertainty in the data. Takeuchi has also calculated h, k, and l for various assumed values of the rigidity of the core. The results are given in Table 5; they

TABLE 5

COMPARISON OF OBSERVED AND CALCULATED VALUES OF LOVE'S NUMBERS

	CALCULATED					OBS.
Rigidity of core......	0	10^7	10^9	10^{11}	10^{13}	....
k..........	0.281	0.275	0.275	0.243	+ 0.055	0.28
h..........	0.606	0.601	0.600	0.530	+ 0.109	....
l..........	0.082	0.081	0.081	0.083	+ 0.092	....
$1+k-h$......	0.675	0.674	0.675	0.713	+ 0.946	0.69
$1+h-3k/2$..	1.184	1.189	1.188	1.166	+ 1.027	1.22
$1+k-l$......	1.199	1.194	1.194	1.160	− 0.37	1.22

show that the rigidity of the core cannot exceed 10^{10} dyne/cm^2. As the bulk modulus is about 5×10^{12}, this indicates that the rigidity is less than $\frac{1}{500}$ of the bulk modulus. This ratio is much less than that for any ordinary solid.

The results obtained do not exclude the possibility that the material of the core might have a very low rigidity but a finite strength in shear, combined with a high absorption for seismic waves. Such a combination of properties is not very likely. It is excluded if the secular variation of the magnetic field is explained by motions in the core (Sec. 6.2).

There is no evidence to show whether the core is above or below its critical temperature; it is therefore possible that it is a gas, in the sense that at the prevailing temperature the liquid and gaseous phases could not coexist at any pressure. It is certain that it is a liquid, in the more important sense that each atom is continually under the influence of several others. It is not known whether the inner core is solid or liquid. For equilibrium it must be denser than the remainder of the core; thus if it is liquid, its bulk modulus must be substantially greater than that of the overlying material in order to give a sufficiently high velocity for compressional waves. This rather improbable supposition may be avoided by assuming it to be solid. The $4\mu/3$ term in equation (1) will then insure that the velocity of P is above that in the liquid part of the core (Bullen, 1950b, 1951, 1953; Ramsey, 1950b).

4. MATERIALS IN THE INTERIOR OF THE EARTH

The materials comprising the continental layers are discussed in chapters 4 and 6 and have also been briefly mentioned in Section 2.3. Informa-

TABLE 6

COMMON ELEMENTS
(Per Cent by Weight)

Element	Sun*	Stony Meteorites	Dunites	Basalts	Granites
C........	16	....	....	....	....
N........	34	....	....	....	....
O........	44	41.0	43.9	44.3	48.3
Na.......	0.2	0.8	0.1	2.4	2.6
Mg.......	2.8	15.8	28.7	3.8	....
Al........	0.2	1.7	0.5	8.5	7.7
Si........	1.7	20.6	19.6	23.4	33.2
S.........	0.7	1.8	....	....	....
K.........	0.0	0.2	0.0	1.2	3.5
Ca.......	0.1	2.0	0.5	6.5	1.4
Cr........	....	....	....	....	....
Fe........	....	15.6	6.4	8.9	2.5

* Excluding hydrogen and helium.

tion about the materials below the crust is necessarily indirect, and it is impossible to reach a conclusion unless some restriction is placed on the field of speculation. The range of possibilities is greatly reduced if only common elements are considered. This amounts to assuming that the elements that are rare at the surface of the earth are also rare inside it. There is considerable justification for this view, since, with some intelligible exceptions (such as the rarity of nitrogen and neon on earth), the relative abundance of the elements shows the same general trend in the sun, the stars, meteorites, and cosmic rays as it does on earth (see chap. 6). The light elements are the common ones, and the heavy elements beyond nickel in the periodic table are extremely rare. The elements constituting more than 1 per cent by weight of the sun and of the average analyses of stony meteorites and of certain igneous rocks are given in Table 6 (Daly, 1933; Brown, 1949; Rankama and Sahama, 1950).

The density of the mantle is 3–6 gm/cm^3, the bulk modulus is in the range 10^{12}–7 $\times$ 10^{12} dynes/cm^2, and the velocity of P waves is in the range 8–14 km/sec. The only compounds of the common elements that will give such a low density and high velocity for P are the silicates, which are, in any case, the natural material to suggest for the mantle, since the material emerging from volcanoes and that found in igneous intrusions consists almost entirely of silicates. Petrological evidence shows that rocks coming from great depths contain little or no free silica, little of the alkali metals, and not much aluminium. They are rocks consisting predominantly of iron and magnesium silicates, such as the isomorphous series forsterite, Mg_2SiO_4; olivine, $(Mg,Fe)_2SiO_4$; fayalite, Fe_2SiO_4; or pyroxenes, such as $(Mg,Fe)SiO_3$. On grounds of density, wave velocity, and petrological associations, dunite—a rock consisting almost entirely of olivine—is usually considered the most likely material to constitute at least the outer part of the mantle. The iron oxides and sulphides would be too dense to constitute any large proportion of the material.

The rapid increase in density which, on Jeffreys' view of the 20° discontinuity, occurs between 400 and 1000 km could be accounted for either by a change in material or by a polymorphic transition. Bernal (1936) has suggested that, at high pressures, olivine may change from the rhombic form, which is stable at ordinary pressures, to a cubic form. Birch (1952) has suggested that the lower part of the mantle consists of a mixture of magnesium, silicon, and iron oxides; this would not differ much from Bernal's high-pressure olivine. The highest pressures that can be maintained for an appreciable time in the laboratory are about 10^{11} dynes/cm^2 (Bridgman, 1948). As this pressure is reached at a depth of 300 km in the earth, it is probable that the changes producing the 20° discontinuity cannot at present be studied by direct experiment.

The core is composed of a liquid which has a density of 10–12 gm/cm^3 and is considerably denser than the mantle. The only common substances substantially heavier than a silicate at atmospheric pressure are iron and its oxides. The molten oxides could not exist in contact with silicates, since they are mutually soluble. The natural choice of material for the core is therefore molten iron. Some plausibility is given to this idea by the occurrence of meteorites composed almost entirely of metallic iron (see chap. 5 of Vol. 4). The existence of these bodies shows that, at some time and place in the solar system, bodies of iron have formed without enough oxygen present to oxidize them. If it could be shown that the iron meteorites were derived from the fragmentation of a planet, it would greatly strengthen the probability that the earth also contains iron. In fact, the origin of the iron meteorites is not certainly known, and they may have no relation to the core of a planet.

Ramsey (1948, 1949, 1950b) has pointed out some difficulties in the supposition that the core of the earth is composed of iron. The most cogent of these is that the density of iron is too high. From Figure 27 it is clear that the bulk modulus of the material of the core is very nearly a linear function of the pressure and that extrapolation of this line runs near the experimental values for solid iron at pressures accessible in the laboratory. Suppose the bulk modulus to be given by

$$k = a + bp,$$

where a is the modulus of solid iron at zero pressure (1.7 $\times$ 10^{12} dynes/cm^2) and b is chosen so as to reproduce Bullen's value of 6.2 $\times$ 10^{12} at the pressure prevailing at the outside of the core (1.37 $\times$ 10^{12} dynes/cm^2). The density at any pressure can then be found by integration of

$$\frac{d\rho}{dp} = \frac{\rho}{k},$$

starting with the density of molten iron at zero pressure, which is 7.0 gm/cm^3 (Stott and Rendall, 1953); the density just inside the core is found to be 10.5 instead of Bullen's value of 9.4. The discrepancy is not large and would be reduced by allowance for the temperature of the core, but the other assumptions made tend to give too small a density. Some concentration of heavier elements toward the base of the mantle is quite possible. With such a concentration, the estimated density in the outer parts of the core must be reduced so as to give the correct mass and moment of inertia for the whole earth. The reduced density in the core implies that the bulk modulus must also be reduced below its value in Bullen's model, in order to give the observed velocity for P. This increased compressibility raises the calculated density of iron. On his model Ramsey finds the density of an iron core to be 12.8, compared with his estimated density of 8.9 just inside the core. The addition of nickel to an iron core would further raise its density.

This objection to iron as the material of the core is a serious one. In order to avoid it, Ramsey has supposed that the mantle and the core are both composed of olivine and that the greater density of the core is due to its being converted into a liquid metal by the great pressure. On this view the boundary of the core occurs at that depth where the pressure is just sufficient to produce the transformation. The change from the mantle to the core under the influence of pressure is the first step in the transformation of matter from its usual form to that which occurs in the interior of a white dwarf star (Ramsey, 1950a). There is no doubt that such a transformation is possible for all substances, that it involves a substantial change in density, and that the high-pressure form is metallic. Unfortunately, no accurate estimate has been made of the change in density to be expected for olivine or of the critical pressure.

Ramsey supposed that his view was consistent with all the inner planets having the same composition. The density now accepted for Mercury is considerably higher than that taken by Ramsey (see Vol. 3), and it appears that it is now impossible to assume that all the inner planets have the same composition. This reduces the probability of Ramsey's view but does not exclude it. It is conceivable that the core consists of an alloy of Ramsey's metallic silicate and iron. This view gains some plausibility from the frequent occurrence of meteorites in which iron and silicate are intimately intermixed. Such a material might be formed if the pressure on an iron-silicate alloy were released. Birch (1952) suggests that the density of an iron core may be reduced by admixture with a little hydrogen. Bullen (1952) has also recently discussed the problem.

In the 200 km immediately above the core, the rate of increase in the velocity of P is less than at shallower depths. This can be seen in Figure 20; S shows some signs of similar behavior, which is not evident in the figure but which can be detected in Table 4. Ramsey suggests that this is due to the excitation of a proportion of the electrons in the olivine into a conduction band; this would be expected to occur at a pressure a little below that at which the transformation to a metal occurs. Urey (1951, 1952) has suggested that this change in slope is due to the admixture of blobs of molten iron with the lower part of the mantle. Some caution is necessary in discussing this feature of the travel-time curve, since the supposed changes occur within about a wave length of the surface of the core and a velocity distribution based on ray optics may be inadequate.

The main uncertainties in the internal constitution of the earth are (a) the nature and depth of the 20° discontinuity; (b) how far the material between the 20° discontinuity and the core is homogeneous; (c) the magnitude of the density jump between the core and the mantle; (d) the constitution of the core; and (e) the properties and constitution of the inner core.

It should be possible to distinguish between Jeffreys' and Gutenberg's views on the 20° discontinuity by a study of earthquakes whose foci lie at depths between 80 and 400 km. Laboratory investigations may also throw light on the phase changes produced by pressure in this range of depth.

The homogeneity of the mantle and the density jump at the boundary of the core are connected, in that a more rapid increase in density with depth in the mantle implies a smaller discontinuity. It is possible that further studies of the amplitudes of waves reflected at the surface of the core will throw light on this. The observation of PcP from an underwater explosion would be particularly valuable, as it would remove the uncertainty about the angular distribution of the initial motion. A knowledge of the free periods of oscillation of the earth would also be helpful if some means could be found of observing them.

It is possible that the theory of the transition of olivine to a metallic state can be improved to a point where the critical pressure and density jump can be predicted. This would greatly clarify the doubts that exist as to the material of the core. A better determination of the density of the planet Mercury is also much to be desired. Birch (1952) and Jacobs (1953) have suggested that the inner core is composed of iron solidified by the high pressure near the center of the earth.

There seems little immediate prospect of learning more about the inner core, and there is grave risk of error in the identification of the numerous and complicated branches of the travel-time curves which should be associated with it. A further study of P at distances between 103° and 142° should show whether the drop in the velocity of P near the outside of the inner core assumed by Jeffreys is really necessary.

The deductions which can be made from experimental and theoretical work on the properties of materials at high pressures are further discussed in Volume **3**. The range of pressure for which information is most required is 10^{11}–4×10^{12} dynes/cm²; this is so far above the pressures at which accurate experimental data exist that extrapolation is dangerous, and yet it is too low for theoretical treatment by simple models assuming complete breakdown of the electron shells. Elsasser (1950a, 1951) doubts whether Ramsey's views are consistent with the facts, and favors an iron core.

5. HEAT FLOW AND RADIOACTIVITY

5.1. Observed Heat Flow

The temperature in mines and borings exceeds the mean annual temperature at the surface of the earth and increases with depth. The rate of increase varies greatly from place to place but usually lies in the range 10–40° C/km; a large body of data has been collected by van Orstrand (in Birch et al., 1942).

The downward increase in temperature implies an upward flow of heat by conduction. The amount of heat flowing out can be found by multiplying the temperature gradient by the thermal conductivity of the rocks. The thermal conductivity of most rocks lies in the range 0.003–0.014 cal/cm °C sec (Birch *et al.*, 1942; Coster, 1948; Birch, 1950, 1954*b*; Misener *et al.*, 1951; Bullard and Niblett, 1951; Leith, 1952). Owing to the large variations of both gradient and conductivity that can occur in a single bore, a reliable heat flow can be obtained only where a considerable number of measurements is available. Even then, the results are subject to disturbance by irregularities of geological structure and by the movement of water, and considerable differences may exist between bores only a few kilometers apart. The measurements up to 1950 have been collected (Landolt-Börnstein, 1952); these, together with a few more recent results (Bullard and Niblett, 1951; Misener *et al.*, 1951; Birch, 1954*b*; Newstead and

TABLE 7

HEAT FLOW

PLACE	NO. OF BORES	HEAT FLOW (cal/cm² sec)		
		Max. $\times 10^{-6}$	Min. $\times 10^{-6}$	Mean $\times 10^{-6}$
South Africa......	7	1.52	0.75	1.10
Persia...........	18	1.22	0.53	0.87
United States.....	10	2.00	0.55	1.45
Canada..........	11*	1.32	0.69	0.95
Europe..........	14	2.87	0.71	1.80
Tasmania........	5	2.54	2.04	2.24
Mean†.......	....	....	....	1.23

* 10 mines and 1 bore, the results from the mines are each equivalent to a group of bores.
† Excluding Tasmania.

Beck, 1953), are summarized in Table 7, which gives the mean heat flow in the areas where it has been determined and the range of values found in different bore holes. The data are far from adequate and come largely from small groups of bores which may not be representative of wider areas; for example, six of the fourteen determinations in Europe are from bores a few miles apart in Nottinghamshire, England. These and a determination in a salt dome at Sperenberg are responsible for the high European average; the other seven determinations give 1.12×10^{-6}. In view of this lack of data, it is impossible to discuss regional variations in heat flow; many local anomalies are known, some of which can be more or less satisfactorily explained; but it is not possible to say whether the heat flow is systematically greater in one country than in another or whether there is a difference between mountainous and low-lying areas.

Similar measurements have recently been made in the Pacific (Revelle and Maxwell, 1952). The heat flow is found to be about 1.2×10^{-6} cal/cm² sec and does not differ significantly from that on the continents. A mean value of 1.0×10^{-6} cal/cm² sec has been found by Bullard (1954a) in the Atlantic. Assuming a flow of 1.2×10^{-6} cal/cm² sec over the whole surface of the earth, the total amount of energy conducted outward is 6.1×10^{12} cal/sec.

The rate of flow of heat from inside the earth is 25,000 times less than that arriving from the sun when it is overhead. The temperature of the surface is therefore controlled by the sun and not by the internal heat. Although the flow of heat is so small, it amounts to a considerable total in the course of geological time. In a million years the total is about 4×10^7 cal/cm². To provide this by burning coal would require the consumption of a seam 40 m thick. This example makes it clear that chemical changes in rocks near the surface cannot provide any large part of the observed heat flow. Similar arguments show that the cooling of dikes and sills is inadequate as a source of heat. Kelvin and most other early writers on the subject supposed the heat arriving at the surface of the earth to be the original heat remaining from a previous time when the earth was molten. Kelvin found that, on this assumption, the earth must have been molten not more than 30 million years ago. The main reason for this result is that the escape of heat from the inside is hindered by the layer of already cooled rock, which increases in thickness as time goes on; if the earth contains no internal source of heat, the outward flow would, after 30 million years, be reduced below that which is observed, even though the inside were still at a temperature of some thousands of degrees. Kelvin's limit could probably be raised substantially by assuming the thermal conductivity to increase with depth (Slichter, 1941); but to raise it to anything approaching the 3×10^9 years, which is at present accepted as the age of the earth, it would be necessary to assume that the thermal conductivity of the material at depths below a few hundred kilometers is of the order of magnitude characteristic of metals (0.1 cal/°C cm sec) rather than of silicates (0.006). Such a high conductivity is excluded if the magnetic secular variation is to be explained by motions in the core (see Sec. 6). It seems almost certain that not more than 20 per cent of the observed heat flow can be derived from the original heat locked up in the earth when it was formed. The rest must come from the radioactivity of rocks.

5.2. RADIOACTIVITY OF ROCKS

All rocks contain measurable amounts of the radioactive elements uranium, thorium, and potassium. The amounts are very variable, as is

shown in Figure 28, but there is a general tendency for the granites and
other acidic rocks to be more radioactive than the basalts and ultrabasic
rocks. Averages are given in Table 8; but, in view of the large variability
and the difficulty in adequate sampling, they can be regarded only as a
general indication of the distribution of the radioactive elements in nature.
The uranium content of stony meteorites depends on two specimens investigated by Davis (1950). There are no modern determinations of the
thorium content of stony meteorites or ultrabasic rocks; the values given
in Table 8 are obtained by assuming the ratio of thorium to uranium to

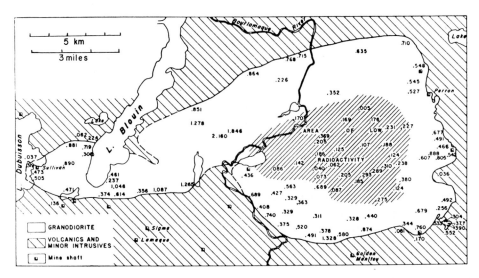

Fig. 28.—Distribution of radioactivity in Bourlamaque batholith (Ingham and Keevil,
1951), expressed as the number of α particles per milligram per hour.

TABLE 8*

RADIOACTIVITY AND HEAT GENERATION IN ROCKS

Rock	Concentration (gm/gm)			Heat Production (cal/gm sec)				Total (cal/cm³ sec ×10⁻¹⁴)
	U ×10⁻⁸	Th ×10⁻⁶	K ×10⁻²	U ×10⁻¹⁴	Th ×10⁻¹⁴	K ×10⁻¹⁴	Total ×10⁻¹⁴	
Granite.......	400	13	3.5	9.2	8.2	3.0	20	53
Basalt........	100	3	1.3	2.3	1.9	1.1	5.3	15
Ultrabasic	2	(0.06)	0.03	0.05	(0.04)	0.03	0.12	0.4
Stony meteorites........	3	(0.10)	0.20	0.07	(0.06)	0.2	0.3	1.0
Iron meteorites	0.5	0.04	0.0	0.012	0.025	0.0	0.04	0.3

* Data from Daly (1933), Evans and Goodman (1941), Arrol, Jacobi, and Paneth (1942), Davis (1947, 1950),
Senftle and Keevil (1947), Davis and Hess (1949), Birch (1951a), and Dalton et al. (1953).

be 3.2, which is the value found in other types of rocks (Senftle and Keevil, 1947). The modern determinations of uranium in meteorites and ultrabasic rocks are usually less than those obtained in the past, by a factor of 10 or more, and the latter are probably best disregarded. Further work is most desirable.

The heat generated by uranium and thorium in equilibrium with their products of disintegration and by potassium is (Bullard, 1942; Birch, 1951a; Slack and Whithan, 1951) given in the accompanying table.

Uranium	2.34×10^{-8} cal/gm sec
Thorium	0.63×10^{-8} cal/gm sec
Potassium	8.5×10^{-13} cal/gm sec

When combined with the amounts of uranium, thorium, and potassium in the rocks, these give the rates of generation of heat given in Table 8. If the rate of generation of heat given in Table 8 for granite extended down to the Mohorovičić discontinuity at a depth of 35 km, the heat generated would be 1.9×10^{-6} cal/cm² sec, which exceeds the observed flow.

If there were 10 km of basalt below 25 km of granite, the heat flow would be 1.5×10^{-6} cal/cm² sec, which is still too high, particularly as no allowance has been made for original heat or for radioactivity below the crust. It is clear that the radioactivity of the crust must be substantially less than the average for granite given in Table 8. This is to be expected, since the radioactive elements tend to be concentrated upward (see chaps. 4 and 6); this can be seen in Figure 28, which shows the distribution of radioactivity over the truncated surface of a batholith (a dome-shaped mass of granite). There is a clear concentration in a ring round the outside of the batholith; this shows that radioactive material has migrated to the outside of the dome and strongly suggests an upward migration.

Owing to the finite age of the earth, the heat produced by radioactivity at depths greater than a few hundred kilometers has not had time to reach the surface. As a rough approximation, the heat coming from below the crust may be taken as equal to that from a semi-infinite solid with a radioactivity equal to that ascribed to ultrabasic rock in Table 8. The heat flow is then $2Q\sqrt{(\kappa_1 t/\pi)}$ (Carslaw and Jaeger, 1947, p. 60), where Q is the rate of heat generation (0.4×10^{-14} cal/cm³ sec), κ_1 is the thermometric conductivity, which may be taken as 6.5×10^{-3}, and t is the age of the earth. With $t = 3.3 \times 10^9$ years, this gives 0.12×10^{-6} cal/cm² sec. Reasonable assumptions (see Sec. 5.3) give 0.3×10^{-6} cal/cm² sec for the heat flow due to the original heat of the earth. The observed surface heat flow on the continents may then be accounted for by taking the rocks of the crust to have half the average radioactivity found in granite at the surface. We then have the values given in the accompanying table.

	cal/cm^2 sec $\times 10^{-6}$
Crust (35 km)......................................	0.9
Mantle...	.1
Original heat......................................	0.3
Total..	1.3

In order to account for the observed heat flow in the oceans, it is necessary to assume that the material of the mantle, that is, the material that gives the 8.2-km/sec P-wave velocity, has a higher radioactivity under the oceans than it has under the continents. This is explicable if the continents are gradually produced from the margins of the ocean basins by a process of differentiation, as is suggested in chapter 4. Such a process would be likely to lead to an upward concentration of uranium and thorium. The continents and oceans would then contain, on the average, the same amount of radioactivity per unit area, but in the oceans it would be distributed through a greater range of depth. There is no evidence to suggest what the vertical distribution is; 250 km of material with a heat generation of 4×10^{-14} cal/cm^3 sec would provide what is required when allowance is made for original heat and for the heat generated in the material above the 8.2-km/sec material. The distribution of the radioactive material through so great a range of depth leads, however, to improbably high temperatures (see Sec. 5.3).

5.3. The Temperature inside the Earth

If all the heat that arrives at the surface of the earth were generated below the crust, the temperature at the base of the crust at depth h would be hH/κ above that at the surface, where H is the heat flow and κ the thermal conductivity. If all the heat were generated by radioactivity spread uniformly through the crust, the temperature would be half this. If $h = 35$ km, $\kappa = 0.006$ cal/cm °C sec, and $H = 1.2 \times 10^{-6}$ cal/cm^2 sec, these temperatures are 700° and 350° C. If, as is suggested above, 0.4×10^{-6} cal/cm^2 sec comes from below the crust and the rest from radioactivity in the crust, the temperature would be 470° C above that at the surface. By a similar method, but using a lower conductivity, Holmes (1944, p. 482) gets 585° C. The conductivity decreases with increasing temperature (Fig. 29); it would not be difficult to allow for this, but it hardly seems worth while in view of the uncertainty in the distribution of radioactivity in the crust. An upward concentration of the radioactivity in the crust would reduce the temperatures.

Since the radioactive material in the crust of the earth is continually decaying, the heat generation must in the past have been greater than it is today. The half-lives of the atoms concerned are (Birch, 1951a; Fleming

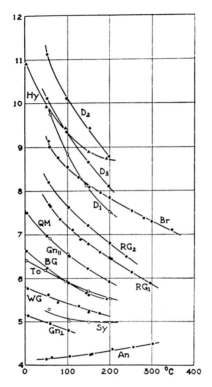

FIG. 29.—Variation of thermal conductivity (in 10^{-3} cal/cm sec degree) of rocks with temperature (Birch and Clark, 1940a). An = anorthosite; Gn = gneiss; Sy = syenite; WG, BG, and RG = granite; To = tonalite; QM = quartz monzonite; Br = bronzite; Hy = hypersthenite; D = dunite.

et al., 1952) given in the accompanying table. Using these values and as-

Isotope.................	U^{238}	U^{235}	Th^{238}	K^{40}
Half-life (10^9 years).....	4.51	0.713	13.9	1.3

suming the rate of heat production by U^{235} to be at present 4.2 per cent of that by U^{238}, one finds that the granite of Table 8 would produce the amounts of heat at various times in the past as given in the accompanying table. Since the temperature at the base of the crust is roughly pro-

Time (10^9 years)...........	0	1	2	3	4
Heat (10^{-14} cal/gm sec)......	20	25	32	45	70

portional to the rate of heat production, it is likely that its base would have been molten between 3 and 4×10^9 years ago. This suggests that conditions at the surface of the earth cannot have resembled those found at present for times longer than this. This is consistent with the ages of the oldest rocks estimated by other methods (see chap. 4). More detailed calculations have been made by Urry (1949).

The estimate of temperatures deeper in the earth is much more speculative. Heat from material at depths of more than a few hundred kilometers has not had time to reach the surface, and the observations of heat flow can therefore give no indication of the temperature or the rate of heat generation at great depths. The only experimental indication is that the electrical resistivity is known to fall to something of the order of 200 ohm cm at a depth of 600–900 km (Chapman and Bartels, 1940, p. 729). The work of Coster (1948) and Hughes (unpublished) shows that such a conductivity is reached by most silicates at a temperature of 1000°–1500° C. Lower temperatures at this depth would be possible only if a substantial proportion of the material were a moderate conductor at lower temperatures. Materials such as some of the iron oxides and sulphides have the necessary properties, but there is no other reason to suppose them to be present. The natural assumption is that the electrical conductivity is due to the high temperature of a silicate mantle. The absence of short periods in the magnetic secular variation and the theory of the geomagnetic "westward drift" (Bullard, 1948b; Bullard et al., 1950; Runcorn, 1954) suggest still higher conductivities and temperatures at greater depths.

More detailed information can be obtained only from calculations based on hypotheses as to the origin and early history of the earth. The following possibilities may be suggested: (a) the earth was formed with both the core and the mantle hot and molten and then cooled to its present state; (b) the earth was formed cold and solid, subsequently melted, and then cooled to its present state; (c) the earth was formed cold and solid and subsequently warmed to its present state. The first possibility would occur if the earth were formed from the sun or by rapid accumulation from a dust cloud. The second would occur if material of high radioactivity accumulated slowly, and the third with slow accumulation and low radioactivity. The plausibility of these processes as theories of the mode of origin of the planets is discussed in Volume **4**; here we are concerned only with their thermal consequences. The consequences of hypothesis *a* have been worked out in detail by Jeffreys (1952*b*).

If the earth were molten originally or became molten after formation, it would almost at once get into a state where the temperature gradient was equal to the adiabatic gradient. It would then cool until the melting point was reached at some depth. The time for this process would probably be well below 10^6 years. While it was going on, it is likely that there would be some chemical differentiation and that the radioactive elements would be concentrated upward.

The *adiabatic gradient* is $aT/\rho C_p$, where a is the coefficient of cubical expansion, T is the temperature, ρ the density, and C_p the specific heat at constant pressure. Estimates of a and C_p can be made by the extrapolation of laboratory data; but Verhoogen (1951) has obtained what is probably a more reliable value of a/C_p by combining Bullen's analysis of the seismic data with relations derived from the theory of solids. He finds that a/C_p decreases from 3.6×10^{-12} gm/erg at a depth of 200 km to 0.8×10^{-12} at 2600 km. From this he gets a mean adiabatic gradient of $0.17°$ C/km. This applies to the present solid mantle but would probably not be very different for a molten mantle.

The point at which the melting point is first reached will depend on whether the rate of increase in the melting point with depth does or does not exceed the adiabatic gradient. If the adiabatic gradient is smaller, solidification will start from the base of the mantle and proceed upward. This must, in fact, happen; for if it did not, the latent heat from the lower part of the mantle would be trapped beneath a layer of poorly conducting solid rock and its latent heat would not be able to escape. The solid mantle found by seismology is therefore evidence that if the earth were ever molten, it must have solidified from below.

The *melting-point gradient* can be obtained from the Clapeyron-Clausius relation, which gives

$$\frac{dT}{dr} = -\frac{Tg}{L}\left(\frac{\rho_S}{\rho_L} - 1\right), \tag{10}$$

where T is the melting point in degrees absolute, L is the latent heat of fusion, and ρ_L and ρ_S are the densities of the liquid and the solid. At ordinary pressures $T = 1300°$ C, $L = 4 \times 10^9$ ergs/gm, and $\rho_S/\rho_L - 1 = 0.08$, which gives a gradient of $3°$ C/km. In the interior of the earth, T

will be greater and L and $\rho_S/\rho_L - 1$ smaller than at zero pressure, but
it is difficult to say how much they will change.

Some idea of the change of gradient with depth may be obtained by
using an empirical formula due to Simon (1937) for the change of melting
point with pressure. This is

$$p = a\left[\left(\frac{T_p}{T_0}\right)^c - 1\right],\tag{11}$$

where T_p is the melting point at pressure p, T_0 that at zero pressure (except
for helium, where T_0 is 0.992°), and a and c are constants. It is found that
c is usually about 2 (Simon and Glatzel, 1929) but varies from 1.55 for
helium (Holland, Huggill, and Jones, 1951) up to 4.75 for caesium. This
formula has been verified for helium up to $T_p/T_0 = 42$.

The rate of change of melting point with pressure at zero pressure derived from the Clapeyron-Clausius expression fixes ac as 1.5×10^{11}. The
temperature at any pressure can then be found from equation (11) for any
value of c. The temperatures found in this way are given in the accompanying table. The value of about 6700° C for $c = 2$ is the most likely.

c	1.5	2.0	3.0	4.0
$T\,(°\,C)$	9300	6700	4600	3600

This gives an average gradient of 2°.2 C/km and a gradient of 1°.3 C/km
at the bottom of the mantle, both of which are substantially greater
than the adiabatic gradient. Solidification would therefore be expected to start at the *bottom* of the mantle and proceed upward, the latent
heat being removed to the surface by convection and there radiated away.
The time required for solidification would probably be not more than
10,000 years. At the end of this time the mantle would be only slightly below the melting point at all depths. Uffen (1952) has obtained a temperature of 5000° C at the bottom of the mantle by using Lindeman's theory of
melting. This is 1700° C below the value estimated from equation (11);
the difference is an indication of the great uncertainty of calculations involving so large an extrapolation.

The core would have the same temperature at the surafce as the mantle
in contact with it and the adiabatic gradient below. The adiabatic gradient
in a fluid core has been discussed by Bullard (1950a), Valle (1952), and
Jacobs (1953); it may be shown to be $g\gamma T/v^2$, where γ is Grüneisen's constant and v is the velocity of compressional waves. With $g = 900$ cm/sec²,
$\gamma = 0.8$, $T = 7000°$ K, $v = 9$ km/sec, this gives 0°.6 C/km and a temper-

ature difference of 2000° C between the center and the outside of the core. These values may be too high; Jacobs gets $0°25$ C/km. If the core is iron, the temperature at the base of the mantle must be above the melting point. The rate of increase in the melting point of iron with pressure is very imperfectly known but is probably much less than that for silicates, owing to the small difference between the densities of the liquid and the solid. The melting point of iron at the top of the core has been estimated in the same way as for the silicate of the mantle, with $L = 2.8 \times 10^9$ erg/gm, $T_0 = 1532°$ C, $\rho_1 = 7.273$, $\rho_2 = 7.019$ (Stott and Rendall, 1953). For iron, c is probably between 3 and 4; the melting point at the base of the mantle is then found to be 3400° C for $c = 3$ and 3000° C for $c = 4$. At the center of the earth it is 4700° C for $c = 3$ and 3800° C for $c = 4$. These figures suggest that the temperature at the base of the mantle is sufficient to melt iron. Very similar results have been obtained by Simon (1953). Jacobs (1954) has suggested that the inner core may be solid iron below its melting point; this would require temperatures lower than those found here. The melting point of the metallic form of silicate proposed by Ramsey as the material of the core is not known. The temperature distribution just after solidification is shown in Figure 30. It is subject to great uncertainty, since the basic assumption of an initial molten state is open to some doubt and equation (11) may be rendered inapplicable because the crystal structure or composition is not the same at all depths within the mantle. The temperatures obtained here are higher than most recent estimates but are lower than those current some years ago.

The thermal history of the earth after solidification can be worked out from the laws of thermal conduction if it can be assumed that no further motion takes place. The temperature, T, is controlled by the conduction equation, which, for a symmetrical temperature distribution, is

$$w \frac{\partial T}{\partial t} = \frac{1}{r^2} \frac{\partial}{\partial r} \left(\kappa r^2 \frac{\partial T}{\partial r} \right) + H\,(r, t), \qquad (12)$$

where w is the heat capacity per unit volume, κ is the conductivity, and H is the rate of heat generation per unit volume. Just after solidification at $t = 0$, T is equal to the melting point everywhere in the mantle. For all $t > 0$, the temperature at the surface may be assumed equal to the present mean surface temperature. At the surface of the core the temperature will not have altered appreciably since solidification. Owing to the gradual reduction in the amount of radioactive material, H should be taken as a decreasing function of the time, but as the half-lives of the elements concerned are all between 0.7 and 14×10^9 years, the decrease in H is very slow and may for many purposes be neglected.

If T_1 is the solution of equation (12) with $H = 0$ and the foregoing boundary and initial conditions, and T_2 is a solution with the actual value of H, the initial temperature equal to zero and the surface temperature zero throughout, then, if w and κ are independent of T,

$$T = T_1 + T_2$$

is the required solution of equation (12). That is to say, the solution may be separated into two parts, one concerning a nonradioactive earth that cools by conduction from the actual initial state and the other concerning an earth initially at zero temperature, which is warmed by radioactivity and loses heat by conduction to the surface. Numerous solutions have been given, of which Slichter's (1941) is the most complete. For present purposes it is convenient to make certain approximations which cannot introduce much error and which lead to an easily intelligible result. We assume (a) that κ and w are the same at all depths; (b) that cooling is appreciable only at depths which are a small fraction of the radius of the earth (the term in eq. [12] containing κ may then be replaced by $\kappa \partial^2 T / \partial r^2$, and the melting-point gradient may be treated as constant); and (c) that H is independent of time and is appreciable only in a layer whose thickness is small compared to the depth to which cooling has extended. The arguments of Section 5.2 suggest that this is a reasonable approximation, at any rate beneath the continents.

With these simplifications, the temperature below the radioactive layer at a depth x is (Jeffreys, 1952b; Bullard, 1939)

$$T = T_s + mx + (S - T_s) \operatorname{erf} \frac{x}{2\sigma t^{1/2}} + \left(1 - \operatorname{erf} \frac{x}{2\sigma t^{1/2}}\right) \frac{Q\bar{x}}{\kappa}, \qquad (13)$$

where T_s is the surface temperature; m is the initial temperature gradient, that is, the melting-point gradient; S is the melting point near the surface; $\sigma^2 = \kappa/w$ is the thermometric conductivity; t is the time since solidification; Q is the total rate of generation of heat per unit area summed throughout the radioactive layer; and $\bar{x}$ is the depth of the center of gravity of the radioactive material.

Initially, the temperature is $S + mx$. The term mx represents the initial melting-point gradient. The decline of the term $(S - T_s) \operatorname{erf} (x/2\sigma t^{1/2})$ as t increases represents the cooling of a nonradioactive earth. $Q\bar{x}/\kappa$ is the temperature rise in the radioactive layer due to the outward escape of the heat Q. The term $-Q\bar{x} \operatorname{erf} (xw/2\sigma t^{1/2})/\kappa$ represents the reversed gradient below the radioactive layer which would be produced by heating of the layer in an initially cold earth.

With $T_s = 0°$ C, $m = 3°$ C/km, $S = 1300°$ C, $w = 1$ cal/cm³, $\kappa = 0.006$ cal/cm ° C sec, and $t = 3 \times 10^9$ years, equation (13) gives

$$T = 3x + 1300 \text{ erf } \frac{x}{480} + \left(1 - \text{erf } \frac{x}{480}\right) 17 \times 10^6 Q\bar{x},$$

where x and $\bar{x}$ are in kilometers and Q in cal/cm² sec. If the radioactivity is distributed uniformly in a radioactive layer of thickness d, the temperature in it will be

$$T = T_s + H_s \frac{x}{\kappa} - \frac{Qx^2}{2\kappa d}, \tag{14}$$

where H_s is the heat flow at the surface. Q can now be chosen so that equations (13) and (14) give the same heat flow at the base of the radioactive layer. This amounts to finding the heat coming from below the radioactive layer by calculation from the assumed initial conditions and subtracting this from the observed heat flow. In this way it is found that if $H_s = 1.23 \times 10^{-6}$ cal/cm² sec, the heat flow at the base of a radioactive layer 35 km thick is 0.32×10^{-6} cal/cm² sec, and the heat produced by radioactivity is 0.91×10^{-6}. The heat production per unit volume in the layer is 26×10^{-4} cal/cm³ sec. The temperatures at any depth can now be found from equations (13) and (14). The results are shown in curve a of Figure 30.

Under the oceans there is some reason to suppose that the radioactivity is distributed through a greater depth than it is beneath the continents (Sec. 5.2). This raises a dilemma which was first pointed out by Dr. R. Revelle (unpublished). If the radioactivity is distributed through too great a depth, the temperature near the base of the radioactive layer will rise above the melting point, which is inconsistent with the propagation of S waves. On the other hand, if the layer is made too thin, the rocks beneath the oceans will have to be assumed to contain an improbably large amount of radioactive material. Temperatures have been calculated for layers 200 and 100 km thick; the results are shown in Figure 30. It appears that the melting point would be exceeded if the thickness were greater than about 150 km. The heat generation needed to give a heat flow of 1.2×10^{-6} cal/cm² sec would be 5.3×10^{-14} cal/cm³ sec for a 200-km layer, and 9.2×10^{-14} for a 100-km layer, after allowance had been made for original heat and for that from 4 km of basalt. These values are so much greater than the observed average of 0.4×10^{-14} cal/cm³ sec for ultrabasic rocks as to raise a real difficulty. It would be of great interest to have more measurements of the radioactivity of basalts and ultrabasic rocks from the oceans and also to examine the amplitudes of S at distances between $10°$ and $20°$ for oceanic and continental paths separately (Sec. 2.4). It is possible that the difficulty may be avoided by the transport of heat by convection in the mantle either continuously or intermittently (see Sec. 5.5), but it would then be necessary to explain why the material beneath the oceans did not become mixed with that beneath the continents. It must be admitted that the relation between the oceanic and continental heat flows raises difficulties to which no satisfactory solution is known.

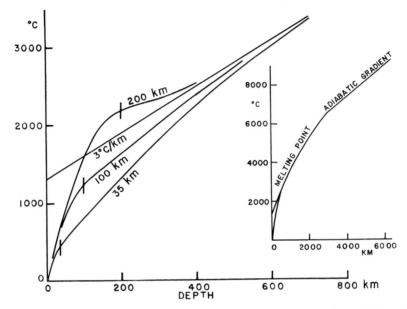

Fig. 30.—Variation of temperature with depth for a surface heat flow of 1.23×10^{-6} cal/cm² sec and a radioactive layer 35, 100, and 200 km thick. The smaller curve shows the variation of melting point with depth.

So far, the temperatures have been calculated on the assumption that the earth was initially fluid and solidified from the bottom upward. It is not inconceivable that the earth was formed by the accretion of small bodies—the planetesimals—and had initially a temperature below the melting point. For this to have happened, the accumulation must have taken place so slowly that the heat produced by the impact of a planetesimal was radiated away before it was covered by further material. The limit that this sets to the rate of accretion has been considered by Benfield (1950a). Even in a slowly accreting planet, the temperature in the interior will be raised by adiabatic compression. Benfield estimates that this would double the initial absolute temperature, that is, if the earth were formed at 0° C, compression would raise the central temperature to about 550° C. In the course of 4×10^9 years the temperature of a material which now has the radioactivity of the ultrabasic rock or iron meteorite in Table 8 would have risen by about 1100°, giving a final temperature of 1600° C. This is the minimum temperature that can reasonably be assumed in the interior of the earth. Such low temperatures seem improbable, for the following reasons:

a) They are too low to melt an iron core (the melting point of Ramsey's metallic silicate is not known).

b) At temperatures so far below the melting point the mantle would have great strength and the approximate isostatic equilibrium of large features and the smallness of the gravity anomalies averaged over large areas would be difficult to account for.

c) Neither convection currents nor contraction would be available to account for mountain-building; in fact, the earth would be slowly heating and expanding instead of contracting. The present state of the surface strongly suggests contraction.

d) The radioactivity of the bulk of the mantle may be nearer that of stony meteorites than that of ultrabasic rock. This would raise the temperature to about 5000° C.

The data on which such calculations are based are little more than a plausible guess, but they do suggest that there is no difficulty in accounting for temperatures of a few thousand degrees in an earth formed by accretion.

The temperature inside the earth is less well known than any other of its physical properties. On the whole, it seems likely that below about 500 km the mantle is only a little below the melting point. This is consistent with the electrical conductivity found from the magnetic observations and allows the material to have a low strength. Fortunately, the temperature is in any case low enough for it to have little effect on the density and elastic constants within the earth. These are predominantly controlled by the nature of the material and the pressure, and only slightly by the temperature. For example, a change in density of 1 per cent is produced in granite by a change in pressure of 5000 kg/cm² or by a change in temperature of 1000° C; since the pressure at the boundary of the core is of the order of 10^6 kg/cm² and the temperature a few thousand degrees, the former is clearly predominant. Certain other properties, particularly mechanical strength, viscosity, and electrical and thermal conductivity, are more affected by temperature than by pressure and are consequently very imperfectly known in the interior of the earth.

5.4. Volcanic Heat

At the bottom of the crust the temperature cannot be much above $450°$ C and is certainly far below the melting point and below the temperature of the lava emerging from volcanoes. There must therefore be some mechanism for providing heat to volcanoes. This mechanism must be local and intermittent in its action; volcanoes are uncommon objects on the earth's surface; they occur only in special places and remain active in a given area for only a fraction of geological time. It may be shown (Gratton, 1945) that chemical action is an inadequate source for the energy; it is also unlikely that the heat comes from an exceptional accumulation of radioactive material. There is no generally accepted view as to where it does come from, but there seems good reason to believe that it is derived from the dissipation of mechanical energy associated with earthquakes.

When an earthquake takes place, energy that has been stored as elastic energy is suddenly released, and part of it is radiated as elastic waves. This energy is gradually dissipated throughout the earth and converted into heat. The energy is only 1.1 ergs/cm³ year and can have no important thermal effects. The remainder of the elastic energy that gave rise to the earthquake is dissipated as heat near the focus by friction at fault planes and by plastic distortion and fracturing of rock. No detailed calculations have been made, but it is likely that this energy is at least as great as that appearing as seismic waves. This heat is produced in a very small fraction of the earth's volume and is probably sufficient to produce melting on a large scale.

As an example, consider the Japan-Kamchatka area shown in Figures 17 and 18 of Gutenberg and Richter's book (1949). If a smooth curve is drawn around the epicenters of the shallow earthquakes shown in these figures, it is found to have an area of 2.0×10^6 km². The total volume down to 60 km—the limit of depth of Gutenberg and Richter's shallow earthquakes—is therefore 1.2×10^{23} cm³. The average energy sent out as seismic waves from this area is (Gutenberg and Richter, 1949, p. 23) 1.7×10^{26} ergs/year. If the heat capacity of the material is 1 cal/° C cm³ and the energy dissipated near the focus is equal to that radiated, the rate of rise of temperature will be 3.4×10^{-5} ° C/year. The temperature will then rise $1000°$ C in 3×10^7 years. As in the absence of this heat the temperature at all depths below 20 km is over 300° C, the whole of the material between 20 and 60 km would be melted. Allowance for the escape of heat upward and for latent heat would make little difference, and the earthquakes below 60 km would produce sufficient heat to prevent the conduction of heat downward. We do not, in fact, need to melt so large a volume of rock, and the energy dissipated may well exceed that in the seismic waves. On both these grounds, the calculated time of 30 million years may be a considerable overestimate of the time needed to melt rock at depth. It might be objected that as soon as the melting point was approached, the rock would soften and be unable to sustain the elastic stresses necessary for the production of further earthquakes and further heating. This objection does not seem insuperable, as rock in such a condition would be likely to convert some of the energy of earthquakes in neighboring stronger rock into heat.

This view ascribes earthquakes and volcanic heat to the mechanical energy associated with the distortion of the crust. It explains very naturally the general association of volcanoes and earthquakes without requiring particular earthquakes to be associated with particular eruptions. On this view it would be expected that volcanic activity would develop later than earthquakes in an area and would continue after the earthquakes had ceased. It is difficult to say whether this is so, but it is possible that Italy, Sicily, and the African Rift Valleys provide examples, as they have active volcanoes and rather minor seismic activity which may be the relic of greater activity in the past. The theory could not account for the volcanoes of the Pacific, as there are very few earthquakes there. This is not a serious objection, as we have other reasons for expecting high temperatures under the oceans (see Sec. 5.3).

Clearly, this theory of the origin of volcanic heat requires more detailed investigation. It would be interesting, for instance, to know whether the position of the volcanoes of the island arcs over the foci of intermediate depth can be accounted for. There may be some difficulty in getting enough energy by mechanical deformation of the crust. If in an area of deformation the crust is compressed to a small fraction of its initial length, the work done per unit volume would be of the order of the crushing strength, that is, about 10^{10} ergs/cm^3. This would raise the temperature by only 240° C. This may be an underestimate, as there are forms of deformation that produce heat without involving a shortening; for example, if the stresses in the crust are produced by convection currents in the mantle, the heat produced by shear at the top of the convective zone will probably greatly exceed that produced by crushing in the crust.

5.5. CONVECTION IN THE MANTLE

Joly (1925), Vening-Meinesz (1947, 1951), Griggs (1939), Anderson (1952), Pekeris (1935), and others have supposed that though the mantle is a solid for forces of short duration such as those occurring in the propagation of earthquake waves and earth tides, it may act as a fluid for stresses of very long duration, an idea suggested by the approximate isostatic adjustment of large topographic features. If this were so, it might be possible for the mantle to be subject to very slow convection currents. Pekeris (1935) has investigated these currents on the hypothesis that they are driven by the difference of weight between equal columns of material beneath the continents and the oceans consequent on differences of temperature. He supposed the radioactivity beneath the oceans to be less than that beneath the continents and hence the temperature to be greater and the density less under the continents than under the oceans. This would lead to currents rising under the continents, flowing out beneath the continental margins, and sinking under the oceans. In view of the recent results obtained from measurements of heat flow at sea, it is probable that the temperatures are higher under the oceans than under the continents and that the direction of flow should therefore be in a direction opposite to that supposed by Pekeris.

The velocity of the hypothetical currents depends on the temperature difference and viscosity assumed. With a temperature difference of $100°$ C and a viscosity of 3×10^{21} gm/cm sec, Pekeris gets velocities of the order of 1 cm a year. He has also calculated the horizontal stresses in the crust, which are of the order of 10^7 dynes/cm^2 and are independent of the assumed viscosity. Such a stress acting on the lower surface of the crust might cause it to buckle and might be the cause of mountain-building.

The arguments in favor of convection currents are somewhat indirect and not entirely conclusive. The supposition that they exist enables a coherent account to be given of the relations of earthquakes, gravity anomalies, volcanoes, and island arcs (Griggs, 1939).

There are some difficulties in supposing convection currents in the mantle. Birch (1951b) has pointed out that the currents can hardly be expected to penetrate the $20°$ discontinuity; if there are to be currents, it is therefore necessary to suppose separate circulations to exist above and below the $20°$ discontinuity. The maintenance of currents also seems to require that the material of the mantle should have no strength for long-continued stresses at temperatures very much below the melting point. The currents will tend to maintain the adiabatic gradient, which will mean that if the upper part of the mantle is near the melting point, the lower part will be hundreds or thousands of degrees below it. It seems unlikely, though not entirely impossible, that the mechanical properties of the mantle are of this very unusual kind. The difficulty would not arise if the melting point and adiabatic gradients were nearly equal; this also does not seem probable. Joly (1925) and Brooks (1941) have suggested intermittent convection currents interspersed with periods during which the gradient is raised by the production of heat. Urey (1951, 1952) has considered the possibility of currents being driven by density differences due to the presence of metallic iron in the crust.

It seems that the existence of large-scale motions in the mantle has not been unambiguously demonstrated and that there are some difficulties in the theory of their maintenance. Their main attraction is that they provide large stresses in the crust and, by suitable hypotheses, can be used to explain a great variety of distortions and movements of the continents and ocean floors.

6. THE EARTH'S MAGNETIC FIELD

6.1. DESCRIPTION OF THE FIELD

To a first approximation, the magnetic field of the earth resembles that which would be produced by a dipole at the center or by uniform magnetization of the material of the earth. The axis of the dipole is inclined at $11°.4$ to the axis of rotation and cuts the surface at the "geomagnetic pole" in latitude $78°.6$ north and longitude $70°.1$ west. The dipole produces a vertical field of 0.63 gauss at the geomagnetic pole and 0.31 on the equator.

A more accurate examination of the earth's field shows that there are substantial and widespread departures from a dipole field. These departures are of two kinds. There are local anomalies due to the presence of magnetic materials, usually magnetite, in the crust. These do not usually exceed a few hundredths of a gauss, but occasionlly, as at Kursk near Moscow, are comparable with the main field and may even reverse it locally. These local anomalies are smoothed out in maps representing the distribution of field over the whole world. Such maps show departures from a dipole field which are smaller than the larger of the local anomalies, but of much greater extent. The departure of the smoothed field from a dipole is shown in Figure 31. This figure shows a complicated field bearing no close relation to the pattern of continents and oceans or to the major geological structures. Such a field can be analyzed in spherical harmonics. By comparing the coefficients derived from the horizontal and vertical components, it can then be divided into a part whose origin lies within the

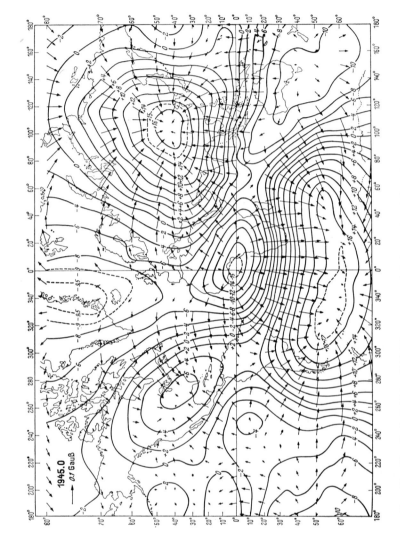

Fɪɢ. 31.—Nondipole field for 1945. The contours give the vertical field at intervals of 0.02 gauss. The arrows give the horizontal component (Bullard *et al.*, 1950).

earth and a part of external origin. It is found that, within the accuracy with which the analysis can be made, *the whole of the field is of internal origin.* This important result applies to the "main field," that is, to the field freed from diurnal variations, magnetic storms, and other short-term phenomena. The latter have their origin in the ionosphere.

When freed from short-period fluctuations, the magnetic field at a point shows a slow change, called the *secular variation.* This change usually continues in the same direction for many years, sometimes for as much as a hundred years. The greatest known change is that in the horizontal force at Cape Town, which has decreased by 32 per cent, from 0.209 to 0.141 gauss, in a hundred years. The rate of change of any component of the field is usually of the order of a few tenths of 1 per cent per year and appears to have a fairly definite upper limit of about 150×10^{-5} gauss/year. The rate of change may alter very suddenly, and there appears to be no limit to the second time differential of the field. An example of a map showing the rate of change of the field is shown in Figure 32. The rate varies only slowly from place to place, and in a general way it may be said that the horizontal scale of the phenomena is similar to that of the nondipole field; in both, the distances between maxima and minima are of the order of several thousand kilometers. It is possible that the nondipole field is largely the integrated effect of the secular variation and that it would be much reduced if averaged over a few hundred years.

The main features of the nondipole field and the secular variation drift westward at a rate of about $0°2$ per year. This drift was discovered by Halley (1692). The dipole field itself moves more slowly, and it is not certain whether what motion it has is systematic. The dipole moment has decreased by about 5 per cent since 1830 but appears recently to have started to increase (Gaibar-Puertas, 1952; Bullard, 1953).

The observations of the magnetic field between 1905 and 1945 have been elaborately reduced and discussed by Vestine *et al.* (1947a, b). This work gives by far the best collection of data and maps that exists and includes spherical harmonic analyses of the field and its rate of change. The nondipole field and the westward drift over the same period have been discussed by Bullard *et al.* (1950).

The field in the remote past has been studied by examining the magnetization of igneous and sedimentary rocks (Johnson *et al.*, 1948; Graham, 1949; Kawai, 1951; Hospers, 1953a, b; Clegg *et al.*, 1954). Both igneous and sedimentary rocks are frequently found to be magnetized in a direction opposite to that of the present field. It is not clear whether this reversal of magnetization is due to a reversal of the field at the time the

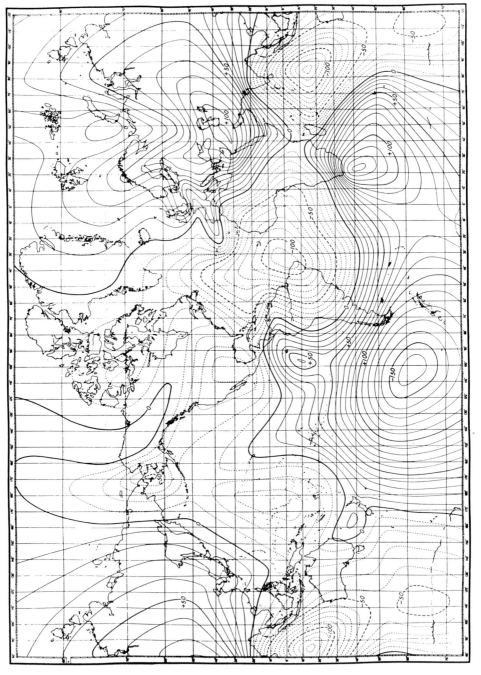

FIG. 32.—Rate of change of the vertical component of the earth's magnetic field in 10^{-5} gauss/year in 1942 (Vestine *et al.*, 1947*b*)

rocks were magnetized or whether it is due to a spontaneous tendency for the rock to become magnetized in a reverse direction to the field. Several mechanisms that will cause reverse magnetization are known (Nagata, 1953). Pre-Jurassic rocks are frequently magnetized in directions not related to the present field; it is possible that this is associated with pole wandering or with continental drift, but only a beginning has been made with the systematic investigation of the problem.

6.2. ORIGIN OF THE MAGNETIC FIELD

The outstanding features to be explained by a theory of the earth's magnetic field are its complexity (Figs. 31 and 32), the lack of correlation with geological features, the fact that it changes by a large fraction of itself in a hundred years, and its internal origin. The lack of correlation with geology practically excludes an origin in the crust. The rapid change makes an origin in the mantle extremely unlikely, since there is nothing in the mantle that can change appreciably in a hundred years. Any motions or temperature changes would cause movements at the surface and would proceed on the geological time scale of millions of years rather than on the magnetic time scale of hundreds of years.

The core, on the other hand, provides a very suitable place for relatively rapid changes to occur. It is fluid and therefore has a possibility of rapid relative motion of its parts that is denied to the mantle and the crust. It is likely to be a conductor of electricity and can therefore carry electric currents. If a means can be found for maintaining motion and a system of electric currents in the core, the general appearance and variability of the field shown in Figures 31 and 32 receive a natural explanation. In the motion of a conducting fluid the lines of current flow and of magnetic field are carried along with the fluid, and a map of the field will in some degree resemble a map of the fluid motion. This is just the kind of complexity that the nondipole field and the secular variation do show; the maps bear a qualitative resemblance to weather maps, and it is plausible that they represent a phenomenon connected with the motion of a fluid. The order of magnitude of the velocities required would be that of the westward drift projected downward onto the core. This is 0.3 mm/sec or 1000 km in 100 years. This view of the earth's field has been developed by Elsasser (1946a, b, 1947, 1950a), Frenkel (1945), and Bullard (1948b, 1949a, b, c, 1954b). Since the currents causing the field are supposed to lie deep in the earth, they cannot produce very local effects at the surface. This explains the absence of features intermediate in size between those associated with ore bodies and those shown in Figures 31 and 32 (Lowes and Runcorn,

1951). Iron just above the melting point has a specific resistance of 1.4×10^{-4} ohm cm (Powell, 1952), and the material of the core probably has a resistance of the same order; the resistance of the lower part of the mantle may be of the order of 10 ohm cm. This relatively good conductivity will screen the effects of rapid changes in the core and will limit the rate of change of the field at the surface of the earth and thus account for the absence of very rapid changes in the field while allowing a large second time differential. The westward drift can also be accounted for (Bullard *et al.*, 1950).

All these results are independent of the cause of the motion in the core or of the electric currents. The cause of the motion has been discussed by Elsasser (1950*b*) and by Bullard (1949*a*). They conclude that the only likely cause is thermal convection due to radioactive heating of the core. The rate of generation of heat required is only a few per cent of that in surface rocks and is of the same order as that in ultrabasic rocks and rather greater than that in iron meteorites. In order that there should be thermal convection, it is necessary that there should be not merely a generation of heat but also a temperature gradient exceeding the adiabatic gradient, and therefore a flow of heat. This involves some difficulty (Bullard, 1950*a*), as it is difficult for heat to escape from the outside of the core, owing to the poor conductivity of the mantle. Elsasser (1950*b*) has suggested that this difficulty can be avoided by assuming the heat to be generated in the inner core. With Jacobs' (1953) low values for the temperatures and for Grüneisen's constant, there is no difficulty. Urey (1952) has suggested alternative causes of motion.

Three mechanisms can be suggested for the maintenance of currents in the core. They might be driven by electromotive forces of thermoelectric, electrolytic, or dynamo origin. The most plausible thermoelectric view (Runcorn, 1954) is that the core and the mantle form the two materials of a thermojunction and that the electromotive force is due to temperature differences at different points on the boundary of the core associated with convection currents. This theory has the disadvantage that the electromotive forces are directed radially and, in a steady state, can be shown to produce no magnetic dipole moment. The electrolytic theory has not been developed in detail; it would depend on the mantle acting as an electrolyte in contact with the metallic core, whose properties would have to be supposed to differ slightly from place to place. Both these views would require temperature differences of hundreds of degrees between different parts of the core-mantle interface, which would imply a heat transport much greater than can plausibly be supposed to occur. The possibility that the motion of the material of the core could cause it to act as a self-exciting dynamo has been investigated by Elsasser (1946a, b, 1947), Bullard (1949a, 1954b), and Takeuchi and Shimazu (1952a, b, 1953). The results are not entirely conclusive, but it seems highly probable that such a process is consistent with Maxwell's equations and considerable progress has been made in working out specific models.

Several other theories of the earth's magnetic field have been suggested. These fall into three general types:

a) Theories that suppose that the material somewhere within the earth is ferromagnetic. As the temperature within the earth is certainly above the Curie point of iron and magnetite, it is necessary to assume that the great pressure raises the Curie point or renders normally nonmagnetic material magnetic. This assumption has no experimental or theoretical support (Birch, 1940a).

b) Theories that suppose that conditions inside the earth cause a separation of charge. The rotation of the charges with the earth's diurnal motion is then supposed to produce the magnetic field. The electrostatic field associated with the charges would be of the order of 10^8 volt/cm and constitutes a great difficulty for such theories (Haalk, 1938, 1950; Benfield, 1950b).

c) Theories that suppose a modification of Maxwell's equations of such a kind that a rotating body is spontaneously magnetized (Wilson, 1924; Blackett, 1947, 1949). There is some difficulty in producing a self-consistent theory of this kind that does not conflict with experiment. In particular, the simplest version predicts the wrong variation of horizontal field with depth within the earth (Runcorn et al., 1951) and leads to other false conclusions (Blackett, 1952).

None of these theories can account for the complexity and the changes in the earth's field. Even if they can account for a simple steady field, they would have to be supplemented by some further mechanism, such as is described above, in order to give anything resembling what is observed. It seems almost certain that, even if the field is not originally produced by motions in the core, such motions must play an essential part in moving and tangling the lines of force. The evidence for this is so strong that it seems safe to use it to supply information about the nature of the core. It gives support to the idea that it is composed of a material which is an electrical conductor, and a liquid with no shear strength and not too great a viscosity. It also suggests the generation of an amount of heat in the core which is not negligible.

REFERENCES

There is a very large number of papers on the subjects discussed in this chapter, and no attempt has been made to collect a complete bibliography. Preference has been given to recent papers, especially those discussing earlier work and having numerous references. Further numerical data may be found in Birch *et al.* (1942) and Landolt-Börnstein (1952). A fuller discussion of most of the topics will be found in Gutenberg (1951*d*) and Jeffreys (1952*b*).

ANDERSON, E. M.	1952	*Geol. Mag.*, **89**, 113.
ARROL, W. J.; JACOBI, R. B.; and PANETH, F. A.	1942	*Nature*, **149**, 235.
BAARS, B.	1951	*Gravity Effect of Earth Tides* (The Hague: Bataafsche Petroleum Maatschappij).
	1952	*Observatory*, **72**, 16.
BAYKAL, O., and WILSON, JAMES T.	1948	*Bull. Seism. Soc. Amer.*, **38**, 41.
BELLAMY, E. F.	1936	*Index Catalogue of Earthquakes* (Newport: County Press).
BENFIELD, A. E.	1950*a*	*Trans. Amer. Geophys. Union*, **31**, 53.
	1950*b*	*Nature*, **166**, 31.
BENIOFF, H.	1951*a*	*Bull. Seism. Soc. Amer.*, **41**, 31.
	1951*b*	*Bull. Geol. Soc. Amer.*, **62**, 331.
	1951*c*	*Trans. Amer. Geophys. Union*, **32**, 508.
	1954	*Bull. Geol. Soc. Amer.*, **65**, 385.
BERNAL, J. D.	1936	*Observatory*, **59**, 268.
BIRCH, F.	1938	*Bull. Seism. Soc. Amer.*, **28**, 49.
	1940*a*	*Amer. J. Sci.*, **238**, 192.
	1940*b*	*J. Geol.*, **48**, 752.
	1941	*Trans. Amer. Geophys. Union*, **22**, 552.
	1943	*Bull. Geol. Soc. Amer.*, **54**, 263.
	1950	*Ibid.*, **61**, 567.
	1951*a*	*J. Geophys. Res.*, **56**, 107.
	1951*b*	*Trans. Amer. Geophys. Union*, **32**, 533.
	1952	*J. Geophys. Res.*, **57**, 227.
	1953	*Bull. Geol. Soc. Amer.*, **64**, 601.
	1954*a*	*Trans. Amer. Geophys. Union*, **35**, 79.
	1954*b*	*Amer. J. Sci.*, **252**, 1.
BIRCH, F., and BANCROFT, D.	1940	*J. Geol.*, **48**, 752.
BIRCH, F., and CLARK, H.	1940	*Amer. J. Sci.*, **238**, 529.
BIRCH, F.; SCHAIRER, J. F.; and SPICER, H. C.	1942	*Handbook of Physical Constants* ("Geol. Soc. Amer. Spec. Papers," No. 36).
BLACKETT, P. M. S.	1947	*Nature*, **159**, 658.
	1949	*Phil. Mag.*, **40**, 125.
	1952	*Phil. Trans. R. Soc. London*, *A*, **245**, 309.

BRIDGMAN, P. W.   1940   *Proc. Amer. Acad. Sci.*, **74**, 11.
                         1948   *Ibid.*, **76**, 55.
BROOKS, H.   1941   *Trans. Amer. Geophys. Union*, **22**, 548.
BROWN, H.   1949   *Rev. Mod. Phys.* **21**, 625.
BROWNE, B. C.   1954   *Proc. R. Soc. London*, *A*, **222**, 398.
BULLARD, E. C.   1939   *M.N.*, Geophys. Suppl., **4**, 534.
                         1942   *Ibid.*, **5**, 41.
                         1948a *Ibid.*, p. 186.
                         1948b *Ibid.*, p. 248.
                         1949a *Proc. R. Soc. London*, *A*, **197**, 433.
                         1949b *Ibid.*, **199**, 413.
                         1949c *Phys. Today*, **2**, 6.
                         1950a *M.N.*, Geophys. Suppl., **6**, 36.
                         1953   *J. Geophys. Res.*, **58**, 277.
                         1954a *Proc. R. Soc. London*, *A*, **222**, 408.
                         1954b *Phil. Trans. R. Soc. London*, *A* (in press).
BULLARD, E. C.; FREED-
  MAN, C.; GELLMAN, H.;
  and NIXON, J.   1950   *Phil. Trans. R. Soc. London*, *A*, **243**, 67.
BULLARD, E. C., and
  GASKELL, T.   1941   *Proc. R. Soc. London*, *A*, **177**, 476.
BULLARD, E. C.; GASKELL,
  T.; HARLAND, W. B.;
  and KERR-GRANT, C.   1940   *Phil. Trans. R. Soc. London*, *A*, **239**, 29.
BULLARD, E. C., and
  NIBLETT, E. R.   1951   *M.N.*, Geophys. Suppl., **6**, 223.
BULLEN, K. E.   1940   *Bull. Seism. Soc. Amer.*, **30**, 235.
                         1942   *Ibid.*, **32**, 19.
                         1947   *An Introduction to the Theory of Seismology* (Cam-
                                  bridge: At the University Press).
                         1949   *M.N.*, Geophys. Suppl., **5**, 355.
                         1950a *Ibid.*, **6**, 50.
                         1950b *Ibid.*, p. 125.
                         1951   *Ibid.*, p. 164.
                         1952   *Ibid.*, p. 383.
                         1953   *Ann. Geofis.*, **6**, 1.
BYERLY, P.   1926   *Bull. Seism. Soc. Amer.*, **16**, 209.
CARSLAW, H. S., and
  JAEGER, J. C.   1947   *Conduction of Heat in Solids* (Oxford: Clarendon
                                  Press).
CHAPMAN, S., and
  BARTELS, J.   1940   *Geomagnetism* (Oxford: Clarendon Press).
CLEGG, J. A.;
  ALMOND, M.; and
  STUBBS, P. H. S.   1954   *Phil. Mag* (7), **45**, 583.
COSTER, H. P.   1947   *M.N.*, Geophys. Suppl., **5**, 131.
                         1948   *Ibid.*, p. 193.

DALTON, J. C.; GOLDEN,
J.; MARTIN, G. R.;
MERCER, E. R.; and
THOMPSON, S. J.   1953   *Geochim. et. Cosmochim. Acta*, **3**, 272.
DALY, R. A.   1933   *Igneous Rocks and the Depths of the Earth* (New
York: McGraw-Hill Book Co.).
DANA, S. W.   1944   *Bull. Seism. Soc. Amer.*, **34**, 189.
        1945   *Ibid.*, **35**, 27.
DAVIS, G. L.   1947   *Amer. J. Sci.*, **245**, 677.
        1950   *Ibid.*, **248**, 107.

DAVIS, G. L., and
HESS, H. H.   1949   *Amer. J. Sci.*, **247**, 856.
DENSON, M. E.   1952   *Bull. Seism. Soc. Amer.*, **42**, 119.
ELSASSER, W. M.   1946*a*   *Phys. Rev.*, **70**, 106.
        1946*b*   *Ibid.*, p. 202.
        1947   *Ibid.*, **72**, 821.
        1950*a*   *Rev. Mod. Phys.*, **22**, 1.
        1950*b*   *Trans. Amer. Geophys. Union*, **31**, 454.
        1951   *Science*, **113**, 105.
ERGIN, K.   1953   *Bull. Seism. Soc. Amer.*, **43**, 63.
EVANS, R. D., and
GOODMAN, C.   1941   *Bull. Geol. Soc. Amer.*, **52**, 459.
EVERNDEN, J. F.   1954   *Bull. Seism. Soc. Amer.*, **44**, 1.
EWING, M., and
PRESS, F.   1950   *Bull. Seism. Soc. Amer.*, **40**, 271.
        1952   *Ibid.*, **42**, 315.
        1954   *Ibid.*, **44**, 127.

EWING, M.; SUTTON,
G. H.; and OFFICER,
C. B.   1954   *Bull. Seism. Soc. Amer.*, **44**, 21.
EWING, M.; WORZEL,
J. L.; HERSEY, J. B.;
PRESS, F.; and
HAMILTON, G. R.   1950   *Bull. Seism. Soc. Amer.*, **40**, 233.
FAUST, L. Y.   1951   *Geophysics*, **16**, 192.
FLEMING, E. H.;
GHIORSO, A.; and
CUNNINGHAM, B. B.   1952   *Phys. Rev.*, **88**, 642.
FRENKEL, J.   1945   *C.R. Acad. Sci. U.R.S.S.*, **49**, 98.
GAIBAR-PUERTAS, C.   1952   *Geofis. Pura. Appl.*, **23**, 2.
GANE, P. G.   1948   *Bull. Seism. Soc. Amer.*, **38**, 95.
GASKELL, T. F.   1954   *Proc. R. Soc. London*, A, **222,**, 356.
GASKELL, T. F., and
SWALLOW, J. C.   1951   *Nature*, **167**, 723.
        1952   *Ibid.*, **170**, 1010.
        1953*a*   *Ibid.*, **172**, 535.
        1953*b*   *Occ. Pap. Chal. Soc.*, No. 3.

GRAHAM, J. W.   1949   *J. Geophys. Res.*, **54**, 131.
GRATTON, L. C.   1945   *Amer. J. Sci.*, **243A**, 135.
GRIGGS, D.   1939   *Amer. J. Sci.*, **237**, 611.
GUTENBERG, B.   1943   *Bull. Geol. Soc. Amer.*, **54**, 473.
                       1944a   *Bull. Seism. Soc. Amer.*, **34**, 85.
                       1944b   *Ibid.*, p. 137.
                       1945   *Ibid.*, **35**, 57.
                       1948a   *Ibid.*, **38**, 121.
                       1948b   *Eng. Sci. Month.*, **11**, 19.
                       1951a   *Bull. Seism. Soc. Amer.*, **41**, 143.
                       1951b   *Bull. Geol. Soc. Amer.*, **62**, 427.
                       1951c   *Trans. Amer. Geophys. Union*, **32**, 373.
                       1951d   *Internal Constitution of the Earth* (2d ed.; New
                                   York: Dover Publications).
                       1952   *Trans. Amer. Geophys. Union*, **33**, 427.
                       1953   *Proc. Nat. Acad. Sci.*, **39**, 849.
                       1954   *Bull. Geol. Soc. Amer.*, **65**, 337.
GUTENBERG, B., and
    RICHTER, C. F.   1936   *Beitr. Geophys.*, **47**, 73.
                       1938   *M.N., Geophys. Suppl.*, **4**, 363.
                       1939   *Beitr. Geophys.*, **54**, 94.
                       1949   *Seismicity of the Earth and Associated Phenomena*
                                   (Princeton: Princeton University Press).
HAALK, H.   1938   *Beitr. Geophys.*, **52**, 243.
                       1950   *Geofis. Pura. Appl.*, **18**, 132.
HALLEY, E.   1692   *Phil. Trans. R. Soc. London*, **17**, 653.
HESS, H. H.   1954   *Proc. R. Soc. London, A*, **222**, 341.
HILL, M.   1952   *Phil. Trans. R. Soc. London, A*, **244**, 561.
HILL, M., and
    SWALLOW, J. C.   1950   *Nature*, **165**, 193.
HILL, M. N., and
    KING, W. B. R.   1953   *Quart. J. Geol. Soc. London*, **109**, 1.
HILL, M. N., and
    LAUGHTON, A. S.   1954   *Proc. R. Soc. London, A*, **222**, 348.
HODGSON, J. H.   1947   *Bull. Seism. Soc. Amer.*, **37**, 5.
                       1953   *Pub. Dom. Obs.*, **16**, 111.
HOLLAND, F. A.;
    HUGGILL, J. A. W.;
    and JONES, G. O.   1951   *Proc. R. Soc. London, A*, **207**, 268.
HOLMES, A.   1944   *Principles of Physical Geology* (London: Nelson).
HOSPERS, J.   1953a   *Proc. Kon. Ned. Akad. Wetensch., B*, **56**, 468.
                       1953b   *Ibid.*, p. 477.
HUGHES, D. S., and
    CROSS, J. H.   1951   *Geophysics*, **16**, 579.
HUGHES, D. S., and
    JONES, H. J.   1950   *Bull. Geol. Soc. Amer.* **61**, 843.
                       1951   *Trans. Amer. Geophys. Union*, **32**, 173.

INGHAM, W. N., and
    KEEVIL, N. B.   1951   *Bull. Geol. Soc. Amer.*, **62**, 131.
JACOBS, J. A.   1953   *Canad. J. Phys.*, **31**, 370.
                           1954   *Nature*, **173**, 746.
JEFFREYS, H.   1932   *M.N.*, Geophys. Suppl., **3**, 60.
                           1937   *Ibid.*, p. 196.
                           1939a   *Ibid.*, p. 498.
                           1939b   *Ibid.*, p. 537.
                           1939c   *Ibid.*, p. 548.
                           1939d   *Ibid.*, p. 594.
                           1941   *Ibid.*, **5**, 1.
                           1943a   *Ibid.*, p. 55.
                           1943b   *Ibid.*, p. 71.
                           1947   *Ibid.*, p. 105.
                           1948   *Ibid.*, p. 219.
                           1950   *Ibid.*, **6**, 137.
                           1951   *The Geocentric Direction Cosines of Seismological
                                   Observatories* (Richmond: Kew Observatory).
                           1952a   *M.N.*, Geophys. Suppl., **6**, 348.
                           1952b   *The Earth* (3d ed.; Cambridge: At the University
                                   Press).
JEFFREYS, H., and
    BULLEN, K. E.   1940   *Seismological Tables* (London: British Association).
JOHNSON, E. A.;
    MURPHY, T.; and
    TORRESON, O. W.   1948   *Terr. Mag.*, **53**, 349.
JOLY, J.   1925   *The Surface History of the Earth* (Cambridge: At
                                   the University Press).
KAWAI, N.   1951   *J. Geophys. Res.*, **56**, 73.
LAMBERT, W. D.   1940   *Report on Earth Tides.* ("U.S. Coast Geod. Surv.
                                   Special Publications," No. 223).
LANDOLT-BÖRNSTEIN   1952   *Zahlenwerte und Funktionen*, Vol. **3** (6th ed.;
                                   Berlin: Julius Springer).
LEET, L. D.   1938   *Practical Seismology and Seismic Prospecting* (New
                                   York: Appleton-Century).
                           1941   *Bull. Seism. Soc. Amer.*, **31**, 325.
LEHMANN, I.   1934   *Geod. Inst. Copenhagen, Medd.*, No. 5.
                           1936   *Bur. Centr. Seism. Trav. Sci.*, **14**, 3.
                           1953a   *Trans. Amer. Geophys. Union*, **34**, 477.
                           1953b   *Bull. Seism. Soc. Amer.*, **43**, 291.
                           1954   *Geod. Inst. Skrift.* (3), **18**, 1.
LEITH, T. H.   1952   *Trans. Amer. Geophys. Union*, **33**, 435.
LOWES, F. J., and
    RUNCORN, S. K.   1951   *Phil. Trans. R. Soc. London, A*, **243**, 525.
MARTNER, S. T.   1950   *Bull. Seism. Soc. Amer.*, **40**, 95.
MEINESZ, F. V.   1947   *Quart. J. Geol. Soc. London*, **103**, 191.
                           1951   *Trans. Amer. Geophys. Union*, **32**, 531.

MISENER, A. D.;
  THOMPSON, L. G. D.;
  and UFFEN, R. J.   1951   *Trans. Amer. Geophys. Union*, **32**, 729.
NAGATA, T.   1953   *Rock-Magnetism* (Tokyo).
NEWSTEAD, G., and
  BECK, A.   1953   *Australian J. Sci.*, **6**, 480.
NISHIMURA, E.   1950   *Trans. Amer. Geophys. Union*, **31**, 357.
NISKANEN, E.   1945   *Ann. Acad. Sci. Fenn.*, Ser. AIII, **10**, 1 ("Pub.
                                      Isos. Inst.," No. 14).

OFFICER, C. B.;
  EWING, M.; and
  WUENSCHEL, P. C.   1952   *Bull. Geol. Soc. Amer.*, **63**, 777.
PEKERIS, C.   1935   *M.N.*, Geophys. Suppl., **3**, 343.
PETTIT, J. T.;
  SLICHTER, L. B.; and
  LA COSTE, L.   1953   *Trans. Amer. Geophys. Union*, **34**, 174.
POWELL, R. W.   1952   *Phil. Mag.* (7), **44**, 772.
PRESS, F., and
  BECKMANN, W.   1954   *Bull. Geol. Soc. Amer.*, **65**, 299.
RAITT, R. W.   1949   *Bull. Geol. Soc. Amer.*, **60**, 1915.
RAMSEY, W. H.   1948   *M.N.*, **108**, 406.
                            1949   *Ibid.*, Geophys. Suppl., **5**, 409.
                            1950*a* *Ibid.*, **110**, 444.
                            1950*b* *Ibid.*, Geophys. Suppl., **6**, 42.
RANKAMA, K., and
  SAHAMA, T. G.   1950   *Geochemistry* (Chicago: University of Chicago
                                      Press).
REICH, H.   1950   *Geol. Jahrb.*, **64**, 243.
REICH, H.; FOERTSCH,
  O.; and SCHULZE, G. A.   1951   *J. Geophys. Res.*, **56**, 147.
REICH, H.; SCHULZE,
  G. A.; and FÖRTSCH, O.   1948   *Geol. Rdsch.*, **36**, 85.
RESEARCH GROUP
  FOR EXPLOSION
  SEISMOLOGY   1953   *Bull. Earthquake Res. Inst.*, **31**, 281.
REVELLE, R., and
  MAXWELL, A. E.   1952   *Nature*, **170**, 199.
ROTHÉ, J. P., and
  PETERSCHMITT, E.   1950   *Ann. Inst. Phys. Globe Strassbourg*, **5**, 3.
RUNCORN, S. K.   1954   *Trans. Amer. Geophys. Union*, **35**, 49.
RUNCORN, S. K.; BENSON,
  A. C.; MOORE, A. F.;
  and GRIFFITHS, D. H.   1951   *Phil. Trans. R. Soc. London*, *A*, **244**, 113.
SCHULZE, G. A., and
  FÖRTSCH, O.   1950   *Geol. Jahrb.*, **64**, 204.
SENFTLE, F. E., and
  KEEVIL, N. B.   1947   *Trans. Amer. Geophys. Union*, **28**, 732.

SHIMAZU, U.   1952   *J. Phys. Earth*, **1**, 11.
SIMON, F.   1937   *Trans. Faraday Soc.*, **33**, 65.
SIMON, F., and
  GLATZEL, G.   1929   *Zs. f. anorg. Chem.*, **178**, 309.
SIMON, F. E.   1953   *Nature*, **172**, 746.
SLACK, H. A., and
  WHITHAM, K.,   1951   *Trans. Amer. Geophys. Union*, **32**, 44.
SLICHTER, L. B.   1941   *Bull. Geol. Soc. Amer.*, **52**, 561.
SOHON, F. W.   1932   *Theoretical Seismology*, Part II (New York: John
                                      Wiley & Sons).
STONELEY, R.   1948   *Bull. Seism. Soc. Amer.*, **38**, 263.
STOTT, V. H., and
  RENDALL, J. H.   1953   *J. Iron & Steel Inst.*, **175**, 374.
TAKEUCHI, H.   1950   *Trans. Amer. Geophys. Union*, **31**, 651.
TAKEUCHI, H., and
  SHIMAZU, Y.   1952*a* *J. Phys. Earth*, **1**, 1.
                              1952*b* *Ibid.*, p. 57.
                              1953   *J. Geophys. Res.*, **58**, 497.
TANNI, L.   1948   *Ann. Acad. Sci. Fenn.*, Ser. AIII, **16**, 1 ("Pub.
                                      Isos. Inst.," No. 18).
TATEL, H. E.;
  ADAMS, L. H.; and
  TUVE, M. A.   1953   *Proc. Amer. Phil. Soc.*, **97**, 658.
TOLSTOY, I.;
  EDWARDS, R. S.; and
  EWING, M.   1953   *Bull. Seism. Soc. Amer.*, **43**, 35.
TOMASCHEK, R.   1952   *M.N.*, Geophys. Suppl., **6**, 372.
UFFEN, R. J.   1952   *Trans. Amer. Geophys. Union*, **33**, 893.
UREY, H. C.   1951   *Geochim. et Cosmochim. Acta*, **1**, 209.
                              1952   *The Planets: Their Origin and Development* (New
                                      Haven: Yale University Press).
URRY, W. D.   1949   *Trans. Amer. Geophys. Union*, **30**, 171.
VALLE, P. E.   1952   *Ann. Geofis.*, **5**, 41.
VERHOOGEN, J.   1951   *Trans. Amer. Geophys. Union*, **32**, 41.
                              1953   *J. Geophys. Res.*, **58**, 337.
                              1954   *Trans. Amer. Geophys. Union*, **35**, 85.
VESTINE, E. H.; LAPORTE,
  L.; COOPER, C.; LANGE,
  I.; and HENDRIX, W. C. 1947*a* *Description of the Earth's Main Magnetic Field and
                                      Its Secular Change, 1905–1945*. ("Carnegie In-
                                      stitution of Washington Publications," No. 578
                                      [Washington, D.C.]).
VESTINE, E. H.; LAPORTE,
  L.; LANGE, I.; and
  SCOTT, W. E.   1947*b* *The Geomagnetic Field: Its Description and Analy-
                                      sis* ("Carnegie Institution of Washington Pub-
                                      lications," No. 580 [Washington, D.C.]).

VOLK, J. A., and
  ROBERTSON, F. 1950 *Bull. Seism. Soc. Amer.*, **40,** 81.
WILLMORE, P. L. 1949 *Phil. Trans. R. Soc. London, A,* **242,** 123.
   1950 *M.N.,* Geophys. Suppl., **6,** 129.
WILLMORE, P. L.;
  HALES, A. L.; and
  GANE, P. G. 1952 *Bull. Seism. Soc. Amer.*, **42,** 53.
WILSON, H. A. 1924 *Proc. R. Soc. London, A,* **104,** 451.
ZISMAN, W. A. 1933 *Proc. Nat. Acad. Sci.,* **19,** 666.

CHAPTER 4

The Development and Structure
of the Crust

By J. TUZO WILSON
University of Toronto

1. INTRODUCTION

THE contributions of astronomers and physicists to our knowledge of the earth have traditionally been similar to those which they have made for the other bodies comprising the universe. For planets, stars, galaxies, and atoms alike, these scientists have studied general properties. They have in large measure discovered the motions, masses, sizes, shapes, ages, and compositions of these bodies. They have speculated upon origins and history. They have also long regarded all these bodies as machines and sought to find the nature of their internal mechanisms and the sources of their energy; but the motions of the interior of the earth, being sluggish and obscure, have proved difficult to study. The earth is recognized to be a heat engine; but even today there is more agreement upon the nature of the nuclear processes which heat the sun and characterize the atoms of different elements than there is about those slow movements within the earth which have generated its powerful magnetic field, developed its mountains, and given structure to its crust.

Our special relation to the earth has enabled another larger group of geologists, geographers, and geodesists to make close and detailed examination of the earth's land surface. Great credit is due these men for their assiduity, care, and often courage in collecting a monumental volume of data about those detailed features which are exposed for them to see.

Unfortunately, a great barrier long existed between these two groups. It was of a double nature. The theoretical physicists and the field men not only looked at different features of the earth on vastly different scales and employed very different methods, but the whole philosophy of their approach was different. Geologists collected voluminous descriptive data from which they deduced the later history of the land and the nature of the surface processes; but they have had to be more concerned with surface effects than with the nature and causes of the deep and fundamental processes. The physicists were formerly unable to analyze or make use of most of the field data and concerned themselves with measuring rates, examining processes, and postulating theories of a much more general character.

Both groups made organized studies for more than a hundred and fifty years without answering the basic problems of the nature and manner of operation of the earth. The fact was that too large a part of the earth remained unexplored. Geological methods and maps stopped at coasts and told little of three-quarters of the surface and practically nothing about the interior.

It is only during the last thirty years that indirect physical methods capable of precisely exploring these vast lacunae have been developed to a useful stage. Like field geology, the application of these methods has required an enormous expenditure of effort, and, for the most part, it has been only in the last five or ten years that this has been begun on a worldwide basis.

Accurate bathymetric charts of the ocean floors are now in process of being made. Surveys of gravity, heat flow, and the thickness of crustal layers are now being rapidly extended on land and sea. The foci, depths, and directions of motion of earthquakes are being accurately plotted. Seismic waves are yielding a precise knowledge of the shells in the interior of the earth. The ages, radioactive content, and modes of deformation of minerals and rocks are being measured. These surveys have already bridged the gap which so long existed in our knowledge, but they are still incomplete. Those who have considered their implications have not yet reached agreement; many who would be in the best position to advance theories are now fully occupied in the hard and sometimes dangerous task of collecting fresh information.

The present is therefore a time of changing ideas and a difficult one at which to write this chapter. A few years ago, only a fragmentary account could have been given. A few years hence, the general theme may have been agreed upon. At present, many old ideas have not yet been abandoned, and the new ones are too numerous, for they have not yet been sorted out and tested. Under the circumstances, the choice is between describing a little bit of many theories and ideas, which would be satisfying to no one, or choosing that scheme which seems soundest and using it as a

frame for describing the earth's crust, remembering that modification of
the theory will not affect the descriptive data.

The following is a summary of the scheme adopted. After a brief section
on sources of information which may prove useful to some in this time of
broadening study of the earth, the distinctions are sketched between the
greatest features—ocean basins and continents—and the nature of the
border between them is mentioned. Then it is shown that rates of erosion,
deposition, and volcanism suggest that continents must be growing at the
expense of ocean basins, which are the older and simpler features. This
growth is clearly connected with the most active parts of the earth, at
present forming two great belts about it. It is suggested that these belts
are made up of only a very few simple types of elements repeated many
times in different stages of development. The next section considers physical theories advanced in explanation of these features. Both the present
belts and a few former ones are examined and described. The continents
are shown to be zoned, with progressively younger belts toward the margins. This suggests that continents may have grown entirely during geological time.

This chapter was written early in 1952, but the editor kindly provided
an opportunity to revise the text two years later. The illustrations have
not been altered except for one addition.

2. SOURCES OF INFORMATION

At a time when studies of the earth are broadening so rapidly, it may be
useful to give a short and necessarily incomplete résumé of the literature.
The work of geologists suffices to fill a large library, but references to any
particular area or subject can be readily found in one or the other of two
serial bibliographies issued, respectively, by the United States Geological
Survey (1923–1950) and the Geological Society of America (1933–1952).
Pearl has written a useful guide (1951). There are regional accounts and
geological maps for many countries and geological maps of all continents,
except Asia and Antarctica. Among many books, four in particular have
dealt with world-wide geology, Suess (1904–1924), Von Bubnoff (1925–
1941), Bucher (1933), and Umbgrove (1947) and, in popular vein, Cloos
(1954), while R. A. Daly in a series of books has discussed particular
problems.

There are structural maps of the United States (King, 1944), Canada
(Derry, 1950), and a few other countries. Structural geology has been
dealt with recently by Anderson (1952) and by Hills (1953).

Textbooks on petrology are numerous, and, of them, Bowen's (1928) has had great influence. Our knowledge of experimental petrology has been largely obtained by the Geophysical Laboratory of the Carnegie Institution of Washington, whose work is summarized, with references, in annual reports. Two recent works dealt with geochemistry (Rankama and Sahama, 1950; Mason, 1952). Chemical arguments are given prominence in *The Planets* by Urey (1952).

The mathematical treatment of the physics of the earth has recently been summarized in two well-known books by Jeffreys (1952) and Gutenberg (1952). There is an abbreviated version of the former without mathematics (Jeffreys, 1951). A volume on geophysics is in preparation in the new edition of the *Handbuch der Physik*. The journals chiefly devoted to this subject include the Geophysical Supplement to *Monthly Notices of the Royal Astronomical Society, Journal of Geophysical Research, Annales de géophysique,* and *Beiträge zur Geophysik*. Many countries publish one or even several journals which deal with geophysics in general.

Annotated references to most papers dealing with the physics of the earth, as well as with exploration geophysics, are given in *Geophysical Abstracts*, published quarterly by the United States Geological Survey. Other geophysical bibliographies are included regularly in *Transactions of the American Geophysical Union, Physical Abstracts, Bibliography of Seismology* (Dominion Observatory, Ottawa), *Journal of Geophysical Research,* and *Bibliographie de géodésie*.

The results of geophysical work are published in a very scattered way, but much of it is eventually reported in one of the many publications of the International Union of Geodesy and Geophysics. The *Bulletin d'information de l'U.G.G.I.* (Laclavère, 1952–1954), issued quarterly, provides a guide to these journals, which also include *Bulletin volcanologique, Bulletin géodésique, International Seismological Summary, Publications of the Isostatic Institute, Catalogue of the Active Volcanoes of the World,* and the *Comptes rendus* of the seven associations which comprise the union.

The distribution of earthquakes and volcanoes has been summarized by Gutenberg and Richter (1949), Kennedy and Richey (1947), and Sapper (1927).

All work on age determinations is summarized, with bibliographies, in the annual reports of the Committee on the Measurement of Geologic Time of the United States National Research Council, while new books in preparation by Rankama, Faul, and Kulp and that published by Libby (1952) will replace the classic *Age of the Earth* by Holmes (1927) and *Bulletin 80* of the National Research Council of the United States on the same subject.

Birch (1942) edited a useful volume on the *Physical Properties of Rocks*.

3. THE GREAT FEATURES OF THE CRUST

The chief structures on the face of the earth are continents and ocean basins. The greater parts of the surfaces of both lie close to one of two definite levels, as is shown in Figure 1. Steep continental slopes form the natural boundaries between them, rather than sea-level, which is subject to minor fluctuations and at present is about 200 meters above the outer edge of the continental shelves.

Suess pointed out that the rocks abundant on the surface of continents are more siliceous or acid in composition and are lighter than those found

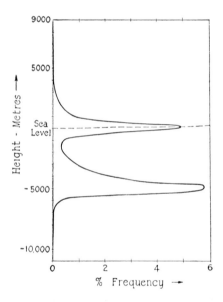

Fig. 1.—Diagram of frequency of levels on the earth's surface (after Wegener and Bucher)

on islands in the deep oceans far from continents or than those dredged from the ocean floors. He suggested that the continents are formed of blocks of siliceous rocks, termed *sal* or *sial* from their two principal elements, silicon and aluminium, resting upon a universal basic layer of magnesium silicates, called *sima* (Suess, 1904–1924).

Recent seismic work has confirmed and elaborated upon this and has shown that the continents are, on the average, about 35 km thick (Tatel, Tuve, and Adams, 1951, 1953; Willmore, Hales, and Gane, 1952; Hodgson, 1953). The velocities measured beneath the continents range from 6.0 km/sec (characteristic of acid rocks, about 65 per cent SiO_2) at the surface, to 6.5 km/sec (probably due to basic rocks, about 50 per cent SiO_2) at 35 km, where the velocities change suddenly at the Mohorovičić discontinuity shown in Figure 2, B, to 8.2 km/sec (probably due to ultrabasic rocks, 40 per cent SiO_2). On the ocean floors there is a thin layer of mud, under which the velocities are those of basic rocks to a depth of about 5 km below the floor, where the velocities change suddenly to those of ultrabasic rocks (Ewing, 1951). These figures show, as do gravity observations, that the continental blocks have quite a different structure from ocean basins; that they are high because they are light; and that continents and ocean basins are in approximate hydrostatic or isostatic equilibrium. It is unlikely, therefore, that any large parts of continents could ever have sunk to form ocean floors. Cf. also chapters 3 and 6.

The shapes and sizes of continents and oceans are irregular, but their disposition is approximately such that if a tetrahedron were placed with its corners in the main continental areas, the oceans would lie opposite to its faces and the continents would be extended along its edges (Gregory, 1899). For a long time no satisfactory explanation for this observation was advanced; this was probably because the continents were usually treated as single blocks, whereas this paper suggests reasons to believe that they have grown steadily. Nevertheless, the location of the nuclei still needs to be explained. Vening Meinesz (1951, 1952), Matschinski (1950, 1952), and Kaufmann (1951) are among those who have recently discussed the origin of continents. Vening Meinesz shows that the shape and position of the continents is compatible with the present or former existence of convection currents in the mantle.

Each continent may be divided into structures of three types—old stable shields, mountain ranges, and continental shelves—and it is becoming apparent that there is a mountain-building process which converts shelves into mountains, while mountains, by processes of erosion, are in time converted into provinces of shields. There seems to be a process of growth by which continents expand and encroach upon ocean basins.

There is a suggestion that ocean floors represent those parts of the original crust of the earth which have been least altered and that they owe their general level to that cause. They will be considered first and then shelves, mountains, and shields, which seem to represent successive stages in the growth of continents over former ocean floors. The height of continents and the thickness of the continental crust are probably closely related to sea-level; the former because erosion tends to reduce them, and the latter because the land appears to rise as the surface is eroded until approximate isostatic equilibrium with the ocean basins is restored.

4. OCEAN BASINS

Since the oceanographic aspects of the ocean basins are dealt with in chapter 5, it suffices to refer here to some of the geophysical and geological aspects.

The examination of the floor of the deep oceans was begun scarcely a hundred years ago and for most of that time depended on soundings made with a weight and line and examination of dredged samples. These methods showed that, on the average, the Pacific Ocean is about 14,000 feet deep and that the Atlantic and Indian Oceans are about 13,000 feet deep, but that all of them contain, near land, long, narrow troughs which slightly exceed 35,000 feet in the deepest places. The old soundings were far apart and not very precisely located. They suggested that the bottom was fairly smooth, although ridges of the dimensions of great mountain ranges were found in all oceans. These ridges emerge in places as islands, of which the Azores, Hawaiian, and Kerguelen Islands are examples. All these islands in the deep oceans far from land are volcanic, and they and igneous rocks obtained by dredging on the ocean floors are of a basic and usually basaltic composition. In most places the ocean floors were found to be overlain by soft muds containing abundant shells of minute marine organisms varying with latitude and water temperature. Although the collection of this information from the oceans of the world was an enormous effort, the methods were such that data accumulated only slowly.

Within the last twenty-five years new methods have been introduced which have vastly increased and altered this information, in spite of the fact that there has not yet been time to apply these methods fully (Kuenen, 1950). First came the development of the echo sounder, to provide continuous profiles of bottom topography accurately located by radio and sonic aids to navigation. Next, Vening Meinesz (1934) developed a method for measuring the acceleration due to gravity at sea from a submarine, which avoided the accelerations due to wave motion. About two thousand such observations have now been made. He found that great variations in gravity accompanied the deep trenches associated with island arcs. After 1930 it was discovered that the trenches are also accompanied by deep-focus earthquakes. Very recently, methods of obtaining cores, up to 70 feet long, of bottom muds and the study of seismic waves propagated from small explosions have greatly increased our knowledge of the nature of sea floors (Bullard and Gaskell, 1941; Ewing et al., 1946, 1954; Hersey and Ewing, 1949; Woollard, 1951; Gaskell and Swallow, 1951; Revelle, 1953; Ewing, 1953; Bullard, 1954).

Rapid progress has been made since the last war, and the results are only now in process of being published. As a result, opinions are not unanimous because older ideas are in process of modification. In this chapter the views of Ewing and his colleagues at Columbia University and of Bullard and the group at the University of Cambridge are followed, both because of the interest of the work they have carried out over the Atlantic Ocean and along its stable coasts, and because their views are in harmony with the ideas upon shelves and upon continental structure to be advanced later in this chapter. Nevertheless, it will be appreciated that the ideas about continental margins obtained by those who have worked along the active, faulted margins of the Pacific (Shepard, 1948) are very likely to be different from those obtained as a result of work off such stable shelves as those on the Atlantic coasts.

As a result of this recent work, it now appears that the topography of the ocean floors is complex, more rugged than that of [continents, and of a very different character. Whereas continents tend to be built along mountain belts and eroded by subaerial forces, oceans are primarily subject to deposition, to a more widespread and active volcanism, and only to very specialized and local erosion.

Ewing (1951) has shown, as a result of more than one hundred seismic studies, that the floors of the Atlantic Ocean and Caribbean Sea have an average thickness of 1 km of mud and a layer of 5 km of basalt resting upon ultrabasic rocks. This is quite a different structure from that of continents. It seems that ocean basins are so low because they are made of dense rocks. This renders it quite improbable that any part of the ocean floors are sunken continental blocks, although that idea has been advocated in the past without any cause for the exchange having been advanced (Ewing, 1953).

So far as is known, the great submarine ridges like the Mid-Atlantic, Hawaiian, and Kerguelen Ridges and many isolated islands and seamounts are all basic volcanic rocks bare, for the most part, of deposits and with a correspondingly rough and irregular topography (Betz and Hess, 1942). Gravity data show that these ridges are uncompensated masses resting upon the ocean floor as loads, showing that the crust has had great strength over long periods of time. Recent observations (Garland, 1950; Innes, in press) of gravity show large anomalies over flat parts of the Canadian Shield which also show no tendency to move into isostatic equilibrium with other parts of the Shield, again suggesting that the crust has permanent strength for areas distinctly smaller than continents. Some of these mid-ocean ridges are seismically active; but, unlike the volcanic arcs near continents and deep trenches, all the earthquakes are shallow.

Besides these great ridges, the exact nature and origin of which is still a matter for speculation, modern investigations have disclosed large numbers of islands and seamounts (which do not reach the surface) of either conical or truncated conical shape. Those that reach the surface are either volcanoes or are capped with coral to form atolls. Presumably, all originated as volcanoes. The flat-topped seamounts in the Pacific (cf. Fig. 1A) number several thousand and appear to occur in groups. They have been called "guyots" by Hess (1946) and used in an ingenious argument to suggest that the oceans are deepening. He noticed that guyots occurred at many depths below a depth of 1000 meters but never between that depth and the surface. He assumed that their shape was due to the erosion of volcanic cones to former levels of the sea and that the depth of 1000 meters coincided with the first evolution of corals during Paleozoic time. Since then, reef-building has been able to keep pace with the rising of sea-level, which has been proceeding at a rate of about 1 meter in 300,000 years, and only atolls have been formed. An alternative explanation is that where there are guyots the ocean floor has not been stable.

Ewing's work in the Atlantic has shown that three types of sea floor predominate. In some parts, especially on seamounts and on the Mid-Atlantic Ridge, the floor consists of bare basic rocks of rugged topography. In flat areas there are undisturbed, fine-grained muds, which have accumulated slowly; but in some places coarse sands and other evidence of great disturbances have been recognized. Some of these disturbed areas extend for hundreds of miles off continental shelves, while others are in the deep trenches. The only satisfactory explanation yet offered is that mud, sliding off the continental slopes, and muddy water, stirred up on the continental shelves, flow from time to time down continental slopes (Heezen and Ewing, 1952, and references given there). In doing so, they tend to be funneled into submarine canyons, which are thus cut back into the edge of the shelves. These currents accelerate as they move, picking up more sediment, and flow as turbidity currents far out over the ocean floors. Earthquakes are known to have started at least some of them. The deep trenches in which many turbidity currents end have been found by seismic measurements to be underlain by great thickness of sediments (Ewing and Worzel, 1954).

As long as the ocean floors were considered to be in part underlain by continental rocks of low density, it was reasonable to believe that the trenches were the surface expression of great downfolds and that these, being composed of light rocks, caused the strips of negative gravity anomalies which have been observed along trenches. Now that Ewing has shown

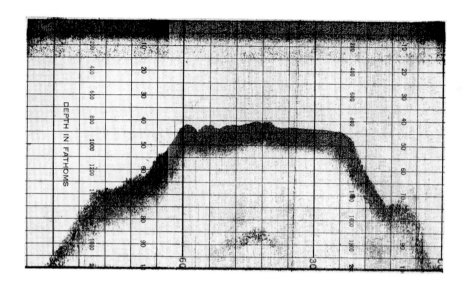

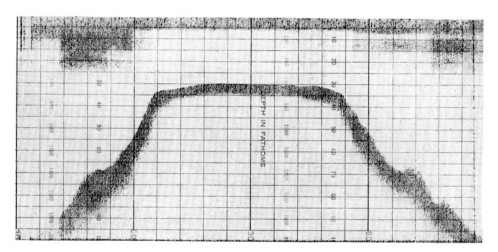

Fig. 1A.—*Above:* Guyot, 20 miles north of Eniwetok Atoll. Hummocky surface on left is area covered by soft oceanic sediment, while smooth right side is hard rock surface, from which sediment has probably been removed. Weak second reflection from bottom appears near center of record. *Below:* Profile of first guyod discovered, October 6, 1944; 8°50′ N., 163°10′ E., "USS Cape Johnson." Upper truncated surface slightly deeper than 600 fathoms and 9 miles across. Note gently sloping shelves at margins of flat top. Near top right-hand side of record, reflections from the "deep scattering layer" near 100 fathoms can be seen—also faintly present in upper figure. This layer is thought to be reflection from marine organisms feeding at this depth in daylight. During the hour after sunset it moves up to surface. (Courtesy Dr. H. H. Hess.)

that light crustal rocks are lacking on the ocean floors, downfolding cannot afford an explanation of negative gravity anomalies; but, as Coulomb (1945) first pointed out, great trenches formed by faulting and filled with many kilometers of unconsolidated and extremely light sediments can provide an explanation both of the anomalies and of how sediments of sufficient thickness to form 35 km of continent can accumulate in places where continents are growing; and this view has been adopted and extended by Ewing (1953).

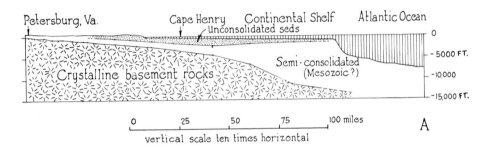

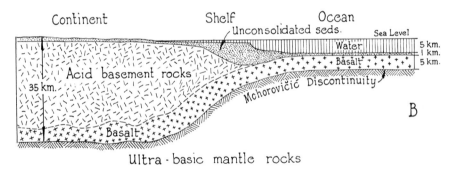

Fig. 2.—*A:* section across Atlantic coastal plain, as measured by Ewing. *B:* generalized section across a stable continental margin.

Much careful seismic work has, to date, been unable to elucidate the vertical structure of continental blocks. It is certain, however, that the surface velocities are those of the visible acid gneisses, while the bottom velocities are those of basalts, below which they change suddenly to those of ultrabasic rocks. If the continents are expanding over the oceans, this would be expected; for the 5 km or so of basaltic rocks on the ocean floors would become the base of the continental crust and would still be preserved there, as the velocities suggest (cf. Fig. 2, *B*).

5. CONTINENTAL SHELVES AND COASTAL PLAINS

The steep continental slopes which mark the structural boundaries between continents and ocean basins do not begin at the water's edge but at a depth of about 200 meters at the edges of the continental shelves, which may be at any distance up to a few hundred miles offshore. Where the shallow continental shelves are wide, they often extend inland as coastal plains of low relief, sometimes underlain by flat-lying, young sediments. Such shelves and coastal plains are found along the Gulf and Atlantic coasts of North America and along the western coasts of Europe and Australia, for example.

Drilling for oil and seismic exploration have made the structure of some of these shelves clear. They are shaped like a series of thick coalescent deltas. This discovery is in keeping with another consideration, which is that rivers have brought down such vast quantities of material that shelves _ ust have been formed by the growth of deltas.

Figure 2, *A*, shows a section across the Atlantic Coast of the United States, which may be taken as an example of a coastal plain and continental shelf. It is based upon sections by Ewing, Worzel, Steenland, and Press (1950) and by King (1951).

The Appalachian Mountains, whose active history ceased about 200,-000,000 years ago, in the Triassic period of the Mesozoic era, have supplied most of the material of this shelf, which is entirely younger than they are. This has been done by steady erosion and intermittent uplift of the land, coupled with a corresponding sinking of the submerged part of the continental margin, which has caused a slight rotational motion or marginal flexure about the coast line (Umbgrove, 1947, p. 97; Chamberlin and Salisbury, 1907, p. 523), so that sediments now deeply buried in the shelves were, in their time, deposited at sea-level. It also implies that there has been some movement of subcrustal material either by flow or by fracturing and displacement.

On no other coastal shelves has so much work been done, but there is no reason to doubt that the others are similar. A striking feature of continental shelves is that no large ones are known to contain any Pre-Cambrian rocks and that, for the most part, they are young structures. As it seems likely that others were formed in the past, they must have been destroyed or changed in some manner. As it is now certain that they did not sink or slip out to sea, they must have become incorporated into the continents by mountain-building processes.

In a later section it will be shown how this could have happened. The roots of old mountains in the shields might then be expected to retain some features of shelves. It is clear that, although the inner parts of shelves may have settled uniformly, the outer parts would contain many slumped and contorted beds. This may be the origin of many of the contorted structures found in shield gneisses, which are granitized and recrystallized rocks of former shelves.

6. RATES OF EROSION, DEPOSITION, AND VOLCANISM

An important consideration about shelves is their rate of accumulation. Fortunately, there are sufficient data to suggest maximum and minimum limits to the rate at which erosion and deposition are occurring. It has been estimated that, at the present time, erosion is reducing the surface of the United States at a rate of 1 meter in 30,000 years (Dole and Stabler, 1909). If these processes had continued at the same rate throughout geological time, a layer about 17 km thick would have been removed from the United States since the beginning of Paleozoic time (5×10^8 years ago), and 110 km thick since one estimated time of the origin of the earth (33×10^8 years ago; Holmes, 1947).

The rock removed must have been redeposited, and these quantities are vastly larger than the volume of sedimentary rocks which have been preserved. It is therefore believed that the rate has not always been so rapid. The chief reason put forward is man's activity in clearing the land, but it is improbable that this can account for the whole difference (Umbgrove, 1947, p. 313). It has also been suggested that the present mountains are unusually high; but this cannot be proved, and it is probable that much sediment must have been metamorphosed and incorporated into the continents. This view is supported by the observations of most geologists who have worked on the exposed rocks of continental basements.

It is also possible to fix a minimum average rate for erosion over the whole period of about 150,000,000 years from Jurassic to present time. In the coastal plain between Texas and Alabama, deep wells prove the presence of at least 2.8×10^6 km^3 of Mesozoic and Cenozoic sediments, to which it is estimated can be added at least as much again for deposits under the submerged continental shelf (Murray, 1953). If this minimum volume of 5.6×10^6 km^3 be assumed to have accumulated in about 1.5×10^8 years as a result of erosion from the Mississippi River Basin of 3.2×10^6 km^2, the average rate of erosion would have been 1 meter in 85,000 years. At that rate, an average of at least 6 km would therefore have been removed from the surface of the Mississippi Basin and deposited along the coast since earliest Cambrian time and at least 40 km since the beginning of the earth.

The conclusion is that many tens of kilometers of rock may have been eroded from the continental blocks and redeposited during geological time. These figures are of the same order as the total thickness of the continents, and they suggest that the continental blocks may have been formed of sediments altered to metamorphic and plutonic rocks.

Older shelves must have existed and disappeared. Eardley (1947, 1951), Kay (1951), and King (1951) have suggested from their structural studies of the Cordillera and the Appalachians that those mountains were formerly marginal shelves with volcanic arcs offshore, which have been converted into mountains. If it is true that mountain ranges were formerly shelves and have been added to the continents, then we arrive at the conclusion already reached by Dana a century ago that all continents "have had their laws of growth" (Dana, 1849; Bucher, 1950). This process could enlarge the surface area of continents at the expense of their thickness but would add nothing to their volume; but there is another process which may have done that.

Rubey (1951), Kulp (1951), and Hutchinson (1947) have produced weighty arguments to suggest that the oceans and the atmosphere have been generated from within the earth by volcanic activity during geological time. Acid volcanoes, which form off many shelves, emit steam and gases and also lava. Could not this lava have been reworked to form the continents?

The West Indies arc has been most fully investigated, and Ewing (1951; Ewing and Worzel, 1954) has shown that the ocean floor on both sides of it consists of a layer of mud only about $\frac{1}{2}$ km thick over a layer of basalt 5 km thick, resting upon the ultrabasic mantle. MacGregor (1938, pp. 70–81) regards the average composition of the volcanic rocks which constitute the arc as being fairly acid (about 60 per cent SiO_2). These lavas could not have been formed by the melting of any pre-existing crust, as there is none. Ewing's suggestion that they are remelted sediments seems unsatisfactory: the sediments accumulate in the wrong place to form volcanics, and acid lavas flow in arcs like the Tonga Islands, where sediments are lacking. It is suggested that they are fresh contributions from the depths which originated interstitially in the mantle, perhaps in Buddington's (1943) hyperfusible layer, and rose along the fractures marked by deep earthquakes.

The present rate of volcanism, if representative, would have been sufficient to form continents, for these have a total area of 1.3×10^8 km², an average thickness of 35 km, and hence a volume of 4.5×10^9 km³, which could have been formed in 3.5×10^9 years at an average rate of only 1.3 km³ per year. Few figures are available for the total annual lava emitted by the world's 500 active volcanoes, which are mostly acid (Kennedy and Richey, 1947); but reports of individual outbursts, like the fall of 4 km³ of rhyolite ash in 1912 in the Katmai Valley, Alaska (Fenner, 1923), and Sapper's estimate of 1 km³ per year since A.D. 1500 (quoted by Kuenen, 1950, p. 388) make it easy to believe in the growth of continents.

The features of volcanic and mountain arcs will next be discussed and then the nature of the processes by which this growth may have taken place.

7. MOUNTAIN AND ISLAND ARCS

7.1 THE TWO ACTIVE BELTS OF FOLDED MOUNTAINS AND ISLAND ARCS

One of the great achievements of field geology has been to show that mountain-building has always been concentrated in narrow, mobile belts. At the present time, two belts, each very roughly a great circle, are active. They contain all the world's young folded mountains, most of its volcanoes, and most earthquake epicenters. One of these belts extends across the Mediterranean, southern Asia, Indonesia, and Melanesia to New Zealand and will be referred to as the "South Eurasian–Melanesian belt." The other surrounds the Pacific Ocean from Indonesia clockwise to Antarctica and will be called the "East Asian–Cordilleran belt." In the past, other belts have been active in different places.

Along the present belts there is a wide variety of volcanic, plutonic, and sedimentary ranges, of single and double island arcs, and of plateaus. These elements are so varied and complex that they defied simple classification until geophysical observations suggested that beneath this apparent complexity there is a simple pattern made up of a few types of features repeated many times in different guises. Chief among these are the primary elements or arcs.

7.2. THE PRIMARY ELEMENTS OR ARCS

Those elements which have deep-seated features associated with them will here be called *primary*, because it is generally agreed that the cause of the mountain-building process lies within the earth and not at its surface. Most primary elements are arcs, and they are all connected into two continuous lines, which are nothing less than two vast and complex zones of fracture about the earth, illustrated in Figure 3. Other mountain elements within the mobile belts, which lack the deep-seated connections, are classed as *secondary*. One of these generally occurs opposite to each junction of two primary arcs. The active primary elements show some or all of the following diagnostic characteristics: (1) they are underlain by

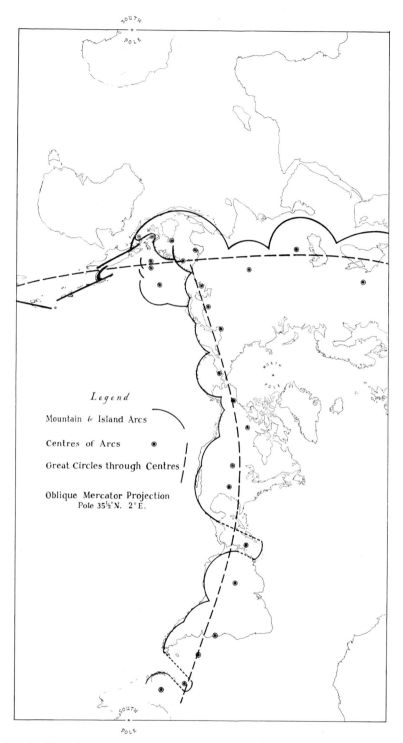

FIG. 3.—The primary arcs or elements of the two active orogenetic belts, connected like a series of scallops.

all the world's deep earthquakes and most of its major shallow ones;
(2) they have associated with them those of the world's active volcanoes
which give acid lavas and the young intrusive rocks or batholiths of
similar composition; (3) they are followed by strips of large negative
gravity anomalies; (4) they are accompanied by the world's greatest oceanic trenches; (5) they rest upon no visible basement of older gneissic rocks;
(6) they contain peculiar sediments, called *ophiolites*, described below.
Most of these elements have two other characteristics, which are not diagnostic, as they are also common to secondary ranges. These features are:
(*a*) most of these elements are roughly circular arcs; (*b*) those in the two
active belts have all been subject to Cenozoic and Recent folding or uplift.

TABLE 1

THE TYPES OF ACTIVE PRIMARY ARCS OR ELEMENTS AND
THEIR CHIEF DISTINGUISHING FEATURES

Name	Shape	Ophiolitic Part Primary Arc	Igneous Part Primary Arc	Example
Single island arc.....	Circular arc	Trench	Volcanic islands	Kurile Islands
Double island arc....	Circular arc	Ophiolitic islands	Volcanic islands	Aleutian Islands at Kodiak Island
Single mountain arc..	Circular arc	Trench	Volcanic and batholithic ranges	Central Andes
Double mountain arc.	Circular arc	Ophiolitic ranges	Volcanic and batholithic ranges	Coast, Cascade, and Sierra Nevada ranges of U.S. (combined)
Fractured arc.......	Straight	Features are irregular		Solomon Islands

The active primary elements do not all look alike; some are mountain
ranges, some are island arcs, but they may be classified into five types,
found in Table 1. The first four are regular and display the same distinguishing features always in the same order. Umbgrove (1947, p. 70) and
Gutenberg and Richter (1949, pp. 24–29) have drawn attention to these
features, which are shown in Table 2 and Figure 4.

7.21. *Single island arcs.*—Many island chains are in the shape of a
circular arc of active acid volcanic islands, concentric with which, at a
distance of from 160 to 200 km on the outer or convex side, there is a deep
ocean trench. Such arcs, like the South Sandwich Islands, the arcs off the
east coast of Asia, or the greater part of the Aleutian chain, are called
"single island arcs" (Umbgrove, 1947, pp. 173–174). Gravity anomalies,
where they have been measured, and shallow and deep earthquakes follow
the order given in Table 2.

7.22. *Double island arcs.*—If the Aleutian Island chain is followed toward Alaska, the single arc of volcanic islands develops into a double arc, in which the place of the ocean trench is gradually taken by a shelf which first displaces and then fills the trench (see Fig. 5; Gibson and Nichols, 1953; Menard and Dietz, 1951; Smith, 1939; Stose, 1946). On this shelf are the Chirikof and Kodiak Islands and the Kenai Peninsula, forming, with the adjacent Aleutian Islands, a double island arc. The outer arc is predominantly composed of sediments which are often of a peculiar type named *ophiolites*. They consist of lava, graywacke, and other sediments derived from lava and cherts, containing oceanic rather than coastal fos-

TABLE 2

FEATURES OF REGULAR, ACTIVE PRIMARY ARCS
(From Convex Side to Concave Side; see Fig. 4)

1. *Ophiolitic part, primary arc*

A deep oceanic trench or a chain of islands or mountains of ophiolitic type of sediments. Sometimes both together, in which case the trench is small and is displaced to lie outside the islands. Shallow earthquakes and a belt of large negative gravity anomalies occur under the islands or mountains or on the inner side of the trench.

2. *Intermediate part, primary arc*

A valley or shallow trough or slope between the ophilitic and igneous parts of primary arcs. Earthquakes at a depth of about 60 km and a belt of positive gravity anomalies occur beneath it.

3. *Igneous part, primary arc*

A volcanic-island arc or mountain arc of andesitic to acid volcanics and granodiorite batholiths, with earthquakes beneath it at about 100 km depth. It parallels the ophilitic part at a distance of about 180 km.

4. *Conical zone of intermediate to deep earthquakes*

Intermediate and deep-focus earthquakes, with foci on a conical zone dipping toward the centers of the arcs and extending in some cases to 700 km in depth.

sils and cut by intrusives of ultrabasic composition. These peculiar rocks have recently been described in the Apennines by Maxwell (1953). In this chapter they will be referred to as "ophiolites," to distinguish them from the more usual types of sediments found in secondary arcs.

7.23. *Double mountain arcs.*—If the double island arc of the Aleutian Islands is followed still farther east, it can be seen to become a double continental mountain system in which the valley occupied by Cook Inlet separates the volcanic and batholithic inner arc of the Aleutian Range from the ophiolitic outer arc on Kenai Peninsula and in the Chugach Mountains.

Bostock (1948) and Fenneman (1931) have pointed to a similar threefold division of the coastal Cordillera for the whole British Columbia and United States coasts. Each is a typical double mountain arc.

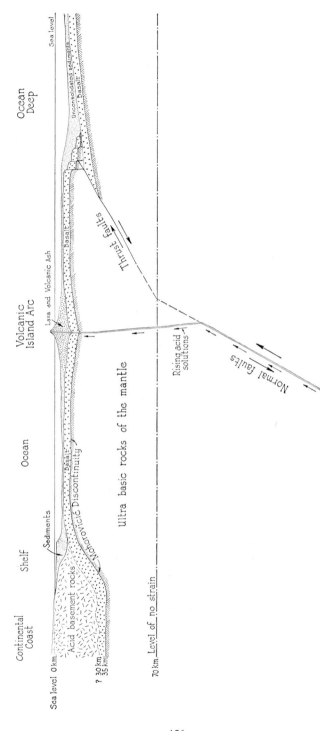

FIG. 4.—Generalized section across an active single island arc

156

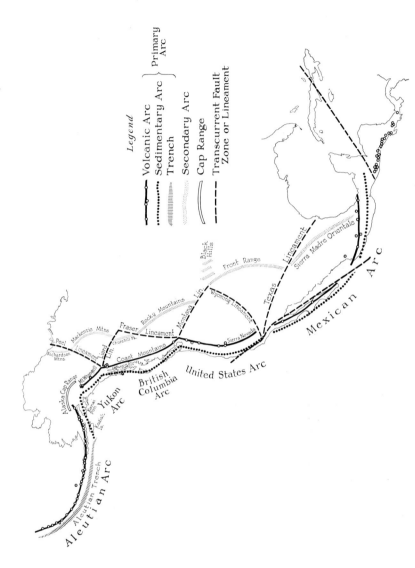

Fig. 5.—Active primary and secondary arcs and lineaments of North America

7.24. *Single mountain arcs.*—In the center of the west coast of South America between Santiago and Ecuador the coastal mountains of the Andes are volcanic and face an ocean trench offshore (see Fig. 6; Stose, 1950; Rich, 1942, p. 165). These mountains are similar to single island arcs, except that they form part of the continent.

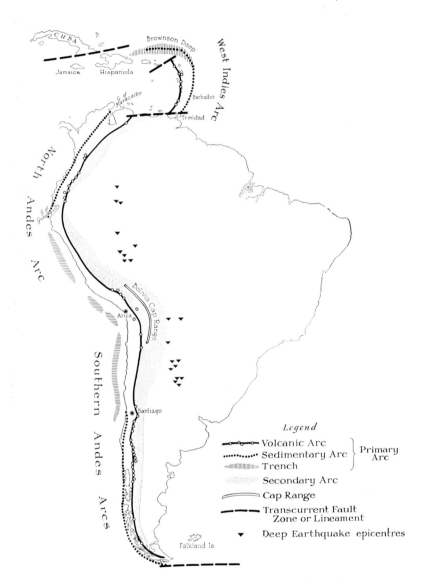

FIG. 6.—Active primary and secondary arcs of South America

7.25. *Fractured arcs.*—It is well known that the San Andreas transcurrent (or strike-slip) fault zone cuts the southern half of the United States double mountain arc, but it does so without destroying the double-arc pattern. In the case of the Philippine fault zone, on the other hand, a long fault with great horizontal displacement is the predominant feature, and only some disorganized aspects of arcuate structure exist, such as a deep ocean trench, scattered active volcanoes of acid composition, and scattered earthquake epicenters at both shallow and great depths (King and McKee, 1949). The simple arcuate pattern either never existed or has been destroyed or torn apart by a transcurrent fault zone. Such composite features will be called *fractured arcs.* The Melanesian arcs from the Philippines to New Zealand are considered to be of this general type (Fig. 7).

7.3. CYCLE OF EVOLUTION AND STAGES OF PRIMARY ARCS

The ages and the geographical distribution of the first four types of regular arcs suggest that the type developed depends upon the age and activity of the arc and its proximity to continents and that the types of arc form an evolutionary sequence, as has already been suggested. The stages of primary arcs are listed in the second column of Table 3.

First a continental shelf forms by deltaic accretion. The Gulf and Atlantic Coast shelves of the United States are examples, which Lawson (1942) has estimated are soon due to start fracturing and volcanic activity.

Next a conical zone of fractures forms (see Fig. 4)—not, as might be expected, within the shelf but farther offshore, with some point in the shelf as center. The existence and location of the fracture zone is not hypothetical but is marked by earthquake foci. Volcanism, which gives rise to the volcanic arc, starts as a consequence of the fracturing. The Aleutian arc is an excellent example of this stage. Most of the arc is far offshore in deep water. In the northern and eastern parts of the Bering Sea is a large shelf, which was, no doubt, fed in the past, as at present, by the Yukon and Anadyr rivers. The center of the Aleutian arc lies within the shelf off the mouth of the Anadyr.

Double arcs, according to Umbgrove, occur where there is a source of sediment to fill the trench and where later movements have squeezed these sediments and elevated them into a string of islands. The Chirikof and Kodiak Islands and Kenai Peninsula provided a splendid example of this, formed where the Aleutian arc approaches and joins North America.

The next step in this evolution is that the rivers of the continents and the volcanoes of the arc both contribute material to fill in the sea behind the arc and often to fill the trough in front of the arc. Examples of arcs

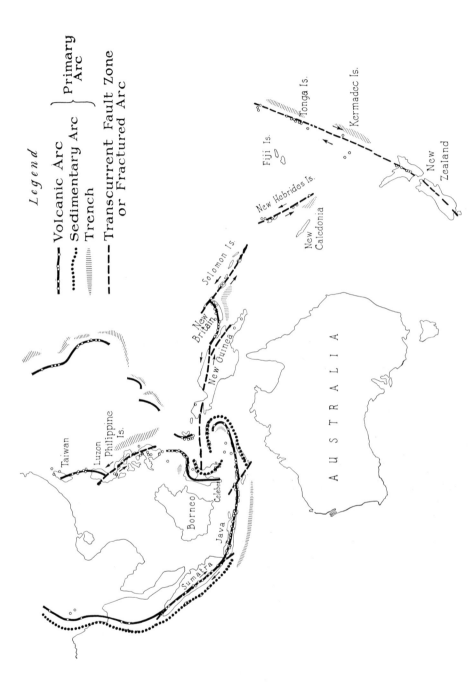

Fig. 7.—Fractured arcs of Melanesia and New Zealand

in which the inland sea is now shallow are the Japanese and Ryukyu arcs and, according to Eardley (1947), the North American Coast Range arcs at the beginning of Mesozoic time.

With further deposition, compression, and uplift, the inland seas become land, and the arcs become joined to the continent as double or single mountain arcs. The great thicknesses of volcanic rocks and sediments derived from them which emerge are sometimes called *eugeosynclines*.

TABLE 3

CYCLE OF STAGES OF PRIMARY AND SECONDARY ARCS
IN OROGENETIC PROCESS

Stage	Primary-Arc Stage	Example	Secondary-Arc Stage	Example
0......	Continental shelf	Atlantic Coast, United States	....	....
1......	Single island arc	Kurile Islands	Small secondary mountain arc	Western Kamchatka
2a*.... or	Double island arc	Aleutian Islands at Kodiak Island	Secondary mountain arc	Alaska Range
2b.....	Single active mountain arc	Central Andes (western ranges)	Secondary mountain arc (sedimentary)	Central Andes (eastern ranges)
3......	Double active mountain arc	Coast, Cascade, and Sierra Nevada Mountains (combined)	Secondary mountain arc (sedimentary)	Rocky Mountains in Canada
4......	Inactive mountain arc (metamorphic part)	Piedmont Province of Appalachian Mountains	Inactive mountain arc (sedimentary part)	Valley and Ridge Province in New York–Pennsylvania
5......	Part or whole of an Archean province of a Pre-Cambrian shield	Grenville Province (more than one arc)	Proterozoic basin	Mistassini Basin, Quebec

* Stages 2*a* and 2*b* are alternates.

The final stages in the suggested cycle can be found, marked by remnants with the same characteristics, in old, inactive mountains and in provinces of shields, as will be shown later.

7.4. TYPES OF JUNCTIONS OF PRIMARY ARCS

It has long been known that mountain ranges join in a few characteristic ways. These are illustrated in Figure 8.

7.41. *Single-fracture systems.*—They are of three kinds.

a) Linkages are the junctions occurring between young island arcs, such as the northeast Asian island arcs (Figs. 9 and 10). They are characterized by the extension of one of the arcs past the junction in a nearly straight ridge, such as Kamchatka or Sakhalin. The extension, which is believed to represent a single-fracture system, is marked by only slight volcanic and seismic activity and no deep earthquakes. The secondary arc is poorly developed, as in western Kamchatka.

b) *Common deflections* are formed where two primary mountain arcs meet at an obtuse angle. This is the type of junction common throughout the Appalachian Mountains and probable also near Santiago in the Andes. The secondary arcs immediately adjoin them, so that there is no median-land, but there is characteristically a graben springing from the continental side which represents a single-fracture system (Fig. 14).

c) *Capped deflections* are a special case of common deflections which apparently occur where the primary arcs meet at an acute angle. The sec-

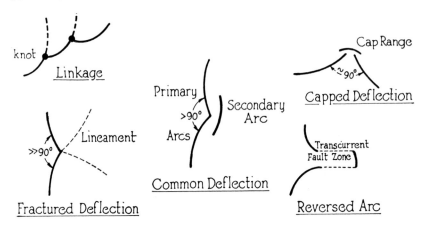

FIG. 8.—Types of junction of primary arcs

ondary arc is then much more highly metamorphosed than usual. It is generally sharply curved. Owing to the slower erosion of metamorphic rocks, it forms a short range of great height, of which the Alps are a fine example, with the Rhine graben as a single-fracture system on the continental side (Fig. 11).

7.42. *Double-fracture systems or fractured deflections.*—They are formed where two primary mountain arcs meet at an obtuse angle and where the primary arcs are separated from the secondary arcs by a wide medianland. Two conspicuous lineaments then spring from the primary junction, cross the medianland apparently as great zones of shearing, and mark the ends of secondary arcs. A good example occurs near Seattle. The Montana and Fraser lineaments cross the medianland and mark the northern and southern ends of the secondary arc of the Canadian Rocky Mountains (Fig. 5).

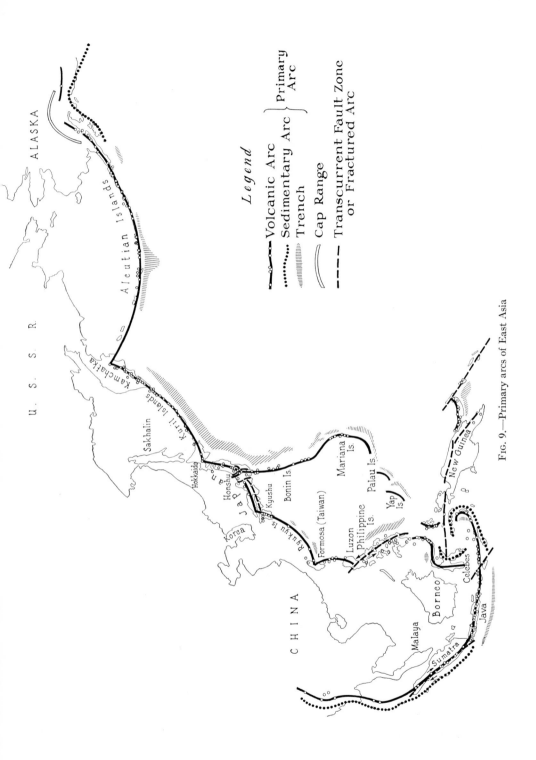

FIG. 9.—Primary arcs of East Asia

Legend

Volcanic Arc ⎫ Primary
Sedimentary Arc ⎬ Arc
Trench
Cap Range
Transcurrent Fault Zone
or Fractured Arc

7.43. *Reversal zones.*—When Hess (1938; Hess and Maxwell, 1953) described the West Indies, he suggested that the arc of the Lesser Antilles was linked to Mexico and to South America by zones of transcurrent faults, that is, straight shear fractures along which there had been horizontal displacements. Since these zones occur where primary arcs change from facing in one direction to facing in another, they will be called *reversal zones.* The transcurrent fault zones have no deep or intermediate earth-

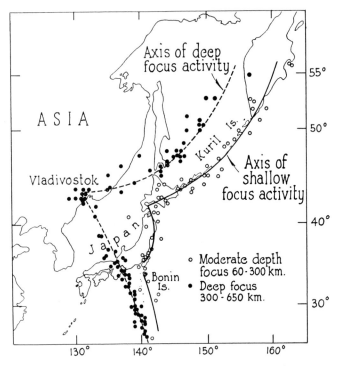

Fig. 10.—Epicenters of shallow and deep-focus earthquakes near the Japanese junction (after Hess).

quakes and appear to be shallow fractures. No secondary arcs form in this case.

7.44. *Other junctions.*—This group includes those junctions hidden by the sea, such as those in Melanesia, concerning which little or nothing is known.

7.5 SECONDARY ELEMENTS OR ARCS

The existence along the active mobile belts of secondary arcs which are without deep-seated features has already been mentioned. These arcs all lie on the concave side of the primary arcs at their junctions. They are

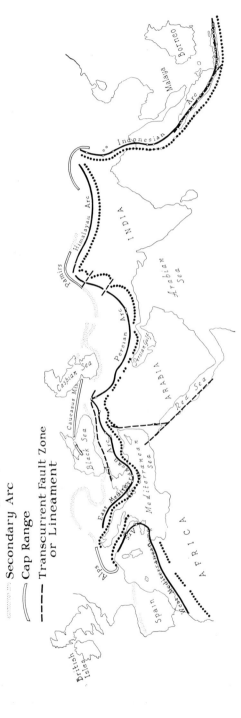

Legend

Volcanic Arc } Primary
Sedimentary Arc } Arc

Secondary Arc

Cap Range

Transcurrent Fault Zone
or Lineament

FIG. 11.—Primary and secondary arcs of southern Eurasia

almost all curved in the opposite direction to primary arcs but are more irregular. They have been formed by the accumulation and subsequent folding and thrust-faulting of thick deposits of sedimentary rocks. Each was laid down upon a basement of gneissic rocks forming a pre-existing part of the continent. These deposits are largely nonvolcanic, include no ophiolites, and are what might be called "normal" sediments. They have been called *miogeosynclines*. Where the sedimentary cover is thin, great blocks of the basement may be faulted up to form ranges in these arcs, as has happened in the Rocky Mountains of the United States. They are without any deep-seated seismic activity. Examples are the Rocky Mountains of Canada and the United States, the Pyrenees, and the Carpathians. Their cycle of stages is given in Table 3.

TABLE 4

CHARACTERISTIC CROSS-SECTION OF AN OROGENETIC BELT
(Examples from Cordillera of British Columbia)

Stage	Feature	Boundary	Example
1.........	Frontland		Pacific Ocean Basin
		Sole of thrust faults of primary arc dipping east	
2a........	Ophiolitic part, primary arc		Vancouver Island and Queen Charlotte Islands
		Valley of Strait of Georgia and Hecate Strait	
2b........	Igneous part, primary arc		Coast Range of British Columbia
		Indefinite	
3.........	Medianland		Central Plateau
		Rocky Mountain trench faults	
4.........	Secondary arc		Rocky Mountains
		Sole of thrusts of secondary arcs dipping west	
5.........	Hinterland		Covered shield of the prairies

7.6 THE CHARACTERISTIC CROSS-SECTION OF AN OROGENETIC BELT

In any cross-section of a complete orogenetic belt the various components always appear in a definite order (Cady, 1950). Proceeding from the convex side of the primary arc toward the concave side, this order is frontland, primary arc, medianland, secondary arc, and hinterland. This is shown in more detail with an example in Table 4. The frontland, primary arc, and hinterland are always present. In most cases the frontland is an ocean, but in the cases of India, Arabia, and northern Africa it is a shield. The medianland has often been referred to as *Zwischengebirge*, or median mass. In those cases in which it is not present, the primary and secondary arcs fit closely together. This is the case in the Andes, of which the western ranges are primary, and the eastern ranges secondary.

There is confusion about frontlands and hinterlands in the literature, because some authors have placed emphasis upon secondary arcs and have referred to what are here called hinterlands as frontlands.

It is agreed with Kyrnine (1948, 1951) that the classes of sedimentary rocks should fit the structural classification, and it is suspected that his graywacke, arkose, and quartzite classes are, respectively, associated with primary arcs, with the late stages of secondary arcs, and with thinly covered hinterlands.

8. THE NATURE OF THE OROGENETIC PROCESS

The foregoing analysis of the principal features of present mountain belts has been descriptive and without explanation. The likelihood that it is a correct generalization would be increased if some explanation could be given for these features in terms of recognized physical laws. At least three methods of tackling the problem have been attempted. Jeffreys (1929) and Urey (1952) have suggested that the origin of the earth is now sufficiently well known that physical and chemical laws can be applied to trace the earth's development from its original state. Each paper deduces important conclusions which must control our speculations, but neither has explained the details of that part of the earth's history recorded in the rocks.

A second approach has been to try to determine the present composition, temperature, and pressure of the materials of which the earth is made at various depths below the surface. If these could be ascertained and if the properties of the same materials at corresponding temperatures and pressures could be measured in the laboratory, then the problem would be precisely soluble. Great progress has been made in laboratory studies at high pressures and temperatures by Bridgman (1951), Griggs *et al.* (1951), Birch (1951), and others. Bullen (1950) has estimated the earth's internal pressures and densities fairly accurately. Jacobs (1954) and Uffen and Misener (1954) have estimated internal temperatures recently; but the composition within the earth is not yet known with certainty. Further study of conditions within the earth is of the greatest importance, but, to date, this information has not been used to explain the origin of any mountain or continent.

A third method has been to try to suggest some physical process which could have given rise to the earth's surface features. According to Griggs

(1939, p. 618), only two mechanisms have been suggested which could cause mountain-building. These are "compression due to thermal contraction and viscous drag of convection currents in the substratum."

It has been amply demonstrated that some forms of both hypotheses would be physically possible and could occur within the earth under conditions that are not unreasonable. In 1929 Jeffreys established the contraction hypothesis in a definite form and argued that the probable amount of contraction was of the right order of magnitude to have produced the known mountain systems, but he did not show exactly how the contraction was linked to any particular geological features. In 1931 Lake pointed out that many orogenetic features were arcuate, and he offered an ingenious explanation for them based on the contraction theory; but the discovery of deep-focus earthquakes showed that his theory could not be quite correct and at least needed modification.

A few years later Vening Meinesz (1934, 1948), Pekeris (1935), and others showed how systems of convection currents could circulate within the earth. These ideas have been developed by many authors, and there is no doubt that convection currents are at present a widely favored mechanism for orogenesis. Papers dealing with convection currents fall into two classes, those suggesting an explanation of the features of particular regions, such as Indonesia (Vening Meinesz, 1954), East Asian arcs (Hess, 1948), or West Indies (Hess, 1938), and those dealing with the subject in a general manner, including, besides those mentioned, important papers by Griggs (1939), Rittmann (1951), Hafner (1951), Vening Meinesz (1952), and several others in a symposium on the subject (Gutenberg, 1951). See also papers by Lees (1952, 1953) and Weeks (1953).

Although it is agreed that convection currents may exist within the earth's mantle, several difficulties have been pointed out which prevent their acceptance as a complete explanation for mountain- and continent-building. These difficulties include (a) the great length and continuity of orogenetic belts; (b) the sharp deflections in the belts; (c) the absence of any evidence of stretching in the crust which should accompany compression if convection currents were operating; (d) the apparently layered nature of the mantle; (e) the evidence provided by deep-focus earthquakes of great strength and stress differences in the mantle which flow should tend to reduce; and (f) the absence of any direct evidence for the existence of currents. This last has led to speculations involving a variety of models of currents and disagreement as to whether convection currents rise or sink under continents and mountains and whether they are continuous or intermittent. Particularly unsatisfactory from the point of view of a résumé such as this is the fact that no paper has yet described the details of the present mountain systems in terms of currents and that no attempt at all has been made to use them to explain the former mountains of Pre-Cambrian time.

Some of these difficulties can probably be overcome. The earth's mechanisms may be complex, and convection currents in the mantle may play, and probably have played, a part in them; but at the present time a development of the contraction theory due to Scheidegger (1953a) appears to provide a more complete explanation. This theory springs from Lake's realization that many mountain and island arcs are approximately circular. Lake's (1931a, b) original suggestion has been extended by Wilson (1949a, 1950) and Scheidegger and Wilson (1950) in the manner set out in Section 7 of this chapter. Scheidegger examined both contraction and convection as possible causes of orogenesis. If the former applies, then the arcuate shapes may be due to rupturing or yielding along the conical zones which deep-focus earthquakes indicate to exist in the outer shells of the earth beneath island arcs. Much is known about the yielding, flow, and rupturing of spherical shells in different states of matter. Scheidegger assumed the outer shells of the earth to be in various conditions, in turn, and could find only one condition and state of matter, not of an *ad hoc* nature, which would produce fractures of the required kind in spherical shells. This fitted Jeffreys' (1929) earlier hypothesis of contraction exactly; and Scheidegger and Wilson (1950) then suggested that failure of the outer shells by sliding rupture could be a satisfactory explanation of the present mountain arcs. Coulomb had independently and earlier come to somewhat similar conclusions about fracturing, but he did not explain why the failures were circular arcs (Coulomb, 1945). Hales (1953) has also discussed the contraction theory.

A year after this chapter was first written and the illustrations completed, Scheidegger (1953b) produced an extension of the theory, which explains, in general, the features found where two arcs join; but the motions of the earth are now found to be more complex: not one arc or two arcs but many arcs are moving and interacting one upon another. This introduces horizontal movements and other complexities; to deal with these the theory needs to be further extended (Wilson, 1951).

The theory of contraction has been attacked on the grounds that the earth cannot be cooling down. Some have claimed this on the supposition that the earth had a cool origin, but Urry (1949) has pointed out that, even so, the earth might still have gone through an intermediate stage of warming up and melting.

Others have suggested that convection currents must arise because the earth is generating so much heat; but Davis and Hess (1947, 1949, 1950) have recently obtained much reduced values for the radioactivity of meteorites and ultrabasic rocks which are considered to represent the material of the earth's interior. The fact of the matter is that little is known about the distribution of radioactivity within the earth (Slichter, 1941; see also chap. 3); but attempts to measure radioactivity have consistently led to results which have later been shown to be too high. Jacobs (1953) has recently concluded that sufficient heat to maintain convection currents in the *core* could flow through the mantle by conduction alone.

While agreement has not yet been reached, it seems quite safe to advance a theory of contraction. Recent data make cooling more probable than when Jeffreys advocated it. The version of the contraction hypothesis presented here appears to fit the geological observations. It explains the pattern of seismicity. It is a sound and precise physical theory by means of which predictions can be made and checked. Even if some other explanation is later found to be more correct, the following discussion will serve to illustrate points requiring explanation.

8.1. OROGENETIC PROCESS PROPOSED TO EXPLAIN PRIMARY ARCS

Jeffreys (1929, pp. 278–279) suggested that cooling has not affected the interior of the earth and that, as a consequence, from the center of the earth to within about 700 km of the surface no appreciable change in volume has yet taken place. He proposed that the layers were cooling, contracting, and becoming thinner from a depth of 700 km to about 100 km and that, because the interior was not altering, these layers were stretched out horizontally. He suggested that there was a level of no strain at about 100 km depth, above which the layers had already largely cooled and were therefore under a horizontal crushing stress (see Fig. 12).

Recently Benioff (1949) has shown that the earthquakes occurring beneath the Andes and the Tonga-Kermadec Islands lie along zones extending to depths of 700 km and that they may be divided into two sequences lying, respectively, above and below a discontinuity at 70 km. Across it he gives reason to believe that there is "no effective mechanical coupling." If Jeffreys' very approximate estimate of 100 km for the depth of the level of no strain be equated to Benioff's observed depth of 70 km, an explanation of Benioff's observations is provided. A level of no strain at a depth of 70 km would provide a zone of no effective mechanical coupling to separate the deep and shallow shocks. Wadati has commented on the scarcity of foci near that depth under Japan, while Table 5 (from Gutenberg and Richter's data) shows that the effect is general.

The shell between 70 and 700 km is considered to be contracting because of cooling, as Jeffreys visualized; and the earthquakes in it are thought to be due to normal faulting, that is, sliding fracture along conical fault zones, as shown in Figure 13. Since these are due to relief of horizontal pressure, these deep cones dip at angles of rather more than 45° (Anderson,

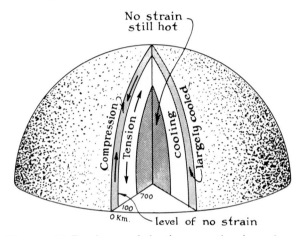

Fig. 12.—Diagram of Jeffreys' proposals for the contraction theory (note that the zones illustrated differ only in temperature and states of strain and do not coincide with zones of different composition).

TABLE 5

FREQUENCY OF LARGE EARTHQUAKES AS FUNCTION
OF THEIR FOCAL DEPTHS

Depth of focus (km)*......	25	50	60	70	80	90	100
Frequency..............	Many	15	5	6	34	11	23

* All depths given precisely in Gutenberg and Richter (1949, Tables 14 and 15) have been plotted. They state that 25 km is the commonest depth for shallow earthquakes. Five depths were 75 km; they were distributed among 70 and 80 km in the ratio in which 70 and 80 occurred.

1952; Hubbert, 1951). Scheidegger could explain these conical zones only if they were centered about points of symmetry or weakness. Many of the centers of arcs are in continental shelves, and it must therefore be assumed that the process of deltaic accumulation eventually gives rise to weakness (by blanketing and heating perhaps?) and hence indirectly to fracture offshore.

On the other hand, the shell above 70 km is in compression due to the

contraction below it and fails by thrust-faulting in conical zones, which
usually lie immediately above those just mentioned. Since the upper
faults are due to compression, the cones dip at less than 45°. The direction
of motion in shallow and deep earthquakes is opposed, one set being due
to normal faulting, the other to thrust-faulting. Opposed directions of
first motion in shallow and deep earthquakes originating in the same region have been reported by Byerly and Evernden (1950).

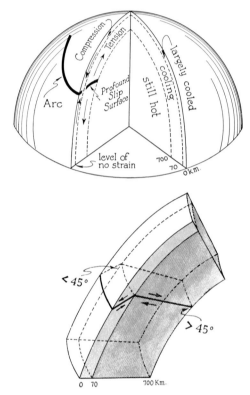

Fig. 13.—Diagram of Scheidegger's development of the contraction theory, with detailed
sketch of part of one arc.

This explains the distribution of earthquakes, and sliding rupture is the
kind of mechanism which should give rise to them. Because the compression is world-wide and the belts are continuous, an orderly pattern for the
release of energy in different parts of the world might be expected and has
been found (Benioff, 1951). The further investigation of these points provides excellent ways to check the validity of this theory.

Geologists have often noticed that mountain ranges show features related to both tension and compression. They have generally assumed that

these succeed each other in cycles; but the present theory suggests that they may be superimposed, with shallow compressional features overlying deep features due to relief of horizontal pressure.

It is considered that the ocean trenches are due to overriding by the inner blocks of arcs, which are thrust up at the surface and which bend down the ocean floor in front of them, as has already been suggested and treated quantitatively by Gunn (1947). Near continents the trenches may become filled, and the filling is then pushed up in the form of islands of the outer ophilitic arcs.

The same overriding and underthrusting probably suffice to explain the occurrence and position of the belts of negative gravity anomalies, which occur over the trenches. It was suggested by Vening Meinesz (1934) that the strips of negative gravity anomalies found over trenches were due to a downfold of the light crust, of which the trench was a surface expression; but Ewing (1951) has shown that there are no light rocks on the floor of the ocean and hence that the downfolding of the crust would not give rise to a decrease in gravity above a fold; he has shown instead that there is a great trough of light sediments under the belt of negative anomalies off Puerto Rico. He has suggested that light sediments are the cause of the deficiency in gravity. If so, they must be very thick and could be metamorphosed in due course to extend the continental block. The reason why volcanoes form over the conical fault zones at those places where they reach a depth of about 100 km is presumably due to subsidiary faulting, which provides channels along which lava and superheated solutions rise from the depths. It is believed that the abundance of acid igneous activity associated with all the deep fractures and its absence in secondary arcs and along shallow seismic fracture zones are evidence that heat and solutions or magma do rise along these fractures. Shallow earthquake zones, like the Mid-Atlantic Ridge, have basic lava associated with them. These associations suggest that basic lavas are due to remelting of the mantle near the surface and that acid lavas rise with much superheat from greater depths.

Since this was first written, several important suggestions have been made. Jeffreys (1952) now believes that cooling has affected layers in the earth below 700 km. This would tend to increase the amount of contraction at the earth's surface during geologic time.

Benioff (1954) has refined his analyses of the distribution of earthquakes. He confirms that changes in the nature of earthquakes occur at depths of about 60 and 300 km; but he associates these with supposed changes in composition, in spite of the fact that these are not the levels

at which well-defined changes are known to occur. He continues to hold
that the great conical fault zones below primary arcs are due to reverse
or thrust faulting at all depths and that the admitted change in angle of
dip of these cones which occurs at depth is due to departures from Anderson's theory of faulting.

Hodgson, in work still largely unpublished, finds that horizontal movements are important along deep-seated fault zones.

Bullen (1953) has made the interesting suggestion that during the cooling and solidification of the earth some less dense layers in the mantle
might have been trapped below more dense layers. In private conversation
he has pointed out that, with reasonable assumptions, the displacement
of these layers could have provided all the energy released by earthquakes
throughout geological time. (This is somewhat analogous to the release of
energy which Urey has shown must have accompanied any separation
and settling of the core.) Bullen considers that this rise of lighter material
could take place only if some process provided channels, and he considers
that fracturing due to contraction would be a suitable process. If both
processes operated, then contraction need only have been small. According to this view, the continents would represent those places where light
matter has risen. If so, it may provide an explanation of why the mantle
seems to be lighter under the oceans than under the continents, as noted
by Bullard in chapter 3.

The fact that continents rise higher than ocean floors would still require explanation, but this might be because of recrystallization of the
lighter material to less dense minerals, particularly feldspars, when it rose
to the surface. Bullen does not envisage a deep-seated granitic layer but
rather a thick zone through which the lighter and lower-melting material
was dispersed in the mantle. This is analogous to Buddington's (1943)
model reached from petrological arguments.

If this view is correct, if the continents have grown, and if the Mohorovičić discontinuity has sunk as shown in Figure 2, B, then this release of
energy seems inescapable. It is very doubtful whether the interpretation
is compatible with convection currents in the mantle at any time since it
solidified.

8.2. A Possible Explanation of the Observed Types of Junctions of Arcs

According to the contraction theory, the active cause of mountain-
building is cooling below 70 km, which gives rise to normal faulting on a
series of conical faults. Scheidegger has recently discussed the phenomena
which might be expected to occur where two such conical zones join. He

has pointed out that downward movement of the inner side of two ad-joining conical surfaces cannot take place unless one or two additional fractures also spring from the line of junction (Scheidegger, 1953*b*).

8.21. *Single-fracture junctions.*—If only one such fracture forms, the movement along it is partly shearing and partly separation. Shearing causes the fracture to be straight, while the separation gives rise to slump-ing to fill the hiatus. In the zone of compression above 70 km, no such frac-ture is necessary, but the slumping below causes slumping and tilting right up to the land surface, and compression causes rather irregular fault-ing to occur at the surface over the slumped fracture. This is held to be the origin of grabens. It is believed that the Appalachian primary arcs join in this fashion, and Figure 14 shows grabens at four out of a possible five primary-arc junctions. They have been named the Saguenay, Ottawa-Bonnechere, Rough Creek–Kentucky River, and Nemaha disturbances. Owing to the dip of the shallow cones above 70 km, the grabens do not quite reach the outcrop of the primary junctions, and the secondary arcs, because of shallow compression, form in the gap against the primary arcs. Small volcanic intrusives are common in graben, and they tend to be of peculiar basic types of rock deficient in silica and characterized by the mineral nepheline.

8.22. *Double-fracture junctions.*—If two fractures form below 70 km, they may both be nearly pure shears, and they give rise to less regular surface features above them, which form the lineaments of the Cordillera illustrated in Figure 5. Scheidegger points out that in this case the pair of lineaments bound the shallow secondary arcs and that the angles at which the primary arcs meet are related as a direct function to the dis-tance between the junction and the secondary arc. Therefore, as the angle of junction is greater at Los Angeles than at Seattle, this theory explains why the American Rocky Mountains are farther from the coast than are the Canadian Rockies.

8.3. Some Irregularities and Their Proposed Explanations

The theory must eventually be extended to apply not only to single arcs and pairs of arcs but to many arcs forming together. This introduces an aspect of interaction due to the adjustments between arcs which is one cause of that geological complexity that is so real and difficult to deal with. A number of irregularities not heretofore mentioned may now be explained by the contraction hypothesis and serve to support it.

8.31. *Different locations of epicenters of deep and shallow earthquakes near Japan.*—It is suggested that the way in which deep earthquakes follow the

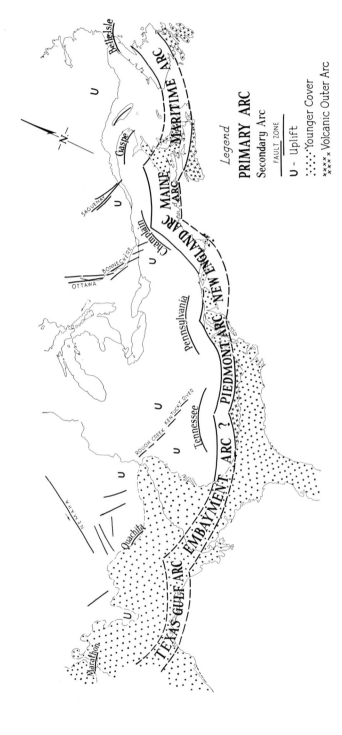

Fig. 14.—Diagram of primary and secondary arcs and fault zones of the inactive Appalachian Mountains

extensions of the Kurile and Bonin arcs to Vladivostok (Fig. 10), whereas the shallow shocks and volcanoes and gravity anomalies cut off this corner and follow northern Japan, is a marked example of the lack of mechanical coupling which Benioff noticed to occur between shallow and deep shocks.

8.32. *"En échelon" structure, an example of the superposition of compression and tension forces.*—With the exception mentioned in the last paragraph, shallow and deep features follow parallel zones, so that apparently the shallow features are usually constrained to lie over the deep zones.

This enables one to explain another feature of the East Asian arcs. It is that the minor folds and lines of volcanoes do not follow the arcs precisely but strike at angles across them, so as to form a system of short, straight, parallel *en échelon* features (see Fig. 15) (Tokuda, 1926; Bucher, 1933). Thus, although the major structures follow arcs, the minor ones do not but are parallel to one another *en échelon*. A similar arrangement of the volcanoes of the Cascade Mountains can be readily seen on the tectonic map of the United States (King, 1944).

The superposition of features due to compression upon those due to tension would give rise to a different arrangement of forces in the outer shell from those in deeper shells, and perhaps this causes the superposition of minor *en échelon* structures upon the major arcuate ones.

8.33. *An explanation of the fractured arcs.*—It has been pointed out that the two active belts meet orthogonally to form a **T**, folded about the earth. Except for the small and irregular New Britain arc, all the arcs along one arm of the **T**, the Melanesian arm, and no other arcs elsewhere are fractured arcs. It is not likely that this distribution is due to chance. The proposed explanation is that the Melanesian arm, and only that arm, has had to undergo two sets of movements approximately at right angles to each other, each corresponding to the general movements of one belt. The interaction of these forces has caused the complexity (Wilson, 1951).

This can be seen by reference to Figure 16, in which the two belts are shown diagrammatically. Along two of the three limbs of the **T**, contraction below the level of no strain and compression above it can take place without horizontal shearing, but along the third side shearing must accompany the shrinkage or compression. This can be demonstrated by arranging three books on a table separated by 1-inch gaps to form a **T**-shaped pattern and then moving them together or apart.

8.34. *Transcurrent faults along arcs.*—The same explanation as that given for the irregular fractured arcs also makes inevitable other less

Echelon Structures
of the
East Asian Arcs
(after S. Tokuda)

FIG. 15.—*En échelon* structures of folds and lines of volcanic craters along the East Asian arcs (after Tokuda and Bucher).

important transcurrent faults elsewhere. Some of the large ones can be seen in the figures showing arcs. The San Andreas rift has been mentioned as an example. Gutenberg (1939) has pointed out that the whole Pacific Ocean is moving north relative to Asia and North America. There are transcurrent faults subparallel to the San Andreas rift between Vancouver Island and the mainland (Buckham, 1947), across Japan at the Fossa Magna, and along the Philippine Fault. Vening Meinesz (1950) has emphasized the southeastward movement of Indonesia between the Philippine and Sumatra fault zones. Other faults, perhaps of similar nature, have been noticed in Peru, Nicaragua, the Aleutian Islands, Turkey, and Eu-

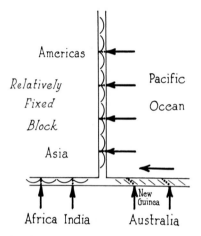

Fig. 16.—Diagram showing directions of motion along belts to explain why all the Melanesian arcs near Australia have been sheared into fractured arcs.

rope. Like the Pacific, the Indian Ocean may be moving north. Its boundaries may be the African rift valleys and the Darling fault zone of western Australia. Many earthquakes have been observed to have large horizontal components of motion (Hodgson and Storey, 1953).

8.35. *Rift valleys and linear island chains.*—The two great orogenetic belts are the only systems of folded mountains active in present or Cenozoic time; but mountains have been built recently in other places by block-faulting and by volcanic accumulation. Most of these mountains do not occur sporadically but along elongated fault systems, of which the most notable are the African rift valleys and the Hawaiian and other linear chains of islands in the Pacific, including the Gilbert, Tuamotu, Society, and Austral Islands.

All these features have the following points in common. Either they branch about at right angles from near one end of an orogenetic belt, or they are far removed from belts; they have only shallow and minor seismic activity; their volcanic rocks are basalts if they are in the oceans and basalts deficient in silica, like those of graben, if on continents. It is suggested that they are primarily due to transcurrent faults and horizontal adjustments in the upper part of the crust, adjustments necessitated by contraction along the orogenetic belts. There are vertical displacements along many of these features which may be a consequence of larger horizontal movements (Anderson, 1952, p. 154). This view has already been advanced as at least part of the explanation for many of these features, by Boutakoff (1948) for the Pacific Islands, by Betz and Hess (1942) for the Hawaiian Islands, and by Quennell (1948) and McConnell (1948) for the rift valleys.

8.36. *Sporadic timing of orogenetic activity.*—It was at one time generally believed that there were only a few great and world-wide periods of mountain-building. Some connected these epochs with supposed heating in the earth's interior and movement of currents. In western Europe and in North America the most accepted epochs of orogenesis have been the Caledonian, Acadian, and Taconic (mid-Paleozoic), the Hercynian and Appalachian (post-Paleozoic), and the Alpine and Cordilleran (post-Mesozoic). The more the matter has been studied, the more complex has each epoch become, and the more numerous have been the exceptions. For example, although Umbgrove (see Fig. 17) fundamentally used this classification, he has employed letters to distinguish no less than 23 different epochs of compression. Knopf (1948) has pointed out the compound nature of orogenies. Gilluly (1949) has shown that the present and recent events in California are sporadic, proceeding "now quickly, now slowly, now in this area, now that."

Rutten (1949, p. 1769) and King (1951, pp. 78–79) have come to the same conclusion, which King states thus: "These terms for orogenic epochs are convenient for references but merely express deformational climaxes that are prominent in one part of the system or another. . . . Where relations are sufficiently plain that the history of an orogenic epoch can be worked out in detail it can be determined that it consists instead of a succession of episodes spread through a considerable span of time. . . . As knowledge increases, differentiation between the succeeding main orogenic epochs becomes correspondingly indistinct."

This again would be a natural consequence of the contraction hypothesis. Cooling is continuous, but its effects are felt now in one place, now in another. To suppose with Stille (1924, 1940) that periods of activity are

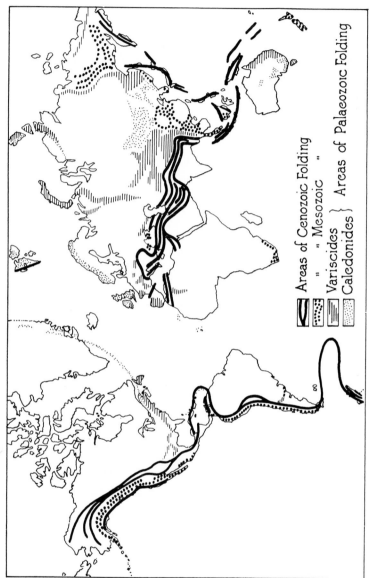

Fig. 17.—World map, showing principal folded mountain ranges

Areas of Cenozoic Folding
" " Mesozoic "
Variscides
Caledonides } Areas of Palaeozoic Folding

world-wide and alternate with world-wide periods of quiescence is held to be contrary to the geological evidence and would require a cyclical cause, the nature of which has never been satisfactorily explained. On the other hand, there is still something to be said for Stille's view: For any part of a continent there was a period when it was being actively mountain-built in a primary arc. That period usually lasted a few hundred million years. Since then any area would have remained quiescent unless a secondary mountain arc was superimposed on it. After these one or at most two cycles, any area has remained an inert part of a shield. Contrary to what has often been supposed, the modern evidence of the ages of the pegmatites in the oldest provinces of shields is that *shields have not been subjected to repeated rebuilding.*

9. DESCRIPTIONS OF SOME OROGENETIC BELTS

9.1. THE PRESENT BELTS

9.11. *North American arcs.*—Of the two active belts, the arcs of the more regular East Asian–Cordilleran belt will be described first, starting with the Cordillera of North America, in which there are four primary arcs. The frontland of all of them is the Pacific Ocean Basin.

The primary or western arcs of the North American Cordillera between Alaska and Honduras consist of four double mountain arcs making up the principal ranges of the western Cordillera. They have been called the Yukon, British Columbia, United States, and Mexican arcs, and they meet in fractured deflections opposite to Skagway, Seattle, and Los Angeles (Wilson, 1950). The principal features are self-explanatory and are illustrated in Figure 5. The position of the Mexican arc was established with the aid of the positions given by Gutenberg and Richter (1949, p. 36) for shallow earthquakes, volcanoes, and large negative gravity anomalies (found by submarine, off the Lower California coast). The medianland is present in North America and forms the Interior System of Yukon and British Columbia (Bostock, 1948) and the Basin and Range Province in the United States (Fenneman, 1931). It is a very complex area, in which metamorphic and igneous rocks are abundant.

The secondary arcs are the Eastern System of Bostock and the Rocky Mountain System of Fenneman. They may be divided into seven ranges or groups of ranges, all without appreciable recent igneous activity. The three principal of these are the Mackenzie Mountains; the Rocky Mountains of British Columbia, Alberta, and Montana; and the Front Ranges of Wyoming, Colorado, and New Mexico. They form great circular arcs, well shown on the tectonic maps of Canada and the United States (Derry,

1950; King, 1944). The centers of these secondary arcs are at the cusps of primary-arc junctions.

The hinterland is the Canadian Shield and covered parts of it under the Interior Plains. In Canada the sedimentary cover thickens into a great marginal basin beneath the foothills, upon which the secondary mountains are encroaching. Emphasis on this secondary encroachment has led some authors to refer to the continental plains as a frontland, which has led to some confusion in terminology. In United States the secondary arc was forced to form east of the basins of thick sediments.

The two lineaments which spring from each of the three fractured deflections are also shown in Figure 5. In each case, that one striking east-southeast is the best developed. Of these six lineaments, the two most southern were described by Ransome (1915). The Montana lineament is well known to those who have worked in Montana (personal communication from W. T. Thom and E. S. Sampson), and there is evidence along some of its component faults that the south side moved east. The three marked in Canada possess properties and directions similar to those in the United States.

All six are valleys, marked by rivers and transportation routes. Along the better-known there are evidences of fault zones. It is suggested that they are due to shear zones at depth, although those that strike to the northeast also have surface thrusts along them. Where they cross the Cordillera, the secondary arcs and other structures either change direction or end abruptly.

The pattern has such impressive regularity that it cannot be due to chance. Some geologists may claim that it has been obtained only by over-simplification and by associating features not of precisely the same age and of such dissimilar nature as the intrusive rocks of the Sierra Nevada and volcanics of the Cascade Mountains. On the other hand, the geophysical data support this simple pattern, and a physical explanation for the properties of these double-fracture junctions has been given already. It may serve as a first approximation whose discrepancies from the complexities of geology need further explanation.

9.12. *The South American arcs.*—These are those which form the Andes Mountains (see Stose, 1950; Weeks, 1947). They join in single-fracture junctions so that the primary and secondary arcs adjoin one another without a medianland. The frontland is the Pacific Ocean. The primary arc consists of the arc of the northern Andes and two or perhaps three other arcs in the southern Andes, illustrated in Figure 6. One junction near Arica at about 19° S. is obvious enough, and Benioff (1949, p. 1854) has pointed to a change in earthquake distribution there. It is classed as a capped deflection, with the Puna block of high (21,000 feet) metamorphic mountains forming the secondary cap range in Bolivia. Theory suggests that a graben should be hidden in the Amazon Basin. Another at Santiago is at latitude 33° S. and is marked by eastward-branching folds (Oppenheim, 1948) and shallow earthquakes in the interior (Gutenberg and Richter, 1949, p. 42), which perhaps mark a graben.

There is an interesting division of the Andes into single and double mountain arcs. From Tierra del Fuego to Santiago there is an outer fringe of islands or a coastal range composed in large part of metamorphic or sedimentary rocks, but partly of unexplored nature (Stose, 1950), and further a main volcanic range. Together they form a double arc.

North of Santiago the volcanoes are close to the sea, "longitudinal structural depressions such as the Vale of Chile do not exist and highlands continue unbroken though with gradually decreasing elevation from the Andean front westward to the ocean" (Rich, 1942, p. 165); but from the Gulf of Guayaquil to the Gulf of Maracaibo, Venezuela, there is again a complex outer sedimentary arc. The central region of single volcanic arcs is fronted by an ocean trench. There are large negative gravity anomalies offshore approximately over the trench (Gutenberg and Richter, 1949, p. 40). The trench lies opposite to the only region to be underlain by deep earthquakes, so that it may be that great activity has kept the trench open.

Oppenheim (1947, pp. 171–172) divides the whole length of the Andes into two provinces, of which the western ranges are primary and have been described. His description of the eastern ranges of the Andes suggests that they are secondary arcs corresponding to the Rocky Mountains in North America and, like them, younger, sedimentary, and overthrust toward the east, but that in the case of the Andes no medianland is present.

The hinterland is the shield area of eastern South America and its covered parts which are under the basins adjoining the Andes.

9.13. *The East Asian arcs.*—These arcs, off the east coast of Asia between Alaska and the Philippine Islands, are the best developed systems of island arcs in the world (Fig. 9). The five most conspicuous are the Aleutian, Kurile, Japanese, and Ryukyu arcs and that from Taiwan (Formosa) to Luzon. They all lie approximately the same distance offshore beyond the continental shelves, between moderately and very deep water, with their centers near the coasts. The arcs become smaller toward the south and increasingly detached from the continent. In the north, the Aleutian arc extends to the continent forming the Aleutian and Chugach

Mountains, which are part of the arc and are as active as are the islands. The junctions are marked by single fractures, well developed along Kamchatka Peninsula and Sakhalin Island. Although Korea looks, from its topography, like another linkage, it is at least partly an older structure. Embryonic secondary arcs form western Kamchatka, southern Hokkaido, Kyushu, Formosa, and western Luzon.

Besides these five arcs, there is another sequence of active but less conspicuous island arcs farther offshore. The Bonin Islands branch almost at right angles from mid-Japan and are followed by the Mariana, Yap, and Palau Islands.

At the junction in Japan a marked change occurs in the properties of the five arcs first described. It suggests that the Mariana belt is in process of displacing the southern half of the older belt as the active locus of orogenetic movements. Southern Japan and the Ryukyu and Taiwan-Luzon arcs are old, for they have few active volcanoes or earthquakes and none that are deep-seated. They contain Paleozoic rocks and underwent an important deformation in mid-Mesozoic time (Kobayashi, 1941; Hess, 1948). On the other hand, the Aleutian, Kurile, Bonin, and Mariana arcs have numerous active volcanoes and earthquakes, many of which are deep-focus (except in the Aleutians). They are younger than the other belt, for no rocks older than Cretaceous have been found on any of these islands.

There is one interesting aspect, already referred to, of the junction in mid-Japan which is shown in Figure 10. The near-surface features, including shallow earthquakes, active volcanoes, and topographic expression, follow the Kuriles, northern Japan, and the Bonins. The deep earthquakes do not. Their epicenters follow what would be an extension of the Kuriles as far as Vladivostok, where they turn sharply to follow what would be an extension of the Bonins and cross Japan by a faulted trough called the Fossa Magna. Thus the deep-seated features do not follow the Japanese arc.

9.14. *The South Eurasian–Melanesian belt.*—The arcs and ranges dealt with thus far have been relatively simple. The components of the other active belt are more complex and irregular, but it is possible to discern many of the same types of primary and secondary arcs along it and to provide a reason for some of the irregularities.

The Alpine and Himalayan mountains, which cross southern Asia, will be treated first, then the Melanesian elements of the southwest Pacific, and, finally, the Celebes junction.

9.15. *The South Eurasian arcs.*—It has long been recognized that the ancestral Alpine and Himalayan mountains grew out of what had previ-

ously been a great intercontinental trough called the "Tethys Sea." The
resulting mountains are the highest and most complex in the world. It is
considered that this complexity is connected with the abundance of sediments which the great continents on either side rapidly provided and with
the presence of land on both sides of the Tethys trough which was less
homogeneous than the ocean floor forming the frontland side of all other
arcs.

In spite of complexity and the lack of deep earthquakes to act as a
guide, the characteristics of inner and outer primary arcs and of secondary
arcs are sufficiently distinct that five great primary arcs can be distinguished, some rather fractured and irregular, but all of about the usual
size and possessing the usual features. All five meet in capped deflections.
These primary arcs, which are illustrated in Figure 11, are the Indonesian,
Himalayan, Persian, East Mediterranean, and West Mediterranean arcs.
In them the usual features of the ophiolitic outer primary arc and the inner
arc of batholiths and of acid volcanoes are well developed. The cap ranges
are the Alps, the Caucasus, the Pamirs, and the mountains of the Burma-
China boundary, including the Ta shuch shan. The Rhine graben is a well-
developed fracture, but the others are either not developed or have not been
recognized. All the primary arcs are convex to the south, and therefore
Africa, Arabia, and India are frontlands, whereas Eurasia is the hinterland
for all five arcs. Secondary arcs, besides the cap ranges, include the Pyrenees, Carpathian, Pontic, and north Persian mountains. The other ranges
of central Asia are older and inactive.

9.16. *The Melanesian fractured arcs.*—The arcs which extend from the
Philippine Islands to New Zealand include some of the world's most active
seismic regions and some of its most irregular arcs, as is shown in Figure 7.
Most of the arcs are nearly straight, and some have ocean deeps on one
side and some on the other. The volcanoes and earthquakes are scattered
irregularly, and shallow shocks occur directly over deep ones.

The reasons advanced as explanations for the complexity of the South
Eurasian ranges do not apply, for there is no evidence of abundant sediments or of previous orogeny or of adjacent continents, but another explanation has already been given.

The evidence for great horizontal movement is well established in the
Philippine fault zone (King and McKee, 1949). It has been suggested that
a great longitudinal fault cuts New Zealand; but not all agree with Wellman (1950) that there has been horizontal movement of 200 miles along it
(Macpherson, 1946). It is not to be expected that much evidence would
have been found in New Guinea (Brouwer, 1951), the Solomon Islands, or

New Hebrides Islands, because all are but little explored and the key localities are hidden by ocean in the latter cases and by alluvium in the Sepik, Ramau, and Markham valleys of New Guinea (Glaessner, 1950).

9.17. *The Celebes junction of belts.*—This junction of the two belts is complex because two sets of forces operating nearly at right angles have acted upon every part and two great belts of failure meet there. It is not surprising, therefore, that features often have a double nature and that they are broken and irregular (Umbgrove, 1947, p. 117).

9.2. OLDER, INACTIVE MOUNTAINS AND SHIELDS

So far, only the young and active mountain belts have been considered. In addition to these, there are many belts of partly eroded mountains in which activity has ceased. The active phases of some of these mountains overlapped the early stages of some arcs of the present belts. For that reason and because we expect a general uniformity in the earth's behavior, the patterns of former belts might be expected to be similar to those of present-day mountains. The simple outlines of the pattern of present mountains were hard enough to find. In the old mountains the problem of detecting the elements will be worse, for many diagnostic features like deep earthquakes will be missing, some parts of old ranges will be covered with later deposits, and erosion will have exposed a different view of other parts.

To gain an idea of what an ancient range might be expected to look like, consider the probable appearance of the Cordillera a few hundred million years hence. There would be no volcanism, only shallow and minor earthquakes. The height of the mountains would be reduced, more batholiths would be unroofed, and much of the present coast might be covered by a coastal plain and shelf of sediments eroded from the mountains. This shelf might extend in places for scores of kilometers out to sea. Weathered down to roots, without volcanic or seismic activity and partly hidden, the primary arcs might be scarcely recognizable.

Farther inland the medianland, which in some other mountain systems is wholly lacking, would be a complex area of metamorphic rocks whose interpretation would prove puzzling. It might be difficult to distinguish from the primary arcs. Inland from these irregular igneous belts and separated from them by a fault zone, one would expect to find the curved outlines of eroded secondary mountains, such as the Alberta Rocky Mountains, forming a series of large arcuate basins concave toward the coast and composed of sedimentary deposits without batholithic intrusions. They would be less likely to be covered than the primary arcs. Relatively mild metamorphism would not have destroyed their folding or their fossils or confused their stratigraphy. The present basins are so deep that much erosion would not have destroyed them. One would expect them to stand out as the most prominent features and the only ones with a clear structure.

9.3. The Inactive Appalachian Mountains

It is suggested that this description suits the Appalachian Mountains of today, which have recently been very clearly described by King (1951) and are illustrated in Figure 14. It also corresponds, in general, to their history as suggested by Kay (1951).

On the geological or tectonic maps of the United States and Canada a series of sedimentary basins, curved and concave toward the ocean, strike one immediately as secondary arcs. Conspicuous are the arcs of the Valley and Ridge Province in Tennessee and in Pennsylvania–New York and the Ouachita Mountains in Oklahoma. According to King, the Marathon uplift in Texas, the hills east of Lake Champlain, the extreme north coast of Gaspé, and the Long Range of northwestern Newfoundland are all narrower but similar basins of altered sediments. They can be presumed to be seven secondary arcs and must be supposed to lie at the cusps, where a series of six primary arcs join one another.

King's description of a belt of metamorphosed sediments in central Newfoundland intruded by many large batholiths corresponds precisely with that of part of an inner primary arc. In the Avalon Peninsula of southeastern Newfoundland the oldest rocks are a vast thickness of slates, conglomerates, and graywackes resting upon volcanics and meeting the requirements for an outer ophiolitic primary arc. There is no medianland. This primary arc, which may be called the "Maritime arc," strikes southwest across Newfoundland under the Gulf of St. Lawrence and presumably turns farther west across northern Nova Scotia to New Brunswick, in so doing giving rise to the large offset of the Newfoundland succession relative to that south of the St. Lawrence. Southern Nova Scotia is underlain by the Maguma series, which is the counterpart of the ophiolitic Avalon series of Newfoundland.

In New Brunswick, opposite the Gaspé secondary arc, the inner primary belt of metamorphic rocks changes direction abruptly to form an arc across Maine. There is another change in the general trend of the intrusives at the New Hampshire border opposite the Lake Champlain cusp, as shown on the Geological Map of North America (Stose, 1946). Two more primary arcs lie to the south, forming the metamorphic rocks of New England–Pennsylvania and of the Piedmont. The next primary arc must be assumed to turn sharply west in Alabama under the cover of young rocks in the Mississippi Embayment to reach the Ouachita cusp. Four of the five single fracture zones or graben are well developed. South of Nova Scotia the outer ophiolitic parts of the primary arcs are hidden.

The southwestern extension of the Appalachian arcs is much less certain. It is, however, clear that the present arcs form belts which are continuous around the world, and it might be expected that former belts had also been continuous. Kay's illustration (1951, Pl. 1) shows the Cordilleran and Appalachian systems as having both been in similar states in early Paleozoic time. He separates them in Mexico but gives no clear evidence to show that a Mexican land existed at that time. A connection between the Cordilleran and Appalachian arcs in Paleozoic time may therefore be speculated upon. Central America may have grown subsequently.

There are many other belts of Paleozoic mountains elsewhere in the world, and some of them are well known, although the details of others have still to be mapped. They are not known to have been analyzed in the fashion just applied to the Appalachians and could not, in any case, be reviewed in the space available, but this classification would appear to fit many of them. Descriptions and maps of these belts have been given recently by Umbgrove (1947). They are shown in generalized fashion in Figure 17. It should be noted that in older arcs there has been a tendency to stress the secondary arcs and neglect the primary parts or to classify the primary arcs as parts of Archean blocks. Umbgrove (1947, chap. 2) gives good regional bibliographies, and Bullard (1944) discusses what is known from age determinations.

9.4. THE PRE-CAMBRIAN SHIELDS

The greater part of every continent is a flat, stable shield of low elevation. These shields are largely covered with a veneer of gently dipping sedimentary rocks; but wherever the basement is exposed or reached by drilling, it is composed of gneisses and igneous rocks contorted into patterns of great complexity and called *Archean* type of rocks. These rocks extend indefinitely downward. They appear to be the stuff of which continents are chiefly made. The overlying rocks in part are fossiliferous rocks of Cambrian and younger age and in part are older rocks, not greatly folded or metamorphosed and called *Proterozoic* type of rocks.

The most useful method of subdividing geological time depends upon the identification of index fossils. Unfortunately, diagnostic and abundant fossils are found only in the rocks from the Lower Cambrian, at the base of the Paleozoic, to the present. These have enabled that span of about

5×10^8 years to be subdivided into 80 stages which can be recognized all over the world. In striking contrast, the few and indeterminate fossils of late Pre-Cambrian time have only suggested a subdivision of the much greater span of Pre-Cambrian time into a younger Algonkian or Protero-zoic part, in which there is evidence of life, and an older Archean or Archeozoic part, without recognizable life. However, this division can hardly be significant, because the Archean types of rocks are now so altered that they might have contained fossils that were destroyed by the metamorphic processes.

Where uncontorted Pre-Cambrian strata occur, they always rest upon basement rocks, and they contain all those few and indeterminate fossils found in Pre-Cambrian rocks. These facts made it easy to suppose that the upper uncontorted Proterozoic strata formed a definite era separated from the deformed rocks of older, early Archean era by a great world-wide unconformity which was everywhere of the same age.

This classification was never proved to be correct, although it was per-haps the best that could be done at the time when it was adopted. The earth's history was then supposed to be relatively short. It ignored the fact that such a subdivision could not have been applied to the better-known fossiliferous rocks, because correlation by index fossils proves that struc-ture and degree of metamorphism are not reliable guides to the age of rocks and that rocks of every age occur in every state of folding and alter-ation in some part of the world. Basement rocks are found under all the continents, but they are by no means everywhere of the same great age.

Some geologists, for example, Leith, Lund, and Leith (1935), have long held that Archean and Proterozoic rock types of one region are not always the time equivalents of Archean and Proterozoic types in a distant region and that the unconformities between them were formed at different times in different places.

More extensive mapping of the Pre-Cambrian rocks and new methods of studying them are now suggesting other subdivisions of a less simple nature which are more in harmony with what has been observed in the young fossiliferous rocks. It has been said: "The trend is clearly towards the recognition of more than two eras. . . . In the absence of fossil evidence of age, radioactive methods are the only real method of estimating time" (Grout, Gruner, Schwartz, and Thiel, 1951, pp. 1019 and 1064). Some Proterozoic types of rocks are now known to be at least 16×10^8 years old (Collins, Lang, Robinson, and Farquhar, 1952), but many Archean types of rocks are much younger, proving that these terms should be used only for *types*, not ages, of rocks (Cumming *et al.*, in press).

Radioactive age determinations, by the isotopic analysis of lead extracted from uranium-bearing minerals, have shown that the oldest rocks are at least 28×10^8 years old (Ahrens, 1950; Allan, Farquhar, and Russell, 1953). Even older ages have been found by studying rubidium, but these perhaps still need some verification (Nicolaysen, Aldrich, and Doak, 1953).

The vast span of Pre-Cambrian time from 28 to 5×10^8 years ago and the patterns revealed by age determinations have led Holmes (1948) to write: "Obviously the time has come to liberate Precambrian geology from the tyranny of a telescoped classification in which the Archean . . . is regraded as a single era of worldwide distribution. Five 'Archean' cycles are already known and there has probably been time enough in the geological past for double that number."

Some important ideas about the probable structure of shields can be gained by comparing them with younger mountains. At several places in the Appalachian region, uranium- and rubidium-bearing minerals have been found in pegmatites and their ages measured. Pegmatites are offshoots of igneous intrusives. The times of deformation and of igneous intrusion in that area have been correlated by means of fossils, and it has been found that all these events lie within the same span of time, which was about 6 to 2×10^8 years ago (Nier, 1939; Nier et al., 1941; Ahrens, 1949; Rodgers, 1952). In the Coast Ranges of North America and in Japan a similar, but younger, correlation has been found.

From this and other similar evidence it seems reasonable to conclude that mountain-building, igneous activity, and the formation of pegmatites have occurred together during limited periods of a few hundreds of millions of years each, which can be dated by pegmatites. The later introduction of minerals not in pegmatites but along fissures and in veins not associated with orogeny leads to younger age determinations. These are confusing unless the minerals from pegmatites and veins are distinguished.

A second important fact which indicates that the Archean should be subdivided was Sederholm's (1910) recognition that the Archean consists of provinces, each of which has a pattern of strike or of foliation, and that at the boundaries between two provinces one pattern often intersects the other, so as to suggest that one is older than the other (M. E. Wilson, 1941; Cooke, 1947; Gill, 1948, 1949). The divisions so indicated have been found to be consistent with the results of radioactive age determinations. Some of these provinces have also been found to have distinctive rock assemblages and patterns of major faults terminating at their boundaries (Jolliffe, 1948; Wilson, 1949b).

All these conclusions agree with one another and suggest that the Pre-Cambrian provinces represent "a long series of orogenic cycles, each of which, though having distinctive peculiarities of its own, is essentially of the same kind as the later Caledonian, Hercynian and Alpine cycles" (Holmes, 1948, p. 254). This restatement of the great "principle of uniformitarianism" suggests that the ideas which were used to guide the classification of the present and Appalachian belts may also be applied to the shield areas.

Consider that geological province of the Canadian Shield lying along the St. Lawrence River, known as the "Grenville" and shown in Figure 18.

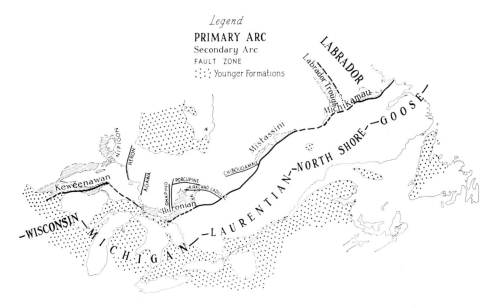

Fig. 18.—Diagram of suggested primary and secondary arcs and fault zones of the former Grenville mountains or province.

As early as 1910, Adams and Barlow (1910, p. 16) said of part of it that "if this district presents the basement of a former mountain range now planed down, the direction of this mountain range was about N 30° E or in a general way parallel to the course of the valley of the St. Lawrence." Its northern boundary has been recognized to be a fault zone (Geological Survey of Canada, 1947, p. 20), and it is shown as such on the tectonic map of Canada (Derry, 1950). The rocks of this province have recently been described by Engel and Engel (1953).

The age determinations from pegmatite minerals in this province lie within the range 11–8 × 10⁸ years old. That period which is similar in

length to the one during which the Appalachians were active may therefore be considered to be the time during which the Grenville Mountain
system was in active process of formation. In the long period since then,
the mountains have lost tens of thousands of feet by uplift and erosion.
A comparison can now be made between the Cordillera and the old Grenville Mountains like that which has just been made between the Cordillera
and the Appalachians. In the case of the Grenville province, greater erosion could be expected to have reduced the size of the secondary arcs and
to have increased the exposures of batholithic and metamorphic rocks. In
fact, the whole region of primary arcs and medianland might be expected
to be one of complex metamorphic and igneous rocks, very difficult to
decipher. On the continental side one would expect to find a fault zone
against which relatively unaltered sediments, resting on a still older basement, lie in small basins concave toward the ocean.

That is exactly the picture of the Grenville province and of its northern
boundary today. The Grenville rocks, which are predominantly metamorphosed sediments of acid composition, still show their original bedding
nearly everywhere as foliation (see Fig. 19; Adams and Barlow, 1910).
They appear to represent the medianland and primary arcs. They become
richer in volcanics to the southeast, which may be an indication of eugeo-
synclinal and ophiolitic deposits. The northern boundary is a great fault
zone, against which are infaulted deep basins of folded Proterozoic rocks,
representing a series of secondary arcs. These basins, which are all concave
toward the coast, are plainly shown on the tectonic map of Canada at the
southern end of the Labrador trough, at Lake Mistassini, by the Huronian
rocks at Sudbury and in Minnesota; and all have been classed as Proterozoic on the basis of their slight alteration. They are regarded as secondary
arcs, and primary arcs presumably join them (Fig. 18).

It has already been suggested that the Archean province to the north
is older on structural grounds (Gill, 1948, p. 29) and because of the age of
radioactive minerals in it (Ellsworth, 1932; Nier, 1939; Hurley, 1949;
Cumming, Wilson, Farquhar, and Russell, in press). It is the Keewatin or
Superior province, and the ages determined in it of over 20×10^8 years
include some of the oldest known. It is considered to be one of the nuclei
from which the continent grew, and its structure is correspondingly interesting. The tectonic map of Canada shows that its structure is different
from that in the Grenville. There are many narrow, sharply curved belts
of greenstone rocks. Some of these belts of greenstones are overlain by
younger synclines of Timiskaming clastics. Lavas are abundant, but
limestones and pure sandstones are entirely lacking.

FIG. 19.—Air photograph of foliation in rocks mapped as pink and gray granites of Killarnean batholithic intrusives around Ada Lake near Rutter Station, Ontario (Ontario Dept. Lands and Forests photo, 1.4 × 0.9 miles).

This was interpreted by Pettijohn (1943) to mean that the province is a multiple one and that the batholiths between the curving lines of greenstone belts are the roots of older primary arcs which gave rise to the Keewatin volcanics forming the first terrain of basic lavas. As this terrain was established, the first clastic sedimentary rocks, now called *Timiskaming*, accumulated between volcanoes. Those in an area near Kirkland Lake have been described by Hewitt (1951):

Examination of the pre-Timiskaming rocks exposed in the area, and study of the nature of the Timiskaming sediments, the pebbles of the conglomerates, and the heavy accessories of the grits and graywackes, allows reconstruction of the provenance area. The distributive province supplying sediments to the Timiskaming trough was composed of basic volcanics and intrusives, a great variety of rhyolites, trachytes, and associated acid porphyries, minor amounts of chert, iron formation, jasper, and slaty graywacke. Metamorphic rocks and large areas of unroofed batholithic granite, granite gneiss and syenite are lacking. Abundant acid porphyry pebbles were supplied.

The Timiskaming sediments are clastic, first-cycle sediments derived by the rapid mechanical disintegration of a rugged, folded Keewatin volcanic terrane. In some areas of the north belt much material was supplied by centers of trachytic Timiskaming volcanism, and trachyte flows and water-laid tuffs make up an important part of the section. The Timiskaming sediments were laid down in a geosynclinal trough flanking the Keewatin highland area and are marginal deposits of a shallow sea.

This earliest recorded time during which the continental nuclei were forming must have been a long and turbulent one. No doubt the nuclei started as single arcs of volcanoes, but apparently it was easier for successive arcs to parallel one another than to be formed elsewhere. As yet we cannot clearly separate, much less date, the successive arcs and belts of this early period. Below the surface the rocks were intruded by, or more likely were converted into, granodiorites, granites, and other plutonic rocks. After so long a period of erosion these unroofed batholiths now form most of the surface.

The Keewatin province is typical of several continental nuclei. In northwestern Canada there is the Yellowknife province of similar rocks and structures, while in South Africa, Sierra Leone, western Australia, southern India, and probably Fenno-Scandia there are other similar provinces of many small parallel belts of greenstone rocks which are the oldest rocks in those continents. They all lack limestones, and for some quite unknown reason all nuclei are rich in gold mineralization.

In Figure 20 all the provinces which have so far been recognized in the Canadian Shield are shown, together with such ages as have been determined for them (Collins, Farquhar, and Russell, 1954). It is realized that these belts are made of arcs, each of which had its own history; but the details have not yet been solved.

FIG. 20.—Known orogenetic provinces of North America (others may be assumed to exist under the interior plains and in the Arctic)

Fig. 21.—Fault boundary between uplifted gneisses of Athabasca province and eroded sandstones resting upon a basement of Yellow-knife province (R.C.A.F. photo A5120-105R).

197

The Keewatin and Yellowknife greenstone provinces have already been discussed. The Athabaska or Churchill province between them was formed between 19 and 16×10^8 years ago with a strong shear along its northern side (Great Slave Lake fault shown in Fig. 21). The Great Slave subprovince is a secondary arc on the north side. No secondary arc seems to have been preserved between the Athabasca and Keewatin provinces (Harrison, 1951). The Labrador province is believed to have been added before the

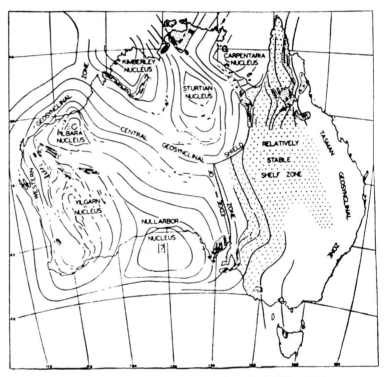

Fig. 22.—Tectonic map of Australia (from E. S. Hills, 1946)

Grenville; the Labrador trough is a characteristic secondary arc. Baffin Island is another primary addition, while Greenland is held to be growing as a separate continent (Noe-Nygaard, 1950). Apart from the young mountains of Ellesmere Island, this is all that has yet been deciphered, for the northern shield is little known and the interior plains are hidden. Figure 25 presents a tentative time scale for North American primary orogenies.

What can be made out for Australia (Hills, 1946; Fairbridge, 1950), southern India (Krishnan, 1949, p. 47; Holmes, Leland, and Nier, 1950a), and South Africa (Holmes, 1948; Holmes, Leland, and Nier, 1950b) is shown in Figures 22–24. Much more has yet to be learned, and many more age determinations are needed. For some areas like Siberia the shields are so extensively covered that little can be discovered except by indirect methods, which still largely await development.

From this study of Pre-Cambrian arcs some further principles emerge. If there is to be a twofold division in the Pre-Cambrian, the boundary should be at the close of the multiple greenstone orogenies of| Keewatin type, which seems to have been about 20×10^8 years ago. Of course, both Archean types and Proterozoic types of rocks occur, but it is held that they

FIG. 23.—Tectonic map of southern India (from Holmes, Leland, and Nier, 1950a)

do not represent two eras of Pre-Cambrian time, but rather that they are
due to primary and secondary arcs, respectively, of many ages. The
Timiskaming-type rocks may turn out to be the equivalent of secondary
arcs to the Keewatin.

It will be seen that the arcs through the Keewatin, Grenville, Appalachian, and Cordilleran ages get progessively larger. The increasing size
of the arcs and the decrease in abundance of volcanics after the Keewatin
follow from the principle of a contracting and cooling earth. As the depth

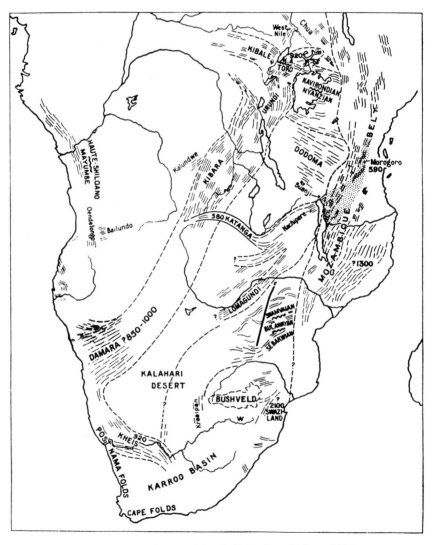

FIG. 24.—Tectonic map of South Africa (from Holmes, 1948)

of cooling became greater, the arcs got larger. The deficiency of sediments in the Keewatin and the nature of the Timiskaming sediments are explained if the continents grew from small volcanic arcs or nuclei and if it was not until later cycles, when plutonic acid rocks like granite had been formed and exposed, that erosion was able to form sandstone and limestone from them. In the Keewatin the small arcs and widespread volcanism suggest that the crust had only just formed (Gill, 1951).

9.5. The Origin and Classes of Igneous Rocks

In this chapter only four broad classes of igneous rocks have been considered. These are acid (or sialic or pacific type), basic (or simatic or atlantic type), intermediate (including nepheline rocks), and ultrabasic. The first two are quantitatively the important rock types. Daly (1933, p. 41) has said: "The igneous rocks of the globe belong chiefly to two types: granite and basalt . . . to declare the meaning of the fact, that one of these dominant types is intrusive and the other extrusive, is to go a long way towards outlining petrogenesis in general." The rocks of intermediate silica content, although petrologically varied and interesting, "are only incidental products."

The ultrabasic rocks, although they are also scarce, are of particular interest because they may be the nearest representatives on the surface of the kind of rocks of which the greater part of the earth's mantle is made. Their modes of occurrence are significant in the study of orogenesis. They never form lavas but occur as small bombs, carried up unmelted in basalts, and as intrusive bodies aligned along mountain belts. These are often associated with faults and appear to have been intruded at one or two periods only along each belt and only at times when orogenetic disturbances reached climaxes. Some may even be blocks upfaulted from the mantle.

The whole question of the origin of the common igneous rocks is a much debated one and not easy to discuss in a few paragraphs. This arises because of the impossibility of observing the behavior of magmas, the liquid melts from which igneous rocks form, and the difficulty of reproducing model systems of sufficient complexity. In particular, we do not know very much about the depths and pressures at which magmas are formed, about the amount and effect of such fugitive constituents as water which escape in volcanic processes, and about the extent to which magmas react with and assimilate the wall rocks of their chambers and passages. Cf. also chapter 6.

Several general principles have been discovered. All geologists agree that these are valid, but there is no agreement upon their relative importance.

For example, it has been established, largely as a result of work by the Geophysical Laboratory of the Carnegie Institution of Washington, that when a silicate melt of suitable basic composition crystallizes, some of the most basic minerals, notably olivine, crystallize early and that these crystals sink and may become separated from the final melt, which is thus of a more siliceous composition. Bands of minerals apparently due to this cause are found in basic intrusives, and few doubt the validity of this idea for basic rocks (Wager, 1948; H. D. B. Wilson, 1953; Walker, 1940).

Likewise, if a basic silicate rock is melted, the first liquid to form is of a higher-than-average silica content. By these processes "Bowen (1928) supposes basaltic liquid to be the direct parent of practically all visible eruptives, and peridotite the probable grandparent, liquid basalt being produced by the selective refusion of solid peridotite" (Daly, 1933, p. 207). According to these views, liquid and solid phases exist together, presumably near the surface of the earth, and hence the liquid phase can have little of that superheat which would be required to melt and assimilate wall rocks. This seems to offer a satisfactory explanation for the basalts of the deep oceans.

Volcanoes, both active and ancient, are fairly common in the deep oceans away from the continental margins and their arcs. They are aligned along straight or curving shapes which have been presumed in some cases to be large fault zones. Small, shallow earthquakes occur along these lines. Since these fault zones are hundreds or thousands of kilometers long, they can be supposed to penetrate some tens of kilometers into the mantle. There the temperatures are high enough that when the faults provide channels and a slight relief of pressure, partial fusion of the mantle could form basalt, which would rise to the surface. On the way, crystal fractionation could provide for sufficient differentiation to form the very small amounts of intermediate and acid volcanic rocks which have been found on some islands (Daly, 1933, p. 467; Shand, 1947, p. 274; Umbgrove, 1947, pp. 70–76). No granite has ever been found on this class of island.

In the oceans the question of assimilation scarcely arises, because the layers of mud and basalt above the ultrabasic mantle are so thin. The basalts must have arisen by the partial melting of ultrabasic rocks. In the resulting series of rocks there is comparative simplicity and order. This is believed to be the origin of the so-called "atlantic suite" of predominantly basic rocks. They are believed to come from relatively shallow depths.

Essentially all the rocks of the ocean basins, which cover two-thirds of the earth, are basic, and they are chiefly olivine basalts. No granite and only infinitesimal amounts of lavas of granite composition have ever been found on islands of the deep oceans, which would seem to be proof enough that basalt is not the parent of granite. Recently Silverman (1951) has shown from a study of isotopes that granite and basalts probably never have been in equilibrium together, as Bowen's theory would require (Bowen, 1948).

Compared with ocean basins, shields have little volcanism. Such volcanism as occurs is all associated with great fracture systems and appears to be similar in nature and perhaps origin to that of the oceans, except for rather more assimilation, resulting in intermediate types of rock. The assimilation is a natural consequence of the passage of basalts with a little superheat through 35 km of pre-existing sialic shield. Intermediate rocks are numerous, however; they have doubtless been formed in several ways.

The chief problems concern the origin of granite (Shand, 1947, pp. 252–265; Read, 1948) and of rocks generally called "granite," although of variable composition and often foliated as gneiss. Such rocks have certainly been formed on an enormous scale out of pre-existing sediments. Suess supposed that this was due to fusion of sediments, but the necessity for supplying heat and additional constituents has eliminated that hypothesis in favor of the action on sediments of hot aqueous solutions or emanations containing silica and alkalis.

To give an answer to this controversy on the relative importance of the various processes which have formed granite that will satisfy everyone is impossible, but the following observations are stated in an attempt to strike a fair balance.

The discussion has been greatly confused by the use of *granite* and *granitic* in two senses. In the restricted sense, granite is a particular form of coarse, acid, igneous rock. In a more general sense granite and the granitic layer are the rocks of the continental basements; but these are not granite in the restricted sense. The shields are predominantly composed of gneisses of more basic composition. In chapter 3 it is shown that the average crustal rocks contain less radioactive elements than true granite. The usual occurrence of negative gravity anomalies over granite batholiths shows that the crust as a whole is denser than granite.

It is along the orogenetic belts that acid igneous activity is chiefly concentrated. Only along them are great masses of granite and other acid rocks formed. It is clear from the disappearance of shelves that these rocks are largely sediments which must have required the addition of much heat and some new material during metamorphism. In part, these altered sediments have become mobile and in that state have intruded overlying and young rocks; but in the old and deeply eroded shields there is less evidence of intrusion. The rocks there are gneisses, which owe their foliation to bedding (Fig. 19). They perhaps owe some of the complexities of their folded structures to the fact that they were the slumped beds of former continental shelves. It will avoid confusion if one realizes that these sediments were formed on continental slopes and on volcanic arcs. Most of them never were the same type of sediments as those which have been studied in the interior of continents but were more like those recently examined with surprise in the Apennines by Maxwell (1953).

It is often said that it would be impossible to form granite (in the restricted sense) from "normal" sedimentary rocks, meaning those found on the surface of continents. This is probably true but is irrelevant if continents are chiefly granodiorite gneiss and were ..ostly formed by the alteration of sediments derived in large part from acid volcanic rocks. According to this view, the continents are being formed by differentiation, but slowly throughout geologic time, not merely in a brief interval early in the earth's history.

What is the common factor that links orogenetic belts with the formation of granites? Surely, it is the deep fractures which earthquakes indicate give access to depths of hundreds of kilometers. There, according to the contraction hypothesis, the cooling of ultrabasic rocks is proceeding, and the residual fluids should be rich in water, silica, and alkalis, forming interstitial hyperfusibles (Buddington, 1943). At that depth these would be superheated and could not escape until fracture zones formed. These liquids would be entirely different from the basalt magma of oceans and rift volcanoes formed by remelting near the surface. They should possess in abundance exactly the heat and constituents required. On the way up they could be expected to melt fractions of the mantle and of sediments and thus to form the variety of acid to basic volcanics which are found along arcs. They could be expected to spread out and granitize the thick muds and ash beds of shelves and arcs. This superheat, with its attendant melting and mixing, can explain the tremendous variety of rock types which renders the classification and terminology of petrology so confusing. The operation of lines of descent by crystallization, as suggested by Bowen, would surely have led to greater order if it had been the chief cause of variation in acid igneous rocks. Order exists only in the basic rocks. It has already been pointed out that the rate of addition might have been such as to grow the continents.

10. CONCLUSION

The manner of origin of the earth, the nature of the processes which act within it, and the composition and present physical state of its interior are matters of the greatest interest. If much was known of any one of these, it would throw light upon the others. Unfortunately, in spite of much able work, much of what is known of these subjects depends upon assumptions or upon indirect evidence. Considerable difference of opinion about the conclusions still exists.

Under the circumstances it is considered that no other evidence about the history of the earth is so abundant and so direct as that provided by the geological history of its surface features. It is unfortunate that lack of fossils and of radioactive age determinations has delayed the interpretation of Pre-Cambrian history which covers the period from at least 28×10^8 to 5×10^8 years ago, so that most arguments have only given weight to the history of the relatively short time since then. In fact, it is the Pre-Cambrian which is the more important.

In this chapter an attempt has been made to describe and analyze the surface features of the earth, in so far as space permitted. The youngest mountain belts have been described and analyzed. The interpretation of the Pre-Cambrian has depended upon the age determinations of Nier, Ahrens, and Collins, and, with some variations, upon the recent work of Holmes, of Hills, Krishnan, Jolliffe, Gill, and other geologists; but it would not be agreed to by all. An attempt has been made to keep descriptions separate from explanations. The only manner so far advanced of explaining any details of orogenetic belts has been the contraction hypothesis, which depends upon the cooling of the earth during the last three billion years. It is possible that some other cause can explain as much or more, but that has yet to be demonstrated. No opinion is offered as to whether the earth started from a cold origin and warmed up before cooling down.

It has been suggested that before the beginning of the geological era, about three billion years ago, the earth had no continents but only a recently solidified cover of ultrabasic rocks, overlain perhaps by a few kilometers of basalt. The surface temperature had reached equilibrium with the sun's radiation, but the temperature gradient just below the surface was much greater than at present.

Cooling caused fracturing, which enabled gases, steam, and lava to escape and form the first atmosphere, the first oceans, and the first chains of volcanoes. Apparently, many subparallel chains formed at several places, and they were intruded by, or were altered in large part to, granodiorites and granites, gradually forming small nuclei of the continents, in which remnants of the lavas now form the Keewatin type of rocks. Upon these nuclei, graywackes, tuffs, and conglomerates collected to form the Timiskaming type of rocks.

Erosion of the nuclei produced sediments of normal kinds, including the first sandstones and limestones which accumulated in great shelves around the margins. The shelves acted as centers controlling the location of new systems of arcuate fractures offshore, along which rose hot gases, alkaline and siliceous solutions, and lavas of predominantly acid composition, from which the atmosphere, oceans, and continents continued to form. These arcs, in turn, grew and became joined to the nuclei as marginal ranges.

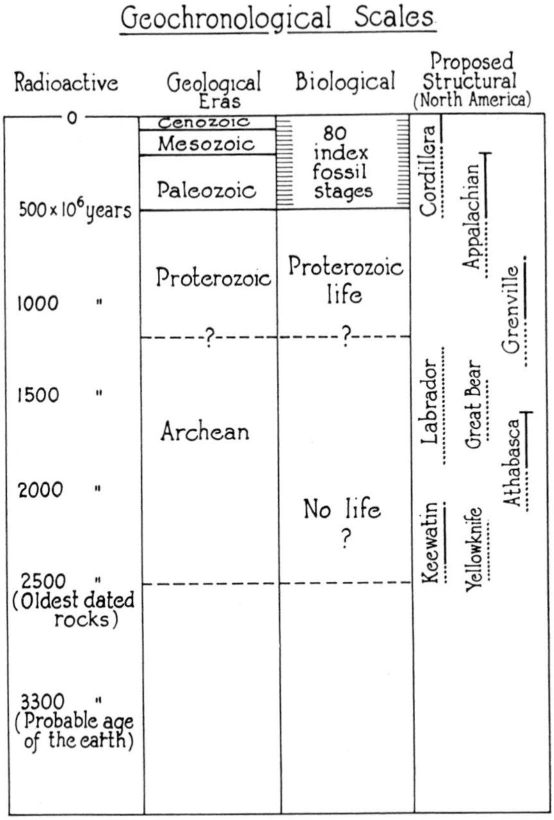

Geochronological Scales

FIG. 25.—Table of comparison between four geological time scales

This process has been repeated in changing patterns to expand the continents ever since and is still proceeding today. As the earth cooled, the thickness of the shells involved in the contraction process got larger, and the radii of curvature of the arcuate fractures increased so that the ranges became steadily larger. The addition of new water from below and the growth of continents have caused the oceans to deepen slowly.

In the mantle below the ocean floors, acid solutions, gases, and accompanying radioactive elements are trapped and can rise only along the arcuate fractures formed as continents grow. The rise of radioactive elements to the surface of shields, where their heat readily escapes, is assumed to explain why shields are inert. This movement of heat-producing elements to the surface may have disturbed the rate at which the earth cools and thus may render uncertain any estimates of a steady decline in the earth's orogenetic activity.

This explanation will not be universally agreed with, and there is much that is not yet known or clear; but the new methods which have been developed for exploring the earth's interior and dating its past history are powerful. As they are widely applied, there is no doubt that the history and processes operating near the earth's surface over the last three billion years will become well known. In the near future we can expect more precise explanations and a larger measure of agreement.

The material for a compilation must be obtained from published literature, but in so broad a subject as this, it is impossible to be acquainted with all that is pertinent or to acknowledge much that has been used. The writer wishes to thank those from whose papers he has drawn and apologize to others whose work should rightfully have been included or mentioned.

He is particularly indebted to his colleagues and students. Among these, A. E. Scheidegger must be mentioned for his proposals concerning the mechanics of the contraction theory; C. B. Collins, R. M. Farquhar, and R. D. Russell for two hundred unpublished isotopic lead age determinations; and G. D. Garland and J. A. Jacobs for ideas regarding gravity and geothermometry. Geophysical research at the University of Toronto has been assisted by grants from the National Research Council of Canada, the Geological Survey of Canada, the Research Council of Ontario, and Imperial Oil, Ltd. Angela Burlinson, Diana Rowley, E. C. Bullard, K. E. Bullen, J. W. Greig, A. Holmes, G. E. Hutchinson, A. E. Scheidegger, H. C. Urey, and W. H. Watson made specific suggestions, while Dorothy Perryman and A. Aiken showed great patience and skill in preparing the manuscript and diagrams. To all of these the writer extends thanks.

REFERENCES

ADAMS, F. D., and		
BARLOW, A. E.	1910	Geol. Surv. Canada, Mem., No. 6.
AHRENS, L. H.	1949	Bull. Geol. Soc. Amer., **60**, 217.
	1950	Nature, **166**, 149.

ALLAN, D. W.; FAR-
QUHAR, R. M.; and
RUSSELL, R. D.   1953   *Science*, **118**, 486.

ANDERSON, E. M.   1952   *The Dynamics of Faulting* (2d ed.; Edinburgh: Oliver & Boyd).

BENIOFF, H.   1949   *Bull. Geol. Soc. Amer.*, **60**, 1837.
   1951   *Ibid.*, **62**, 331.
   1954   *Ibid.*, **65**, 385.

BETZ, F., and
HESS, H. H.   1942   *Geog. Rev.*, **32**, 99.

BIRCH, F.   1942   *Geol. Soc. Amer., Spec. Paper*, No. 36.
   1951   *Trans. Amer. Geophys. Union*, **32**, 533.

BOSTOCK, H. S.   1948   *Geol. Surv. Canada, Mem.*, No. 247.

BOUTAKOFF, N.   1948   *Internat. Geol. Cong., Report 18th Sess.*, Part 13, Sec. M.

BOWEN, N. L.   1928   *The Evolution of the Igneous Rocks* (Princeton: Princeton University Press).
   1948   *Geol. Soc. Amer. Mem.*, No. 28, p. 79.

BRIDGMAN, P. W.   1951   *Bull. Geol. Soc. Amer.*, **62**, 533.

BROUWER, H. A.   1951   *Quart. J. Geol. Soc. London*, **106**, 231.

BUBNOFF, S. VON   1925–
   1941   *Geologie der Erde* (Berlin: Borntraeger).

BUCHER, W. H.   1933   *The Deformation of the Earth's Crust* (Princeton: Princeton University Press).
   1950   *Trans. Amer. Geophys Union*, **31**, 495.

BUCKHAM, A. F.   1947   *Trans. Canadian Inst. Min. and Met.*, **50**, 460.

BUDDINGTON, A. F.   1943   *Amer. Mineralogist*, **28**, 119.

BULLARD, E. C.   1944   *Mem. Manchester Lit. Phil. Soc.*, **86**, 55.
   1954   *Proc. R. Soc. London, A*, **222**, 287.

BULLARD, E. C., and
GASKELL, T. F.   1941   *Proc. R. Soc. London, A*, Vol. **172**, No. 971.

BULLEN, K. E.   1950   *M.N.*, Geophys. Suppl., **6**, 57.
   1953   *Seismology* (London: Methuen & Co.), p. 110.

BYERLY, P., and
EVERNDEN, J. F.   1950   *Bull. Seism. Soc. Amer.*, **40**, 291.

CADY, W. M.   1950   *Trans. Amer. Geophys. Union*, **31**, 780.

CHAMBERLIN, T. C., and
SALISBURY, R. D.   1907   *Geology* (New York: Henry Holt & Co.), **3**, 523.

CLOOS, H.   1954   *Conversation with the Earth* (London: Routledge & Kegan Paul).

COLLINS, C. B.; FAR-
QUHAR, R. M.; and
RUSSELL, R. D.   1954   *Bull. Geol. Soc. Amer.*, **65**, 1.

COLLINS, C. B.; LANG,
A. H.; ROBINSON, S. C.;
and FARQUHAR, R. M.   1952   *Proc. Geol. Assoc. Canada*, **63**, 15.

COOKE, H. C.   1947   *Geol. Surv. Canada* ("Econ. Geol. Ser.," No. 1;
                                  3d ed.), p. 20.
COULOMB, J.   1945   *Ann. géophys.*, **1,** 244.
CUMMING, G. L.;
  WILSON, J. T.;
  FARQUHAR, R. M.;
  and RUSSELL, R. D.   1954   *Proc. Geol. Assoc. Canada* (in press).
DALY, R. A.   1933   *Igneous Rocks and the Depths of the Earth* (New
                                  York: McGraw-Hill Book Co.).
DANA, J. D.   1849   *U.S. Explor. Exped. under the Command of Charles
                                  Wilkes, U.S.N.* (Philadelphia), **10,** 436; quoted
                                  from BUCHER, 1933, p. 379.
DAVIS, G. L., and
  HESS, H. H.   1947   *Amer. J. Sci.*, **245,** 677.
                          1949   *Ibid.*, **247,** 856.
                          1950   *Ibid.*, **248,** 107.
DERRY, D. R.   1950   *Tectonic Map of Canada* (Geol. Assoc. Canada).
DOLE, R. B., and
  STABLER, H.   1909   *U.S. Geol. Surv. Water-Supply Paper*, **234,** 78.
EARDLEY, A. J.   1947   *J. Geol.*, **55,** 309.
                         1951   *Structural Geology of North America* (New York:
                                 Harper & Bros.).
ELLSWORTH, H. V.   1932   *Geol. Surv. Canada* ("Econ. Geol. Ser.," No. 11).
ENGEL, A. E. J., and
  ENGEL, C. G.   1953   *Bull. Geol. Soc. Amer.*, **64,** 1013.
EWING, M.   1951   Papers read at International Union of Geodesy and
                                 Geophysics, Ninth General Assembly, Brussels.
                         1953   *Bull. Geol. Soc. Amer.*, **64,** 1419.
EWING, M.; WOOLLARD,
  G. P.; VINCE, A. C.;
  and WORZEL, J. L.   1946   *Bull. Geol. Soc. Amer.*, **57,** 909.
EWING, M., and
  WORZEL, J. L.   1954   *Bull. Geol. Soc. Amer.*, **65,** 165 and 195.
EWING, M.; WORZEL,
  J. L.; STEENLAND,
  N. G.; and PRESS, F.   1950   *Bull. Geol. Soc. Amer.*, **61,** 877.
FAIRBRIDGE, R. W.   1950   *Scope* (Univ. of Western Australia), **1,** 22–29.
FENNEMAN, N. M.   1931   *Physiography of Western United States* (New York:
                                 McGraw-Hill Book Co.).
FENNER, C. N.   1923   *Nat. Geog. Soc., Contrib. Tech. Papers*, Katmai Ser.,
                                 No. 1.
GARLAND, G. D.   1950   *Pub. Dom. Obs., Ottawa*, **16,** 1.
GASKELL, T. F., and
  SWALLOW, J. C.   1951   *Nature*, **167,** 723.
GEOL. SOC. AMER.   1933–
                         1952   *Bibliog. and Index of Geol. Exclusive of North
                                 America*, Vols. **1–17.**

GEOL. SURV. CANADA	1947	"Econ. Geol. Ser.," No. 1 (3d ed.).
GIBSON, W., and		
NICHOLS, H.	1953	*Bull. Geol. Soc. Amer.*, **64**, 1173.
GILL, J. E.	1948	*Trans. Canadian Inst. Min. and Met.*, 50th Anniv. Vol., p. 29.
	1949	*Trans. Ry. Soc. Canada*, Ser. 3, **43**, 61.
	1951	*Bull. Geol. Soc. Amer.*, **62**, 1442.
GILLULY, J.	1949	*Bull. Geol. Soc. Amer.*, **60**, 561.
GLAESSNER, M. F.	1950	*Bull. Amer. Assoc. Pet. Geol.*, **34**, 856.
GREGORY, J. W.	1899	*Geog. J.*, **13**, 236.
GRETENER, P. E. F.;		
FARQUHAR, R. M.; and		
WILSON, J. T.	1954	*Trans. R. Soc. Canada*, Ser. 3, Vol. **48** (in press).
GRIGGS, D. T.	1939	*Amer. J. Sci.*, **237**, 611.
GRIGGS, D. T., *et al.*	1951	*Bull. Geol. Soc. Amer.*, **62**, 853, 863, 1385.
	1953	*Ibid.*, **64**, 1327.
GROUT, F. F.;		
GRUNER, J. W.;		
SCHWARTZ, G. M.;		
and THIEL, G. A.	1951	*Bull. Geol. Soc. Amer.*, **62**, 1017.
GUNN, R.	1947	*Geophysics*, **12**, 238.
GUTENBERG, B.	1939	*Science*, **90**, 456.
GUTENBERG, B. (ed.)	1951	*Trans. Amer. Geophys. Union*, **32**, 497.
	1952	*Internal Constitution of the Earth* (2d ed.; New York: McGraw-Hill Book Co.).
GUTENBERG, B., and		
RICHTER, C. F.	1949	*Seismicity of the Earth* (Princeton: Princeton University Press; 2d ed., 1954).
HAFNER, W.	1951	*Bull. Geol. Soc. Amer.*, **62**, 373.
HALES, A. L.	1953	*M.N.*, Geophys. Suppl., **6**, 458 and 486.
HARRISON, J. M.	1951	*Bull. Geol. Surv. Canada*, **20**, 33.
HEEZEN, B. C., and		
EWING, M.	1952	*Amer. J. Sci.*, **250**, 849.
HERSEY, J. B., and		
EWING, M.	1949	*Trans. Amer. Geophys. Union*, **30**, 5.
HESS, H. H.	1938	*Proc. Amer. Phil. Soc.*, **79**, 71.
	1946	*Amer. J. Sci.*, **244**, 772.
	1948	*Bull. Geol. Soc. Amer.*, **59**, 417.
HESS, H. H., and		
MAXWELL, J. C.	1953	*Bull. Geol. Soc. Amer.*, **64**, 1.
HEWITT, D. F.	1951	*Bull. Geol. Soc. Amer.*, **62**, 1450.
HILL, M. N.	1952	*Phil. Trans. R. Soc. London, A*, **244**, 561.
HILLS, E. S.	1946	*J. and Proc. R. Soc. New South Wales*, **79**, 67.
	1953	*Outlines of Structural Geology* (3d ed.; London: Methuen & Co.).
HODGSON, J. H.	1953	*Pub. Dom. Obs., Ottawa*, **16**, 113.

HODGSON, J. H., and
   STOREY, R. S.   1953   *Bull. Seism. Soc. Amer.*, **43**, 47.
HOLMES, A.   1927   *The Age of the Earth* (London: Harper & Bros.).
                     1947   *Endeavour*, **6**, 99.
                     1948   *Internat. Geol. Cong., Report 18th Sess.*, Part 14, p. 254.

HOLMES, A.; LELAND,
   W. T.; and
   NIER, A. O.   1950*a*   *Amer. Mineralogist*, **35**, 19.
                  1950*b*   *Amer. J. Sci.*, **248**, 81.
HUBBERT, M. K.   1951   *Bull. Geol. Soc. Amer.*, **62**, 355.
HURLEY, P. M.   1949   *Science*, **110**, 49.
HUTCHINSON, G. E.   1947   *Ecol. Mono.*, **17**, 299.
INNES, M. J. S.   1954   *Pub. Dom. Obs., Ottawa* (in press).
JACOBS, J. A.   1953   *Nature*, **171**, 835.
                     1954   *Ibid.*, **173**, 258.
JEFFREYS, H.   1929   *The Earth* (2d ed.; Cambridge: At the University Press).
                     1951   *Earthquakes and Mountains* (2d ed.; London: Methuen & Co.).
                     1952   *The Earth* (3d ed.; Cambridge: At the University Press).
JOLLIFFE, A. W.   1948   *Internat. Geol. Cong., Report 18th Sess.*, Part 14, Sec. M.
KAUFMANN, G. F.   1951   *Proc. Third World Pet. Cong., The Hague*, Sec. 1.
KAY, M.   1951   *Geol. Soc. Amer., Mem.*, No. 48.
KENNEDY, W. Q., and
   RICHEY, J. E.   1947   "Catalogue of the Active Volcanoes of the World," *Bull. volcanologique*, Ser. 2, Vol. **7**, Suppl.
KING, P. B.   1944   *Tectonic Map of the United States* (Amer. Assoc. Pet. Geol.).
                     1951   *The Tectonics of Middle North America* (Princeton: Princeton University Press).
KING, P. B., and
   McKEE, E. M.   1949   *Bull. Geol. Soc. Amer.*, **60**, 1829.
KNOPF, A.   1948   *Bull. Geol. Soc. Amer.*, **59**, 649.
KOBAYASHI, T.   1941   *Jour. Fac. Sci., Imp. Univ. Tokyo*, Sec. II, **5**, 219.
KRISHNAN, M. S.   1949   *Geology of India and Burma* (Madras).
KUENEN, P. H.   1950   *Marine Geology* (New York: John Wiley & Sons, Inc.).
KULP, J. L.   1951   *Bull. Geol. Soc. Amer.*, **62**, 326.
KYRNINE, P. D.   1948   *J. Geol.*, **56**, 130.
                     1951   *Trans. Amer. Geophys. Union*, **32**, 743.
LACLAVÈRE, G.   1952–
                     1954   *Internat. Union Geodesy and Geophys, News Letter.* Vols. **1–3**.

LAKE, P.   1931a   Geog. J., **78**, 149.
                                 1931b   Geol. Mag., **68**, 34.
LAWSON, A. C.   1942   Bull. Geol. Soc. Amer., **53**, 1253.
LEES, G. M.   1952   Quart. J. Geol. Soc. London, **108**, 1.
                                 1953   Ibid., **109**, 217.

LEITH, C. K.; LUND,
   R. J.; and LEITH, A.   1935   U.S. Geol. Surv. Prof. Paper, **184**, 10.
LIBBY, W. F.   1952   Radiocarbon Dating (Chicago: University of Chica-
                                         go Press).

McCONNELL, R. B.   1948   Internat. Geol. Cong., Report 18th Sess., Part 14,
                                         p. 199.

MacGREGOR, A. G.   1938   Phil. Trans. R. Soc. London, B, **229**, 1.
MACPHERSON, E. O.   1946   New Zealand Dept. Sci. and Indust. Res. Geol.
                                         Mem., No. 6.

MASON, B.   1952   Principles of Geochemistry (New York: John Wiley
                                         & Sons).

MATSCHINSKI, M.   1950   C.R. Acad. Sci. Paris, **230**, 1882.
                                 1952   Proc. Kon. Ned. Akad. Wetensch., **55**, 411.
MAXWELL, J. C.   1953   Bull. Amer. Assoc. Pet. Geol., **37**, 2196.
MENARD, H. W., and
   DIETZ, R. S.   1951   Bull. Geol. Soc. Amer., **62**, 1263.
MURRAY, G. E.   1953   Trans Amer. Geophys. Union, **34**, 296.
NICOLAYSEN, L. O.;
   ALDRICH, L. T.; and
   DOAK, J. B.   1953   Trans. Amer. Geophys. Union, **34**, 342.
NIER, A. O.   1939   Phys. Rev., **55**, 150 and 153.
NIER, A. O.;
   THOMPSON, R. W.;
   and MURPHEY, B. F.   1941   Phys. Rev., **60**, 112.
NOE-NYGAARD, A.   1950   Grønlandsbogen (Copenhagen: Schultz Forlag),
                                         p. 114.

OPPENHEIM, V.   1947   Amer. J. Sci., **245**, 158.
                                 1948   Ibid., **246**, 578.
PEARL, R. M.   1951   Introduction to Geologic Literature (New York: Mc-
                                         Graw-Hill Book Co.).

PEKERIS, C. L.   1953   M.N., Geophys. Suppl., **3**, 343.
PETTIJOHN, F. J.   1943   Bull. Geol. Soc. Amer., **54**, 925.
QUENNELL, A. M.   1948   Internat. Geol. Cong., Report 18th Sess., Part 14,
                                         p. 55.

RANKAMA, K., and
   SAHAMA, T. G.   1950   Geochemistry (Chicago: University of Chicago
                                         Press).

RANSOME, F. L.   1915   Problems of North American Geology (New Haven:
                                         Yale University Press), chap. 6.

READ, H. H.   1948   Geol. Soc. Amer. Mem., **28**, 1.
REVELLE, R.   1953   Trans. Amer. Geophys. Union, **34**, 329.
RICH, J. L.   1942   Amer. Geog. Soc. Spec. Pub., Vol. **26**.

RITTMANN, A. 1951 *Arch. d. sci. (Génève)*, **4**, 274.

RODGERS, J. 1952 *Amer. J. Sci.*, **250**, 411.

RUBEY, W. W. 1951 *Bull. Geol. Soc. Amer.*, **62**, 1111.

RUTTEN, L. M. R. 1949 *Bull. Geol. Soc. Amer.*, **60**, 1755.

SAPPER, K. 1927 *Vulkankunde* (Stuttgart: Engelhorns).

SCHEIDEGGER, A. E. 1953a *Bull. Geol. Soc. Amer.*, **64**, 127.

1953b *Canadian J. Phys.*, **31**, 1148.

SCHEIDEGGER, A. E.,
and WILSON, J. T. 1950 *Proc. Geol. Assoc. Canada*, **3**, 167.

SEDERHOLM, J. J. 1910 *C.R., Cong. Geol. Internat. XI*, **1**, 686.

SHAND, S. J. 1947 *Eruptive Rocks* (3d ed.; New York: John Wiley & Sons).

SHEPARD, F. P. 1948 *Submarine Geology* (New York: Harper & Bros.).

SILVERMAN, S. R. 1951 *Geochim. et Cosmochim. Acta*, **2**, 26.

SLICHTER, L. B. 1941 *Bull. Geol. Soc. Amer.*, **52**, 561.

SMITH, P. S. 1939 *U.S. Geol. Surv. Prof. Paper*, No. 192.

STILLE, H. 1924 *Grundfragen der vergleichenden Tektonik* (Berlin: Gebr. Borntraeger).

1940 *Einführung in den Bau Amerikas* (Berlin: Gebr. Borntraeger).

STOSE, G. W. 1946 *Geol. Soc. Amer. Geologic Map of North America.*

1950 *Geol. Soc. Amer., Geological Map of South America.*

SUESS, E. 1904–
1924 *The Face of the Earth* (5 vols.; Oxford: Clarendon Press).

TATEL, H. E.;
TUVE, M. A.;
and ADAMS, L. H. 1951 *Internat. Assoc. Seism., XI Conf., Résumés*, p. 27.

1953 *Proc. Amer. Phil. Soc.*, **97**, 658.

TOKUDA, S. 1926 *Japanese J. Geol. and Geog. Trans.*, **5**, 41.

UFFEN, R. J., and
MISENER, A. D. 1954 *Nature*, **173**, 259.

UMBGROVE, J. H. F. 1947 *The Pulse of the Earth* (The Hague: Martinus Nijhoff).

U.S. GEOLOGICAL SURVEY 1923–
1950 *Bibliography of North American Geol.*, Bulls. 746, 747, 823, 937, 938, 949, 952, 958, 968.

UREY, H. C. 1951 *Geochim. et Cosmochim. Acta*, **1**, 209.

1952 *The Planets: Their Origin and Development* (New Haven: Yale University Press).

URRY, W. D. 1949 *Trans. Amer. Geophys. Union*, **30**, 171.

VENING MEINESZ, F. A. 1934 *Gravity Expeditions at Sea, 1923–1932* (Netherlands Geodetic Comm.), Vol. **2**.

1948 *Quart. J. Geol. Soc. London*, **103**, 191.

1950 *Proc. Kon. Ned. Akad. Wetensch.*, **53**, 1.

1951 *Ibid.*, **54**, 3.

1952 *Ibid.*, **55**, 527.

1954 *Bull. Geol. Soc. Amer.*, **65**, 143.

VERHOOGEN, J.   1949   *Nature*, **164**, 72.
WADETI, K.   1940   *Sixth Pacific Sci. Cong., 1939, Calif. U.S.A.*, **1**, 142.
WAGER, L. R.   1948   *Internat. Geol. Cong., Report 18th Sess.*, Part 2, p. 140.
WALKER, F.   1940   *Bull. Geol. Soc. Amer.*, **51**, 1059.
WEEKS, L. G.   1947   *Bull. Amer. Assoc. Pet. Geol.*, **31**, 1194.
                         1952   *Ibid.*, **36**, 2071.
WELLMAN, H.   1950   *Interim Proc., Geol. Soc. Amer.*, Part 1, p. 12.
WILLMORE, P. L.;
   HALES, A. L.; and
   GANE, P. G.   1952   *Bull. Seism. Soc. Amer.*, **42**, 53.
WILSON, H. D. B.   1953   *Econ. Geol.*, **48**, 370.
WILSON, J. T.   1949a   *Nature*, **164**, 147.
                         1949b   *Trans. Canadian Inst. Min. and Met.*, **52**, 231.
                         1950   *Proc. Geol. Assoc. Canada*, **3**, 141.
                         1951   *Proc. R. Soc. Tasmania*, **1950**, 85.
WILSON, M. E.   1941   *Geol. Soc. Amer.*, 50th Anniv. Vol., p. 271.
WOOLLARD, G. P.   1951   *Trans. Amer. Geophys. Union*, **32**, 634.

CHAPTER 5

Oceanography

By H. U. SVERDRUP

Director, Norsk Polarinstitutt, Oslo, Norway

1. THE OCEAN BASINS

THE oceans of the earth cover an area of 361×10^6 km², representing 70.8 per cent of the earth's surface. By far the greater ocean areas are found in the Southern Hemisphere, as is evident from Table 1, in which are entered the ocean and land areas between parallels of latitude.

TABLE 1*

DISTRIBUTION OF WATER AND LAND BETWEEN PARALLELS

LATITUDE	NORTHERN HEMISPHERE				SOUTHERN HEMISPHERE			
	Water (10^6 km²)	Land (10^6 km²)	Water (Per Cent)	Land (Per Cent)	Water (10^6 km²)	Land (10^6 km²)	Water (Per Cent)	Land (Per Cent)
90°–75°.......	7.266	1.496	82.9	17.1	0.522	8.239	6.0	94.0
75 –60.......	9.993	15.652	38.9	61.1	19.721	5.924	76.9	23.1
60 –45.......	17.540	23.137	43.0	57.0	40.087	0.590	98.3	1.7
45 –30.......	29.246	23.586	55.4	44.6	48.098	4.734	91.0	9.0
30 –15.......	40.082	21.261	65.4	34.6	47.035	14.308	76.8	23.2
15 –0........	50.568	15.149	77.0	23.0	50.901	14.816	77.4	22.6
Total....	154.695	100.281	60.7	39.3	206.364	48.611	80.9	19.1

* From Kossina (1921).

Geographically, the seas of the earth comprise the three oceans, the Atlantic, the Pacific, and the Indian Ocean; and a number of adjacent seas, including the large mediterranean seas (the Mediterranean and the Black seas, the Arctic, the American, and the Asian mediterranean seas); the small mediterranean seas, such as the Baltic Sea, Hudson Bay, and others; and the marginal seas, such as the North Sea, the Bering Sea, and

215

others. Table 2 shows the area, volume, and mean depth of oceans and seas.

Until about 1920 our knowledge of the topography of the ocean bottom was very inadequate, because soundings had to be carried out by means of lead and wire, requiring many hours where the depth to the bottom was great. This time-consuming method has now been replaced by the use of echo-sounding equipment, by means of which a continuous record of the depth to the bottom can be obtained from a ship under way. The result is that soundings are being accumulated so fast that it is impossible to keep the bathymetric charts up to date.

When only a few deep-sea soundings were available, it was generally believed that the deep basins of the oceans were characterized by a flat and

TABLE 2*

AREA, VOLUME, AND MEAN DEPTH OF OCEANS AND SEAS

Region	Area $(10^6$ km$^2)$	Volume $(10^6$ km$^3)$	Mean Depth (Meters)
Atlantic Ocean..................	82.441	323.613	3926
Pacific Ocean...................	165.246	707.555	4282
Indian Ocean...................	73.443	291.030	3963
(all excluding adjacent seas)			
Large mediterranean seas.........	29.518	40.664	1378
Small mediterranean seas.........	2.331	0.402	172
Marginal seas..................	8.079	7.059	874
All oceans and adjacent seas..	361.058	1370.323	3795

* From Kossina (1921).

contourless bottom; but the echo soundings have revealed that generally the bottom of the sea is as irregular as the surface of the land. Mountain ranges or isolated mountains rise from great depths without reaching the sea surface, and in several areas deep and narrow trenches are present. The greatest depth which has so far been reported has been found in the Mariana Trench in the Pacific, in about lat. 11° N., long. 143° E. Gr. According to a critical analysis by Carruthers and Lawford (1952), the depth is 5940 fathoms or 10,863 meters. Table 3 shows some of the other greatest depths which have been found in the different oceans.

In general, the ocean bed is covered by sediments, but ridges and isolated peaks may be free from sediments because of the action of currents. All sediments in shallow water and most of the sediments in near-shore areas are derived from the adjacent land and are called *terrigenous*, in contrast to the sediments of the deep-ocean basins, which are called *pelagic*. The latter may be mainly of organic origin, in which case they are called *oozes;* or they may be mainly of inorganic origin and are called *red clays.* The oozes are calcareous or siliceous. Of the former, the globigerina ooze dominates, formed by the tests of the pelagic Foraminifera. Of the latter, diatom ooze, formed by the frustules of diatoms (microscopic plants), covers the larger areas. All told, 268,000,000 km² of the ocean bottom are covered by pelagic deposits; 126,000,000 km² by globigerina ooze; 31,000,-000 by diatom ooze; 102,000,000 by red clay; and the remaining 9,000,000 by other oozes. All these sediments are very fine, the red clay being by far the finest. The median diameters of the particles in the three types are 7.8, 7.0, and 1.1 μ, respectively.

TABLE 3

SOME OF THE GREATEST DEPTHS OF THE OCEANS

Ocean	Locality	Depth (Meters)
North Atlantic......	Puerto Rico Trough	8,750
South Atlantic......	South Sandwich Trench	8,264
North Pacific........	Japan Trench	10,374
	Philippines Trench	10,497
	Mariana Trench	10,863
South Pacific........	Tonga-Kermadec Trench	9,427
	Peru Basin	7,635
Indian.............	Sunda Trench	7,455

The total thickness of the sediment carpet covering the ocean bottom has been determined by means of seismic methods developed by W. Maurice Ewing and used by him in the North Atlantic; by Hans Pettersson on board the Swedish research vessel, the "Albatross," in the tropical parts of all three oceans; and by Russell Raitt of the Scripps Institution in the North Pacific. In the Atlantic the total thickness of the sediments was found to be up to 4000 m, but in the Pacific and the Indian oceans the recorded thickness nowhere exceeds 300–400 m. It has been suggested that in the latter oceans the deeper sediments may have been covered by lava flows. In several places where soft sediments were expected, the bottom was found to be formed by lava of recent origin.

At present the rate of growth of the deep-sea deposits is very slow. According to the more recent estimates, the average rate of deposition of globigerina ooze is of the order of 2 mm in 1000 years, and that of red clay is about 1 mm in 1000 years. For red clay, values as low as 0.04 mm in 1000 years have been reported (Pettersson and Rotschi, 1952, p. 88).

Recently it has become possible to obtain undistorted cores of a length of up to 20 m, using the Kullenberg piston corer. In red clay such a core may represent material which has been laid down during the last 20,000,-000 years or more, that is, during a period of time which is significant even from a geological point of view. The study of these cores and of others which have been obtained previously by other methods has revealed that in globigerina ooze warm- and cold-water Foraminifera alternate, indicating that large changes in the temperature of the ocean waters have taken place in the time interval during which the sediments were deposited. These matters are being further investigated.

The nickel content of the deep-sea deposits has attracted considerable attention. Pettersson and Rotschi (1952) have pointed out that the nickel content of the red clay is considerably higher than the average nickel content of the uppermost crust of the earth, the maximum values being ten times higher than the continental average. They also found the highest nickel values, about 0.05 per cent nickel, in material with a low rate of deposition; and they assumed that the lower values may be ascribed to the dilution effect of calcareous or siliceous microfossils. Furthermore, in long cores of red clay or radiolarian ooze they found conspicuous variation of the nickel content with depth, with maxima two or three times higher than the average value for the same core.

When looking for an explanation of the high nickel values, the authors arrive at the conclusion that it is difficult to explain the observed concentrations as a result of deposition of terrestrial material or as originating from lava ejected over the ocean floor. The latter possibility appeared to be ruled out by the fact that samples of submarine lava showed no more nickel than did the average rocks at the surface of the earth. In view of these difficulties, the authors suggest that the high nickel values in the red clay may be due to the accumulation of *meteoric* or *cosmic dust*. On the basis of this assumption, they estimate that, on an average, the total contribution of extra-terrestrial material to the earth in the course of one year reaches a value of the order of 1,000,000 tons, whereas F. Watson, on the basis of meteor counts, has estimated the same amount at somewhat less than 2000 tons.

Because of this great discrepancy, the authors submitted their calculations to authorities on meteors and cosmic dust and learned that their conclusions appear to be in fair agreement with more recent calculations. Watson states that the figure based on meteor counts must be taken as a lower limit, while F. L. Whipple, who has developed the theory of micrometeorites (1950*a*, *b*), is of the opinion that the total mass of invisible micrometeorites may be 10,000 times greater than that of the visible meteorites.

In concluding their paper, Pettersson and Rotschi point out that an analysis of the platinum and palladium content of the red-clay samples that are rich in nickel may provide a crucial test of the hypothesis as to the cosmic origin of the nickel. According to Goldschmidt, the average content of platinum and palladium in iron meteorites is 20 and 10 gm/ton, respectively, whereas in continental rocks the values are about 10,000 times less. While this is being written, analysis of the palladium content is in progress, and the investigation of the nickel content of cores is being continued. These studies probably represent the oceanographic work that is of the most direct interest to astronomers.

2. THE WATER OF THE OCEANS

2.1. The Salt Content of Sea Water

The sea water is such a complex solution of salts that it is impossible by direct chemical analysis to determine its total content of dissolved solids. The *salinity* of the sea water has, therefore, been defined as "the total amount of solid material in grams contained in one kilogram of sea water when all the carbonate has been converted to oxide, the bromine and iodine replaced by chlorine, and all organic matter completely oxidized." The numerical value of the salinity as defined in this manner is slightly lower than the exact amount of dissolved solid matters in grams per kilogram.

Analyses of a large number of samples from different parts of the oceans have revealed that, regardless of the absolute concentrations, the relative amounts of all the major constituents are virtually constant. Therefore, the salinity of a water sample can be computed by determining the amount of only one of the major components. Chlorine is present in relatively large quantitites and can be determined easily and accurately; for this reason the determination of the *chlorinity* of the sea water has been standardized and is now in general use. The empirical relation between salinity and chlorinity is

$$\text{Salinity} = 0.03 + 1.805 \times \text{chlorinity} .$$

Both salinity and chlorinity are expressed in parts per thousand, or "per mille," for which the symbol "‰" is used.

Of the known elements, 49 have been found in sea water, but a few of these are present in such small quantities that so far it has not been possible to determine their concentration. Radium, which can be determined with precision, is present in amounts of about 1×10^{-13} gm/kg.

2.2. DENSITY OF SEA WATER

The density of sea water depends in a complicated manner upon temperature, salinity, and pressure. Figure 1 shows the character of the relationship at atmospheric pressure for the temperatures and salinities that are encountered in the open sea. For precise determinations, comprehensive tables must be used. When computing currents from the observed dis-

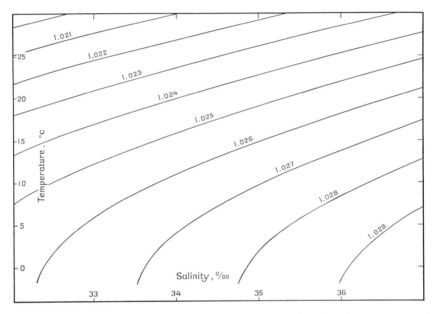

FIG. 1.—Density of sea water at atmospheric pressure as a function of temperature and salinity.

tribution of mass (see p. 245), the specific volume is used instead of the density, and it must be known with an accuracy of about one unit in the fifth decimal place. Therefore, the temperature must be determined with an accuracy of $0°.02$ C, and the salinity with an accuracy of about 0.01 ‰.

2.3. SOME THERMAL PROPERTIES OF SEA WATER

The salt content of the water leads to a lowering of the freezing point, which is nearly proportional to the salinity. At a salinity of 30 ‰, the freezing point is at $-1°.63$ C, and at 35 ‰ it is at $-1°.91$ C.

The thermal expansion of sea water is influenced by the salinity of the water, the most important feature being that the temperature of maximum density decreases with increasing salinity. Pure water has its maximum density above the freezing point, at $4°$ C; but at a salinity of 24.70 ‰ the temperature of maximum density coincides with the freezing point, $-1°.332$ C; and at a higher salinity, freezing begins before the maximum density has been attained. These features have a bearing on the conditions for the formation of ice at sea.

The specific heat of sea water is somewhat smaller than that of pure water, but the difference is rarely significant. The heat of vaporization is considered equal to that of fresh water.

Since sea water is slightly compressible, its temperature changes if a mass is brought *adiabatically* from one pressure to another. If a sample of sea water of salinity 35 ‰ and temperature $0°$ C is brought adiabatically from the sea surface to a depth of approximately 5000 m, where the pressure is 500 bars (one bar equals 10^6 dynes cm^{-2}), its temperature increases by $0°.49$ C. Within many of the deep-ocean basins a temperature increase toward the bottom has been observed. When this increase was first recorded, it was ascribed to an effect of the heat flux from the interior of the earth; but subsequently it has been shown that the increase never exceeds the value that may result from the effect of adiabatic processes.

The thermal conductivity of sea water is slightly smaller than that of pure water of the same temperature, but the value which has been determined in the laboratory has no bearing upon processes of conduction of heat in the sea, because sea water is always in a state of *turbulent motion*, by which the processes of heat transfer are completely altered. The ordinary coefficient of thermal conduction must be replaced by an "eddy coefficient," which is very much larger and which depends so much on the state of motion that the effects of salinity, temperature, and pressure can be disregarded. The "eddy conductivity" will be dealt with below.

2.4. The Characteristics of the Sea in Regard to Radiation

When considering the characteristics of the sea in regard to radiation, it should first be stated that we are concerned with the radiation from the sun and the sky and the radiation from the sea surface itself. The radiation from the sun, including the part that reaches the surface of the earth as scattered radiation from the sky, falls in the wave-length range 0.3–2 μ and is referred to as *short-wave* radiation, in contrast to the radiation from the sea surface itself and from the clouds and the water vapor in the atmosphere, which is called *long-wave* radiation because it falls in the wave-length range 10–15 μ. Water radiates as a black body, and the long-wave radiation from the sea surface therefore depends only upon the temperature of the surface.

Part of the short-wave radiation that reaches the sea surface is reflected from the surface. The reflection of the direct radiation from the sun depends upon the altitude of the sun. With the sun 60°, 30°, and 10° above the horizon, the reflected amounts are 2.1, 6.0, and 34.8 per cent, respectively. For diffuse radiation a reflection of 17 per cent has been determined theoretically. On clear days, measurements have given values in agreement with the foregoing; but on overcast days, when one might expect the radiation to be diffuse, values between 8 and 15 per cent have been found (Neiburger, 1948). The measurements were carried out with a high sun. The lower values were found with a thin or moderately thick cloud cover, and the higher with thick cloud covers, perhaps indicating that with a thin cloud cover part of the radiation may be directed.

Even on a clear day, part of the radiation received at the sea surface is diffuse, and this circumstance must be taken into account when computing the reflection loss on a clear day for different altitudes of the sun. One obtains the approximate values given in the accompanying tabulation.

Altitude of sun	5°	10°	20°	30°	40°	50°	90°
Percentage reflected	40	25	12	6	4	3	3

These values are applicable if the sea surface is smooth. In the presence of waves, the reflection may be decreased by about 20 per cent.

The part of the incoming radiation from the sun and the sky which is not reflected will penetrate the sea surface and is absorbed in the upper layers of the sea. When dealing with the absorption of radiation in pure water, a coefficient of absorption at wave length λ, κ_λ, is defined by the equation

$$d I_\lambda = - \kappa_\lambda I_\lambda dn .\tag{1}$$

Here I_λ is the energy at wave length λ, and dI_λ is the decrease in energy in the direction of the beam in an infinitesimal layer of thickness dn. Integrating equation (1) between the limits $n = N$ and $n = N + L$, one obtains

$$\kappa_\lambda = \frac{1}{L} \ln \frac{I_{\lambda, N}}{I_{\lambda,\ N+L}} .\tag{2}$$

This equation also serves as a definition of the coefficient of absorption, the numerical value of which depends upon the unit of length used. In physics this unit is 1 cm; but in oceanography 1 m is commonly used as the unit of length; thus the numerical values given here are 100 times larger than the corresponding values in physics texts. At the same time, the coefficient is defined such as to be, not the absorption coefficient, but the *extinction coefficient*. The reason is that in oceanography the main interest attaches to the manner in which the radiation decreases with depth. This rate can be expressed by means of an extinction coefficient, defined by

$$\kappa_\lambda = \ln \frac{I_{\lambda, z}}{I_{\lambda, z+1}}, \tag{3}$$

where z is the depth, taken positive downward.

With a clear sky the extinction coefficient depends upon the altitude of the sun, because the direct radiation from the sun penetrates obliquely into the sea. This dependence is, however, not very important, partly because the refraction is so great that, even with the sun close to the horizon, the sun's rays form an angle of 49° with the vertical after having passed the sea surface, and partly because of the powerful scattering which rapidly reduces the obliquity of the rays. Furthermore, the effect of the scattering on the rate of decrease of the incident radiation is so great and so variable that the effect of the sun's altitude becomes less important.

Laboratory measurements of the coefficient of absorption of distilled water have not given quite consistent results, but they all show that the coefficient is small in the visible part of the spectrum and very large in the infrared. The effect of this selective absorption in pure water is shown schematically in Figure 2,[1] from which it is seen that at a depth of 100 m the spectrum has been reduced to a narrow band around $\lambda = 0.5 \mu$.

In the ocean numerous measurements of the extinction coefficient have been carried out, using photoelectric or photronic cells and various colored filters in order to determine the coefficient within narrow bands of wave length. These measurements have shown that in the sea the extinction coefficient for a given wave length varies between very wide limits. Even in the clearest oceanic water it is greater than the corresponding coefficient for pure water, and in turbid coastal water it is very much larger.

The great variability of the extinction coefficient of sea water is illustrated in Figure 3, which shows the coefficient as a function of the wave length for different types of sea water (Jerlov, 1951). It is seen that, with the increasing turbidity of the water, the region of minimum extinction coefficient (maximum transparency) is shifted toward the red end of the spectrum.

1. Figures 2, 5, 6, 7, 8, and 9 are from H. U. Sverdrup, Martin W. Johnson, and Richard H. Fleming, *The Oceans* (copyright 1942 by Prentice-Hall, Inc., New York), pp. 105, 493, 684, 727, 748, 753. Reproduced by permission of the publishers.

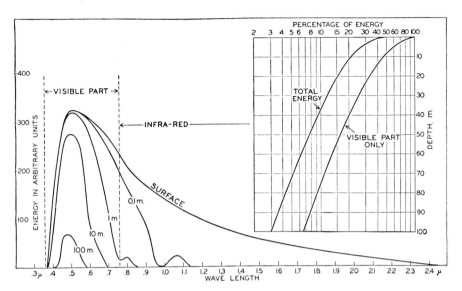

FIG. 2.—Schematic representation of the energy spectrum of the radiation from the sun and the sky which penetrates the sea surface, and of the energy spectra in pure water at depths of 0.1, 1, 10, and 100 m. *Inset:* Percentages of total energy and of energy in the visible part of the spectrum reaching different depths.

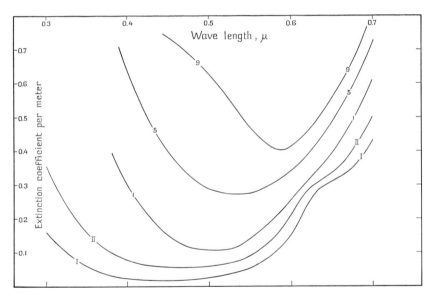

FIG. 3.—Extinction coefficients of radiation in different types of sea water. Coefficients in clear and average oceanic water shown by curves marked *I* and *II;* in coastal water of different turbidity by curves marked *1, 5,* and *9.*

There are two reasons for the large values of the coefficient. In the first place, the ocean waters always contain some very fine suspended matter which increases the scattering. In the second place, varying amounts of certain metabolic products are generally present, derived from plants or animals, which are all included in a common term, "yellow substance." This yellow substance absorbs strongly at wave lengths shorter than 0.5μ. It is present in appreciable quantities in turbid coastal waters, where it causes the wave length of maximum transparency to be shifted from about 0.45μ (for pure water) to 0.55μ or even a little higher.

It may be of interest to observe that at very low light-intensities the maximum sensitivity of the human eye lies at a wave length of 0.503μ and that, according to experiments, the eyes of at least one species of fish are of similar sensitivity. This may imply that the fish eye has been developed to take advantage of the weakest light in the sea; and since the human eye has similar characteristics, one is tempted to assume that after the reptiles emerged from the sea, during some remote geological period, the eyes of land animals have undergone no further development as to the region of maximum sensitivity for weak illumination.

2.5. Eddy Viscosity, Conductivity, and Diffusivity

The coefficients of viscosity, heat conductivity, and diffusion, determined in the laboratory, are applicable to conditions in the sea only if the water is at rest or in laminar motion. Since these conditions are never fulfilled, it is necessary to replace the ordinary coefficients by "eddy coefficients," which depend upon the degree of turbulence.

In the presence of turbulence, momentum, heat, or dissolved substances are carried from one layer to another by the random motion of smaller or larger masses of the fluid, whereby the transfer rates are greatly increased. The random motion is superimposed upon a more or less simple average flow pattern.

The concept of eddy viscosity was introduced into oceanography in 1902, when V. W. Ekman examined the effect of winds in producing currents. At that time he dealt only with the effect of exchange of momentum in a vertical direction; but subsequently it has been shown that it is equally necessary to introduce a horizontal eddy viscosity when dealing with strictly horizontal motion. The numerical values of the vertical and horizontal eddy viscosities differ greatly, in accordance with the fact that there exist fundamental differences between the random motions in a vertical and in a horizontal plane. In the vertical direction the dimensions of eddies are limited by the depth to the bottom, and—what is generally of

greater importance—vertical motion is impeded because of a stable stratification of the waters. Where the stratification is stable (density increasing
with depth), a small mass of water that has been brought to another level
will be subjected to the Archimedean force that is directed toward the
level at which the mass has the same density as its surroundings. In the
case of horizontal motion the boundaries exercise a far less restricting influence on the eddy dimensions, and at the same time the motion is not
impeded by the Archimedean force.

Another effect of the stable stratification is that numerically the coefficient of eddy diffusivity becomes smaller than the corresponding kinematic eddy viscosity. G. I. Taylor has shown that such must be the case,
and Jacobsen has pointed out that whereas elements in turbulent motion
may rapidly give off their momentum to the surroundings, other properties may be exchanged slowly and that, before equalization has been attained, the elements may be moved to new surroundings by gravitational
forces.

Numerical values of *vertical* eddy coefficients have been computed,
either directly from observed conditions or by making use of theoretical
results based on laboratory studies of turbulence. The wide range of the
computed values and their magnitude as compared to the true coefficients
are evident from the accompanying brief compilation. The enormous

Kinematic viscosity..................	$0.019–0.009$ cm^2 sec^{-1}
Kinematic eddy viscosity.............	$2–7500$ cm^2 sec^{-1}
Diffusivity........................	2×10^{-5} cm^2 sec^{-1}
Eddy diffusivity....................	$0.02–100$ cm^2 sec^{-1}

range in the values of the eddy coefficients is generally attributed to effects
of stability and current velocity, because intense turbulence is associated
with small stability and strong currents.

The *horizontal* coefficients vary within even wider limits, from values of
the order of 10 up to 10^8 cm^2 sec^{-1}. The smallest values are applicable to
diffusion as observed, for instance, with small spots of dye, and the
largest to diffusion on an ocean-wide scale. These results clearly indicate
that the coefficients to be used depend upon the scale of the phenomenon,
a conclusion which is in agreement with recent theories of turbulence (see
Stommel, 1949). These theories assume that turbulence can be characterized by a continuous series of eddies of all sizes. When dealing with
horizontal motion, the average flow pattern upon which the random fluctuations are superimposed is obtained by averaging over a smaller or
larger area. When averaged over a small area, the corresponding random

fluctuations will be small and the eddy coefficients correspondingly small, whereas when averaged over a very large area, the corresponding random fluctuations will be large, and the same will be true for the eddy co-efficients.

When a continuous series of eddies is present, energy must be supplied to the larger in order to maintain a steady state. In the case of the oceans the energy for maintenance of the larger eddies is supplied by the wind, and this energy is transferred to smaller and smaller eddies and is finally transformed to heat.

Theoretically, the eddy coefficients applicable to isentropic turbulence are proportional to $L^{4/3}$, where L represents the linear dimensions of the region under consideration. Small-scale experiments in the sea have indicated that this so-called $\frac{4}{3}$-law holds when dealing with horizontal diffusion; but the complete problem is too complicated to be dealt with fully here. It must suffice to emphasize that the horizontal eddy coefficients vary with the dimensions of the area under examination and that for ocean-wide areas the value is of the order of 10^8 cm² sec⁻¹. This value will be used later in the discussion of how the large-scale ocean currents are maintained.

3. THE HEAT BUDGET OF THE OCEANS

3.1. GENERAL

The exchange of energy between the earth and its surroundings is determined by processes of radiation only. The solar energy which is received at the limit of our atmosphere is lost partly by reflection and partly by radiation to space from the surfaces of the earth, the clouds, and the atmosphere. Assuming that the solar energy that reaches the outer limit of the atmosphere amounts to 1.94 cal cm⁻² min⁻¹ and that 36 per cent of this energy is reflected, one finds that the effective radiating temperature of the earth and its atmosphere, taken as a whole, is 250° K.

The distribution of temperature over the surface of the earth is, however, not determined by processes of radiation only. While for the earth as a whole the amounts of energy received and lost by radiation are in balance, this is not true at any given latitude. Both the effective insolation (the incoming radiation from the sun minus the reflected part) and the outgoing terrestrial radiation decrease from the equator to the poles; but at the equator the effective insolation is greater than the terrestrial radiation, whereas at the poles it is less. In computing these quantities, different authors have reached somewhat different results, but they all agree as to the main features. Table 4 contains the average annual values of the incoming effective insolation and the outgoing terrestrial radiation between parallels of latitude in the Northern Hemisphere, according to Baur and Phillips (1933). Between the equator and about 35° N. the earth receives more energy than it loses, whereas north of latitude 35° N. the loss exceeds the gain. The last column of Table 4 shows the total amounts of gain or loss for the areas between the parallels. These figures should sum up to zero if the computations were exact; actually, the sum is -0.07×10^{16} cal min^{-1}, which is satisfactory, since the values of effective insolation and terrestrial radiation have been computed independently.

It follows from the data in Table 4 that if only radiative processes were active, heating would take place in lower latitudes and cooling in higher.

TABLE 4

AVERAGE ANNUAL VALUES OF EFFECTIVE INSOLATION AND TERRESTRIAL
RADIATION BETWEEN PARALLELS OF LATITUDE IN
NORTHERN HEMISPHERE

Range of Latitude (Degrees)	Area (10^{16} cm^2)	Effective Insolation* (cal cm^{-2} min^{-1})	Terrestrial Radiation (cal cm^{-2} min^{-1})	Diff. (cal cm^{-2} min^{-1})	Total Diff. (10^{16} cal min^{-1})
0–10.........	44.1	0.354	0.296	+0.058	+2.56
10–20.........	42.7	.346	.299	+ .047	+2.00
20–30.........	40.2	.336	.298	+ .038	+1.53
30–40.........	36.3	.297	.291	+ .006	+0.22
40–50.........	31.5	.236	.269	− .033	−1.04
50–60.........	25.6	.185	.253	− .068	−1.74
60–90.........	34.3	0.135	0.240	−0.105	−3.60

* The calories used are gram calories throughout.

Since there is no evidence of any persistent change in the temperature of the atmosphere or the oceans, it must be concluded that, on an average for the whole year, heat is transported from lower to higher latitudes. This transport reaches its maximum a little north of 35° N., where it attains a value of 6.31×10^{16} cal min^{-1}. It is mainly effected by the atmosphere but, as will be shown later on, also to some extent by the ocean currents. This applies particularly to conditions in the Northern Hemisphere, for which the figures in Table 4 have been computed. A corresponding detailed computation has not been made for the Southern Hemisphere, but from other data it appears probable that there the ocean currents are less important in the transport of heat into polar latitudes.

The oceans play another and even more important role in regulating the temperature distribution. Where surplus energy is received, it is used mainly for evaporation; and later this surplus energy becomes available to

the atmosphere when condensation takes place, often in a region far removed from where the evaporation occurred. Knowledge of the heat
budget of the ocean and of ocean currents and the interaction between
ocean and atmosphere are, therefore, indispensable to an understanding
of the temperature distribution at the surface of the earth and in the
atmosphere.

For all oceans and for the whole year the average amounts of energy
received and lost must balance, because there is no evidence that the temperature of the waters changes appreciably over periods as short as a
century or so. The oceans receive or lose energy mainly by processes of
radiation, by exchange of sensible heat with the atmosphere, and by evaporation from the sea surface or condensation on the surface. The effects
of other processes, such as the conduction of heat from the interior of the
earth, the transformation of kinetic energy into heat, and energy derived
from chemical processes in the sea, are of no importance to the heat
budget; but the energy that is transmitted to the sea by the stress of the
wind on the sea surface is, as will be shown, of prime importance in the
maintenance of the currents.

The heat flux from the interior of the earth has been estimated at about
40 cal cm^{-2} year^{-1}, that is, 10^{-4} cal cm^{-2} min^{-1}. The kinetic energy that is
transmitted to the sea by the stress of the wind and part of the energy of
the tidal currents are dissipated by friction and transformed into heat; the
average amounts are of the same order of magnitude as the heat flux from
the interior of the earth. Both quantities are very small compared to the
entries in Table 4. Finally, in areas with abundant plant life, up to 0.8 per
cent of the incoming radiation is used by the plants for photosynthesis;
but again this is small if compared with the average for all oceans and the
whole year.

3.2. Processes of Radiation

The average annual amount of energy which the sea receives from sun
and sky varies with latitude; and in a given latitude it varies with the
cloudiness. Measurements have been carried out over some ocean areas;
but where no direct observations are available, the average amount (in
cal cm^{-2} min^{-1}) may be computed from the empirical relation

$$Q = k \left(1 - 0.071\bar{C}\right) \bar{h},$$

where $\bar{C}$ is the average cloudiness on the scale 0–10, $\bar{h}$ is the average altitude of the sun in degrees, and k is a factor which depends upon the transparency of the atmosphere and which appears to vary between 0.023 at
the equator and 0.027 in latitude 70°.

As already explained, part of the radiation from sun and sky is reflected from the sea surface. The remaining part, Q_s, penetrates into the sea, where it is absorbed. By far the greatest fraction of this energy is absorbed close to the sea surface, because water has an appreciable transparency only in the wave-length range 0.4–0.6 μ (Fig. 3, p. 224). This feature is illustrated in Figure 4, which shows the percentage amounts of energy that reach different depths under different conditions.

The great absorption of radiation near the sea surface does not lead to the development of a thin, warm surface layer. The reasons are that part

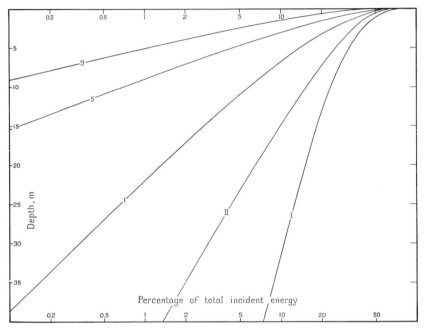

FIG. 4.—Percentages of total energy reaching different depths in clear and average oceanic water (curves *I* and *II*) and in coastal water of different turbidity (curves *1, 5,* and *9*).

of the energy is lost immediately by long-wave radiation, part is used for evaporation from the surface, part is given off to the atmosphere as sensible heat, and the remaining part is rapidly distributed over a thicker layer because of the eddy conductivity. Only on an absolutely calm day with a smooth sea may the afternoon temperature at the surface be a few degrees higher than the temperature at a depth of a few meters. Because of the combined effect of the processes mentioned, the range of the diurnal variation of the surface temperature is always small, generally less than 1°; and the range of the annual variation of surface temperature is small also, except in some coastal waters, where a layer of fresh water may effectively suppress the mixing processes.

Only during the hours of the day when the sun is above the horizon does the sea receive energy by radiation from sun and sky. During all hours it loses energy by its own long-wave radiation; but at the same time it also receives radiation from the water vapor and the carbon dioxide in the air and from the clouds. The net result is a radiation loss which will be called *back-radiation*, Q_b. With a clear sky, the back-radiation amounts to 0.15–0.20 cal cm^{-2} min^{-1}. With a completely overcast sky, it is, on an average, reduced to only 17 per cent of the value with a clear sky under corresponding conditions; but, depending upon the thickness of the clouds, the percentage may vary between 75 and 0.

The average amount of radiation that penetrates the sea surface, Q_s, is greater in all latitudes than the loss of energy from the sea surface by back-radiation, Q_b. Averaged for the whole year and all oceans, the radiation surplus $Q_r = (Q_s - Q_b)$ must be given off to the atmosphere, but not necessarily when and where it was received. Part of the surplus may be carried by currents to other regions, and part may be stored during the warm season and given off during the cold season. Thus the oceans exercise a great equalizing influence on the climate of the earth.

Let Q_c be the amount of energy that is carried by the ocean currents into, or out of, any given area; Q_e the energy used for evaporation within the area; and Q_h the energy that is given off to the atmosphere as sensible heat. The energy budget of the area may then be written

$$Q_s - Q_b = Q_c + Q_e + Q_h . \tag{4}$$

For the oceans as a whole and for the whole year, Q_c must be zero.

3.3. Exchange of Heat between the Ocean and the Atmosphere

The heat flux from the sea surface to the air or vice versa is practically equal to the heat flux in the air directly above the sea surface:

$$Q_h = - c_p A \frac{dT}{dz}, \tag{5}$$

where c_p is the specific heat of the air, A is the eddy conductivity of the air, and $-dT/dz$ is the temperature gradient (the lapse rate) close to the sea surface. The positive z-axis is directed upward and, because of the minus sign, the lapse rate is positive when the temperature decreases with height, that is, when the air is colder than the sea surface. To be exact, the potential temperature of the air and not the ordinary temperature should appear in equation (5); but within a thin layer near the sea surface the gradient of the potential temperature differs so little from that of the ordinary temperature that no appreciable error is introduced by using the latter.

The term $c_p A$ has to be introduced instead of the ordinary coefficient of heat conductivity because the air is always in a state of turbulent motion. Since the eddy conductivity, A, increases with increasing distance from the surface, the numerical value of the temperature gradient decreases.

In the tropics the sea surface temperature is, on the average, about $0°.8$ C above the air temperature at a height of about 10 m. In middle and higher latitudes conditions are much more variable, with great differences between summer and winter. In summer the sea surface is often colder than the air, particularly in regions with south-flowing currents; but in winter the sea surface may be much warmer than the air. Averaged for the whole year and the entire sea, the sea surface is warmer than the air; and the difference, sea surface *minus* air, is greater than in the tropics.

Knowledge of the eddy conductivity of the air close to the sea surface and of the temperature gradients is too inadequate for a study of the heat flux from the sea to the air; but, as will be shown, it is possible to compute the ratio between the flux of sensible heat and the flux of latent heat associated with evaporation.

3.4. EVAPORATION

The flux of water vapor is

$$F_e = - A \frac{d f}{d z}, \tag{6}$$

where f is the specific humidity, that is, the mass of water vapor per unit mass of moist air. The specific humidity can be expressed by means of the vapor pressure in the air, e, thus:

$$f = \frac{0.622 e}{p - e},$$

where p is the atmospheric pressure, always large compared to e. Introducing the vapor pressure, equation (6) becomes, approximately,

$$F_e = - A \frac{0.622}{p} \frac{d e}{d z}. \tag{7}$$

In general, the vapor pressure at the sea surface is higher than that in the air and depends upon the temperature and the salinity of the water:

$$e_s = e_d (1 - 0.000537 \ S),$$

where e_s is the vapor pressure over sea water, e_d the vapor pressure over distilled water of the same temperature, and S the salinity per mille of the water. Since the salinity of the surface waters of the open oceans never deviates much from 35 ‰, the vapor pressure at the sea surface is generally 2 per cent lower than that over distilled water of the same temperature. This implies that if the air is saturated with moisture, the vapor pressure in the air and at the sea surface are equal if the surface temperature is about $0°.3$ higher than the air temperature. In general, the air is not saturated, and the sea surface is more than $0°.3$ warmer than the air. Therefore, near the sea surface the vapor pressure generally decreases with height, and evaporation takes place. In middle and higher latitudes conditions may be reversed when warm air flows in over cold water. In such cases the water vapor is condensed on the sea surface, and this process in most cases is accompanied by the formation of fog (Grand Banks of New Foundland and part of the coast of California). However, evaporation predominates all over the open oceans, particularly in winter off the eastern coasts of the continents of the Northern Hemisphere, where cold continental air frequently flows out over the warm sea.

The heat taken by evaporation from the sea surface equals

$$Q_e = - AL \frac{0.622}{p} \frac{de}{dz}, \tag{8}$$

where L is the heat of vaporization at the temperature of the surface ($L \cong 596 - 0.52T$, in which T is expressed in $°$ C).

The ratio between the flux of sensible heat and the flux of latent heat associated with evaporation is

$$R = \frac{Q_h}{Q_e} = \frac{c_p}{L} \frac{p}{0.622} \frac{dT/dz}{de/dz} \simeq 0.66 \frac{p}{1000} \frac{T_s - T_a}{e_s - e_a}, \tag{9}$$

where the numerical values $c_p = 0.240$ and $L = 585$ have been introduced. The ratio R is called the "Bowen ratio" because it was first used by I. S. Bowen. The air pressure at the sea surface does not vary significantly, so that R depends mainly upon the ratio between the temperature and humidity gradients in the air at short distances from the sea surface. These gradients have been measured in a few instances only, but they can be replaced approximately by differences between the temperature and the vapor pressure at the sea surface (T_s and e_s) and the corresponding values in the air at a height of a few meters (T_a and e_a). These values can be obtained from charts of sea surface temperatures and climatological charts of the oceans. On the basis of such data, Jacobs (1942, 1943) has computed the values of the Bowen ratio for the oceans of the Northern Hemisphere and for different seasons; corresponding calculations have not yet been made for the Southern Hemisphere because of a lack of climatological charts.

In the Northern Hemisphere the ratio is small in low latitudes, where it varies little during the year. In middle latitudes the ratio is greater and varies with the season. In winter it may in some regions exceed 0.5, and in others it may in summer drop to -0.2. Negative values imply that heat is conducted from the air into the sea.

The evaporation could be computed from equation (7) if the eddy diffusivity and the humidity gradient near the sea surface were known, but they are not known with sufficient accuracy. From the energy equation and the knowledge of the Bowen ratio it is, however, possible to compute the evaporation between parallels of latitude, assuming that no energy is transported by ocean currents. Then we have

$$Q_e = \frac{Q_s - Q_b}{1 + R}. \tag{10}$$

The evaporation can also be computed in another manner. From knowledge of the character of the eddy diffusivity of the air and its relation to the wind velocity, it appears probable that the evaporation can be found from a relation of the form

$$E = K(e_s - e_a)w, \tag{11}$$

where E is the amount of evaporated water expressed in a suitable unit, e_s and e_a represent the vapor pressures at the surface and in the air at a height of 8–10 m, respectively, and w is the wind velocity as observed at a height of 8–10 m. The coefficient K has to be adjusted so that for all oceans the evaporation as computed from equation (11) agrees with that found on the basis of energy considerations (eq. [10]).

Finally, the evaporation can be determined by direct observations from pans on board ships; but since the values obtained in this manner do not apply to the sea surface, a correction factor has been derived by elaborate and somewhat uncertain methods.

Some of the main results of such investigations are summarized in Table 5, from which it is evident that there is a reasonable agreement between the values derived from meteorological observations and those from direct measurements. Between the equator and 30° N. these values are systematically lower than the values computed from the radiation surplus, whereas north of 30° N. they are systematically higher. In the Southern Hemisphere, from which only values based upon pan measurements on board ships are available, no such systematic difference is apparent.

3.5. Heat Transport by Ocean Currents

The results contained in Table 5 suggest that in the Northern Hemisphere considerable amounts of heat are transported by the ocean currents. Table 6 summarizes the values that can be derived from the data in Table 5.

TABLE 5

Results of Studies of Evaporation from the Oceans

Latitude Range	Ocean Area (10^{16} cm²)	(Q_s-Q_b) (cal cm⁻² min⁻¹)	$1+R$	Q_e (cal cm⁻² min⁻¹)	Evaporation (mm day⁻¹) from		
					Q_e	Met. Obs.	Direct Obs.
60°–50° N.....	10.9	0.056	1.31	0.043	1.03	1.78	1.18
50 –40.......	15.0	.079	1.21	.065	1.58	2.00	2.11
40 –30.......	20.8	.114	1.15	.100	2.44	3.32	2.90
30 –20.......	25.1	.166	1.11	.149	3.69	3.56	3.50
20 –10.......	31.5	.176	1.10	.160	3.95	3.66	3.61
10 – 0.......	34.0	.166	1.10	.151	3.73	3.11	3.20
0°–10° S.....	33.7	.152	1.10	.138	3.40	....	3.36
10 –20.......	33.4	.159	1.10	.145	3.55	....	3.60
20 –30.......	30.9	.160	1.11	.144	3.52	....	3.36
30 –40.......	32.3	.133	1.14	.117	2.86	....	2.69
40 –50.......	30.5	.083	1.17	.071	1.69	....	1.76
50 –60.......	25.4	0.047	1.20	0.039	0.94	....	0.71

TABLE 6

Average Amounts of Heat Carried by Currents *Out* of Areas between Parallels, Northern Hemisphere

Latitude Range (° N.)	Q_c in 10^{16} cal min⁻¹ from (Q_s-Q_b) and		Latitude Range (° N.)	Q_c in 10^{16} cal min⁻¹ from (Q_s-Q_b) and	
	Met. Obs.	Direct Obs.		Met. Obs.	Direct Obs.
60–50........	−0.42	−0.08	30–20.......	+0.16	+0.23
50–40........	− .32	− .41	20–10.......	+ .41	+ .49
40–30........	−0.85	−0.44	10– 0.......	+0.95	+0.82

Table 7 shows the amounts of heat that are carried across parallels of latitude in the Northern Hemisphere. The table gives the total amounts and the fractions that are transported by the ocean currents and by the wind systems of the atmosphere. Only the values that are derived from the meteorological observations have been used, since these appear to be the more trustworthy, being based on a far better coverage of the oceans. In arriving at the figures applicable to the oceans, it has been taken into account that in the Atlantic Ocean an amount of heat estimated at about 0.4×10^{16} cal min^{-1} is carried across the equator; there is a considerable exchange of water between the North and the South Atlantic oceans, warm water being carried to the north in the upper layers and cold water to the south at greater depths. There is no information about a possible transport of heat across the equator by winds.

The essential feature which is brought out in Table 7 is that in the Northern Hemisphere the ocean currents contribute materially to the transport of heat from lower to higher latitudes. The data in Table 5 indicate that the currents do not play a correspondingly important role in the Southern Hemisphere.

TABLE 7

AVERAGE AMOUNTS OF HEAT CARRIED ACROSS PARALLELS OF
LATITUDES, NORTHERN HEMISPHERE
(Units: 10^{16} cal min^{-1})

LATITUDE (° N.)	TOTAL AMOUNT	AMOUNT CARRIED BY		LATITUDE (° N.)	TOTAL AMOUNT	AMOUNT CARRIED BY	
		Oceans	Atmosphere			Oceans	Atmosphere
0.........	0.4	0.4	0.0	40.........	6.7	1.1	5.6
10.........	3.0	1.4	1.6	50.........	5.7	0.8	4.9
20.........	5.0	1.8	3.2	60.........	3.9	0.3	3.6
30.........	6.5	1.9	4.6				

From a more detailed analysis it appears that the greater transport of heat by the ocean currents takes place in the Atlantic Ocean, where it also reaches into higher latitudes. The latter feature is related to the contours and bottom configuration of the ocean. Directly and indirectly, the ocean currents are largely responsible for the very mild climate of the northern part of Northwestern Europe.

4. THE DEEP-WATER CIRCULATION OF THE OCEANS

The atmosphere can be regarded as a thermodynamic machine in which heat is transformed into kinetic energy. This model requires that heating occur at higher pressure and cooling at lower pressure. In the atmosphere this condition is fulfilled because heat is added near the surface of the earth, where the principal condensation of water vapor takes place, whereas heat is lost mainly by radiation from the upper surface of clouds or by direct radiation from the water vapor in the air.

Direct heating and cooling cannot maintain an intense circulation in the ocean, because both heating and cooling take place near the sea surface, at nearly the same pressure. Therefore, the ocean must be a very inefficient thermodynamic machine. On this basis it may appear surprising that in the Northern Hemisphere the oceans can transport such large amounts of heat into higher latitudes; it will be shown that this is possible because the currents in the upper layers of the sea are maintained not by heating and cooling but by the frictional drag that the prevailing winds exert on the sea surface and that the meridional currents are related to the lateral boundaries of the oceans. Still, a direct thermal, or rather thermo-haline, circulation in the sea is also present and accounts for the distribution of temperature and salinity in the large masses of water that fill the deeper parts of the oceans. We shall first examine this circulation.

When dealing with the deep-water circulation it should be stated that the stratification of the waters in the oceans is stable; that is, the water of the greatest density is found at the greatest depth. Furthermore, it should be borne in mind that the density can be altered only at the surface of the sea, by heating or cooling, by evaporation or precipitation, or by freezing of ice. Near the coasts the addition of river water is important to the density; but we are dealing here with the open-ocean areas only.

On the basis of these simple considerations we expect that the deep ocean basins are filled by water which originates from surface regions where the waters have attained their greatest density. At first, we would expect to find these regions in high latitudes, where cooling has taken place; but in most such areas the effect of the cooling is counteracted by the excess of precipitation over evaporation, by which the density is reduced. Surface water of high density is formed mainly where water of high salinity is carried into high latitudes and cooled. Since such conditions exist in the North Atlantic Ocean, an appreciable deep-water circulation is found in the Atlantic Ocean.

The deep water of the North Atlantic is formed in the Irminger Sea between Iceland and Greenland and in the Labrador Sea between Greenland and Labrador. One of the last branches of the Gulf Stream system carries Atlantic water of salinity above 35 ‰ into these regions, where it mixes with arctic water, which is carried south by the East Greenland Current or the Labrador Current, respectively, and which has a salinity of about 34 ‰. The mixture attains a salinity close to 34.9 ‰ and, when cooled to about 3° C, its density, about 1.02782 at atmospheric pressure, is sufficiently high for the water to sink to the greatest depths. This water, therefore, fills all deeper parts of the North Atlantic Ocean and flows slowly toward the south. According to estimates, the average flow for the whole year is about 4×10^6 m³ sec⁻¹.

The flow to the south is strengthened by the outflow from the Mediterranean Sea of water of very high salinity (38.6 ‰) and relatively high temperature (13°.0 C). The Mediterranean Sea is characterized by its own deep and bottom water. Through the Strait of Gibraltar a surface current toward the east carries Atlantic water of a salinity of about 36.4 ‰ into the Mediterranean, where the salinity of the water is greatly increased by excess evaporation. When cooled in winter, this water attains in some areas a temperature of about 13° and sinks, forming the deep and bottom water, which in part flows out along the bottom of the Strait of Gibraltar and mixes with the waters of the Atlantic Ocean. It is estimated that the average outflow of Mediterranean Water amounts to nearly 2×10^6 m^3 sec^{-1}. In the North Atlantic this water spreads at depths of about 1200 m. Part of the Mediterranean Water is carried into the South Atlantic Ocean, where it gradually mixes with the waters above and below and where, because of its slightly higher temperature and salinity, it can be traced at depths that increase from about 1400 to about 2000 m. The effect of the Mediterranean Water can be recognized even in latitude 50° S., to the east of South Africa.

Deep and bottom water is also formed around the Antarctic Continent, but by a different process. The salinity of the water is increased when ice freezes, because most of the salts remain in the water. Freezing may therefore lead to the formation of deep and bottom water, but only in regions in which the salinity initially is uniform from the surface to the bottom. In the Arctic this condition is fulfilled in some localities which are isolated from the ocean by submarine ridges so that bottom water formed in this manner does not enter the North Atlantic Ocean. In the Antarctic the condition is fulfilled within some of the shallow areas off the continent, and there water of high density may be formed. This water flows down the continental slope and, in doing so, mixes with the somewhat warmer waters off the coast. When reaching the bottom, the mixed water has a temperature of $-0°.4$, a salinity of 34.66 ‰, and a density (at atmospheric pressure) of 1.02784.

This Antarctic Bottom Water has the highest density of all the water masses of the open oceans. It is mainly formed to the south of the Atlantic Ocean, whence it spreads around the Antarctic Continent and, what is here more important, to the north along the bottom of the three oceans. This flow to the north is particularly conspicuous in the Atlantic, where the Antarctic Bottom Water, because of its low temperature and low salinity, can be traced to at least latitude 30° N. In the other oceans it reaches only to about 20° S.

The formation of the deep and bottom water of the oceans is practically limited to the Atlantic Ocean, where it takes place both in high northern and high southern latitudes. Of the two other oceans, only the Pacific Ocean reaches into high northern latitude, but no deep and bottom water is formed there because no current carries water of high salinity to the north. In the northern part of the Pacific Ocean, including Bering Sea, the great excess of precipitation over evaporation leads to the development of a surface layer of low salinity. Winter cooling brings about an overturn of this surface layer; but the greater salinity of the deep water prevents convection currents from reaching to great depths. The deep parts of the North Pacific Ocean are all filled by water of a very uniform character, temperature $2°0–1°5$, salinity $34.66–34.69 \%_0$, and density close to 1.02775. This water represents water of Atlantic origin which has been diluted by admixture of Antarctic water and also by a slight admixture of the low-salinity surface water of the North Pacific itself.

Water also sinks at convergences in lower latitudes; and after it has left the surface, it spreads at the depth to which it "belongs" because of its density. In general, the surface density increases from lower to higher latitudes. Therefore, in general, water that has left the surface at a higher latitude is found at a greater depth than water than has left the surface at a lower latitude. Consequently, below a locality in lower latitude the change of density of the water in a vertical direction corresponds to the change of density in a horizontal direction when proceeding along the surface to higher latitudes. This means that in a vertical direction we find a distorted picture of the meridional density distribution at the sea surface.

The most conspicuous convergence is found in the Southern Hemisphere, where the Antarctic Convergence can be traced all around the Antarctic Continent. The convergence does not follow a parallel of latitude, because its location appears to be influenced by the land and bottom contours. It lies between latitudes 60° S. and 48° S.; but the surface water that sinks at the convergence has the same character in all areas, a temperature of $2°2$, a salinity of $33.80 \%_0$, and a density of 1.02702.

In all oceans, the water that sinks at this convergence, the Antarctic Intermediate Water, spreads to the north at depths of 700–800 m; but as it advances to the north, it mixes with the waters above and below and gradually attains a higher temperature and a higher salinity. Again there exists a striking difference between conditions in the Atlantic Ocean and in the two other oceans. In the Atlantic the Antarctic Intermediate Water continues across the equator and can be traced to nearly 30° N.; but in the Indian and Pacific oceans it reaches only to about 20° S. In the Northern

Hemisphere corresponding convergences are present, but they are less important, particularly in the Atlantic Ocean.

In lower latitudes, regions of convergence are found in the subtropics, but the water masses which sink within these areas contribute only to the formation of the upper layers of the oceans. Within these layers we find the permanent large-scale currents, which will be discussed later.

The conditions which have been described are illustrated in Figures 5 and 6, which show the distribution of temperature, salinity, and oxygen content in vertical meridional sections of the Atlantic and the Pacific. The content of dissolved oxygen (in ml/l) has been added, because this content is closely related to the circulation.

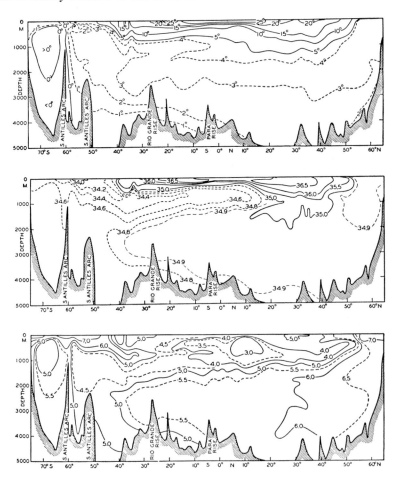

FIG. 5.—Vertical sections showing distribution of temperature, salinity, and oxygen in the western Atlantic Ocean (after Wüst).

The sections demonstrate that higher temperatures are found in the upper layers only and are limited to a latitude range of roughly 45° S.–45° N. Only in the western North Atlantic, in the region of the Sargasso Sea, are temperatures above 10° found to a depth of nearly 1000 m. Similarly, regional differences in salinity are present only in the upper layers; and below a depth of 1500 m the salinity is remarkably uniform, particularly in the Pacific Ocean. In the western Atlantic the Antarctic Intermediate Water appears in the salinity section as a tongue of low-salinity water, and it also shows up in the temperature and oxygen sections as tongues of low-temperature or high-oxygen content, respectively. In the

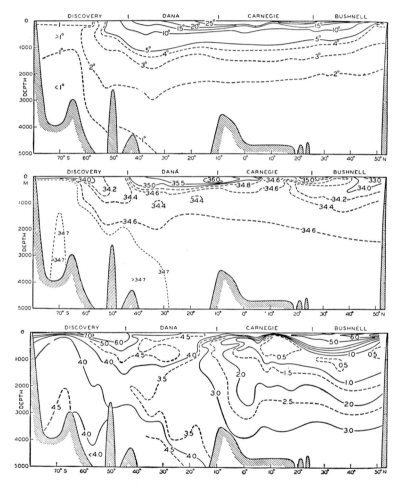

FIG. 6.—Vertical sections showing distribution of temperature, salinity, and oxygen in the Pacific Ocean, approximately along the meridian of 170° W.

North Atlantic between 10° N. and 45° N., the high salinity at depths of 800–1000 m is due to admixture of Mediterranean Water. Below a depth of about 1500 m one recognizes the relatively warm (2°–3°) and saline water that sinks in the northern part of the Atlantic and spreads to the south, and also the cold and less saline bottom water that spreads to the north from the Antarctic. The high-oxygen content of the North Atlantic Deep Water demonstrates that this water has recently left the surface, because the water takes up oxygen only when in contact with the atmosphere and in the deep water the oxygen is gradually consumed by the oxidation of organic matter that drops to the bottom.

In the Pacific Ocean the distributions of temperature and salinity are simpler. No layer of high salinity is found at intermediate depths because no Mediterranean Sea borders upon the Pacific. The Antarctic and Arctic Intermediate Waters can be recognized by their low salinities, but corresponding low temperatures do not appear. The oxygen content of the deep water is low, indicating that deep and bottom water is not formed within the Pacific area. In particular, the deep water of the North Pacific is lacking in oxygen because this water is renewed very slowly by a slight exchange with the South Pacific.

Summarizing the preceding description, we arrive at the following picture of the deep meridional circulation of the oceans: In the Atlantic Ocean, deep water from the northern part and from the Mediterranean flows south, crosses the equator, and rises around the Antarctic Continent. Bottom water forms in the Antarctic and flows north, where it can be traced to the north of the equator. It mixes with the south-flowing deep water and returns to the Antarctic with this water. Antarctic Intermediate Water also flows north, continues across the equator, mixes with the deep water, and returns with this to the Antarctic. In the Indian and Pacific oceans no meridional deep-water circulation is found to the north of the equator. To the south of the equator, Antarctic Bottom Water and Intermediate Water flow north, mix with the deep water, which to a great extent is of Atlantic origin, and returns with this to the Antarctic.

This picture has no similarity to the simple planetary circulation which one should expect if it were exclusively thermally controlled. The actual circulation is different because of the importance of the salinity to the density of the waters; but the resulting complications cannot explain why in the Atlantic Ocean there exists a large exchange of water between the two hemispheres. This feature must be caused by transport of surface water across the equator, brought about by the action of the prevailing winds and the effects of the coasts. We may therefore consider the deep-water circulation of the Atlantic Ocean as a circulation that is conditioned by processes of heating and cooling but is maintained by the action of the wind.

The picture of the deep-water circulation described has been inferred from the distribution of temperature and salinity and is not based upon any measurements of the velocities. Actually, the flow of the deep water is probably far too slow to be detected by direct means. The rapid ocean currents are all confined to the upper layers of the oceans, in general less than 1000 m from the surface. Except within the Gulf Stream off the east coast of the United States, where the current probably reaches to a depth of nearly 2000 m, measurable velocities are rarely found below 500 m.

5. THE CURRENTS WITHIN THE UPPER LAYERS OF THE OCEANS

5.1. THE EQUATIONS OF MOTION

Ships' observations have given us fairly complete knowledge of the semipermanent surface currents of the oceans; but our knowledge of the subsurface currents, the "pure wind" current, and certain types of wave motion is based mainly on applications of the hydrodynamic equations of motion.

In oceanography a left-handed co-ordinate system is generally used, with the z-axis positive downward. The equations of motion then take the form

$$\frac{d\,v_x}{dt} = \frac{\partial\,v_x}{\partial t} + \frac{\partial\,v_x}{\partial x}\,v_x + \frac{\partial\,v_x}{\partial y}\,v_y + \frac{\partial\,v_x}{\partial z}\,v_z = -\,a\,\frac{\partial p}{\partial x} + 2\omega\,\sin\phi\,v_y + aR_x,$$

$$\frac{d\,v_y}{dt} = \frac{\partial\,v_y}{\partial t} + \frac{\partial\,v_y}{\partial x}\,v_x + \frac{\partial\,v_y}{\partial y}\,v_y + \frac{\partial\,v_y}{\partial z}\,v_z = -\,a\,\frac{\partial p}{\partial y} - 2\omega\,\sin\phi\,v_x + aR_y, \quad (12)$$

$$\frac{d\,v_z}{dt} = \frac{\partial\,v_z}{\partial t} + \frac{\partial\,v_z}{\partial x}\,v_x + \frac{\partial\,v_z}{\partial y}\,v_y + \frac{\partial\,v_z}{\partial z}\,v_z = -\,a\,\frac{\partial p}{\partial z} + g - 2\omega\,\cos\phi\,v_E$$

$$-\,\frac{v^2}{a} + aR_z.$$

These equations state that the acceleration equals the sum of the acting forces, the pressure force (a = specific volume, p = pressure), the gravitational force (g = acceleration of gravity), the Coriolis force (ω = angular velocity of earth, ϕ = latitude, v_E = east component of current), the centrifugal force (a = radius of earth), and the frictional force. To these equations must be added the equation of continuity,

$$\frac{\partial\,v_x}{\partial x} + \frac{\partial\,v_y}{\partial y} + \frac{\partial\,v_z}{\partial z} = -\,\frac{1}{a}\frac{d\,a}{dt}$$

and the boundary conditions.

In the foregoing form the equations of motion apply to the Northern Hemisphere. When dealing with the Southern Hemisphere, we must reverse the signs of the Coriolis terms.

5.2. THE PRESSURE FIELD

Equations (12) are never used in their complete form, but simplifications are introduced, depending upon the character of the problem. When dealing with the ocean currents, one always considers the vertical velocities as negligible; and on the right-hand side of the last equation (12) the last three terms are negligible compared to the first two. This equation, therefore, is reduced to the hydrostatic equation,

$$a\,dp = g\,dz\,, \tag{13}$$

from which distances between isobaric surfaces can be found by numerical integration:

$$z_2 - z_1 = \int_{p_1}^{p_2} \frac{a}{g}\,dp\,, \tag{14}$$

provided that the specific volume is known as a function of pressure. The latter condition is fulfilled if temperature and salinity have been determined at a sufficient number of depths, because, in the first approximation, the pressure increases by 1 decibar (1 bar $= 10^6$ dynes cm^{-2}) when the depth increases by 1 m. In carrying out the computation, several short cuts have been introduced. On the right-hand side of equation (14) the specific volume is entered as the sum of two terms—the specific volume of water of salinity 35 ‰ and temperature 0°, $a_{35, 0, p}$—and an anomaly, δ, which depends upon the observed values and can always be expressed by a small number. The distances between isobaric surfaces are then expressed as the sum of a standard distance and an *anomaly*.

Where oceanographic observations are available at a number of localities, the anomalies can be used for preparing *charts* of the topography of one or more isobaric surfaces relative to one isobaric surface that is selected as a reference surface. If this reference surface coincides with a level surface, the charts represent true topographies of the other isobaric surfaces; otherwise, they represent only relative topographies. Strictly speaking, the oceanographic observations that are used should be simultaneous, but conditions in the sea change so slowly that this requirement need not be met.

In general, the topographies are not based on the anomalies as expressed in units of length but in units of work. The practical unit of work is called 1 *dynamic meter* and is numerically nearly equal to 1 m of length. The appearances of the charts are, therefore, quite similar, whether units of length or units of work are used. Charts of topographies of isobaric surfaces represent the *field of pressure* from which conclusions can be drawn as to the character of the semipermanent currents of the oceans.

5.3. COMPUTATION OF CURRENTS

For computing currents, it is assumed that accelerations and frictional forces are negligible, whereby the first two equations of (12) are reduced to

$$\lambda \, v_y = a \, \frac{\partial p}{\partial x}, \qquad \lambda \, v_x = - \, a \, \frac{\partial p}{\partial y}, \tag{15}$$

where $\lambda = 2\omega \sin \phi$.

In some instances it is practical to replace the horizontal pressure gradient by the slope of the isobaric surface.

The x-profile of an isobaric surface is defined by

$$\frac{\partial p}{\partial x} \, dx + \frac{\partial p}{\partial z} \, dz = 0 ; \tag{16}$$

or, using the hydrostatic equation (13),

$$\frac{\partial p}{\partial x} \, dx + \frac{g}{a} \, dz = 0 . \tag{17}$$

Therefore, the slope in the x-direction is

$$i_{p,x} = \frac{dz}{dx} = - \frac{a}{g} \frac{\partial p}{\partial x},$$

meaning that

$$a \, \frac{\partial p}{\partial x} = - \, g i_{p,x} ; \tag{18 a}$$

and, similarly,

$$a \, \frac{\partial p}{\partial y} = - \, g i_{p,y} . \tag{18 b}$$

Consequently, the currents are obtained from the equations

$$v_x = \frac{g}{\lambda} \, i_{p,y} , \qquad v_y = - \frac{g}{\lambda} \, i_{p,x} . \tag{19}$$

The computed currents represent true currents if the slopes of the isobaric surface refer to a level isobaric surface at which the horizontal motion vanishes. In this case equations (15) correspond to the equation of the geostrophic wind, which is used extensively in meteorology. In oceanography a great deal of effort has been directed toward the establishment of a "surface of no motion," to which the computed currents can be referred. Here it must suffice to state that in the Pacific Ocean good agreement between observed and computed currents is obtained by selecting a surface of no motion at a constant depth of about 1500 m; but in the Atlantic Ocean a variable depth must be introduced, in agreement with the much more complex circulation in the Atlantic, discussed above.

The components of the total mass transport by currents are

$$M_x = \int_0^d \rho \, v_x d z, \qquad M_y = \int_0^d \rho \, v_y d z, \qquad (20)$$

where d represents "the depth of no motion." Similarly, the components of the volume transport equal

$$T_x = \int_0^d v_x d z, \qquad T_y = \int_0^d v_y d z. \qquad (21)$$

The mass and volume transports can be computed directly from the observed distribution of mass without first finding the velocities. We define a function

$$P = \int_0^d p \, d z \qquad (22)$$

which can be computed by making use of the hydrostatic equation. Integration of equation (15) then gives

$$M_x = -\frac{1}{\lambda}\frac{\partial P}{\partial y}, \qquad M_y = \frac{1}{\lambda}\frac{\partial P}{\partial x}. \qquad (23)$$

Figures 7 and 8 show the mass transports by the permanent currents of the North Atlantic and North Pacific oceans. The direction is given by streamlines and the transport, in 10^6 m^3 sec^{-1}, by inserted numbers. A comparison with any chart of surface currents shows that there exists a great similarity between the general course of the surface currents and the stream lines of the total transport.

Equations (15), on which the computation of currents is based, state only that, neglecting acceleration and friction, there exists a mutual relationship between the field of pressure and the field of motion. If the field of pressure is known, as has been assumed, the field of motion can be computed; but, conversely, we may also state that if the field of motion were known, we could have computed the corresponding field of pressures. Therefore, we cannot claim that the currents are caused by the distribution of pressure, which, in turn, is determined by the distribution of mass. We can only state that, neglecting acceleration and friction, a mutual relationship exists.

However, friction cannot be completely neglected, although a good approximation is obtained by disregarding it. Actually, kinetic energy is always being dissipated, and therefore the existing circulation cannot prevail unless energy is added. We have already pointed out that in the ocean only negligible amounts of heat are transformed into kinetic energy. The only possibility is, therefore, that the ocean currents are maintained by the prevailing winds. An inspection of Figures 7 and 8 suggests that such is the case, because there is, in general, a striking agreement between the directions of the prevailing winds and of the prevailing currents. In the

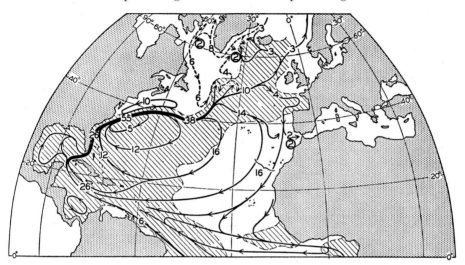

FIG. 7.—Transport of Central Water and Subarctic Water in the Atlantic Ocean. The lines with arrows indicate the direction of the transport, and the inserted numbers indicate the transported volumes in millions of cubic meters per second. Full-drawn lines show warm currents; dashed lines show cold currents. Areas of positive temperature anomaly are shaded.

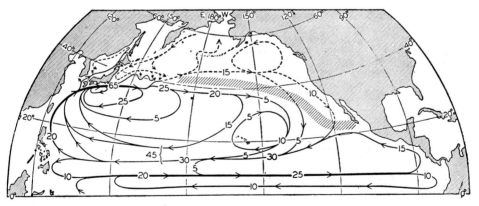

FIG. 8.—Transport chart of the North Pacific. The lines with arrows indicate the approximate direction of the transport above 1500 m and the inserted numbers indicate the transported volumes in millions of cubic meters per second. Dashed lines show cold currents; full-drawn lines show warm currents.

regions of the trade winds the currents run in the direction of the wind, toward the west; and, similarly, between 35° N. and 50° N., where winds from the west dominate, the currents run to the east. Between latitudes 20° N. and 35° N. anticyclonic circulation prevails, both in the atmosphere and in the ocean, whereas north of about 50° N. cyclonic circulations are present (Gulf of Alaska, Bering Sea, Labrador Sea, Norwegian Sea).

There exist, however, two striking discrepancies between winds and currents: north of the equator a countercurrent toward the east is imbedded between the westward equatorial currents; and in both oceans the western parts of the anticyclonic gyrals are compressed so that the transport to the north takes place by narrow and swift currents (the Gulf Stream and the Kuroshio). A theory of the relationships between winds and currents must explain these discrepancies also. It will be shown that this can be done; but we will first consider the more immediate effects of winds in producing currents and piling up water.

5.4. THE PURE WIND CURRENT

In order to deal with the "pure wind current," we return to the first two equations of motion and omit all terms except the Coriolis terms and the frictional terms. When dealing with the latter, we assume that only the effect of vertical turbulence enters. The frictional stress exerted on a horizontal surface then has the components

$$\tau_x = \mu_e \frac{d\,v_x}{d\,z} \quad \text{and} \quad \tau_y = \mu_e \frac{d\,v_y}{d\,z}, \tag{24}$$

where μ_e is the eddy viscosity. The frictional force per unit mass has the components

$$aR_x = a \frac{d}{d\,z}\left(\mu_e \frac{d\,v_x}{d\,z}\right) \quad \text{and} \quad aR_y = a \frac{d}{d\,z}\left(\mu_e \frac{d\,v_y}{d\,z}\right). \tag{25}$$

The equations of horizontal motion then take the form

$$\lambda\rho\,v_y + \frac{d}{d\,z}\left(\mu_e \frac{d\,v_x}{d\,z}\right) = 0, \quad \lambda\rho\,v_x - \frac{d}{d\,z}\left(\mu_e \frac{d\,v_y}{d\,z}\right) = 0. \tag{26}$$

The boundary conditions are

$$\tau_{a,x} = -\mu_{e,0}\left(\frac{d\,v_x}{d\,z}\right)_0, \quad \tau_{a,y} = -\mu_{e,0}\left(\frac{d\,v_y}{d\,z}\right)_0, \tag{27}$$

where τ_a is the stress that the wind exerts on the sea surface, and

$$v \to 0 \quad \text{when} \quad z \to \infty. \tag{28}$$

The first condition states that the stress that the wind exerts on the water must balance the stress that the water exerts on the air.

Using these boundary conditions, we obtain, by integration,

$$M_x = \frac{1}{\lambda}\, \tau_{a,y}, \qquad M_y = -\frac{1}{\lambda}\, \tau_{a,x}. \tag{29}$$

This means that the total transport by the wind current is directed 90° to the right of the stress of the wind (in the Southern Hemisphere, to the left). This result is independent of the manner in which the eddy viscosity varies with depth.

In order to learn how the velocity of the wind current varies with depth, it is necessary to introduce certain assumptions as to the character of the eddy viscosity. The simplest assumption, $\mu_e = $ Constant, was introduced by V. W. Ekman in 1902 when he first discussed the problem. Integration gives

$$v_x = v_0\, e^{-(\pi/D)z} \cos\left(45° - \frac{\pi}{D}z\right),$$

$$\tag{30}$$

$$v_y = v_0\, e^{-(\pi/D)z} \sin\left(45° - \frac{\pi}{D}z\right),$$

$$v_0 = \frac{\tau_a}{\sqrt{\mu_e \rho 2\omega \sin\phi}}, \tag{31}$$

where

$$D = \pi\sqrt{\frac{\mu_e}{\rho\omega \sin\phi}}. \tag{32}$$

The character of the current is very simple: At the surface the current is deflected 45° to the right of the direction of the stress (the wind), and the angle of deflection increases linearly with depth. The velocity decreases logarithmically with depth (Fig. 9). Other assumptions have been made regarding the eddy viscosity, but in all cases similar major features have been found.

The transport at right angles to the wind accounts for the *upwelling* of cold subsurface water that occurs off the coasts of California, Morocco, Peru, and Southwest Africa. Where the wind blows more or less permanently parallel to the coast and with the coast to the left (right in the Southern Hemisphere) of an observer with his back to the wind, the warm surface layer is carried *away* from the coast. Near the coast the water must be replaced by water that rises toward the surface. Observations show that this water comes from a depth of only 200–300 m but has a temperature that is many degrees below the average surface temperature of the latitude in question. This process is responsible for the low temperature off the coasts that were mentioned.

5.5. Piling-Up of Water by Wind

The foregoing results apply to the open ocean, where the stress of the wind may be balanced by the total effect of the Coriolis force. When dealing with a narrow body of water, the stress has to be balanced in a different manner. Consider a long, shallow bay with the wind blowing toward the bottom of the bay. In this case the slope of the sea surface cannot be

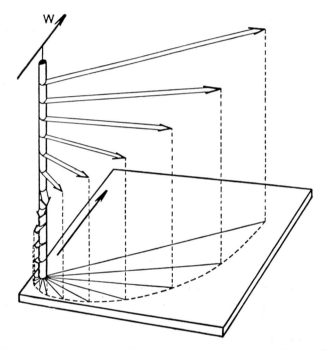

Fig. 9.—Schematic representation of a wind current in deep water, showing the decrease in velocity and change of direction at regular intervals of depth (the Ekman spiral). W indicates direction of wind.

neglected. Omitting acceleration but retaining the friction term in the previous form, integration of the equations of horizontal motion gives

$$\tau_{a,x} + \tau_{d,x} = -\lambda M_y - \int_0^d g \rho i_{p,x}\, dz ,$$

$$\tau_{a,y} + \tau_{d,y} = \lambda M_x - \int_0^d g \rho i_{p,y}\, dz ,$$

(33)

where d is the depth to the bottom and τ_d is the stress at the bottom. Placing the x-axis in the direction of the bay, considering that the transverse transport (M_y) must be zero, and assuming the water to be homogeneous, so that the inclination of the isobaric surface is independent of depth, we obtain

$$\tau_a + \tau_d = -\, g \rho i_p d \,. \tag{34}$$

In this case the sum of the stresses exerted at the upper and lower surfaces of the body of water is balanced by the component of gravity acting on the entire body of water.

Equation (34) has been used for computing the stress as a function of wind velocity. In an area like the Gulf of Bothnia the inclination of the sea surface can be derived from records of sea-level, and a rational assumption can be made as to the value of τ_d. The stress of the wind has been found to be proportional to the square of the wind velocity and to the density of the air:

$$\tau_a = 2.6 \times 10^{-3} \rho_a w^2 \,. \tag{35}$$

Though this relation is in agreement with results based on the theory of turbulent flow over a rough surface, it remains somewhat uncertain.

Piling-up of water also takes place in the open ocean. In the tropics, where the trade winds blow steadily from the east, the light surface water is accumulated in the western part of the oceans. At a depth of a few hundred meters the temperature and salinity do not vary with longitude, indicating that there the isobaric surfaces do not slope in an east-west direction. The sea surface, on the other hand, must rise toward the west because of the piling-up of the warm and light surface water. The oceanographic observations indicate a slope of 3.8×10^{-8} in the Atlantic and of 4.5×10^{-8} in the Pacific.

5.6. GENERAL RELATION BETWEEN WINDS AND CURRENTS

Having dealt with these special cases of the effects of the wind stress toward transporting water or maintaining slopes of isobaric surfaces, we can return to the general problem of the relation between the prevailing winds and the prevailing currents. For this purpose we again make use of the equations of motion, taking the effects of both vertical and horizontal eddy viscosities into account. We write the components of the frictional term in the form

$$aR_x = a \frac{\partial}{\partial z} \left(\mu_e \frac{\partial v_x}{\partial z} \right) + a h_x \,,$$

$$aR_y = a \frac{\partial}{\partial z} \left(\mu_e \frac{\partial v_y}{\partial z} \right) + a h_y \,, \tag{36}$$

and introduce

$$H_x = \int_0^d h_x d z \,, \qquad H_y = \int_0^d h_y d z \,. \tag{37}$$

Omitting the field accelerations, which, according to experience, are small, and integrating the equations, we obtain

$$\frac{\partial M_x}{\partial t} = -\frac{\partial P}{\partial x} + \lambda M_y + \tau_x + H_x,$$

$$\frac{\partial M_y}{\partial t} = -\frac{\partial P}{\partial y} - \lambda M_x + \tau_y + H_y, \tag{38}$$

where τ_x and τ_y now represent the components of the wind stress. We recognize that previously we have used the first two terms on the right-hand side of equations (38) for computing the mass transport from the distribution of pressure, the second and third terms for computing the mass transport by the pure-wind current, and the first and third terms for computing the slopes of isobaric surface under specialized conditions.

We now eliminate P by cross-differentiation, observing that, for an incompressible fluid, continuity requires

$$\frac{\partial M_x}{\partial x} + \frac{\partial M_y}{\partial y} = 0 \tag{39}$$

and that, with the x-axis east-west, $\lambda = 2\omega \sin \phi$ is independent of x. Using the designation $\beta = d\lambda/dy$, we obtain

$$\frac{\partial}{\partial t}\left(\frac{\partial M_x}{\partial y} - \frac{\partial M_y}{\partial x}\right) = \beta M_y + \left(\frac{\partial \tau_x}{\partial y} - \frac{\partial \tau_y}{\partial x}\right) + \left(\frac{\partial H_x}{\partial y} - \frac{\partial H_y}{\partial x}\right). \tag{40}$$

This is a vorticity equation which states that the local change of vorticity equals the sum of three terms which we may call "vorticity tendencies" and which all have their specific physical significance. We must, however, assume that, on the average, a steady state exists. The condition which in that case has to be fulfilled can be written thus:

$$\left(\frac{\partial \tau_x}{\partial y} - \frac{\partial \tau_y}{\partial x}\right) = -\left(\frac{\partial H_x}{\partial y} - \frac{\partial H_y}{\partial x}\right) - \beta M_y, \tag{41}$$

meaning that in every locality the wind-stress vorticity must be balanced by vorticity related to lateral friction and by the term βM_y, which Ekman calls the "planetary vorticity."

Using this equation, Stommel (1951) has given a qualitative explanation of the westward intensification of the ocean currents. Assume a symmetrical anticyclonic wind circulation over a closed ocean area in the Northern Hemisphere, meaning that the wind-stress vorticity is negative over the entire area. We may offhand expect that this stress will produce an anticyclonic circulation in the sea. The effect of horizontal friction at the boundaries must be to counteract the effect of the wind stress, and the first term on the right-hand side of equation (41) must be positive. The second term is negative for a water mass that moves to the north, and positive for a mass that moves to the south. This is a consequence of the conservation of angular momentum or, what is equivalent, of the variation of the Coriolis parameter with latitude.

A symmetrical oceanic circulation would imply that the vorticity of the frictional term would be the same at the western and eastern boundaries and that the planetary vorticity would have the same numerical value but the opposite sign. The vorticity of the wind stress is the same at both boundaries, because the wind system is assumed to be symmetrical.

Calling the numerical values of the three terms in equation (41) a, b, and c, respectively, it follows that, with symmetrical currents, we must have

$$\text{Off western boundary:} \quad -a + b - c = 0 \text{ ,}$$

$$\text{Off eastern boundary:} \quad -a + b + c = 0 \text{ .}$$

These conditions require $c = 0$; that is, no north-south transport off the boundaries, contrary to the assumption.

An anticyclonic circulation is possible only if the transport to the north off the western boundary is greatly increased, whereby the lateral shearing stresses are increased correspondingly. Over the remaining part of the ocean the transports may be small and the lateral stresses correspondingly small. Stommel illustrates this situation by tabulating some arbitrary values of the vorticity terms in an asymmetric circulation, as shown in the accompanying table.

Vorticity Terms	Strong North Current off Western Boundary	South-Flowing Currents over Rest of Ocean
Wind stress (a).........	− 1.0	−1.0
Frictional (b)...........	+10.0	+0.1
Planetary (c)..........	− 9.0	+0.9
Total.............	0.0	0.0

Stommel concludes that the interesting consequences of this reasoning are "(1) the fact that although energy is added to the oceans by the work of the wind over the entire surface, it is dissipated chiefly in the strong western current; (2) that a good representation of the circulation outside of the western currents can be obtained from a knowledge of the wind stress alone, independent of friction."

Before the general theory had been developed, Sverdrup (1947) had showed, in agreement with Stommel's conclusion, that the equatorial countercurrent could be computed from a knowledge of the stress of the wind only and that it developed in the region of minimum stress.

In order to tackle the general problem, it is necessary to find an expression for the lateral frictional force. This is done by introducing a stress, τ', acting on a vertical surface. This stress has the components

$$\tau'_x = A \frac{\partial v_x}{\partial x}, \qquad \tau'_y = A \frac{\partial v_y}{\partial y}, \tag{42}$$

where A is the lateral eddy viscosity. Assuming A to be a constant, we find

$$H_x = A \frac{\partial^2 M_x}{\partial x^2}, \qquad H_y = A \frac{\partial^2 M_y}{\partial y^2}. \tag{43}$$

The final equations can be written in a more elegant form by introducing a mass-transport stream function ψ, such that $M_x = -\partial \psi / \partial y$ and $M_y = \partial \psi / \partial x$. In this case the boundary conditions take the form:

$$\text{At the boundary: } \psi = 0, \qquad \frac{\partial \psi}{\partial \nu} = 0,$$

where ν is normal to the boundary.

Solutions of the general equations have been obtained by Munk (1950), Munk and Groves (1950), Munk, Groves, and Carrier (1950), and Hidaka (1950a, b; 1951). In carrying out numerical calculations, the value $aA = 10^8$ cm^2 sec^{-1} has been used according to estimates by other methods. The stress of the wind has been obtained from wind data, using empirical and semitheoretical relations between wind and stress.

For the North Atlantic and the North Pacific the computed currents show a pattern which is in close agreement with those that are derived from oceanographic observations (Figs. 7 and 8), but in the case of the Gulf Stream the computed values of the transport are about half the observed ones—a discrepancy which may be due to the crude values of the wind stress.

So far, the computations have been directed toward explaining the major currents in the Northern Hemisphere. However, the general theory applies also to the Southern Hemisphere, where similar westward intensifications are found in the South Atlantic Ocean (the Brazil Current) and in the Indian Ocean (the Agulhas Current). A corresponding current is lacking in the South Pacific, but the wind system over this ocean is very complicated, and the western boundary is very irregular.

The Antarctic Circumpolar Current belongs in a separate class. Here we have to deal with a current which flows around the Antarctic Continent without being impeded by land barriers. Since the current is directed west-east, the effect of the variable Coriolis parameter disappears, and the current should be expected to represent a system within which balance exists between the wind stress and the lateral friction. Assuming this to be the case, Munk and Palmén (1951) obtained a transport which is 10–100 times greater than the transport according to oceanographic observations. They suggest that the lateral stresses are not sufficient to balance the wind stress and that "the balancing stress probably is applied at the bottom, largely where the major submarine ridges lie in the path of the currents."

5.7. MINOR FEATURES

The relation between the prevailing winds and currents, discussed earlier, deal with the large-scale, climatological features. Superimposed upon these large-scale features are many irregularities, some of which are easily understood and others which are yet unexplained.

It is not surprising that numerous eddies of varying dimensions are present. The transient wind systems with their convergences and divergences must bring about local increases or decreases in sea-level and thus set up pressure gradients that may reach to the bottom and induce motion at all depths. These eddies are responsible for the large-scale horizontal mixing which is reflected in the large values of the horizontal eddy viscosity.

It is, however, surprising to find that a major current like the Gulf Stream off the American east coast is far more concentrated than the average values indicate and also that the narrow streaks with swift current in the direction of the main flow alternate with weaker countercurrents (Fuglister and Worthington, 1951). This structure, which was first demonstrated in 1950, appears to be typical of the Gulf Stream; and marked streakiness of currents has also been found in other areas. A similar tendency toward concentration of momentum is also present in the atmosphere, but the underlying reason for this pattern is not known.

6. INTERACTION BETWEEN ATMOSPHERE AND OCEAN

The interaction between atmosphere and ocean has been dealt with in several of the preceding sections; a brief summary will now be presented.

The atmosphere can be considered as a thermodynamic machine in which heat is converted to kinetic energy, which, in turn, is dissipated by friction. On the average, the machine runs with constant speed, meaning that, on the average, the rate of dissipation balances the rate at which kinetic energy is produced. The major ocean currents are maintained by the work of wind stresses on the sea surface, and the energy that is transferred to the ocean in this manner is dissipated in the ocean. Any change in the intensity of the atmospheric circulation must lead to a change in the water transport by the current, which, in turn, must influence the circulation of the atmosphere. The reason for this is that the atmosphere derives a substantial part of its heat, probably about 40 per cent, from condensation of water vapor, and the water vapor is supplied mainly by evaporation from the sea surface.

The maximum evaporation takes place where cold air flows over warm water; in the Northern Hemisphere this occurs in the winter off the eastern coasts of the continents. Off these coasts swift currents (the Gulf Stream and the Kuroshio) transport large-scale quantities of warm water to the north, and when cold continental air flows out over this warm water, evaporation becomes intense (Jacobs, 1942, 1943). Energy which was stored in lower latitudes is given off to the atmosphere. A change in the transport by the current must lead to a change in the rate of evaporation, that is, in the energy supplied to the atmosphere, and thus influences the circulation of the atmosphere.

At present the problem of interaction has been only touched. Knowledge of the regional and seasonal distribution of evaporation is of recent date, and the understanding of the large-scale relation between wind stress and currents is even more recent. Here we can only draw attention to the problems and emphasize that, for an understanding of the general distribution of temperature over the earth and for an analysis of possible fluctuations, the entire system—atmosphere *and* ocean—has to be considered.

REFERENCES

BAUR, F., and PHILLIPS, H.	1933	*Gerlands Beitr. z. Geophys.*, **45**, 82.
CARRUTHERS, J. N., and LAWFORD, A. L.	1952	*Nature*, **169**, 601.
FUGLISTER, F. C., and WORTHINGTON, L. V.	1951	*Tellus*, **3**, 1.
HIDAKA, K.	1950*a*	*Geophys. Notes*, Vol. **3**, No. 23.
	1950*b*	*Ibid.*, No. 38.
	1951	*Ibid.*, Vol. **4**, No. 3.
JACOBS, W. C.	1942	*J. Marine Res.*, **5**, 37.
	1943	*Ann. New York Acad. Sci.*, **44**, 19.
JERLOV, N. G.	1951	*Rept. Swedish Deep-Sea Exped., 1947–48*, **3**, No. I, 1.

KOSSINA, E.   1921   *Veröff. Berlin U. Inst. Meereskunde*, N.F. *A*, Vol. **9.**
MUNK, W. H.   1950   *J. Meteorol.*, **7**, 79.
MUNK, W. H., and
  GROVES, G. W.   1950   *Tellus*, **2**, 158.
MUNK, W. H.;
  GROVES, G. W.; and
  CARRIER, G. F.   1950   *J. Marine Res.*, **9**, 218.
MUNK, W. H., and
  PALMÉN, E.   1951   *Tellus*, **3**, 53.
NEIBURGER, M.   1948   *Trans. Amer. Geophys. Union*, **29**, 647.
PETTERSSON, H., and
  ROTSCHI, H.   1952   *Geochim. et Cosmochim. Acta.*, **2**, 81.
STOMMEL, H.   1949   *J. Marine Res.*, **8**, 199.
                            1951   *Bull. Amer. Meteorol. Soc.*, **32**, 21.
SVERDRUP, H. U.   1947   *Proc. Nat. Acad. Sci.*, **33**, 318.
WHIPPLE, F. L.   1950a   *Proc. Nat. Acad. Sci.*, **36**, 687.
                            1950b   *Ibid.*, **37**, 19.

  For references to earlier literature see
SVERDRUP, H. U.;
  JOHNSON, W.; and
  FLEMING, R. H.   1942   *The Oceans* (New York: Prentice-Hall Book Co.).

CHAPTER 6

The Geochemistry of the Crust[1]

By BRIAN MASON
Indiana University[2]

1. THE GEOCHEMICAL STRUCTURE OF THE EARTH

In the simplest terms, geochemistry may be defined as the science concerned with the chemistry of the earth as a whole and of its component parts. It is both more restricted and more extensive in scope than geology. Geochemistry deals with the distribution and migration of the chemical elements within the earth in space and time. The science of the occurrence and distribution of the elements in the universe as a whole has been called "cosmochemistry." The main tasks of geochemistry can be summarized thus:

1. The determination of the relative and absolute abundances of the elements and of the atomic species (isotopes) in the earth and the interpretation of these abundances in terms of cosmic abundances.

2. The study of the distribution and migration of the individual elements in the various parts of the earth (the atmosphere, hydrosphere, crust, etc.) and in minerals and rocks, with the object of discovering principles governing this distribution.

Geochemically the earth may be considered a *closed* system as this term is used in physical chemistry. This concept can be criticized as an oversimplification; some material—meteorites and meteoritic dust—is continually being received from outer space, and some hydrogen and helium are being lost by escape from the upper atmosphere. However, these gains and losses are insignificant compared with the system as a whole. By the nature of things, the geochemist is concerned mainly with the

1. Much of the material in this chapter is adapted from the author's *Principles of Geochemistry* (New York: John Wiley & Sons, Inc., 1952).

2. Now curator, American Museum of Natural History, New York 24, N.Y.

crust of the earth, since it is the only part accessible to direct examination. Nevertheless, the internal structure of the earth and its mode of origin are matters of prime importance to him, since the crust can be considered only as the end-product of a chemical differentiation, first, of the earth as a whole and, second, of the entire universe.

Seismological data indicate the presence of two major discontinuities within the earth—the Mohorovičić discontinuity, at a depth of about 33 km beneath the continents, and the Wiechert-Gutenberg discontinuity, at a depth of 2900 km. The earth is thus divided into three parts—the *crust*, the *mantle*, and the *core*. The crust is heterogeneous and varies in thickness from place to place. Marked differences exist, especially between the continents and the ocean basins. For the continental areas Jeffreys (1939a) recognizes two principal layers, an upper shell of granitic or granodioritic composition of mean thickness 15 km and density about 2.65, and a lower shell whose composition is approximately that of gabbro and basalt, of mean thickness 18 km and density about 2.9. These two shells correspond to the sial and the sima (sial = material composed largely of *si*licon and *al*uminum; sima = material composed largely of *si*licon and *ma*gnesium). According to the principles of isostasy, the sial layer is in hydrostatic equilibrium with respect to the sima. In the ocean basins the sial is thin or absent. Over the whole earth there is a discontinuous skin of sedimentary and metamorphic rocks, which may be 10 km or more thick in geosynclinal belts but which is nevertheless insignificant in amount compared to the total mass of the crust.

The Mohorovičić discontinuity separates the heterogeneous crust from the much more homogeneous mantle. The identification of the material making up the mantle is largely based on information obtained from laboratory experiments on the elasticity of rocks. The experiments indicate that only three rock types—dunite (olivine), peridotite (olivine and pyroxene), and eclogite (garnet and pyroxene)—have elastic properties of the right order to give the observed seismic-wave velocities. Goldschmidt (1922) postulated an oxide-sulphide zone in the lower part of the mantle, partly by analogy with the occurrence of ferrous sulphide in meteorites; this idea has not been generally accepted, but the cosmic abundance of sulphur suggests that an iron sulphide phase is probably present in the earth, most likely disseminated rather than concentrated into a single layer. Urey (1951) adduces evidence to support the hypothesis (originally proposed by Williamson and Adams, 1923) that the lower part of the mantle contains a considerable amount of disseminated nickel-iron. The Wiechert-Gutenberg discontinuity between the mantle and the core is a sharp one, and its position is known with considerable accuracy (± 5 km, according to Jeffreys, 1939b).

The belief that the earth has an iron core predates the geophysical evidence for its existence. The idea apparently originated with J. D. Dana in 1873; before that time the earth was generally considered to be a great ball of granite, chemically homogeneous throughout. The idea of an iron core has become firmly intrenched in geophysical and geological thought. However, Ramsey (1948) has put forward the idea that the Wiechert-Gutenberg discontinuity, instead of being due to a change from silicate material to an iron alloy, is the result of a pressure transition. He points out that a breakdown of atomic structure is to be expected at very high pressures, whereby the atomic volume can be greatly reduced, the process involving the loss of the molecular and crystal bindings. Hence his suggestion that the mantle and core are, respectively, molecular and "metallic" phases of magnesium-iron silicate. Elsasser (1950) has discussed this suggestion and points out that the probable densities to be expected at pressures such as those within the mantle and core can be predicted from quantum theory. These results indicate that even a breakdown of the atomic structure of magnesium-iron silicate could not produce the density required for the core. He therefore concludes that Ramsey's suggestion is untenable and shows that the density changes predicted from quantum theory corroborate the usual assumption that the mantle consists mainly of silicates, whereas the core is iron or an iron-nickel alloy.

The earth may therefore be considered as made up of an iron core, a fairly homogeneous silicate mantle, and a heterogeneous silicate crust. This picture of its internal structure and composition is consistent with its mass, its moment of inertia, and the presence of discontinuities indicated by seismic waves. The succession of material with decreasing silica content on passing through the crust into the mantle agrees with petrological experience. The probable composition of an earth of this kind is also consistent with the relative abundances of the elements. To complete the picture, we must add to the crust, mantle, and core three further zones—the atmosphere, the hydrosphere, and the biosphere. The *atmosphere* is the gaseous envelope which surrounds the earth. The *hydrosphere* is the discontinuous shell of water, fresh and salt, making up the oceans, lakes, and rivers. The *biosphere* is the totality of organic matter distributed through the hydrosphere, the atmosphere, and on the surface of the crust. Table 1 gives the important features of these zones, and Table 2 gives data on the thickness, volume, mean density, and mass of each.

The atmosphere, the hydrosphere, and the biosphere, although geochemically important, contribute less than 0.03 per cent of the total mass of the earth. Hence in arriving at an average composition for the earth, these zones may be ignored. Even the crust makes up less than 1 per cent of the whole. Thus the bulk composition of the earth is essentially determined by that of the mantle and the core. On the assumption of a peridotite mantle and a nickel-iron core, the bulk composition of the earth is as

TABLE 1

THE GEOCHEMICAL STRUCTURE OF THE EARTH

Name	Important Chemical Characters	Important Physical Characters
Atmosphere......	N_2, O_2, H_2O, CO_2, inert gases	Gas
Biosphere........	H_2O, organic substances, and skeletal matter	Solid and liquid, often colloidal
Hydrosphere.....	Salt and fresh water, snow, and ice	Liquid (in part solid)
Crust...........	Normal silicate rocks	Solid
Mantle.........	Silicate material, probably largely $(Mg,Fe)_2SiO_4$; some iron sulphide?	Solid
Core or sidero-sphere.........	Iron-nickel alloy	Upper part liquid, lower part possibly solid

TABLE 2

VOLUME AND MASSES OF EARTH SHELLS*

	Thickness (km)	Volume ($\times 10^{27}$ cm³)	Mean Density (gm/cm³)	Mass ($\times 10^{27}$ gm)	Mass (Per Cent)
Atmosphere.......				0.000005	0.00009
Hydrosphere.......	3.80 (mean)	0.00137	1.03	0.00141	0.024
Crust............	30	0.015	2.8	0.043	0.7
Mantle..........	2870	0.892	4.5	4.056	67.8
Core............	3471	0.175	10.7	1.876	31.5
Whole earth.......	6371	1.083	5.52	5.976	100.00

* Data for the biosphere are not included, on account of its relatively small mass and the lack of precise figures.

follows (Mason, 1952): Fe 35, O 28, Mg 17, Si 13, Ni 2.7, S 2.7, Ca 0.61, Al 0.44, Co 0.20, Na 0.14, Mn 0.09, K 0.07, Ti 0.04, P 0.03, Cr 0.01. These figures indicate that about 90 per cent of the earth is made up of four elements: Fe, O, Mg, and Si. The only other elements that may be present in amounts greater than 1 per cent are Ni, Ca, Al, and S. Seven elements —Na, K, Cr, Co, P, Mn, and Ti—may occur in amounts from 0.1 to 1 per cent. Thus the earth is made up almost entirely of fifteen elements, and the percentage of all the others is negligible, probably 0.1 per cent or less of the whole.

2. THE GEOCHEMICAL CLASSIFICATION OF THE ELEMENTS

A geochemical classification of the elements was suggested by Goldschmidt (1926). He coined the terms *siderophile, chalcophile, lithophile,* and *atmophile* to describe elements with affinity for metallic iron, for sulphide, for silicate, and for the atmosphere, respectively. The geochemical differentiation of the earth resulted in the concentration of siderophile elements in the nickel-iron core, the lithophile elements in the silicate mantle and crust, the gaseous elements and those that form stable gaseous compounds in the atmosphere. Chalcophile elements are those which combine with sulphur rather than form silicates or remain in the native state. The classification of an element as lithophile, chalcophile, or sidero-

TABLE 3

GEOCHEMICAL CLASSIFICATION OF THE ELEMENTS

Siderophile	Chalcophile	Lithophile	Atmophile
Fe Co Ni	Cu Ag	Li Na K Rb Cs	H N (C) (O)
Ru Rh Pd	Zn Cd Hg	Be Mg Ca Sr Ba	Inert gases
Os Ir Pt	Ga In Tl	B Al Sc Y	
Au Re Mo	(Ge) (Sn) Pb	Rare earths	
Ge Sn	As Sb Bi	(C) Si Ti Zr Hf Th	
C P	S Se Te	(P) V Nb Ta	
(Pb) (As) (W)	(Fe) (Mo) (Cr)	O Cr W U	
		(H) F Cl Br I	
		(Tl) (Ga) (Ge)	
		(Fe) Mn	

phile has been based largely on its distribution between the silicate, sulphide, and nickel-iron phases of meteorites. Table 3 presents this geochemical classification of the elements.

Some elements show affinity for more than one group, because the distribution of any element is dependent to some extent on the physical and chemical environment of the system as a whole. For instance, chromium is a strongly lithophile element in the earth's crust; but if oxygen is deficient, as in iron meteorites, chromium is decidedly chalcophile, entering almost exclusively into the sulpho-spinel daubréelite, $FeCr_2S_4$. Similarly, under strongly reducing conditions, carbon and phosphorus are siderophile. The mineralogy of an element, although a general guide, may not be altogether indicative of its geochemical character. For example, although thallium minerals are all sulphides, the greater part of the thallium in the earth's crust is contained in potassium minerals, in which the Tl^+

ion proxies for the K^+ ion. In general, the classification of an element as lithophile, chalcophile, or siderophile refers to its behavior in liquid-liquid equilibria between melts. When an element shows affinity for more than one group, it is given in parentheses under the group or groups of secondary affinity.

The geochemical character of an element is largely governed by the electronic configuration of its atoms and hence is closely related to its position in the periodic system (Table 4). Lithophile elements are those which readily form ions with an outermost 8-electron shell; the chalcophile elements are those of the B subgroups, whose ions have 18 electrons in the outer shells; the siderophile elements are those of Group VIII and some

TABLE 4

THE GEOCHEMICAL CLASSIFICATION OF THE ELEMENTS IN
RELATION TO THE PERIODIC SYSTEM

H					Atmophile: N												He
					Lithophile: Na												
Li	Be	B	C		Chalcophile: Zn									N	O	F	Ne
					Siderophile: Fe												
Na	Mg	Al	Si											P	S	Cl	A
K	Ca	Sc	Ti	V	Cr	Mn	Fe	Co	Ni	Cu	Zn	Ga	Ge	As	Se	Br	Kr
Rb	Sr	Y	Zr	Nb	Mo		Ru	Rh	Pd	Ag	Cd	In	Sn	Sb	Te	I	Xe
Cs	Ba	La-Lu	Hf	Ta	W	Re	Os	Ir	Pt	Au	Hg	Tl	Pb	Bi			
			Th		U												

neighboring elements, whose outermost shells of electrons are, for the most part, incompletely filled. These factors are reflected by other properties also. Goldschmidt pointed out the marked correlation between geochemical character and atomic volume. If the atomic volume of the elements is plotted against atomic number, the resulting curve shows maxima and minima. All siderophile elements are near the minima; the chalcophile elements are on sections where the atomic volume increases with the atomic number; they are followed by the atmophile elements, whereas the lithophile elements are near the maxima and on the declining sections of the curve.

Brown and Patterson (1948) have shown that if the heat of formation of an oxide is greater than that of FeO, the element is lithophile; the difference between the two heats of formation is a measure of the intensity of the lithophile character. Similarly, those elements whose oxides have heats of formation lower than FeO are chalcophile or siderophile; those for which the heat of formation of the sulphide is equal to or greater than that of FeS are generally chalcophile. A semiquantitative measure of lithophile, siderophile, or chalcophile character is also provided by the electrode potential. Elements with high positive potentials (1–3 volts), such as the alkali and alkaline-earth metals, are lithophile; the noble metals, with high negative potentials, are siderophile; elements falling in the intermediate range are generally chalcophile.

3. THE COMPOSITION OF THE CRUST

The average composition of the crust is, in effect, that of igneous rocks, since the total amount of sedimentary and metamorphic rocks is insignificant in comparison to the bulk of the igneous rocks and, in any case, their average composition is not greatly different. Clarke and Washington (1924) estimate that the upper 10 miles of the crust consist of 95 per cent igneous rocks, 4 per cent shale, 0.75 per cent sandstone, and 0.25 per cent limestone. Where sedimentary rocks are present, they form a relatively thin veneer on an igneous basement, except where locally thickened in orogenic belts.

Clarke and Washington made an exhaustive study of the data available for computing an average composition of igneous rocks. The basis for their computations was Washington's compilation of 5159 "superior" analyses. The analyses were grouped geographically, and the averages of these groups agreed fairly well with one another. In other words, the composition of the earth's crust is approximately the same in different regions, provided that these are large enough to eliminate local variations. However, the SiO_2 percentage is markedly lower for rocks from oceanic areas, such as the islands of the Atlantic and Pacific Oceans, further evidence for the belief that the sial shell is thin or absent below the ocean basins. Clarke and Washington's estimate of the average composition of igneous rocks, which is sometimes used as the average composition of the crust, is, in effect, the *composition of continental areas* rather than the crust, as this term has been used earlier in this chapter.

The over-all average of the 5159 analyses, expressed in elements, is given in the accompanying tabulation. This composition does not corre-

O	Si	Al	Fe	Ca	Na	K	Mg	Ti	P	H	Mn	All Others
46.59	27.72	8.13	5.01	3.63	2.85	2.60	2.09	0.63	0.13	0.13	0.10	<0.10

spond to any common igneous rock but is intermediate between that of granite and basalt, which make up the bulk of all igneous rocks.

Numerous objections have been raised to the method of arriving at an average composition of igneous rocks by averaging analyses, but a more satisfactory procedure has yet to be proposed. The principal objections are as follows: (1) the uneven geographical distribution of analyses; (2) their nonstatistical distribution over the different rock types; and (3) the lack of allowance for the actual amounts of the rocks represented by the analyses.

The basis for the first objection is, of course, that Europe and North America have been more adequately investigated and are represented by far more analyses per unit area than are other parts of the earth. However, Clarke and Washington showed that the averages for the individual continental areas show a marked agreement, in spite of the widely different coverage, a fact which suggests that the results can probably be accepted as a reasonable approximation.

The second objection is valid, in that an average of published rock analyses inevitably gives undue weight to the rare and unusual rock types and insufficient weight to the abundant and uniform types, such as granites and basalts. This objection is probably not so serious as has been asserted, however, since in a large number of analyses the unusual types will be drawn from the whole range of rock composition and will tend to give a true average. Also, as Clarke and Washington point out, their 1924 average was made from analyses of fresh unaltered rocks only, thus eliminating many analyses of unusual rocks.

The third objection, that all analyses are given equal weight regardless of the areas occupied by the rocks and therefore of their relative amounts, can also be countered if it can be shown that, on the average, the variations due to this cause offset one another. It is true that one rock, say a basalt, is exceedingly abundant, whereas another may be merely a narrow dike. Such differences may not affect the mean appreciably, however, since the relatively insignificant rocks range in composition just as the more abundant rocks do. Furthermore, the surface exposure of a rock is no certain measure of its real volume and mass, for a small exposure may be merely the peak or crest of a large subterranean body and a large exposure may represent only a thin layer.

The figures of Clarke and Washington show that eight elements—O, Si, Al, Fe, Ca, Na, K, Mg—make up nearly 99 per cent of the crust. Of these, oxygen is absolutely predominant. As Goldschmidt (1928) first pointed out, this predominance is even more marked when the figures are recalculated to atom per cent and volume per cent (Table 5). The earth's crust consists almost entirely of oxygen compounds, especially silicates of aluminum, calcium, magnesium, sodium, potassium, and iron. In terms of numbers of atoms, oxygen exceeds 60 per cent. If the volume of the different atoms, or rather ions, is calculated, oxygen makes up more than 90 per cent of the total volume occupied by the elements. Thus the crust of the earth is essentially a packing of oxygen anions, bonded by silicon and ions of the common metals; as Goldschmidt remarked, the lithosphere may well be called the *oxysphere*.

TABLE 5

THE COMMONER CHEMICAL ELEMENTS IN
THE EARTH'S CRUST

Element	Weight (Per Cent)	Atom (Per Cent)	Radius (A)	Volume (Per Cent)
O.........	46.60	62.55	1.32	91.97
Si.........	27.72	21.22	0.39	0.80
Al.........	8.13	6.47	0.57	0.77
Fe.........	5.00	1.92	0.82	0.68
Mg.........	2.09	1.84	0.78	0.56
Ca.........	3.63	1.94	1.06	1.48
Na.........	2.83	2.64	0.98	1.60
K.........	2.59	1.42	1.33	2.14

4. THE INITIAL GEOCHEMICAL DIFFERENTIATION
OF THE CRUST

Comparison of the chemical composition of the crust with the bulk composition of the earth and with the probable cosmic abundance of the elements reveals information of great geochemical significance. Table 6 presents the numerical data, expressed as atomic abundances (atoms per 10,000 atoms Si). The cosmic abundances are taken from Kuiper (1952), except for He, where recent measures indicate a somewhat lower abundance; those for the bulk composition of the earth and for the crust are calculated from the weight percentages given in the previous sections; the composition of the mantle is taken as that of an average peridotite; and the figures for meteoritic silicate are calculated from the data of Brown and Patterson (1948). The comparison, in effect, uses silicon as an arbitrary standard; although this is fairly satisfactory, it should be remembered that silicon is twice as abundant in the crust as in the earth as a whole.

Comparing, first, the elemental abundances in the cosmos and in the earth, we see that the major difference is the deficiency in the earth of the volatile elements and these which form volatile compounds: H, He, C, N,

Ne (the remaining rare gases also show this deficiency). Oxygen is diminished in relative amount, but not to the same extent, evidently because it forms stable nonvolatile compounds with many elements. For the remaining elements—Fe, Si, Mg, S, Ni, Al, Ca, Na—the relative abundances are quite similar both in the cosmos and in the earth. The differences in cosmic and terrestrial abundances of the nonvolatile elements may reflect differences in the methods of arriving at the estimated abundances in the cosmos and the earth, rather than being significant of real differences. The chemical differentiation between the cosmos and the earth is the impoverishment of the earth in the gaseous elements and those that form stable

TABLE 6

ELEMENTAL ABUNDANCES (ATOMS/10^4 ATOMS SI) IN COSMOS, IN METEORITIC SILICATE, AND IN EARTH, MANTLE, AND CRUST

Element	Atomic No.	Cosmos	Earth	Meteoritic Silicate	Mantle	Crust
H......	1	3.5×10^8	....	....	....	1,400
He.....	2	1.4×10^7	....	....	....	....
C......	6	38,000	....	....	....	27
N.	7	83,000	....	....	....	3
O.....	8	140,000	38,000	35,000	38,600	29,500
Ne.....	10	160,000	....	....	....	....
Na.....	11	490	130	460	130	1,250
Mg....	12	11,000	15,000	8,900	15,500	870
Al.....	13	870	350	880	360	3,050
Si......	14	10,000	10,000	10,000	10,000	10,000
S......	16	4,300	1,800	....	....	....
K......	19	66	40	70	39	670
Ca.....	20	690	330	670	340	920
Ti.....	22	26	18	27	21	133
Fe.....	26	5,400	13,500	3,750	1,730	910
Ni.....	28	380	1,000	86	....	1

gaseous compounds. Such impoverishment is explicable on either of the commonly accepted modes of origin of the earth. Condensation from incandescent solar material would result in the loss of volatile elements in the high-temperature stage of the earth's history; the formation of the earth by the accretion of solid particles at a low or moderate temperature would mean an initial lack of the volatile elements. Aston (1924) pointed out that not only are He and Ne deficient in the earth, but the heavier rare gases also. Since Kr and Xe should be retained even by an incandescent earth, this fact favors an origin of the earth by accretion.

Comparing, now, the composition of the crust with that of the mantle, we find that the crust is much richer in K, Na, Al; contains relatively more Ca; and is poorer in Fe and especially Mg. Expressed in mineralogical terms, the crust shows a concentration of feldspar, the mantle a concentration of ferromagnesian minerals. This is the relation that would be expected if the crust and the mantle are the result of fractional crystallization of a silicate melt whose original composition was that of mantle plus crust. Laboratory investigations of synthetic melts indicate that from such a system olivine, $(Mg,Fe)_2SiO_4$, would be the first phase to crystallize. The original composition of the system would be such that by far the greater part of it would crystallize as olivine before any other phase appeared. The next phase to crystallize would be pyroxene, probably first $(Mg,Fe)SiO_3$ and later $Ca(Mg,Fe)Si_2O_6$. The implication is that the mantle originated as an accumulation of olivine crystals, possibly accompanied in the later stages by pyroxene. Removal of these crystals would cause the composition of the liquid to change toward that of a basalt or gabbro. Further fractional crystallization of a basaltic liquid could ultimately produce as an end-product a feldspar-quartz rock, a granite or granodiorite. The fractional crystallization of an originally homogeneous silicate melt could thus bring about the differentiation of mantle and crust.

In this connection it is interesting to compare the composition of the crust and the mantle with that of meteoritic silicate. Study of the figures in Table 6 shows that the average composition of meteoritic silicate is intermediate between that of the mantle and the crust, being closer to that of the mantle. Some anomalies can be seen, notably the high iron content in meteoritic silicate. The iron content of silicate material will, however, be dependent on the chemical environment at the time of formation, whether oxidizing or reducing; in effect, the more oxygen or the less hydrogen, the greater the amount of iron combined as silicate rather than as the free metal. The figures in Table 6 indicate that the earth's mantle and crust may well have resulted from the differentiation of material similar in composition to that of meteoritic silicate.

The manner in which this differentiation of the earth has come about is of vital concern not only to the geochemist but also to the astronomer. The uniformity of conditions at and near the earth's surface throughout geological time, as indicated by the geological record, suggests that the major separation into crust, mantle, and core was probably completed at an early period in the earth's history. However, Urey (1951) believes that the formation of the earth's core has been a continuing process throughout geological time.

The geochemical differentiation of the earth has been essentially a phase segregation under the gravitational force of the earth itself, the major phases being nickel-iron, silicate material, iron sulphide (possibly), and a gas phase, the atmosphere. It is highly significant that the distribution of elements under these conditions is controlled not by their densities or atomic weights but by their affinities for the major phases present. This, in turn, is controlled by the electronic configuration of their atoms. Thus uranium and thorium, although of high density, are concentrated in the crust, not in the deep interior, whereas siderophile elements, including most of the world's gold and platinum metals, are presumably concentrated in the iron core.

The internal structure of the earth, with its marked density stratification, suggests that it was at one time *liquid*, whereby this gravitational differentiation would have taken place within a comparatively short time. This might be thought to favor an origin for the earth as an incandescent mass torn from the sun. However, a liquid earth might well be formed by the accretion of solid material; the kinetic energy of in-falling particles and the compression of the material would generate great heat, perhaps sufficient to liquefy the growing earth. In addition, radioactive disintegrations, particularly those of short-lived nuclei such as K^{40} would also be an important source of heat. By postulating the initial conditions, it is possible to deduce therefrom the probable chemical and physical evolution of the earth. This has been done for an initial state as a mass of incandescent vapor of solar composition (Nutting, 1943; Eucken, 1944) and for an earth formed by accretion in a cosmic-dust cloud (Latimer, 1950; Urey, 1951). On either postulate the evolution of the earth results in the same final state—an iron core and a silicate mantle and crust.

Whether the initial crust of the earth was granitic in composition is still a matter on which no general agreement exists among geologists and geophysicists. Some authorities prefer the view that the initial crust was basaltic and that the predominantly granitic continents are the result of later processes of erosion and sedimentation, accompanied by metasomatism produced by gases and solutions rising to the surface from the underlying layers. Some theories for the origin and evolution of the earth seem to imply that it never has passed through a liquid state, in which case the chemical differentiation of mantle and crust by any liquid → crystal process would be ruled out. It is not possible, at least on present information, to decide this question by geological evidence; nowhere has any area which might have formed part of the initial crust been recognized as such. Its existence is inherently improbable; the older the rocks, the more likely they are to have undergone metamorphism, whereby their original characters have been partly or wholly destroyed. The oldest parts of the earth's crust which have been accurately dated are in the Keewatin province of Canada, in northern Sweden, and in Southern Rhodesia, all of which contain pegmatites whose minerals have been dated at about 2200 million years (Ahrens, 1952). In the Keewatin province of Canada the ancient rocks are predominantly altered lavas of basaltic composition, and Wilson (1952) cites this as evidence for an originally basaltic crust. In northern Sweden, however, rocks of this type are not common, and the rocks are predominantly quartz-rich gneisses, many of which appear originally to have been silica-rich lavas or tuffs. The answer to the question of the nature of the original crust, therefore, awaits further evidence. As in so many other questions of the sort, the answer may well be that the initial crust was basaltic in some places, granitic in others. However, the crust below the deep ocean basins has probably been basaltic throughout geological time.

5. THE GEOCHEMISTRY OF MAGMATIC PROCESSES

Whatever the nature of the initial crust, it has been subjected to a variety of processes throughout geological time and has undergone great changes. Vast amounts of magma have been poured out on the surface through volcanic vents or have crystallized within the crust. The earth's surface has been subjected to weathering and erosion, with the chemical and mechanical breakdown of pre-existing rocks and the transportation of the debris in suspension or solution. Most of this material has eventually come to rest in the sea, and some has ultimately returned to the land areas in the form of sedimentary rocks. Then, again, both sedimentary and igneous rocks may be transferred through geological processes to the lower parts of the crust, where, by the action of heat, pressure, and chemically active fluids, they have been transformed into metamorphic rocks or perhaps have been partially or wholly remelted. We may consider the geochemical history of the crust in three parts—the *magmatic*, essentially controlled by the liquid → crystal reactions in a silicate melt; the *sedimentary*, controlled by reactions taking place at ordinary temperatures and pressures in the presence of water; and the *metamorphic*, controlled by reactions occurring at elevated temperatures and pressures in an essentially crystalline medium. If the temperatures become sufficiently high, the rocks begin to melt, and magma is regenerated.

In discussing the geochemistry of magmatic processes, we must first consider the nature of a silicate melt. Barth and Rosenquist (1949) have pointed out that the entropy of fusion of silicates is not high, and hence the atoms or ions in the molten silicate have a degree of order not greatly different from that in the solid. It thus appears that a good deal of the structural arrangement is preserved after fusion. Since the silicon-oxygen bonds are much stronger than other links in silicate structures, it is reasonable to assume that these bonds are present to some extent in the liquid also, i.e., the anions in the melt are predominantly polymerized silicon-oxygen tetrahedra, linked together by sharing oxygens into one-, two-, or three-dimensional networks, similar to those in crystalline silicates but more irregular. The high viscosity of silicate melts is evidently due to the presence of these complex silicon-oxygen groupings.

The degree of polymerization of the silicate anions is markedly affected by the ratio of Si (and Al) to O. The linking of the silicon-oxygen tetrahedra will be greatest at an Si:O ratio of 1:2 and will decrease as the proportion of Si decreases. This is borne out by the increase in viscosity of silicate melts as the SiO_2 content increases. The presence of other ions is also significant. In alkali silicate melts, the viscosity decreases in the sequence $K > Na > Li$; evidently sodium is more effective than potassium in disrupting the Si-O bonds and thereby breaking up the polymerized anions into smaller units, and lithium even more so. Probably bivalent cations are even more effective in this respect; iron-rich melts are of notably low viscosity, even at high SiO_2 contents. Laboratory experiments have shown, however, that small amounts of H_2O have a particularly remarkable influence in decreasing the viscosity. This is evidently due to the strong tendency for the reaction $H_2O + O^{2-} = 2(OH)^-$ to take place. The oxygen links between silicon-oxygen tetrahedra are thereby destroyed, and the polymerized anions are broken down into simpler groups. Since the "molecular weight" of OH is low, a small weight per cent of H_2O in a silicate melt is very effective in eliminating links between silicon-oxygen tetrahedra.

Through the study of crystallization in artificial silicate melts of known composition, great advances have been made in the understanding of the geochemistry of igneous rocks. Fundamentally, the laws of crystallization in a magma are the same as those in an artificial melt. The principles of heterogeneous equilibrium govern crystallization from a liquid; they express the conditions under which only one of the possible crystallization products is to be expected and under what conditions more than one may appear simultaneously. The basic relation is, of course, the *phase rule*, which states that in any system the number of phases (P) plus the number of degrees of freedom (F) are equal to the number of components plus 2, or $P + F = C + 2$. The phase rule has been extended in the consideration of geochemical processes in the following way: In any system the maximum number of phases can be reached only when the number of degrees of freedom is at a minimum. This state can be realized by fixing both temperature and pressure. However, it is extremely unlikely that such conditions will occur during magmatic crystallization, since it proceeds, as a rule, over a great P-T range, i.e., these factors remain variable and thus give two degrees of freedom. Under these circumstances the phase rule becomes $P = C$, i.e., in a system of n components at arbitrary temperature and pressure, no more than n phases (minerals) can be mutually stable. This extension of the phase rule is due to Goldschmidt (1911) and is sometimes known as the *mineralogical phase rule*.

Despite their wide range in chemical composition, igneous rocks have a comparatively simple mineralogy, in that probably 99 per cent of igneous rocks are made up essentially of seven minerals or mineral groups: quartz, feldspars, feldspathoids, olivine, pyroxene, hornblende, biotite. This limitation in the number of phases normally formed by the crystallization of a magma is clearly understandable in terms of the phase rule. Actually, considering a magma as an eight-component system of O, Si, Al, Fe, Mg, Ca, Na, and K, it is improbable that as many as eight phases would crystallize from any composition in that system, because the individual components are not completely independent, some of them being capable of replacing one another, atom for atom, in minerals.

From the study of crystallization in artificial silicate melts and the coordination of the results thereby obtained with the observations of igneous petrology, important conclusions have been established regarding magmatic crystallization. Simple eutectic crystallization, once believed to be common and important in magmas, probably never occurs. Practically all rock-forming minerals are solid-solution series, and crystallization of systems containing such compounds takes place over a range of temperature, and the phases separating have a considerable range of composition; eutectic crystallization is not possible under such conditions. The course of crystallization is dependent upon the rate of solidification and the presence or the removal of early-formed crystals, whereas in eutectic crystallization the rate of solidification has no influence, and the final condition is always the same, whether or not early-formed crystals are removed. Another significant feature in silicate systems is the frequent occurrence of incongruent melting, when one solid phase will be converted into a different phase by reaction with the liquid. Thus crystallization in a magma is characterized by reactions of two kinds: continuous reaction in a solid-solution series, whereby early-formed crystals change uninterruptedly in composition by reaction with the melt, and discontinuous reaction, whereby an early-formed phase reacts with the melt, giving a new phase with a different crystal structure and a different composition. This concept of *reaction* as the fundamental phenomenon of magmatic crystallization is due to Bowen (1928) and has been developed by him into the *reaction principle*.

Bowen showed that the common minerals of igneous rocks can be arranged into two series, a discontinuous reaction series, comprising the ferromagnesian minerals, and an essentially continuous reaction series of the feldspars (Fig. 1). In effect, each of the ferromagnesian minerals is itself a continuous reaction series, since they are all solid solutions. The reac-

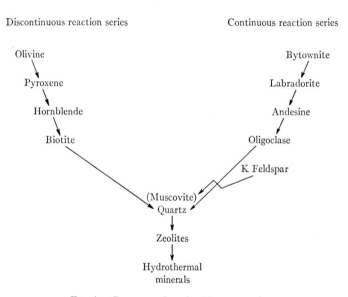

FIG. 1.—Common minerals of igneous rocks

tion series which Bowen set up, largely on the basis of laboratory study of silicate melts, parallels the general sequence of magmatic crystallization, as indicated by the petrology of the igneous rocks.

The petrological significance of the reaction principle may be illustrated by considering briefly the crystallization of a basaltic magma of such a composition that olivine and bytownite are the first phases to form. As the temperature falls, they will react more or less completely with the melt and be converted into pyroxene and labradorite; and if no fractionation takes place, the melt will solidify as a pyroxene-labradorite rock, a basalt or gabbro. If fractionation takes place and some of the early-formed olivine and bytownite is removed from the system, the reaction process will continue further, and the remaining melt will act upon pyroxene and labradorite to form hornblende and andesine. The greater the degree of fractionation, the more extensive the reaction process. With a high degree of fractionation, the whole reaction series is gone through, and the final liquid will be a watery solution rich in silica.

According to the reaction principle, therefore, the fractional crystallization of a basaltic magma under suitable conditions can lead to the successive formation of more siliceous rocks until ultimately a granitic composition is reached. This sequence has been confirmed in many areas of igneous rocks, e.g., the Oslo region, the Caledonian plutonic rocks of western Scotland, the Duluth lopolith, etc. Nevertheless, as Bowen himself points out, fractional crystallization is a very flexible process, and two magmas of approximately the same initial composition may produce very different rock types. Processes other than fractional crystallization may also be of significance in the diversification of igneous rocks; the mixing of two different magmas, the assimilation of solid material, and the splitting of a magma into two immiscible liquids have been suggested as responsible for certain types of igneous rocks. In some occurrences of igneous rocks it is apparent that the parent-magma had a distinctly aberrant composition, as in certain areas—for example, Fen in Norway and Alnö in Sweden—where primary carbonates are present in considerable amount.

The reaction principle expresses succinctly the concept of differentiation by fractional crystallization. It illustrates how a magma may solidify as a single rock type or may give rise to many rock types. The basaltic magma we have discussed might solidify as a gabbro consisting of pyroxene and labradorite, or it might give rise to rocks varying from dunite to granite, depending upon the degree of fractionation and the extent to which early-formed phases were removed from further reaction with the melt. This type of crystallization should be contrasted to eutectic crystallization, whereby a melt of a certain composition will always give the same solid phases of the same composition in the same proportions, whether cooling is fast or slow, whether early-formed phases are removed or remain in the system, or whether solidification proceeds at a uniform rate or discontinuously.

The reaction series provides us with a concise statement of the segregation of the major elements during magmatic crystallization. The first-formed minerals, olivine and calcic plagioclase, are low in silica, and the magma is thereby enriched in this component; the olivine is rich in magnesium, the plagioclase in calcium, and so the concentration of these elements in the liquid is decreased. The crystallization of olivine also changes the Mg-Fe ratio in the magma, since this ratio is always higher in the crystals than in the liquid from which they separate. In effect, olivine and all the other ferromagnesian minerals are individual continuous series, in which the early-formed crystals are magnesium-rich, the late-formed ones iron-rich. As crystallization proceeds, pyroxene becomes the stable phase instead of olivine, and calcium may now be removed from the melt both as plagioclase and as augite. The magma is becoming relatively enriched in Na, K, and Si. As the concentration of calcium in the liquid falls, the sodium content of the plagioclase progressively increases; with the appearance of hornblende as a stable phase in the discontinuous reaction series, some sodium may be incorporated in this mineral also. Potassium remains in the liquid until a late stage, since it can be removed in appreciable amounts only in biotite and in potash feldspar.

The reaction principle thus describes the general distribution of the major elements among igneous rocks developed by fractional crystallization. It depicts the sequence of phase separation as the temperature drops and as the composition of the liquid changes by the removal of some elements in the solid phases. The reaction principle, however, is essentially descriptive, not explanatory. It describes how the major elements distribute themselves among the different minerals, but not why they act in this way; and it does not tell us anything regarding the fate of the minor elements. The explanation must ultimately depend upon thermodynamic considerations—the energy changes involved in assembling ions of differing size and charge in particular crystal lattices.

The thermodynamics of magmatic crystallization is controlled by the nature of the ions present, their concentration, the temperature and pressure, and the type of crystal lattices formed. In effect, the question posed is "How do changes in the composition and physical conditions of the magma affect the solubility of the many different possible compounds?" A solid A will crystallize from a liquid containing A if the chemical potential of A is less in the solid than in the liquid. However, although we can state the problem, we cannot solve it, since the necessary thermodynamic data are not available. From the viewpoint of thermodynamics, magmatic crystallization is characterized by the energy and entropy changes involved in removing ions from the liquid and packing them in an orderly fashion in a crystal lattice, in which the constituent atoms or ions tend to take up positions whereby their total potential energy is reduced to a minimum. This tendency can be expressed quantitatively in terms of *lattice energies*. The lattice energy of an ionic crystal, generally represented by U, is defined as the energy absorbed when a mole of the crystal is dispersed into infinitely separated ions. The lattice energy depends upon the balancing of (1) the electrostatic forces between ions of opposite charge, which gives a resultant attraction, falling off with the square of the distance, and (2) the internuclear repulsive forces, which fall off very rapidly with distance. The attractive and repulsive forces result in an equilibrium position of minimum potential energy, which, summed over all the ions, is numerically equal to the lattice energy of the crystal, which is equal to the amount of work per mole which must be expended to disperse the crystalline substance into an assemblage of widely separated ions. As such, it cannot be equated with any directly measurable quantity and is not to be identified either with the heat of sublimation, which is the energy necessary to disperse the substance into a molecular gas, or with the heat of solution, which also includes the heat of hydration of the ions, or with the heat of formation, which is the heat evolved by the combination of the constituent elements. Born (1919) and Haber (1919) devised a thermochemical cycle by means of which lattice energies can be calculated from measurable thermal data. Unfortunately, the required thermal data have not yet been measured for many of the common silicate minerals. Under these circumstances attempts have been made to devise empirical methods of determining lattice energies. The consideration of geochemical processes in terms of lattice energies has been of particular interest to Fersman and other Russian geochemists. In an attempt to get a simple method of determining lattice energies, Fersman (1935) introduced the EK concept, which is an empirical constant for each element, representing the contribution of that element to the lattice energies of its compounds. Thus, for NaCl,

$$U_{NaCl} = K\,(EK_{Na} + EK_{Cl}) \qquad (K \text{ is an independent constant}) .$$

From known lattice energies, Fersman was able to assign EK values to most of the elements. However, the application of these values to the calculation of lattice energies of silicate minerals and thence to the interpretation of geochemical processes has so far given ambiguous results. The differences in calculated lattice energies of corresponding amphiboles and pyroxenes, for example, are small—smaller than the probable error. One serious criticism of Fersman's approach is that it allows only for the energy associated with a specific number of ions of different elements but fails to consider the energy associated with the crystal lattice as such. For example, the previous equation will clearly give the same lattice energies for all polymorphs of the same substance.

A concept rather similar to that of Fersman's EK values is the activation energy of migration of an ion, or the E value, introduced by Wickman (1943). To some extent, Wickman's E value is the contribution of a single ion to the lattice energy of a crystal, but it differs from Fersman's EK value in that it is a function not only of the ion itself but also of the surrounding ions and hence takes into account structural differences. The E-value concept is, however, qualitative only, as no means have yet been devised for expressing E values in figures.

The fate of an element during magmatic crystallization is linked with its concentration in the magma and the nature of the structural lattices which may form. The silicon and aluminum content of the magma and the temperature are the factors controlling the sequence of crystal lattices. These crystal lattices act as a sorting mechanism for the cations. A cation can enter a crystal lattice only if it is of suitable size and can attain its appropriate co-ordination number. Since, in general, there will be a number of different ions which can satisfy this requirement, that ion will enter the lattice in largest amount, relative to its concentration in the liquid, which holds its position in the lattice with greatest tenacity. This is, in effect, the ion which will make the greatest contribution to the lattice energy of the crystal, i.e., has the largest EK value (Fersman) or E value (Wickman). As mentioned previously, quantitative figures for these energy contributions are as yet imperfectly known. However, from studies of crystal structures and quite independently of energy considerations, Goldschmidt (1934) formulated the following empirical rules as a general guide to the course of an element during liquid $\rightarrow$ crystal formation in a multicomponent system:

1. If two ions have the same radius and the same charge, they will enter a given crystal lattice with equal facility.

2. If two ions have similar radii and same charge, the smaller ion will enter a given crystal lattice more readily.

3. If two ions have similar radii and different charge, the ions with the higher charge will enter a given crystal lattice more readily.

These rules have wide application in the study of the geochemistry of igneous rocks. Calcium enters the feldspar lattice more readily than sodium does, on account of its higher charge, and so is concentrated in the early-formed plagioclase. The potassium ion is considerably larger than sodium, and potash feldspar is generally one of the last minerals to crystallize. The magnesium ion is somewhat smaller than the ferrous ion, and magnesium is always concentrated in the early-formed ferromagnesian minerals, whether olivine, pyroxene, amphibole, or biotite. However, Goldschmidt's rules have had their greatest utility in predicting the order of removal from a magma not only of the major elements but of the minor elements also.

When a minor element has the same charge and an ionic radius similar to a major element, we speak of it as being *camouflaged* in the crystal lattice containing the major element. Thus, Ge^{4+} (0.44 A) is camouflaged in silicate minerals (Si^{4+}, 0.39 A), Ga^{3+} (0.63 A) is camouflaged in aluminum minerals (Al^{3+}, 0.57 A). When a minor element has a similar ionic radius but a higher charge, or the same charge but a lesser radius, than that of a major element, it is said to be *captured* by the crystal lattice containing the major element. Thus, Ba^{2+} (1.43 A) is captured by potassium minerals (K^+, 1.33 A). Finally, when a minor element has a similar ionic radius but a lower charge, or the same charge but a greater radius, than that of a major element, it is said to be *admitted* into the crystal lattice containing the major element. Thus Li^+ (0.78 A) is admitted into magnesium minerals (Mg^{2+}, 0.78 A). In capture and admission the charge balance is maintained by concomitant substitution elsewhere in the crystal lattice. Goldschmidt's rules indicate that it is possible from a knowledge of the ions in a magma and their sizes to predict in which phase or phases a particular element is likely to be found. Study of specific regions of igneous rocks has confirmed the validity of these rules. A brief summary follows; for more detailed information see the papers of Nockolds and Mitchell (1948) and Wager and Mitchell (1951).

Rubidium is a large ion, and the only major element it can replace should be potassium, and this is found to be true. Rubidium forms no minerals of its own, being always incorporated in potassium minerals. In igneous rocks it is present in the micas and in potash feldspar; since Rb^+ is considerably larger than K^+, rubidium should be admitted into potassium minerals. Observation has shown that the Rb/K ratio increases in the later-formed potassium minerals. Barium, an ion similar in size to rubidium, is also found in potassium minerals, but barium is concentrated in the early-formed potassium minerals; evidently, the barium ion is captured on account of its higher charge. Strontium, whose ion is smaller than potassium and somewhat larger than calcium and sodium, appears in both potash feldspar and plagioclase feldspar; strontium should be captured by potash feldspar and admitted to plagioclase. That this is so is indicated by an increase of Sr/Ca in passing from early to late plagioclase, and a relative concentration of Sr in early-formed potash feldspar.

A number of minor elements—scandium, nickel, cobalt, and lithium—have ionic radii about 0.8 A, close to those of ferrous iron and magnesium. As is to be expected, these minor elements appear in the ferromagnesian minerals of igneous rocks, but the pattern of concentration varies. Scandium, on account of its higher charge, should be captured by such minerals, and pyroxenes generally show a relative concentration of this element; it is not concentrated in the earlier-formed olivines, evidently because of the difficulty of balancing the excess positive charge, thus introduced, by other suitable replacements. Nickel behaves as if its effective radius were somewhat less than magnesium, the Ni/Mg ratio being highest in early-formed minerals (especially olivine), and declining steadily in the later-formed rocks and minerals. The Co/Mg ratio, however, remains practically constant throughout an igneous rock series, indicating effective camouflage of cobalt by magnesium. Lithium, with the same radius as magnesium but a lower charge, should be admitted into ferromagnesian minerals; and this is borne out by the steady increase in the Li/Mg ratio in later-formed rocks and minerals. A considerable amount of lithium evidently remains in the liquid until a very late stage of differentiation, since pegmatites often show a particular concentration of this element, which in the practical absence of magnesium forms individual minerals, such as lepidolite, spodumene, amblygonite, and petalite.

Chromium, vanadium, and titanium are generally removed from magmas in association with iron. If they are present in sufficient concentration, chromium and titanium may form individual minerals, chromite ($FeCr_2O_4$) and ilmenite ($FeTiO_3$); otherwise, they enter the ferromagnesian minerals, the pyroxenes, amphiboles, and biotite, as does vanadium.

Germanium and gallium are two elements which are characteristically camouflaged by major elements. The Ge^{4+} ion has the same charge and practically the same radius as Si^{4+} and can therefore proxy for Si^{4+} in the whole series of silicate structures; this is reflected in a practically constant Ge/Si ratio in a rock series. The Ga^{3+} ion bears a similar relationship to Al^{3+}, and the Ga/Al ratio in igneous rocks and their minerals is practically constant, indicating effective camouflage of gallium in aluminum minerals.

The remaining lithophile elements are those which, on account of too great difference in ionic radius and ionic charge, do not replace the major elements. On account of low concentration in the original magma, they remain in solution and hence are enriched in the residual liquid of magmatic crystallization. These elements are: B^{3+} (0.20 A), Be^{2+} (0.34 A), W^{6+} (0.78 A), Nb^{5+} (0.69 A), Ta^{5+} (0.68 A), Sn^{4+} (0.74 A), Th^{4+} (1.10 A), U^{4+} (1.05 A), the rare earths (0.99–1.22 A), and Cs^+ (1.64 A). They are concentrated in pegmatite minerals, which are the only economic source of most of them.

The chalcophile elements in a magma associate with sulphur and lesser amounts of arsenic, antimony, bismuth, selenium, and tellurium to form sulphides and related compounds. Some sulphides may separate from a magma at an early stage of crystallization, but they characteristically segregate at a late stage and are ultimately deposited in veins formed at comparatively low temperatures. This is probably on account of the low thermal stability of most sulphides. The separation of sulphides must also depend upon a sufficient concentration of sulphide ions in the magma. This may not be attained until a large part of the lithophile elements have been removed by crystallization of the silicates.

As well as a differentiation of the elements in a single magmatic evolution, there is some evidence of differentation of the elements in time. This was first brought out by Rankama (1946), who showed that certain elements (Li, Be, Rb, Cs, Ba, rare earths, Ta, and Pb) increase in concentration in granites of successively younger geological age, whereas others, such as Y, decrease in concentration in younger granites, as compared with the old Pre-Cambrian granites.

So far we have been considering the solid products of magmatic crystallization. In addition, all magmas contain *volatile material;* its amount and composition are not well known, since no means of directly sampling it have yet been devised. As a result, the significance of this material has been the subject of extreme controversy. It has been maintained that magmas are essentially "dry." This opinion has been largely discarded, however, since water has been found to be universally present both in volcanic exhalations and in the gases evolved from fresh igneous rocks by heating *in vacuo.* Nevertheless, even this evidence has been subjected to doubt. It has been suggested that primary magma is rich in hydrogen, which by surface or near-surface oxidation has produced the water or a considerable part of it. Similar differences of opinion are current as to the amount of volatile matter in magmas. Here, again, we are dependent on indirect evidence, such as observations on volcanoes, petrographic examination and chemical analysis of igneous rocks, and experimental determination of the solubility of water and other volatiles in silicate melts. This evidence is in part contradictory. Some volcanologists have stated that in certain eruptions, such as that of Vesuvius in 1906, the mass of gas evolved outweighted the solid matter ejected; in other eruptions the proportion of gas in the material ejected has been estimated as low as 0.3 per cent. Different volcanoes, and the same volcano at different times, evidently present very dissimilar appearances. The data on the solubility of water in artificial silicate melts have indicated that the limiting solubility of water in a granitic melt is about 10 per cent, which suggests that magmas probably contain less than this amount. All igneous rocks contain some volatile matter, mostly water, which can be extracted by heating *in vacuo*, and Clarke's average of the analyses of fresh igneous rocks shows 1.5 per cent H_2O; this figure may perhaps be taken as a lower limit for the average water content of a magma. Current estimates run from about 1 to 8 per cent of water in magmas.

As mentioned earlier, the composition of the volatile components cannot be directly determined. Here again we have to fall back on analyses of the gases evolved on heating igneous rocks, on observations of materials deposited in fumaroles, and on analyses of gases collected around volcanoes. The last procedure, while most direct, is technically difficult and personally uncomfortable or dangerous. The most satisfactory collections yet made are those of the gases evolved from the lava lake at Kilauea on Hawaii (Shepherd, 1938). Analyses of these gases show that the major constituents of the volatile matter at this place are H_2O, CO_2, and sulphur compounds and that H_2O is dominant. Observations on other volcanoes confirm this general picture. Water is always the major constituent, generally making up over 80 per cent of the whole by volume; CO_2, H_2S, S, SO_2, HCl, and NH_4Cl are often abundant; and HF, N_2, H_2, CH_4, B_2O_3, and CO have been recorded in lesser amounts. In addition, gaseous emanations from magmas collect, transport, and deposit many other elements. Such minerals as magnetite, hematite, molybdenite, pyrite, realgar, galena, sphalerite, covellite, sal ammoniac, ferric chloride, and many others have been found in the throats of fumaroles, where they have been deposited directly from gases. The Valley of Ten Thousand Smokes provides us with one of the best-documented examples of the role of volcanic emanations. The work of Allen and Zies (Zies, 1938) showed that the principal gas in all the fumaroles was water vapor, the percentage by volume ranging from 98.8 to 99.99. Other gases recognized were CO_2, O_2, CO, CH_4, H_2S, H_2, N_2, A, HCl, and HF. Although these were present in very small percentages, the total amount evolved was enormous. Thus the average concentration of HCl was 0.117 per cent, and of HF 0.032 per cent, but the total quantity of HCl evolved in 1919 was estimated as 1,250,000 tons, and of HF 200,000 tons. One difficulty in discussing the geochemical significance of these figures is that of determining how much of the emanations are primary, i.e., were contained in the original magma, and how much secondary, i.e., assimilated by the magma from surrounding rocks during the rise to the surface. Allen and Zies believe that much of the water vapor given off at the Valley of Ten Thousand Smokes was ground water heated by the igneous material. The same difficulty arises in assessing the amount of material in mineral springs that is magmatic in origin. Allen and Day (1935) suggest that perhaps 90 per cent of the water in the geysers and hot springs at Yellowstone is activated ground water. Precise information on those points would greatly advance our knowledge of the geochemical significance of magmatic emanations; but it is evident that igneous activity during geological time has brought vast amounts of water and other volatile matter to the earth's surface.

6. THE GEOCHEMISTRY OF SEDIMENTARY PROCESSES

A cursory examination of sedimentary processes suggests that they would tend to produce an average mixture of the individual components present in the parent-material and thus work against any chemical differentiation. This, however, is not the case; weathering, erosion, and sedimentation lead generally to a marked separation of the major elements. As Goldschmidt (1922) pointed out, the cycle of matter at the earth's surface can be likened to a chemical analysis, and to a quantitative analysis at that. The chemical differentiation which results is remarkable. The steps in this geochemical separation process are as follows:

1. Minerals which are especially resistant to chemical and mechanical breakdown collect as granular material. Of these, the commonest is quartz, and the product is a quartz sand or a sandstone showing a marked enrichment in silicon with respect to the parent-material. This may be compared to the separation of silica in the first stage of a rock analysis.

2. The products of chemical breakdown of aluminosilicates accumulate, giving a mud consisting essentially of the clay minerals. This results in concentration of aluminum and also of potassium by adsorption. The process corresponds to the second step in a rock analysis, the separation of alumina and other easily hydrolyzed bases.

3. Along with the formation of argillaceous sediments, but often separated in space and time, iron is precipitated as ferric hydroxide. In this process oxidation from the ferrous to the ferric state precedes precipitation by hydrolysis. Concentration of iron is the result, sometimes to the extent of the formation of iron ores.

4. Calcium is precipitated as calcium carbonate either by purely inorganic processes or by the action of organisms. Limestones are formed, and calcium is thereby concentrated. This may result in practically quantitative separation of calcium, as in a chemical analysis. Limestone can be partly or wholly converted to dolomite by the metasomatic action of magnesium-rich solutions, and magnesium is thereby precipitated and concentrated together with calcium.

5. The bases which remain in solution collect in the ocean, from which they are removed in quantity only by evaporation, giving rise to salt deposits. The most important of these bases is sodium, but lesser amounts of potassium and magnesium also accumulate in sea water.

The chemical breakdown of a rock by weathering can be represented by the following scheme:

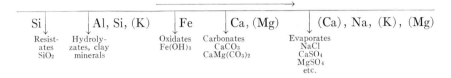

Si	Al, Si, (K)	Fe	Ca, (Mg)	(Ca), Na, (K), (Mg)
Resistates SiO_2	Hydrolyzates, clay minerals	Oxidates $Fe(OH)_3$	Carbonates $CaCO_3$ $CaMg(CO_3)_2$	Evaporates NaCl $CaSO_4$ $MgSO_4$ etc.

This scheme indicates the course followed by the major elements during sedimentation and gives a useful geochemical classification of sediments into *resistates, hydrolyzates, oxidates, carbonates,* and *evaporates.* Goldschmidt (1944) recognized a further class, the *reduzates,* which include coal, oil, sedimentary sulphides, and sedimentary sulphur. Coal and oil are of organic origin, and sedimentary sulphides and sulphur often owe their formation to organic processes also, although possibly indirectly.

The fate of the major elements during sedimentation has been fairly well worked out. Silica concentrates in the resistate sediments, alumina in the hydrolyzates, iron and manganese in the oxidates, and calcium and magnesium in carbonates; a good part of the sodium remains in solution and eventually accumulates in the ocean; potassium is adsorbed by the clays and may form the mineral illite. The fate of the minor elements during sedimentation has not been thoroughly investigated, and much less is known about their behavior under these circumstances than during magmatism. This is due in part to a lesser interest in the chemistry of sedimentary rocks than of igneous rocks, and in part to the lack of guiding principles, such as are provided by Goldschmidt's empirical rules for capture and admittance of ions by crystal lattices. Sedimentary processes are more complex in this respect, and many factors may play a part in determining the transportation and deposition of an element—ionic potential (Z/r, where Z is the ionic charge and r the radius), pH and oxidation potential of the medium, colloidal properties, adsorption, and so on. Hence it is not yet possible to make categorical statements regarding the fate of many of the minor elements during sedimentation.

The resistates form the important group of sands and sandstones. Quartz is far and away the commonest and most abundant of residual minerals, and sands and sandstones are sources of silica for industrial uses. Many other minerals may appear in small amounts in sands and sandstones, but most of these can be decomposed and removed by intense weathering. Zircon ($ZrSiO_4$) is one of the most persistent of minerals, and the main ore deposits of zircon are sands from which it can be profitably separated. Magnetite (Fe_3O_4) and ilmenite ($FeTiO_3$) are fairly resistant minerals and accumulate in sands; other industrially important constituents of some sands are rutile (TiO_2), monazite ($CePO_4$), cassiterite (SnO_2), and, of course, gold and the platinum metals.

The hydrolyzate sediments consist in great part of the clay minerals. Tropical weathering often produces aluminum hydroxides rather than hydrated aluminum silicates, and high-alumina clays and bauxites result. In either case the end-product represents a concentration of aluminum over the average amount in the earth's crust. Many other elements, especially those in Groups III and IV of the periodic table, may be expected to precipitate in hydrolyzate sediments, and the meager data on minor elements in sedimentary rocks bear this out. Shales show concentrations of elements of medium ionic potential and of elements like potassium that are readily adsorbed by colloidal particles; they are sometimes enriched in chalcophile elements, evidently precipitated as sulphides by the H_2S often generated in marine muds. The most remarkable hydrolyzate sediments from the geochemical viewpoint are the black bituminous shales and the bauxites, both of which have originated under rather special conditions. The black shales were deposited slowly in a strongly reducing marine environment rich in organic matter. Sulphide ions were evidently present, produced by the reduction of sulphate. Analyses of black shale are characterized not only by a considerable content of organic carbon but generally also by much sulphur, present mainly as FeS_2. Enrichment of the following minor elements has been noted: V, U, As, Sb, Co, Cu, Ni, Cd, Ag, Au, and metals of the platinum group. It has been suggested that the minor elements were accumulated by the vital activity of the organisms now represented by bituminous material, but this is far from certain. The chalcophile nature of many of these elements suggests that precipitation from solution as sulphides is a more reasonable explanation. A linear increase of uranium with increasing carbon content has been demonstrated in some of these shales, but this does not necessarily imply that the uranium was present in the organisms that furnished the carbon. The uranium content also shows an excellent correlation with the abundance of colloidal-sized grades in the sediment, which might suggest that this element is present in the clay mineral, which in these black shales is generally illite. The evidence indicates that the concentration of uranium is not the result of biological activity but of later chemical processes, probably related, in part at least, to the presence of organic matter in the sediments. Some phosphatic shales, such as those which occur in the Phosphoria formation in Wyoming, Idaho, and Montana, show similar geochemical features, especially in the enrichment in vanadium and uranium; they seem to have been deposited under similar conditions, i.e., oxygen-deficient marine environments where organic material was accumulating and the rate of sedimentation was very slow. Bauxites have a different pattern of enrichment and often show a concentration of beryllium, gallium, niobium, and titanium; of these, gallium is actually being extracted as a by-product from the production of aluminum.

The most important oxidate is ferric hydroxide, which, if pure, gives rise to a sedimentary iron ore. Manganese is also deposited as an oxidate sediment in the form of hydrated manganese dioxide, and such deposits or their metamorphosed equivalents are the significant sources of manganese ore. The absorptive power of precipitated ferric hydroxide and manganese dioxide hydrate is very great, and hence many minor elements are found in oxidate sediments. Vanadium, phosphorus, arsenic, antimony, and selenium have been reported in sedimentary iron ores in larger amounts than their average abundance in the crust; Li, K, Ba, B, Ti, Co, Ni, Cu, Zn, Pb, and W have been reported in notable concentrations in manganese ore.

The common carbonate sediment is limestone. Limestone generally represents an accumulation of the skeletal remains of marine organisms, although some limestones may have been formed by inorganic precipitation. The calcium carbonate content of sea water approaches the saturation value, and under special conditions (warm water, high salinity, low CO_2 content) saturation may be exceeded. Calcium carbonate may be deposited as calcite or as aragonite, but it is doubtful whether aragonite will persist for any considerable time in a geological formation, since it is a monotropic form and tends to change to calcite. Whether calcium carbonate was originally deposited as calcite or as aragonite may have significant geochemical consequences, however; the structure of aragonite permits ready substitution by larger cations, such as strontium, lead, etc., but not the smaller cations, whereas for calcite the reverse is true. Hence the minor elements in a limestone will probably differ in kind and amount according to the nature of the calcium carbonate in the original sediment.

The evaporates are quantitatively unimportant as sediments but are highly significant in the interpretation of geological history. Geochemically, they are of special interest as a type of deposit whose mode of formation can readily be reproduced in the laboratory. As early as 1849 Usiglio made experiments aimed at elucidating the conditions of formation of salt deposits; but his results were unsatisfactory, since he worked with sea water, a highly complex solution, with which he failed to get reproducible results. Later the problem was tackled from the other direction by van't Hoff (1912) and his co-workers, who began by studying the solubility relations of all the possible compounds which might be produced by the evaporation of sea water. Working initially at 25°, they determined the equilibrium relations in the simple two-component salt-water systems and then extended these researches to multicomponent systems. Similar investigations were made at 83°, and specific reactions involving the appearance or disappearance of individual compounds were studied at the temperature of reaction. Van't Hoff's success in working out phase relations and applying these results to natural occurrences of evaporates (especially the Stassfurt deposits) was one of the first fruits of the application of physicochemical principles (in this case the phase rule) to geological problems.

As sea water evaporates under natural conditions, calcium carbonate is the first solid to separate. The precipitation of calcium carbonate may be followed by that of dolomite, but there is no evidence that extensive deposits of dolomite have been formed in this way. Indeed, evaporation of sea water in a closed basin cannot give rise to thick carbonate deposits— sea water 1000 m deep would give only a few centimeters of limestone.

With continued evaporation, calcium sulphate is deposited. Depending on temperature and salinity, either gypsum ($CaSO_4 \cdot 2H_2O$) or anhydrite ($CaSO_4$) may be formed. In salt solutions of approximately the composition of sea water at 30°, gypsum will begin to separate when the salinity has increased to 3.35 times the normal value; after nearly half the total amount of calcium sulphate has been deposited, anhydrite becomes the stable phase. When the solution has been concentrated to one-tenth the original bulk, halite starts to separate. Anydrite and halite then precipitate together, until the field of stability of polyhalite, $K_2Ca_2Mg(SO_4)_4 \cdot 2H_2O$, is reached.

Most evaporate deposits contain calcium carbonate, calcium sulphate, and sodium chloride; evidently, conditions under which other salts could be deposited have seldom been attained. Only when an evaporating body of sea water has been reduced to 1.54 per cent of the original volume, do potassium and magnesium salts begin to crystallize. Important deposits of these salts are worked in Germany, in the Texas–New Mexico area of the United States, and in the province of Perm in the U.S.S.R.

The total amount of sedimentation during geological time is clearly a figure of great importance for the quantitative geochemistry of the crust, and a number of attempts have been made to calculate it. Such calculations are generally based upon data regarding the amount and composition of ocean water and the average composition of igneous and sedimentary rocks. Goldschmidt (1933a) made these calculations in the following way. For each square centimeter of the earth's surface, there are 278 kg of sea water; and, since sea water contains 1.07 per cent sodium, the 278 kg contains 2.975 kg of sodium. The average sodium content of igneous rocks is 2.83 per cent, and of sedimentary deposits approximately 1 per cent. In the process of weathering, a certain amount of the material is leached away, and Goldschmidt estimated that the mass of the sedimentary deposits is 0.97 of the original igneous rocks that gave rise to them. Now

Let X be the amount igneous rock eroded per cm^2 of earth's surface,

Let Y be the amount of clastic sediments deposited per cm^2 of earth's surface;

Then:

$$Y = 0.97X,$$

$$\text{Sodium content of igneous rocks per square centimeter} = \frac{2.83}{100} \cdot X,$$

$$\text{Sodium content of clastic rock per square centimeter} = \frac{1}{100} \cdot Y.$$

But the sodium content of ocean water per square centimeter = 2.975 kg. Hence

$$\frac{2.83}{100} X - \frac{Y}{100} = 2.975;$$

or

$$X = 160 \text{ kg/cm}^2; \qquad Y = 155 \text{ kg/cm}^2.$$

The value of 160 kg/cm^2 gives a figure of about 3×10^8 km^3 for the total amount of igneous rock weathered during geological time.

These calculations overlook, on the one hand, the sodium removed from the ocean during geological time in the form of salt deposits and, on the other, that added by way of volcanic exhalations and in solution in magmatic waters. Both these items are probably small in relation to the sodium cycle as a whole, and they work in opposite directions. In addition, of course, the calculations fail to take into account the sodium which may have been present in the primitive ocean; any such sodium would reduce the amount of weathering necessary to produce the present sodium content of sea water.

Goldschmidt also calculated the quantity of calcium and magnesium carbonate in sedimentary rocks. He estimated the average content of non-carbonate CaO in sandstones and shales to be 0.6 per cent and concluded, therefore, that CaO in excess of this figure is present as calcium carbonate. Similarly, the average amount of noncarbonate MgO was estimated to be 2.6 per cent. A balance sheet for the cycle of calcium and magnesium in sedimentation was then derived and is given in the following table:

In the ocean Ca........ $0.00042 \times 278 = 0.117$ kg/cm^2
        Mg........ $0.00130 \times 278 = 0.361$ kg/cm^2

	CaO	MgO
In igneous rocks............................	5.08 per cent	3.49 per cent
In carbonate-free sediments.................	0.6 per cent	2.6 per cent
160 kg of igneous rocks contain.............	8.128 kg	5.584 kg
155 kg of carbonate-free sediments contain.....	0.930 kg	4.030 kg
278 kg of sea water contain.................	0.117 kg Ca,	0.361 kg Mg
Corresponding to........................	0.164 kg CaO,	0.598 kg MgO

Therefore, the following amounts of calcium and magnesium carbonates (per square centimeter) must be present in the sediments:

7.034 kg CaO	0.956 kg MgO
5.519 kg CO$_2$	1.043 kg CO$_2$
———	———
12.553 kg CaCO$_3$	1.999 kg MgCO$_3$

Assuming that all the magnesium carbonate in sediments is there as dolomite, $CaMg(CO_3)_2$, we obtain these figures: 10.170 kg $CaCO_3$, 4.372 kg $CaMg(CO_3)_2$. Hence the total amount of sedimentary rocks per square centimeter of the earth's surface is 155 kg clastics, 10.2 kg limestone, and 4.4 kg dolomite, and the combined CO$_2$ in sediments in thus 6.562 kg/cm^2. From the above figures and the densities of these rock types, the total average thickness of sediments can be calculated, as shown in the accompanying table, i.e., the total volume of sediments produced during

	Mass/cm^2 (kg)	D	V (cc)	Thickness (m)
Clastics (sandstones and shales)	155	2.65	58,491	585
Limestone.................	10.2	2.7	3,777	38
Dolomite.................	4.4	2.9	1,517	15
Total.	169.6	....	....	639

geological time corresponds to a rock shell about 640 m thick, enveloping the whole earth.

Kuenen (1950) has criticized these figures and has concluded from several lines of evidence that the total amount of sediments is considerably greater. The calculations of Wilson (chap. 4) point in the same direction. Kuenen believes that the major source of error in previous calculations is the figure for the average sodium content of sedimentary rocks, which he considers too low. He estimates that the total volume of sediments is $7 \times 10 \text{ km}^3$, of which $5 \times 10^8 \text{ km}^3$ is in deep-sea deposits, mainly red clay. He stresses the importance of the deep ocean basins as collecting grounds for vast amounts of sediment throughout geological time and predicts that the average thickness of such sediments is about 3 km. His predictions have been supported by some recent geophysical measurements of sediment thickness on the ocean bottoms, which have given figures of the order he suggested. Cf. chapter 5, Section 1.

A number of estimates for the relative amounts of the common sediments are collected in the accompanying small table. The lack of agree-

	1*	2	3	4	5
Shale ⎫ Sandstone ⎭ · · · · · · · · · · · · · · ·	91	⎰80 ⎱15	82 12	46 32	57 14
Limestone (and dolomite)	9	5	6	22	29

* The numbers in these boxheads refer to the following sources: (1) Goldschmidt (1933); (2) Clarke and Washington (1924); (3) Leith and Mead (1915); (4) Leith and Mead (1915) (708,000 ft. of sediments in North America, Europe, Asia); (5) Kuenen (1941) (for the sedimentary rocks of the East Indies).

ment is due to several causes. The estimates derived from actual measurements of stratigraphic sections are weighted in favor of the proportions of these sediments on the continental shelves, which is not the same as that for the earth as a whole; Kuenen points out that the deposits of the deep sea, which hardly appear in terrestrial outcrops, are by no means insignificant. Since calcareous deposits form a greater proportion of the shelf sediments, and red clay those of the deep sea, the sedimentary rocks show more limestone and less argillaceous material than the average for the whole earth. The identification of a formation as a limestone, a sandstone, or a shale is liable to be very gross; shales usually contain considerable sand, sandstones, and considerable clay; and the term "limestone" is applied to many rocks with only 50 per cent or so of carbonate. Hence the disparity between the different estimates is not surprising, and the agreement is more remarkable than the disparity. It is clear, however, that limestones are more prominent in the geological column than one might expect from geochemical calculations; this is certainly significant and confirms the idea that shallow-water environments are the great places of carbonate deposition, whereas much clayey matter is permanently deposited in the ocean deeps.

7. THE GEOCHEMISTRY OF METAMORPHIC PROCESSES

Metamorphism may be defined as the sum of the processes which, working within the crust, cause the recrystallization of rock material. During metamorphism the rocks remain essentially solid; if remelting takes place, a magma is produced, and metamorphism has passed into magmatism. Metamorphism is induced in solid rocks as a result of pronounced changes in temperature, pressure, and chemical environment. These changes affect the physical and chemical stability of a mineral assemblage, and metamorphism results from the effort to establish a new equilibrium. In this way the constituents of a rock are changed to minerals which are more stable under the new conditions, and these minerals may arrange themselves with the production of structures which are likewise more suited to the new environment. Metamorphism accordingly results in the partial or complete recrystallization of a rock, with the production of new structures and new minerals.

The three factors of heat, pressure, and chemically active fluids are the impelling forces in metamorphism. The heat may be due to the general increase of temperature with depth or to contiguous magmas. Pressure may be resolved into two kinds: hydrostatic or uniform pressure, which leads to change in volume; and directed pressure or stress, which leads to change of shape or distortion. Uniform pressure results in the production of granular, nonoriented structures; stress results in the production of parallel or banded structures. Whether stress has a distinctive influence on the mineralogical composition of metamorphic rocks, that is, whether stress affects chemical equilibria, is still a controversial topic. Uniform pressure affects chemical equilibria by promoting a volume decrease, i.e., the formation of minerals of higher density. The action of chemically active fluids is a most important factor in metamorphism, since even when they do not add or subtract material from the rocks, they promote reaction by solution and redeposition. Where they add or subtract material, the process is called *metasomatism*. Probably some degree of metasomatism accompanies most metamorphism. Water is the principal chemically active fluid, and it is aided by carbon dioxide, boric acid, hydrofluoric and hydrochloric acids and other substances, often of magmatic origin.

Metasomatism or allochemical metamorphism raises the question as to how the introduction or removal of material has taken place. Three ways may be suggested: transportation in a gas phase, transportation by liquids, and transportation involving neither of these. The last process may be visualized as a migration of atoms or ions along crystal boundaries or even through solids, and its significance in metamorphism is a subject of acute controversy. That such a process is possible is universally accepted. The controversy, like so many others in geology, rages around the magnitude of the effects that this form of material transfer has actually produced in the rocks. Some workers ascribe to it the alteration of enormous volumes of material; specifically, it has been stated (Perrin and Roubault, 1949) that granite masses of batholithic dimensions are the result of allochemical metamorphism of pre-existing rocks without the intervention of liquid or gas phases. Other workers state that migration of ions in and through solids is, at best, an insignificant factor in metamorphism, being completely overshadowed by other types of transportation, and that in any case the requirements for extensive migration of this kind are unlikely to be realized under the usual condition of metamorphism.

On the whole, the evidence favors the latter view. Measurements of diffusion in silicates indicate that the rate of migration of ions in solids of this kind is much too slow to produce extensive changes, even in the time available during cycles of metamorphism. These experimental data are complemented by deductions based on energy considerations. Diffusion in and through solids is conditioned by the kinetic energy of the ions and the presence of defects in the crystal lattices. Rising temperatures will promote such diffusion, by increasing the kinetic energy of the ions and the degree of disorder in crystal lattices. However, as Bowen (1948) has pointed out, diffusion is insignificant until the temperature approaches the melting point of the solid; in fact, there is a threshold value below which diffusion is ineffective. For silicates this threshold value is given as 0.8–$0.9T$, where T is the melting temperature (in degrees absolute) of the individual silicate. As Bowen observes, if this condition holds rigidly, diffusion in the solid state may be ruled out as a metamorphic process, since an assemblage of minerals will begin to melt at a temperature far below the melting point of any individual mineral. Hence magma will be regenerated at temperatures well below those at which ions would begin to diffuse in and through the individual minerals. In this connection the presence of zoning in feldspars and other minerals shows that differences of chemical composition over microscopic distances can persist over vast periods of time and through severe changes in physical conditions.

The controversy regarding diffusion in the solid state as an agent of metamorphism has tended to overshadow the significance of other processes of transportation. Water and other volatile substances are practically omnipresent, at least in small amounts, in all rocks and are also set free in large amounts by igneous activity, thereby providing a universal and effective medium for the transportation of material. Field observations and laboratory experiments indicate that metasomatism is essentially the result of the introduction or removal of material by liquids or gases rather than by transfer in and through solids.

If the temperature continues to rise during metamorphism, any rock must eventually melt. In this way a magma is generated, and the further geochemical evolution is no longer part of metamorphism. The regeneration of magma will not, however, take place at a definite temperature and pressure, but over a range of temperatures and pressures; the process may not proceed to completion and may be halted at any stage. Mixed rocks or *migmatites* are formed thereby, whose characters partake of those of both igneous and metamorphic rocks.

The process can be looked upon as the reverse of magmatic crystallization. In the melting of rocks, we may expect that the first liquid to form will resemble the last liquid fraction of a magma and be rich in silica, soda, potash, alumina, and water. The process of differential fusion or *anatexis* can be conceived as beginning with the "sweating" of the low-melting fraction from the main mass of the rock and its segregation into lenses. In the light of laboratory work on the crystallization of hydrous feldspar melts, differential fusion of rocks may be expected to begin at temperatures of 600°–700°. If the process ceases at this point, the fused material will crystallize as an aggregate of quartz and feldspar as lenses within the more refractory material, giving rise to the rock type which has been called "venite," a particular variety of migmatite. A similar product could be formed by the injection of the last fraction from magmatic crystallization between the layers of solid rock, and the resulting rock has been called "arterite," to distinguish it from one formed by differential fusion. In the field it is often difficult to decide whether a migmatite is an arterite or a venite, and, indeed, both processes outlined above may have been active at the time of formation.

Under conditions of ultra-metamorphism the regenerated magma will most likely be granitic. Some granites may well have been formed by the actual remelting of material of suitable composition. However, granites may also originate without remelting. The mineral association of granite—quartz, alkali feldspar, biotite, and muscovite—is typical of a particular set of temperature-pressure conditions, and any body of rock whose bulk composition corresponds to that of granite (or is converted thereto by metasomatism) will recrystallize to give this typical mineral association under those conditions. Generally, as a result of directed pressure during crystallization, the product will be a gneiss; but if directed pressure is weak or lacking, a normal granite may result. Thus granites may be produced in several ways—by the fractional crystallization of a magma, by the crystallization of a melt produced by the differential fusion of a pre-existing rock, and by the recrystallization without fusion of a pre-existing rock. Any body of granite may include within it representatives of all these types of origin. Deciding the mode of formation of a particular granite may require all the resources, field and laboratory, of a geologist, and, even so, the answer may not be unequivocal. The volume of discussion on the origin of granite is an eloquent expression of the difficulty in determining the boundary between magmatic and metamorphic processes in actual rocks.

8. THE GEOCHEMICAL CYCLE

One of the few subjects upon which universal agreement seems to prevail is that the earth was not created in its present state. The geochemical evidence supports the idea that its internal structure is probably the result of forces originating within the earth itself. The earth is a physicochemical system with considerable mass and thus exerts a gravitational force on its own components. The resulting gravitational field has affected the distribution of material by concentrating the heavier phases toward the center and the lighter phases toward the surface. The rate of such a gravitational differentiation clearly depends upon the viscosity of the system; it will be more rapid in a gas than in a liquid, more rapid in a liquid than in a solid. The idea of an earth at one time liquid is attractive, as enabling such gravitational differentiation to take place within a comparatively short time. Geophysical data sustain the theory that the earth has a layered structure due to separation of its material into shells of different density. Goldschmidt (1933b) termed this the *primary geochemical differentiation*. It was a differentiation due to gravity acting on a system in which iron, oxygen, and silicon were the major components. Iron was the principal component, and the distribution of the elements between a metallic core and a silicate mantle was controlled by their oxidation potential with respect to that of iron. Elements more readily oxidized than iron concentrated in the mantle; elements less readily oxidized formed the core. Hence the fate of an element in this primary geochemical differentiation is, in effect, a reflection of the number and arrangement of its orbital electrons. Those elements forming ions with a noble-gas structure went into the silicate phase; the transition elements, on the other hand, concentrated in the metallic core or in a sulphide phase.

The separation of crust, mantle, and core enables us to consider the outer part of the earth as a distinct physicochemical system. The migration of the elements within the crust has been discussed in terms of the processes of magmatism, sedimentation, and metamorphism. We have seen that the fate of an element during magmatic crystallization is primarily a function of its ionic size. A particular element appears in those minerals in whose lattices it fits most readily and with the greatest decrease of free energy. The distribution of the elements by ionic size in this way was described by Goldschmidt as the *secondary geochemical differentiation*. Magmatic crystallization also adds important amounts of a few elements to the atmosphere and hydrosphere.

The processes of sedimentation can be looked upon as leading to a further degree of geochemical differentiation. At the comparatively low temperature of sedimentary processes, ionic substitution in minerals is much less prominent, although still significant. Co-precipitation under a particular set of physicochemical conditions is, however, an important way in which certain elements become associated in particular types of sediment. The controlling factors are those pertaining to the properties of ions in aqueous solutions, and the ionic potential is of primary importance. Geochemical differentiation during sedimentation is therefore governed in large part by interrelationships between ionic radius and ionic charge.

Sedimentation also involves an interaction of the hydrosphere and the atmosphere with the lithosphere. Water and carbon dioxide are incorporated in sedimentary minerals; soluble ions, especially sodium, are contributed to the hydrosphere. Processes involving living organisms are intimately associated with sedimentation but can be considered separately; and these processes are even more closely linked with the hydrosphere and the atmosphere. Photosynthesis has probably been directly responsible for the present composition of the atmosphere; and the balance of dissolved material in the ocean is largely a function of the organic life therein. Thus in the biosphere a further geochemical differentiation takes place through the metabolic action of organisms. A detailed discussion of the cycles involved is found in chapter 8.

The series of changes so far discussed have led, on the whole, to an increasing degree of geochemical differentiation. This tendency is reversed by metamorphism. In general, metamorphism tends toward uniformity of distribution of the elements. One can visualize unlimited metamorphism as resulting in an ideal condition in which the whole lithosphere reaches a uniform composition. This may seem an exaggerated view; but that such a tendency exists is evidenced by the comparatively monotonous chemical and mineralogical composition of ancient geological formations. Compared to the chemically diverse rock types of younger ages, the Archaean is dominantly made up of gneisses of relative uniformity, which is probably due in considerable degree to long-continued metamorphic and metasomatic reactions.

Thus in the beginning the relative abundances of the elements were determined by the stability of their isotopes, i.e., by the number of neutrons and protons in the nucleus and the binding energy. The processes by which the earth was formed led to a first separation of elements according to their volatility or ability to form volatile compounds; the earth is evidently impoverished in the more volatile elements and compounds in comparison to the universe as a whole. The separation of the earth into an iron core and a silicate mantle and crust resulted in a strong fractionation of the elements according to their affinity for metal or for silicate; this fractionation was controlled by the number and arrangement of the outer electrons. The next step in the evolution of the earth was the solidification of mantle and crust, which led to a further fractionation, this time determined largely by the role of the different elements in liquid → crystal equilibria. The major controlling factor was ionic size. During geological time considerable fractionation of the elements has taken place at the earth's surface as a result of sedimentary processes; the fate of an element under these conditions is largely a matter of its ionic potential, the ratio of ionic size to ionic charge. The absolute abundance of an element is conditioned by its nuclear structure; its abundance in a particular part of the universe or of the earth is conditioned by more superficial atomic characters, such as the number and arrangement of the orbital electrons, the size of the atom or ion, and so on. The geochemical behavior of each element depends on its individual properties under the physicochemical conditions at each stage in the geochemical cycle.

The geochemical cycle provides us with an over-all picture of the migration of the elements and can best be illustrated by means of a diagram (Fig. 2). In the lithosphere the geochemical cycle begins with the initial crystallization of a magma, proceeds through the alteration and weathering of the igneous rock and the transportation and deposition of the material thus produced, and continues through diagenesis and lithification to metamorphism of successively higher grade until eventually magma is regenerated. Like any ideal cycle, the geochemical cycle may not be realized in practice; it may be indefinitely halted at some stage, short-circuited, or its direction reversed. The geochemical cycle is not a closed one,

either materially or energetically. It received "primary" material from below, bringing energy with it in the form of heat. The surface receives an
insignificant contribution of meteoritic matter which nevertheless is detectable in deep-sea deposits, where the rate of sedimentation is very low.
The surface receives energy from outside the earth in the form of solar
radiation, practically all of which is, however, reradiated into space.

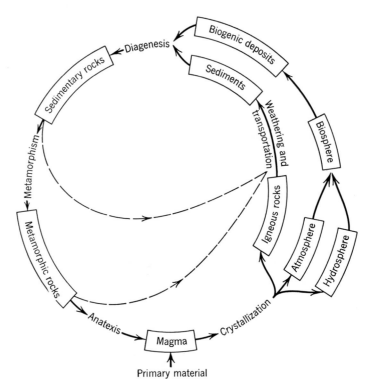

Fɪɢ. 2.—The geochemical cycle

The geochemical cycle provides a useful concept as a basis for the discussion of many aspects of geochemistry and particularly the course followed by a specific element in proceeding through the different stages. A
complete understanding of the cycle in terms of the individual elements is
one of the major objectives of geochemistry. An element may tend to concentrate in a certain type of deposit at some stage or may remain dispersed
through the entire cycle. The geochemical cycle of a few elements has been
worked out in considerable detail, but for many our knowledge is fragmentary.

REFERENCES

AHRENS, L. H. 1952 *Trans. Amer. Geophys. Union*, **33**, 193.

ALLEN, E. T., and
DAY, A. L. 1935 *Pub. Carnegie Inst. Washington*, No. 466.

ASTON, F. W. 1924 *Nature*, **114**, 786.

BARTH, T. F. W., and
ROSENQUIST, T. 1949 *Amer. J. Sci.*, **247**, 316.

BORN, M. 1919 *Verh. deutsch. phys. Gesellsch.*, **21**, 13.

BOWEN, N. L. 1928 *The Evolution of the Igneous Rocks* (Princeton: Princeton University Press).

1948 *Mem. Geol. Soc. Amer.*, **28**, 79.

BROWN, H., and
PATTERSON, C. 1948 *J. Geol.*, **56**, 85.

CLARKE, F. W., and
WASHINGTON, H. S. 1924 *U.S. Geol. Surv. Prof. Paper*, No. 127.

ELSASSER, W. M. 1950 *Rev. Mod. Phys.*, **22**, 1.

EUCKEN, A. 1944 *Nachr. Gesellsch. Wissensch. Göttingen*, p. 1.

FERSMAN, A. E. 1935 *C.R. Acad. Sci. U.R.S.S.*, **2**, 564.

GOLDSCHMIDT, V. M. 1911 *Norsk. Vidensk. Skr.*, No. 1.

1922 *Ibid.*, No. 11.

1926 *Beitr. Geophys.*, **15**, 38.

1928 *Neues Jahrb. Min. etc.*, Beilage Band **47**, Abt. A, 1119.

1933a *Fortschr. Min. Krist. Petrog.*, **17**, 112.

1933b *Handwörterbuch der Naturwissenschaften*, **4**, 886.

1934 *Geol. Fören. Förh.*, **56**, 385.

1944 *Chem. Products*, p. 1.

HABER, F. 1919 *Verh. deutsch. phys. Gesellsch.*, **21**, 750.

JEFFREYS, H. 1939a *M.N.*, Geophys. Suppl., **4**, 424.

1939b *Ibid.*, p. 537.

KUENEN, P. H. 1941 *Amer. J. Sci.*, **239**, 161.

1950 *Marine Geology* (New York: John Wiley & Sons).

KUIPER, G. P. (ed.) 1952 *The Atmospheres of the Earth and Planets* (rev. ed.; Chicago: University of Chicago Press), p. 329.

LATIMER, W. M. 1950 *Science*, **112**, 101.

LEITH, C. K., and
MEAD, W. J. 1915 *Metamorphic Geology* (New York: Henry Holt & Co.).

MASON, B. 1952 *Principles of Geochemistry* (New York: John Wiley & Sons).

NOCKOLDS, S. R., and
MITCHELL, R. L. 1948 *Trans. R. Soc. Edinburgh*, **61**, 533.

NUTTING, P. G. 1943 *J. Washington Acad. Sci.*, **33**, 121.

PERRIN, R., and
ROUBAULT, M. 1949 *J. Geol.*, **57**, 357.

RAMSEY, W. H. 1948 *M.N.*, **108**, 404.

RANKAMA, K.	1946	*Bull. comm. géol. Finlande*, No. 137.
SHEPHERD, E. S.	1938	*Amer. J. Sci.*, **235A**, 385.
UREY, H. C.	1951	*Geochim. et Cosmochim. Acta*, **1**, 209.
VAN'T HOFF, J. H.	1912	*Untersuchungen über die Bildungsverhältnisse der ozeanischen Salzablagerungen* (Leipzig: Akademische Verlagsgesellschaft).
WAGER, L. R., and MITCHELL, R. L.	1951	*Geochim. et Cosmochim. Acta*, **1**, 129.
WICKMAN, F. E.	1943	*Geol. Fören. Förh.*, **65**, 371.
WILLIAMSON, E. D., and ADAMS, L. H.	1923	*J. Washington Acad. Sci.*, **13**, 413.
WILSON, J. T.	1952	*Trans. Amer. Geophys. Union*, **33**, 195.
ZIES, E. G.	1938	*Amer. J. Sci.*, **235A**, 385.

CHAPTER 7

The Atmosphere Up to 30 Kilometers

By HORACE R. BYERS

Chairman, Department of Meteorology, University of Chicago

THE division of the atmosphere at 30 km for treatment in two separate chapters of this book, while arbitrary, is not entirely without logic. At 30 km, under average middle-latitude conditions, the nearly isothermal region of the stratosphere ends. It is overlain by extensive but tenuous layers of very high and very low temperatures. Restricting the name "stratosphere" to the isothermal layer, Chapman (1950) calls its upper boundary the *stratopause*. This chapter thus may be said to deal with the atmosphere below the stratopause or with the troposphere and the stratosphere.

It is convenient to treat the upper atmosphere separately from the troposphere and stratosphere because, at the present state of development of physical science, both the methods of measurement and the matters of primary interest are distinct in the two regions. The lower region is the domain of day-to-day study in terms of hydrodynamics and thermodynamics of air in motion and ultimately the determination of instantaneous distributions of meteorological elements, affecting what may be called, broadly, "the weather." Measurements are made by nearly world-wide simultaneous soundings by meteorological balloons released twice daily or oftener or by various types of personal observations and measurements. The upper atmosphere is of interest in a more static sense—for its unique conditions of equilibrium, its ionized layers, photochemical reactions, special constituents, etc. It is measured or explored sporadically by high-altitude rockets and by indirect effects on optical, acoustical, electrical, and magnetic phenomena.

1. COMPOSITION AND HEAT BALANCE OF THE ATMOSPHERE

The atmosphere is a medium that selectively absorbs the solar and terrestrial radiations. It also receives energy through conduction and convection of air parcels from the heated earth, including heat of vaporization released through cloud condensation and precipitation. It loses energy to space by radiation emitted at certain wave lengths. Scattering and reflection of solar radiation, the latter mainly from cloud layers, are of great importance. The mechanism by means of which a heat balance is maintained at the surface of the earth and in the atmosphere is highly complicated. The variable atmospheric constituents and the intricate patterns of air circulation are largely responsible for the complexities.

1.1. COMPOSITION OF THE ATMOSPHERE

The atmosphere consists of a mechanical mixture of several gases, sometimes called the *permanent* gases, that remain in fixed proportion to the

TABLE 1

COMPOSITION, BY VOLUME, OF THE ATMOSPHERE

Constituent	Per Cent	Parts per Million
Nitrogen.................	78.084 ± 0.004	....
Oxygen.................	20.946 ± 0.002	....
Carbon dioxide...........	0.033 ± 0.001	....
Argon...................	0.934 ± 0.001	....
Neon...................	....	18.18 ± 0.04
Helium.................	....	5.24 ± 0.004
Krypton................	....	1.14 ± 0.01
Xenon..................	....	0.087 ± 0.001
Hydrogen...............	....	0.5
Methane (CH_4)...........	....	1.5
Nitrous oxide (N_2O).......	....	0.5

IMPORTANT VARIABLE GASES

| Water vapor....... | 0 –2 per cent |
| Ozone............ | $\begin{cases} 0 –0.07 \text{ p.p.m. (ground level)} \\ 1–3 \text{ p.p.m. (20–30 km)} \end{cases}$ |

total and other gases that vary markedly with time and location. A number of tabulations of the composition of the air have been made by various investigators, all in fairly close agreement. Table 1 is taken mainly from recent sources compiled by Glueckauf (1951). Cf. also chapter 9.

Throughout the troposphere and most of the stratosphere the permanent gases exist in nearly the same proportion at all heights, the remaining constituents showing generally a rapid decrease in percentage with height.

It is interesting to note that although water vapor comprises usually less than 2 per cent of the gases even with moist conditions at sea-level, it absorbs nearly six times as much solar radiant energy as all the other gases combined. Furthermore, it accounts for nearly all the absorption by gases of the terrestrial radiation.

Ozone is of special interest because of its photochemical reaction to certain wave lengths of the solar radiation, particularly in the ultraviolet. The height of maximum ozone density is at 20–30 km. Oxygen molecules are dissociated by the solar radiation into atomic oxygen, which combines with other oxygen molecules to form ozone ($O + O_2 \rightarrow O_3$), which itself is dissociated to form O_2 and O. The three forms O, O_2, and O_3 react to achieve an equilibrium mixture which is different at various heights. For a detailed discussion of these effects the reader is referred to chapters 12 and 13.

Suspended in the atmosphere are certain particles. By far the most important are the liquid water and ice particles of clouds. Not only in the radiation balance but in the whole problem of heat transfer in the atmosphere they play a predominant part. Other particles are present which have less direct meteorological effects. They include dust, smoke, industrial effluents, various chemical particles that may be classified separately from dust and smoke, things of an organic nature such as pollens, spores, bacteria, fibers, etc., and particles recognizable only as ions or radiation particles.

1.2. Radiation Balance

Outside the atmosphere the solar radiation, at normal incidence, has a mean intensity of about 1.94 gram-calories per square centimeter per minute (List, 1951). This value is called the *solar constant*. At the surface of the earth the solar radiation that can be absorbed is very much less because the rays at any given time are normal at only one point in the tropics and, more important for our considerations here, a considerable fraction of the radiation is depleted in the atmosphere. The depletion depends on the length of the optical path, determined by latitude, date, and time, and on the nature and quantity of absorbing, reflecting, and scattering matter in the atmosphere. The radiation reaching the earth or any point on a horizontal surface, including both direct and sky radiation, is called the *insolation* at that point. Figure 1 gives an example of the effects of the atmosphere on this quantity during the course of the year at Washington, D.C.

To get an idea of what happens to the solar radiation after it enters the atmosphere, one can make up a table, like Table 2, based on the best estimates of reflection, scattering, and absorption with and without clouds and for the average cloud cover of the earth, which is 52 per cent, according to C. E. P. Brooks. It is seen that, under average clear-sky conditions, about 70 per cent of incident radiation outside the atmosphere is absorbed at the surface of the earth but that, under average overcast condi-

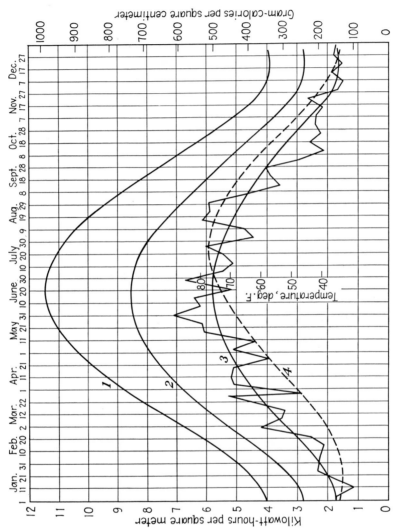

Fig. 1.—Solar radiation and temperature. Curve 1, computed insolation per day outside the atmosphere at Washington, D.C. Curve 2, insolation received at the ground at Washington, with cloudless sky. Curve 3, the same for average sky conditions. Curve 4, normal daily temperature-curve for Washington. The irregular solid line represents actually observed daily values, averaged by weeks, of the total solar and sky radiation at Washington during a representative year—1925.

tions, only about 35 per cent gets through. Thus with slightly more than half the earth obscured by clouds on the daylight side, about 50 per cent of the solar energy intercepted by the planet is absorbed at its surface.

From Table 2 it can be seen that the *average albedo* of the earth, including its atmosphere, should be 52 per cent of 0.55 plus 48 per cent of 0.15, or 0.36. This should be compared with the albedo computed by other means in chapter 15 of this volume. The values in Table 2 are taken from data given by Kimball, Baur and Phillips, Fritz, List, Neiburger, and Haurwitz and are based on measurements within the atmosphere. The details can be obtained by reference to the original articles.

TABLE 2

FRACTION OF INCIDENT SOLAR RADIATION DEPLETED AND RECEIVED AT SURFACE
UNDER AVERAGE CONDITIONS WITH CLEAR SKIES, OVERCAST
SKIES, AND MEAN CLOUDINESS

Clear skies:

    Reflection and back-scattering:

        Atmospheric scattering 0.09

        Surface reflection 0.06

          Total 0.15

    Absorption:

        By water vapor 0.13

        By other gases, dust, etc. 0.03

          Total 0.16

    Total depletion 0.31

    Absorbed at surface (1–0.31) 0.69

Overcast skies:

    Reflection and back-scattering 0.55

    Absorption 0.10

        Total depletion 0.65

        Absorbed at surface (1–0.65) 0.35

Mean cloudiness of 0.52 over whole earth:

    Absorbed at surface in clear spaces (0.48 of area)

        0.48 × 0.69 . . . . 0.33

    Absorbed at surface under cloud-covered spaces (0.52

        of area) 0.52 × 0.35 . . . . 0.18

        Total (mean fraction absorbed over the surface of the

        earth as a whole) 0.51

In geological history there have been periods when the earth was warmer or cooler than at the present time; and it seems at once evident that this must have been caused either by changes in the radiation balance or by internal changes in the earth and atmosphere. If the surface of the earth is now getting hotter or colder, it is doing so at such a slow rate that we may consider that there is, over a year or more, a heat balance on the earth and in its atmosphere. This being the case, the same amount of energy must go out to space as comes in. Except for direct reflection and scattering, this energy goes out as terrestrial (including atmospheric) radiation. This low-temperature, or infrared, emission cannot be investigated so easily as the solar radiation can, and our present knowledge of it it inadequate. Lack of sufficient information concerning the water-vapor transmission in the infrared has been a serious handicap to progress.

The absorption spectrum of the atmosphere is treated in chapter 9 of this volume. It should be noted that, in the absence of clouds, thick smoke, or dust, the principal absorption in the infrared is by water vapor. Carbon dioxide also absorbs strongly, but it is not an abundant gas in the atmosphere, and some of its strongest absorption lines are in a portion of the spectrum where strong water-vapor lines are also found. A feature of the water-vapor absorption is the existence of a "window" at the wave lengths of maximum emission, approximately between 8 and 13μ. Here 1 cm of precipitable water in vapor form—a reasonable value for the whole atmosphere—transmits more than 90 per cent of the radiated energy. This transparent band is sharply cut off on the long-wave-length side by a strong absorption band of carbon dioxide in the normal atmosphere (cf. chap. 9).

In the unclouded parts of the atmosphere the terrestrial radiation may, for simplicity, be considered as transmitted in two forms: one part which goes out into space through the atmospheric window, and the other part largely absorbed in the atmosphere but having a fraction re-emitted to space by radiation from the "top" of the atmosphere. Through the troposphere the temperature and water-vapor content normally decrease with height, so that the absorption and emission fall off rapidly. In the isothermal stratosphere the water-vapor content is small but does not seem to decrease with height, at least in middle latitudes. As a simplification, one may assume that in the bands of water-vapor and carbon dioxide absorption, energy is emitted to space as black-body radiation at the temperature of the stratosphere. In those large sections of the earth not having an isothermal layer in the stratosphere, this assumption is not valid, and the calculation of atmospheric emission is difficult.

At this point it is of interest to look at some values of the water-vapor content of the troposphere and stratosphere. In North America the amount of precipitable water in the troposphere varies from 1 or 2 mm during invasions of winter arctic air to 6 or 7 cm in summer tropical air. Data for the stratosphere moisture are scarce, but in three balloon flights carrying special radiosonde equipment incorporating an electronic dew-point hygrometer, Barrett, Herndon, and Carter obtained the measurements given in Table 3; the amounts are about 0.1 m.

A set of computations by Simpson of outgoing radiation from the earth to space at various latitudes is presented graphically in Figure 2. Although based on questionable water-vapor absorption data, it is useful in demonstrating some of the effects, at least in a relative sense. The curve for clear

TABLE 3

WATER VAPOR IN THE STRATOSPHERE

DATE	LAUNCHING SITE	TEMPERATURE (° C) AND PRESSURE (mb)		TOTAL WATER (gm cm^{-2})
		Tropopause	Top of Flight	
July 1, 1949.....	Camp Ripley, Minn.	$\{$ $-$ 62°4 157	$-38°2$ 14 $\}$	6.85×10^{-3}
Aug. 26, 1949...	Camp Ripley, Minn.	$\{$ $-$ 57°6 206	$-39°4$ 9 $\}$	7.94×10^{-3}
Jan. 7, 1950.....	St. Louis, Mo.	$\{$ $-$ 57°2 212	$-59°1$ 16 $\}$	12.62×10^{-3}

skies shows the effects of higher surface temperatures in lower latitudes, except that near the equator the colder stratosphere results in a reduced emission in the opaque bands of the water-vapor spectrum. For overcast skies the transmission from the surface of the earth through the atmospheric window is absent, and the only radiation is the black-body emission at the temperature of the stratosphere, which is known to *increase* with latitude. Curve *III* in the figure is for the mean cloudiness. In the polar regions it is assumed that clouds make little or no difference, since, on the average, they are at about the same temperature as the surface of the earth and about equally effective as radiating surfaces.

A summary of the heat balance of the earth and atmosphere is given graphically in Figure 3, computed from the best available data averaged for all latitudes and all seasons. On the left of the diagram the reflection, scattering, and absorption of the solar radiation are represented, and on the right the terrestrial effects are shown. On the left 100 units of solar energy are represented as coming into the atmosphere and 36 going out again from reflection and scattering. On the right the remaining 64 units go out through the transparent region (17 units) and the opaque region

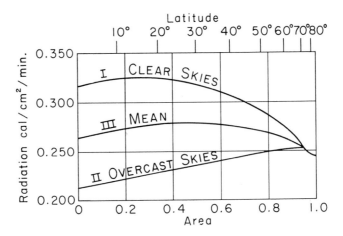

FIG. 2.—Terrestrial radiation versus latitude under various sky conditions

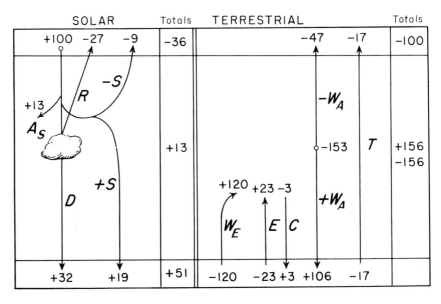

FIG. 3.—The heat balance of the earth and its atmosphere (see text)

(47 units) to make up the external balance. The various symbols and quantities are as follows:

A_s = Solar radiation absorbed in the atmosphere—13 units

R = Reflected solar radiation (depicted as coming from cloud, although some comes from surface)—27 units

$-S$ = Solar radiation scattered upward—9 units

$+S$ = Solar radiation scattered downward (sky radiation)—19 units

D = Direct solar radiation reaching the earth—32 units

W_E = Emission from the earth in the absorbing portion of the water-vapor spectrum —120 units

$+W_A$ = Downward flux of infrared radiation from the atmosphere in the absorbing portion—106 units reach ground

$-W_A$ = Upward flux of infrared radiation from the atmosphere in the absorbing portion—47 units leave at top

T = Emission from the earth in the transparent region—17 units

E = Heat carried to the atmosphere in the hydrologic cycle (evaporation, condensation, precipitation)—23 units

C = Heat transported downward by eddy currents—3 units to the surface

The balance is maintained as shown in the following tabulation.

BALANCE TO SPACE

In	Out	
100	$-S$.....	9
	R....	27
	$-W_A$...	47
	T....	17
		——
	Total.........	100

SURFACE BALANCE

In		Out	
D....	32	W_E.....	120
$+S$.....	19	E......	23
$+W_A$...	106	T......	17
C....	3		——
	——		
Total.........	160	Total.........	160

ATMOSPHERIC BALANCE

In		Out	
W_E.....	120	$-W_A$...	47
E......	23	$+W_A$...	106
A_s.....	13	C....	3
	——		——
Total.........	156	Total.........	156

2. DISTRIBUTION OF TEMPERATURE

The temperature at any point in the atmosphere is determined by the flux of solar and terrestrial radiation to and from that point *plus* heat transported by horizontal and vertical air motions and exchanged through condensation and evaporation. For the last few years the almost world-wide system of soundings at least once daily at several hundred land stations and ships at sea has been in operation and has provided ample data concerning the temperature distribution up to 20 km or more. In this chapter only a general survey of the temperature distribution will be given.

Summer and winter meridional temperature cross-sections prepared by the United States Weather Bureau from soundings throughout the Northern Hemisphere averaged for each latitude belt are reproduced in Figures 4 and 5. The isotherms are drawn, and the position of the average tropopause is indicated by the heavy line.

A conventional way of subdividing the atmosphere is by considering it to have three main parts—the *troposphere*, where the temperature normally decreases with elevation; the *tropopause*, the height where this decrease in temperature ceases; and above it the *stratosphere*, where, up to an average height of about 30–35 km, the temperatures change relatively little with height.

The troposphere averages from 8 to 16 km deep but varies widely, depending on latitude and local perturbations. It is, on the average, highest near the equator and lowest over the poles. The so-called "isothermal stratosphere" is only approximately isothermal; in the tropics the temperature increases above the tropopause, while in middle and higher latitudes there is a tendency for an increase of temperature with height in the summer stratosphere and a slight decrease in winter.

There is a wide variation in the structure of the lowest layers of the troposphere, depending upon the different relationships of heat transfer between these layers and the surface of the earth by radiation, convection, and conduction. Over land areas there is a marked diurnal variation in surface temperature, and at most points in middle latitudes there are pronounced interdiurnal changes brought about by alternating influxes of cold and warm air masses. In the polar regions, especially in winter, *temperature inversions*, i.e., increasing temperature with height, are common in the lowest layers. Over the tropical regions, heat is added to the lower layers by the relatively warm oceans and continents, thus preventing the formation of temperature inversions except in a shallow layer over land areas at night.

In middle latitudes the contrasts between land and sea are marked. Continental regions react more quickly than oceans to changes in the ratio between solar and terrestrial radiation, so that in summer, when the solar heating is intense, the continents quickly achieve high temperatures,

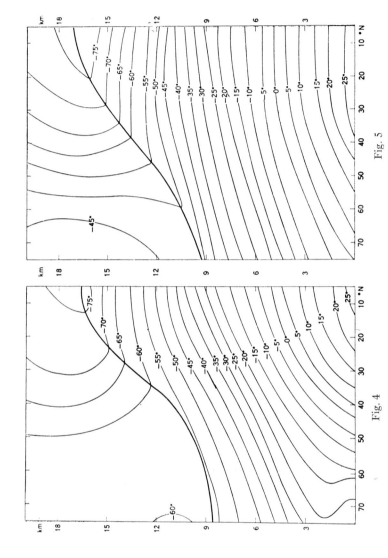

Figs. 4–5.—Fig. 4, vertical cross-section of the average-temperature field, Northern Hemisphere, in ° C, for January. Fig. 5, same as Fig. 4, for July.

and in winter the low temperatures become quite pronounced. Over the
oceans the summer surface temperatures are relatively lower, and in winter
considerably higher, than over land. This results in a tendency for the
creation of temperature inversions over land in winter and over the oceans
in summer.

In Figure 6 average soundings for some representative stations are
plotted in terms of temperature versus height, for winter and for summer.
For comparison purposes, the N.A.C.A. (National Advisory Committee

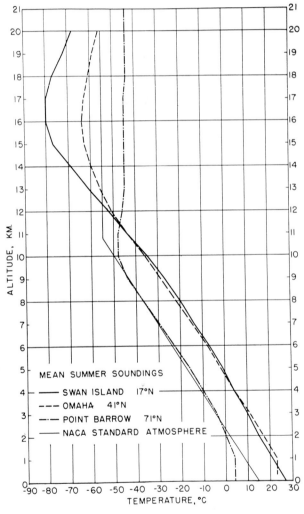

MEAN SUMMER SOUNDINGS

——— SWAN ISLAND   17°N
- - - OMAHA   41°N
—·— POINT BARROW   71°N
——— NACA STANDARD ATMOSPHERE

ALTITUDE, KM.

TEMPERATURE, °C

Fig. 6.—Mean temperature soundings, winter and summer, for selected stations in North
America, with NACA "Standard Atmosphere" shown for comparison.

for Aeronautics) Standard Atmosphere, a quasi-mean atmospheric temperature distribution used as an engineering and altimetry standard, is included. The curves show some of the features just described.

2.1. Comparison with Adiabatic Equilibrium

It is of interest to compare the temperature lapse rate of the troposphere with that which would occur if all air particles were free to move up and down and thorough mixing occurred. Parcels of air going up would expand with the decreasing pressure, and those coming down would be compressed by the increasing pressure. The absorption and emission of radiant energy in the free atmosphere does not appreciably affect the temperature over periods of several hours or less; so, by neglecting this effect and also, for the moment, heat exchanged by condensation and evaporation, we may assume that the expansions and compressions are adiabatic.

It is convenient to write the adiabatic equation as derived from the first law of thermodynamics in terms of temperature, T, and pressure, p, with the following result:

$$C_p \frac{dT}{T} - R \frac{dp}{p} = 0 \,,$$

where C_p is the specific heat at constant pressure and R is the gas constant for dry air. In the atmosphere the hydrostatic relation determines the vertical distribution of pressure, such that

$$\frac{dp}{dh} = - \rho g$$

where h is the height, ρ is the density of the air, and g is the acceleration of gravity. If ρ is expressed in terms of T and p in the equation of state for an ideal gas, a substitution gives the dry adiabatic rate as

$$\frac{dT}{dh} = - \frac{g}{C_p} .$$

Since C_p is here expressed in mechanical units, it has a value of $0.24 \times 4.187 \times 10^7 = 1.004 \times 10^7$ ergs; dT/dh then has the value $-9.8 \times 10^{-5} \,^\circ$ K cm^{-1}, or approximately 1° C/100 m. It is essentially a constant throughout the denser part of the atmosphere.

In the middle and upper troposphere the observed lapse rate usually is between 0.5 and 0.8° C/100 m, and an observation showing a superadiabatic lapse rate is usually regarded with suspicion. Such rates occur only near the ground on a hot, sunny day. The N.A.C.A. Standard Atmosphere has a lapse rate of 0.65° C/100 m in the troposphere.

Thus it can be shown that the "normal" atmosphere will resist vertical convection or other displacements, at least in the absence of condensation. The buoyancy acceleration upward on a unit mass of density ρ' in an environment of density ρ is given by

$$a = g \, \frac{\rho - \rho'}{\rho}$$

or

$$a = g \, \frac{T' - T}{T}.$$

If the adiabatic lapse rate is designated by γ and the environment lapse rate by a, the acceleration upward after leaving a level of temperature equilibrium where $T = T' = T_0$ will be

$$a = g \, \frac{(T_0 - \gamma \Delta h) - (T_0 - a\Delta h)}{T_0 - a\Delta h} = \frac{g\Delta h \, (a - \gamma)}{T},$$

showing that, if Δh is positive, the acceleration would be upward if $a > \gamma$ and downward if $a < \gamma$. A lapse rate less than adiabatic is therefore stable, since it suppresses vertical motions; a superadiabatic portion of the atmosphere is unstable. A layer of temperature inversion represents great stability.

If condensation occurs during ascent, the latent heat of vaporization is realized from the water, and, if freezing or crystallizing, the heat of fusion is added. Although this releases some 600 cal/gm of condensed water, under atmospheric conditions the effects of the expansion outweigh this heat release, so that the parcel still decreases in temperature with ascent. The resulting rate of temperature decrease with height is called the *condensation-adiabatic* or *pseudo-adiabatic rate*. Leaving off terms of negligible magnitude in the atmosphere, one may express it by the same equation as for the dry adiabatic process, but with a term $dw \times L/T$ added. Here dw is the amount of water vapor in grams per gram of dry air condensing in the expansion through the pressure interval dp, and L is the latent heat of condensation at the temperature T. We then have

$$C_p dT - RT \, \frac{dp}{p} + L dw = 0.$$

The condensation adiabatic rate varies considerably with the temperature and pressure, since w, the saturation water-vapor mixing ratio, is itself a complicated function of temperature and pressure. At $10°$ C and a pressure of 850 mb, the rate is about half the dry adiabatic; at $-10°$ C and the same pressure it is about 0.8.

It turns out, therefore, that the atmosphere is commonly in a state such that if it is moist enough and some means of setting up ascending motion is present, condensation can occur and the atmosphere will be unstable for condensation-adiabatic ascent. This is what happens in convective rain showers and thunderstorms. The ascent is complicated by mixing of environment air with the ascending mass of air, so that the actual computation of the instability is difficult.

2.2. TEMPERATURES THROUGH THE GEOLOGIC AGES

Quite apart from temperature variations which might have occurred during the formation of this planet, the earth has been undergoing temperature changes of a slow, irregular, oscillatory nature throughout the geological past, right up to the present time. We are now in a period of rapid recovery from the last ice age.

In Figure 7 is a reconstruction of the temperature record through geologic time for the latitude 40°–90° N., reproduced by permission from C. E. P. Brooks (1951). Two records are given, one empirical, estimated from paleogeographic data presented by Dacqué, and the other theoretical, calculated by Brooks through a process of weighing different factors in geographical change at the surface of the earth. Fluctuations of relatively short period, such as the various glacial ages of the Quaternary, are not shown.

In his review of past climates, Brooks summarizes the various theories as to how the changes have been brought about. In brief outline, the theories may be stated as follows:

I. Theories of climatic change dependent on external influences
   A. Variations of solar radiation
      1. Direct temperature effects
      2. Effect of increased precipitation with increased solar radiation to produce ice age (Simpson's inverse temperature effect)
   B. Changes in the elements of the earth's orbit
      1. Obliquity of the ecliptic
      2. Eccentricity of orbit
      3. Precession of the equinoxes
   C. Tidal variations, which vary the breakup at the edge of the ice cap, affecting the number of icebergs and thus the ocean temperature
II. Theories of climatic change due to terrestrial causes
   A. The hypothesis of continental drift, i.e., no climatic change over earth as a whole but continents moved to different climatic zones
   B. The geographic control of climate
      1. The geographic cycle of elevation and erosion
      2. Effects of mountain-building
        a) Lower temperature characteristic of higher altitude
        b) Increased cloudiness, causing increased reflection of solar radiation

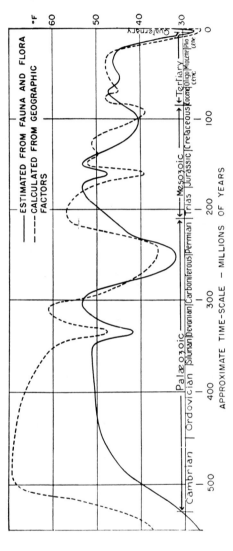

Fig. 7.—Variations of the mean temperature for 40°–90° N. in geological time, after C. E. P. Brooks

      c) Increased area of snow and ice

      d) Increased evaporation due to increased precipitation

    3. The role of polar icecaps in accentuating climatic changes

    4. Changes in ocean currents due to large-scale changes of distribution of continents and oceans

    5. Special effects on ocean and air currents such as in the Late Paleozoic

  C. Humphreys' theory of volcanic dust during periods of great volcanic activity and its effects on insolation and atmospheric radiation

  D. Variations of carbon dioxide and effects on radiation absorption

Selecting from the terrestrial causes, Brooks used four factors which could be determined from paleogeographic data and calculated the curve given by the dashed line in Figure 7. The four factors used are: height of continents, continentality, ocean currents, vulcanicity. In places the maxima and minima of the two curves disagree by several million years; but, considering the limited number of factors used in calculating the curve, one is inclined to look upon it favorably. It does not take into account the possibility of variations in solar radiation. This possibility is purely speculative and without astronomical foundation (see Vol. **1,** chap. 2, by B. Strömgren).

3. ATMOSPHERIC CIRCULATION

As a result of heat and pressure differences over the globe, a circulation of air from certain parts of the atmosphere to others must develop. The primary circulation is that which exchanges air between high and low latitudes. Differences in temperature between the oceans and land masses give rise, in certain regions, to circulations to and from summer-heated and winter-cooled continents—the monsoon circulations. There are numerous other minor circulations resulting from a variety of local effects, many of them diurnal in character. Superimposed on these circulations are the large perturbations in the air flow, associated at the surface with cyclones and anticyclones, which, in addition to producing day-to-day weather changes, cause somewhat disorderly break-throughs in the primary circulation exchange of the earth.

3.1. THE GENERAL CIRCULATION

A direct thermal circulation between the equator and the poles cannot develop in the atmosphere because of the effects of the rotation of the earth. The Coriolis force acts toward the right in the Northern Hemisphere and toward the left in the Southern Hemisphere. The driving force of the circulation can be expressed in terms of a pressure-gradient force or in terms of the slopes of constant-pressure (isobaric) surfaces and the force of gravity. Except in cases of strong friction, of sharp curvature, or of other accelerations having a small effect, there is a tendency for the air motions to approach *geostrophic* flow, in which the pressure-gradient force exactly balances the Coriolis force. Over small sections of the earth where certain curvature terms are not significant, this balance can be expressed for the horizontal wind in simple Cartesian co-ordinates as follows:

$$\frac{1}{\rho}\frac{\partial p}{\partial x} = f v, \qquad \frac{1}{\rho}\frac{\partial p}{\partial y} = - f u,$$

along a horizontal surface, or

$$\left(\frac{\partial h}{\partial x}\right)_p = \frac{- f v}{g}, \qquad \left(\frac{\partial h}{\partial y}\right)_p = \frac{f u}{g},$$

along an isobaric surface. In these equations, f is the Coriolis parameter, $2\Omega \sin \phi$, where Ω is the angular velocity of the earth's rotation and ϕ is the latitude; the x-axis points east, and the y-axis points north; u and v are the x and y components, respectively, of the velocity. This balance means that the wind tends to follow the isobars, with high pressure to the right in the Northern Hemisphere and to the left in the Southern Hemisphere, or, on a constant-pressure chart, to follow the height contours in the same way. At the equator, the Coriolis force vanishes; so this balance does not hold in very low latitudes.

A direct thermal circulation with warm air rising at the equator, flowing northward and southward, sinking at the poles, and returning to the equator at the ground could not exist because of this deflecting force. The result would be westerlies aloft and easterlies at the ground in both hemispheres. Neither of these situations is in agreement with observation.

A useful way of looking at this problem is from the point of view of conservation of angular momentum. A particle carried away from the equator toward the polar axis, conserving its angular momentum, would be flung eastward, while a particle going equatorward from rest at one of the poles would have a deficit of west-to-east momentum with respect to the earth and would have to curve toward the west. A mass initially at the equator with no zonal motion would, if carried meriodionally to latitude 60° while conserving its angular momentum, achieve a west-to-east speed relative to the earth of 233 m/sec. A similar east-to-west speed would be attained by a mass displaced to that latitude from the pole.

In actuality, the mean meridional circulation breaks down into cells, as depicted by Bergeron. The circulation, as given by this tricellular system modified by Rossby, is shown in Figure 8, with the meridional components of the cells shown in vertical cross-section and the sea-level circulation in map plan. It is seen that the three cells are associated with three wind

zones: the tropical easterlies or trade winds, the middle-latitude westerlies, and the polar easterlies. The polar front in its mean position separates
the westerlies from the low-level polar easterlies where these two wind
systems converge. In the horse-latitude high-pressure belt, the air diverges
horizontally between the westerlies and the trade winds. At the equator,
the Northern and Southern Hemisphere trade winds converge at the surface into the equatorial convergence zone of low pressure. In the upper
troposphere, westerly winds prevail at all latitudes. In all cases the mean
meridional components are extremely small compared with the zonal
components.

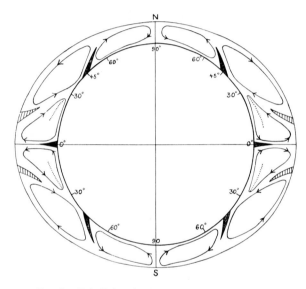

FIG. 8.—Tricellular circulation, Rossby's 1941 model

The polar and tropical meridional circulation cells are in accordance with
the expected circulation on a rotating planet with a cold pole, but the
middle cell cannot be explained easily. Rossby, Palmén, and others have
described the middle cell as a much smaller cell than that depicted by
Bergeron and have linked it more closely with the polar front. This will
be discussed in more detail in a subsequent section. The sinking in the
horse latitudes appears to come about by net heat losses by radiation at
the upper levels. It appears that, on the average, the atmosphere is losing
heat at a rate of 1° or 2° C per day in the upper troposphere of these
latitudes. Until more accurate data on the water-vapor absorption and
emission at these levels have been obtained, this cooling cannot be specified with certainty, however.

On the day-to-day charts of the atmosphere, one never sees these meridional circulations. The behavior of the atmosphere is so variable that mean charts may suppress the most important factors because of their changing location. The atmospheric perturbations play an important part in the meridional heat exchange, not indicated by the mean circulation data. In Figure 9 is reproduced a chart prepared by Petterssen showing the rate of alternation between cyclones and anticyclones in the Northern

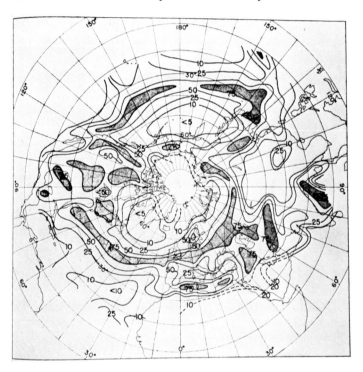

FIG. 9.—Rate of alternation (per cent) between cyclones and anticyclones in winter, after Petterssen. The computation is made by taking the percentage frequencies of cyclone and anti-cyclone centers, F_c and F_A, in squares of 10^5 km^2 and forming the ratio F_c/F_A when $F_c < F_A$ or the ratio F_A/F_c when $F_c > F_A$. This ratio is defined as the rate of alternation. Shaded areas have rates above 75 per cent.

Hemisphere in winter. From 40 years of weather maps the positions of all centers of cyclones and anticyclones were located to the nearest degree of latitude and longitude, and were grouped for each 5° square. To correct for the difference in area of various 5° squares, the frequencies were reduced to a standard area of 100,000 km^2, or approximately the area of a 5° square in latitude 70° N. The numbers are the ratio of cyclone frequency to anticyclone frequency, expressed in percentages. The summer chart, not reproduced here, is similar. These charts demonstrate the importance of the alternating cyclones and anticyclones and the various currents and air masses they bring with them in exchanging air across the latitudes. Anyone experiencing the day-to-day changes in winds and air masses in the middle-latitude regions of maximum activity—and most of the readers of this volume must live in such regions—is certainly aware of this exchange.

How the atmospheric circulation breaks up into complicated flow patterns is demonstrable in fluid-model experiments. Fultz has reproduced circulations remarkably similar to those of the atmosphere in his "dishpan" experiments, in which a shallow pan filled with water and a tracer material is rotated at the center and heated below the rim. A flow pattern obtained in the case of a rotation at 3.86 rpm is shown in Figure 10. And for comparison the 500-mb pressure contour map for 0300 GMT on February 17, 1952, is shown in Figure 11. Such properties of motion in a rotating fluid with a heat source have been studied with remarkable success by Fultz in the laboratory.

3.2. The Jet Stream and Its Perturbations

The experiments of Fultz agree with the observed motions in the atmosphere and in the oceans, in showing a pronounced concentration of west-to-east motion in a narrow band. In the atmosphere, this concentrated current, called the "jet stream" by Rossby, Palmén, and co-workers, is centered just below the tropopause in middle latitudes around the earth; but it varies its position considerably, appearing as a fast-moving meandering stream. These meanders are the perturbations in the upper westerlies, associated with the cyclones and anticyclones of the layers near the surface. Thus we find that from about 3 km upward into the lower stratosphere, westerlies prevail at all latitudes but tend to be concentrated in one or more jet streams. The perturbations appear on upper-air maps as troughs and ridges radiating from the great polar cyclonic vortex. Mean contour charts of the 500-mb surface for winter and summer, as prepared by the United States Weather Bureau under the direction of H. Wexler, show the mean picture (Figs. 12 and 13). Vertical cross-sections representing the meridional temperature and wind distribution averaged for all the meridians of the Northern Hemisphere have been prepared for winter and summer by Petterssen and are shown in Figures 14 and 15. As might be expected, the zones of strongest temperature gradient, greatest slope of the isobaric surfaces, and strongest zonal winds more or less coincide.

As was pointed out by Namias and others, the atmosphere goes through

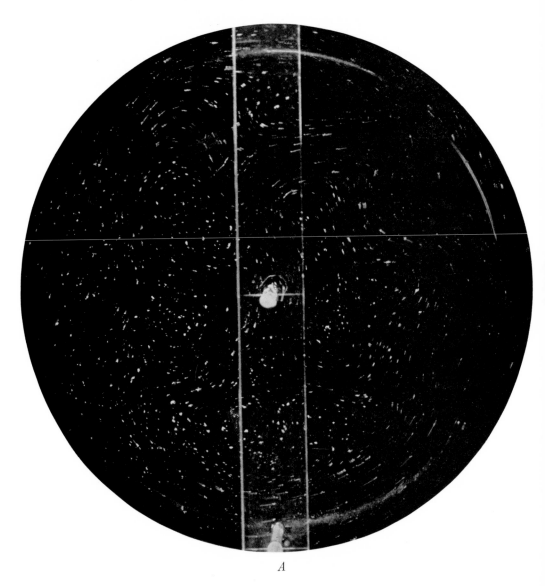

A

FIG. 10.—Flow pattern in Fultz's "dishpan" experiment. *A* is a photograph of "dishpan" heated at the rim; it is a time exposure, and streaks are caused by the motions of tracer material in the water. *B* is a streamline analysis of relative motions at surface of dishpan. Taken on July 11, 1951.

periods of perhaps a week to as much as two months, in which the circulation over a large portion of the Northern Hemisphere is largely zonal. This is followed by a period of troughs and ridges of increasing amplitude, many, as demonstrated by Palmén, leading to completely cutoff circulations. Petterssen shows that during the periods of predominantly zonal motion there is a deficit of exchange of mass (and heat) between low and high latitudes, and during the periods of marked perturbations there is an excess of such exchange. Thus the mean circulation statistics, by damping out the irregular perturbations, fail to reveal the required exchange.

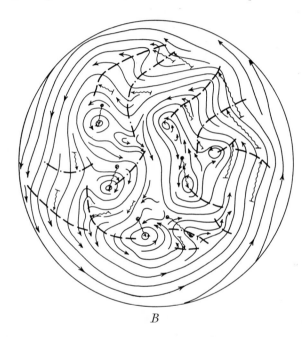

B

FIG. 10.—*Continued*

Palmén points out that the mean representation has the further weakness that it overemphasizes a secondary, but more or less stationary, jet stream of low latitudes. The winter cross-section of Figure 14 shows the jet stream centered at about latitude 25° N. According to Palmén, this is not the really strong, meandering jet associated with the principal atmospheric activity. At a given instant in the atmosphere, *two* jet streams are usually found, the one at 25°–30° latitude and another, stronger one at a higher latitude. This more northerly jet, Palmén shows, is the one that is associated with the polar front. The cross-section in Figure 16 illustrates this. With isotherms and lines of equal zonal velocity both indicated, it is

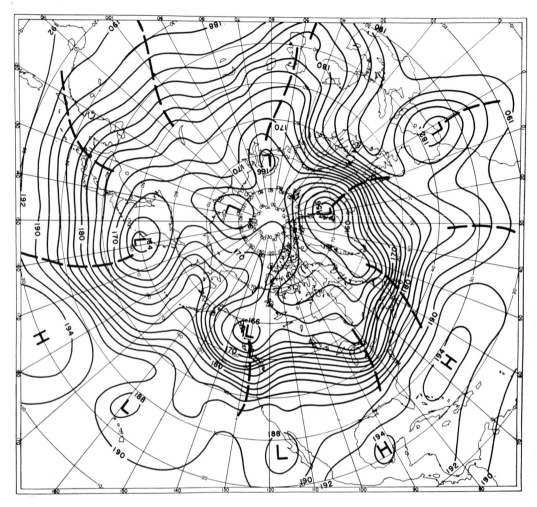

FIG. 11.—Chart of contours, which roughly approximate streamlines, of 500-mb surface in the Northern Hemisphere at 0300 G.M.T. on February 17, 1949, showing similarity to Fig. 10, turned 90°. Contour intervals are 200 feet.

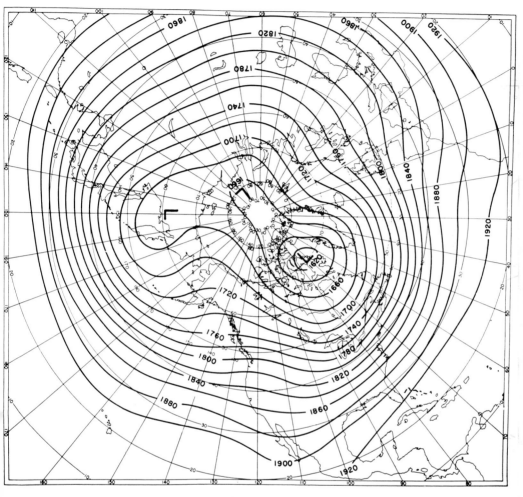

Fig. 12.—Mean 500-mb chart for the Northern Hemisphere in January taken from "Normal Weather Charts of the Northern Hemisphere," U.S. Weather Bureau, 1952.

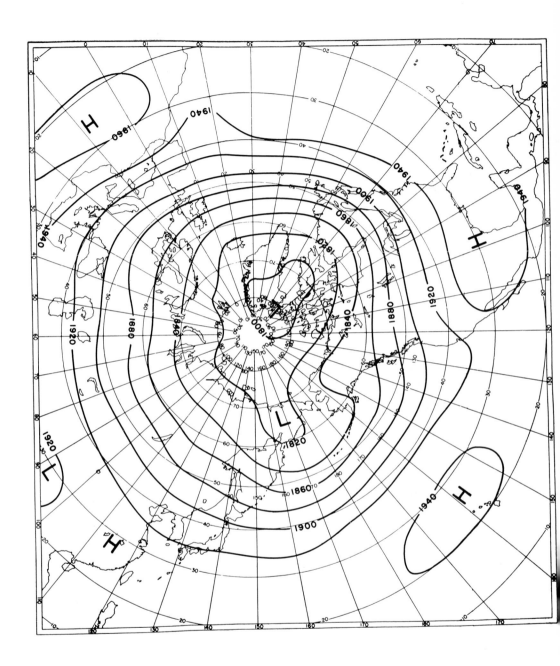

324

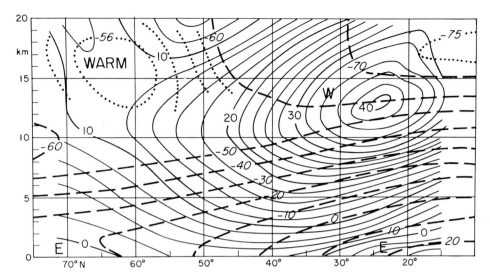

FIG. 14.—Meridional cross-section of mean zonal component of the geostrophic wind in meters per second (*solid lines*) and mean isotherms in ° C (*broken and dotted lines*), both for winter season. Data are the means of all longitudes in the Northern Hemisphere (after Petterssen).

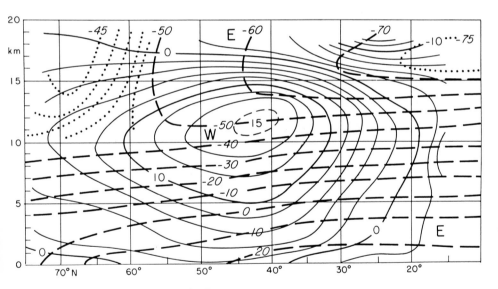

FIG. 15.—Same as Fig. 14, for summer

seen that the northern jet is in the vicinity of the strongest south-north temperature gradient, where the heavy lines designate the polar front. It is also seen that the tropopause is broken at that point, permitting tropospheric air to flow more or less horizontally into the lower stratosphere. This is the typical situation. The perturbations of the jet stream are associated with the perturbations of the polar front, where stormy conditions develop. As the air ascends upward along the slope of the front, con-

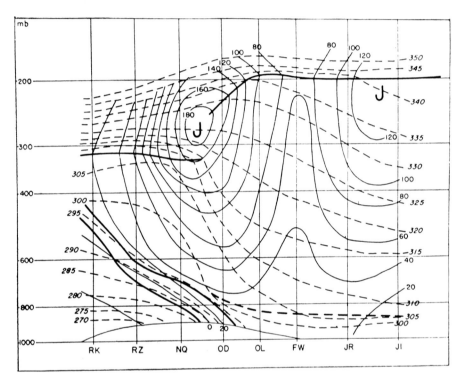

Fig. 16.—Vertical cross-section, Bismarck, North Dakota (*RK*) to Brownsville, Texas (*JI*), January 29, 1947, 03h, G.M.T. Thin solid lines are lines of equal geostrophic zonal-wind speed (m.p.h.); broken lines are isotherms of potential temperature (temperature reduced adiabatically to 1000-mb pressure); and heavy solid lines are tropopauses and boundaries of frontal layer. The letter *J* represents regions of west-wind maximum. From Riehl (1947).

densation and precipitation occur. This is therefore an important region for the transport of latent heat into the various levels of the troposphere.

Keeping the picture of the basic flow pattern in mind, we will now proceed to examine the possible mechanisms for its development and the theories for meridional exchange in the face of this essentially zonal flow pattern. Two theories will be invoked: one concerning the transport of west-to-east angular momentum poleward from low latitudes, as originally suggested by Jeffreys; the other, due to Rossby, derived from the tendency toward conservation of the vertical component of vorticity in the circumpolar westerlies. The first explains the state of affairs between the jet stream and the equator and gives a basis for meridional exchange, whereas the second explains the jet stream and the conditions encountered to poleward.

Palmén has given a clear treatment of the momentum effects, and the discussion which follows is essentially taken from his work. He demonstrates that the transfer of angular momentum per unit time through an imaginary wall extending around the earth at latitude ϕ and from height h_1 to h_2 can be given by

$$[M_\phi]\,_{h_1}^{h_2} = 2\pi a^2 \cos^2 \phi \left\{ \int_{h_1}^{h_2} \Omega a \, \cos \phi \, \overline{\rho \, v} \, dh + \int_{h_1}^{h_2} \overline{\rho u \, v} \, dh \right\},$$

where a is the radius of the earth, Ω is the angular velocity of rotation of the earth, and u and v are the x and y (eastward and northward) velocity components, respectively. The first term is the momentum flux due to the rotation of the earth and the drag of the atmosphere with it; the second term is the transport of relative momentum, due to the rotation of atmospheric particles around the latitude with relative linear speed u.

Over a long time the mass north and south of latitude ϕ is conserved, so that

$$\int_0^\infty \overline{\rho \, v} \, dh = 0 \, .$$

Thus the first term vanishes if the integration is through the entire atmosphere. Therefore,

$$[M_\phi]\,_0^\infty = 2\pi a^2 \cos^2 \phi \int_0^\infty \overline{\rho u \, v} \, dh \, ,$$

or, on pressure surfaces, since $dp = -\rho \, g dh$,

$$[M_\phi]\,_{p_0}^0 = \frac{2\pi a^2 \cos^2 \phi}{g} \int_0^{p_0} \overline{u \, v} \, dp \, ,$$

where p_0 is the mean surface pressure at latitude ϕ. It is seen that the net meridional transfer of angular momentum depends on a correlation of u and v. This last integral can be divided into two components, to give

$$[M_\phi]\,_{p_0}^0 = \frac{2\pi a^2 \cos^2 \phi}{g} \left\{ \int_0^{p_0} \bar{u} \, \bar{v} \, dp + \int_0^{p_0} \overline{u' \, v'} \, dp \right\},$$

where $\bar{u}$ and $\bar{v}$ are the mean values of u and v components and u' and v' are the fluctuations from the individual mean, so that $\overline{uv} = \bar{u} \bar{v} + \overline{u' v'}$.

The first term of this last equation gives the net flux due to meridional flow, called by Priestley the *drift term*. The second term, having the formal character of a Reynolds stress, gives the net flux due to fluctuations in the flow at the latitude ϕ. Priestley calls it the *eddy flux term*.

Surface friction has the effect of injecting west-to-east momentum into the surface easterlies and extracting it from the westerlies. So the source of M is in the easterlies and the sink in the westerlies. Therefore, $[M_{\phi}]_{p_0}^{0}$ reaches its maximum value at the horse-latitude high-pressure belt, which is the boundary between the easterly trades and the middle-latitude westerlies.

The drift term depends upon the existence of one or several circulation cells in the meridional plane. In going around a latitude circle, one must come back to the same pressure; therefore, the mean value of the geostrophic meridional flow, which depends on this pressure distribution, must be zero. The mean drift is given by the mean value of the *ageostrophic* component, $\overline{\Delta v}$. The drift term is positive if, in the vertical, there is a positive correlation between $\bar{u}$ and $\overline{\Delta v}$. Therefore, there is a poleward flux only if a poleward drift occurs, on the average, in layers with stronger west-wind components, $\bar{u}$, than in layers of equatorward drift. The poleward drift would be most effective if it occurred at the tropopause, where $\bar{u}$ is strongest, with an equatorward drift in the weaker winds above and below.

Since the poleward flux in the drift term depends on $\bar{u}\,\bar{v}$, the maximum must be where we have the strongest increase of u with height. Therefore, the drift term gives the strongest contribution above the horse latitudes, where calms exist at the surface and the statistical subtropical jet stream is immediately above.

The eddy flux term probably is more important than the drift term. It is provided for by the large perturbations of the atmosphere forming superscale eddies. Practice has shown that these eddies are easily identifiable and need not be treated statistically, as in usual turbulence studies. They are the great meanders seen in the jet streams, most of them associated with polar-front cyclones at the ground. The cutting-off of cold cyclonic vortices equatorward and warm anticyclones poleward from the main jet are striking examples of the exchange by these perturbations.

Palmén concludes that the angular momentum injected into the atmosphere in the tropical source region is transported poleward by the large-scale disturbances. This eddy transport is made possible by transforming part of the absolute momentum of the earth into relative momentum. A mean toroidal circulation, with poleward drift in the upper troposphere and equatorward drift in the lower troposphere, is visualized. This circulation derives its energy from the heat sources and sinks of the atmosphere.

Palmén's meridional circulation scheme, represented in Figure 17, consists of three cells in each hemisphere: (1) the conventional tropical cell; (2) the extra-tropical or polar-front cell; and (3) the polar or subpolar region, which does not have a well-defined circulation cell. The tropical cell is the principal source of angular momentum in the atmosphere. This cell has the subtropical jet at its poleward boundary. The polar front is given in dashed lines in the surface layers and in the upper troposphere to emphasize the necessity for exchange there in the form of intermittent

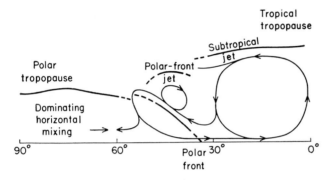

FIG. 17.—Palmén's meridional circulation scheme

"break-throughs." The polar front is not a continuous boundary. It should be noted also that there is a gap in the tropopause above the polar front and its jet, a gap through which water vapor can enter the stratosphere. The polar front is given in its winter position. In summer it would be nearer the pole, although the general picture would be about the same.

Behind the polar front, former tropical air comes in aloft and is transformed as it converges with an upper polar current, sinks, and then spreads out in the lower levels. The convergence shown around 60° N. has been associated with the polar front by Bergeron and Rossby; but, according to this picture of Palmén's, that is incorrect. The stratosphere is not included in this representation, but it is to be expected that there is a weak poleward drift in the lower part and equatorward components above.

Palmén states that the whole region north of 60° has large-scale horizontal mixing and quasi-constant absolute vorticity. This is in agreement with Rossby's theory for the circumpolar motions and the jet stream. Rossby has shown that complete lateral mixing in a thin hemispherical shell of uniform thickness would result in the establishment of a zonal-velocity profile such that the vertical component of the vorticity of the absolute motion would be independent of latitude.

Figure 18 was used by Rossby to demonstrate the effects. In that figure a comparison is made between some observed zonal-wind profiles at the tropopause level and the particular profile obtained from a constant vorticity corresponding to 2Ω, where Ω is the angular velocity of the earth.

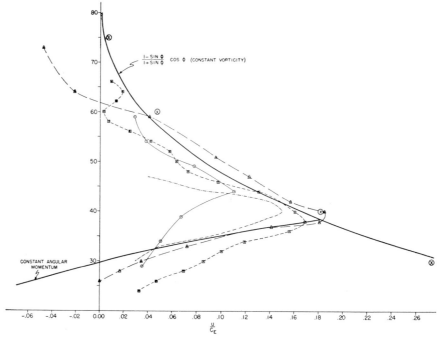

FIG. 18.—Rossby's comparison between theoretical wind profiles obtained from vorticity and momentum considerations (*heavy lines*) and some observed geostrophic wind profiles at the tropopause level (*thin lines*). The ordinate is north latitude and the abscissa is wind velocity expressed in the nondimensional ratio of zonal-wind speed to linear equatorial velocity of the solid planet. Large circles represent solar rotation data; but their relevance is uncertain (**1**, 556–57).

Below latitude $38°$ a profile corresponding to constant angular momentum is connected to the constant-vorticity profile. Also entered in the diagram are the observed data on the sun's rotation, expressed as motion relative to a hypothetical solid rotation corresponding to the sun's period of rotation at its poles, assumed to be 34.00 days. The relative velocities have been reduced to nondimensional form through division by the linear equatorial velocity of the corresponding planetary solid rotation. On the terrestrial curves, but not in the solar data, the velocity decreases sharply from the jet stream to the equator. The good agreement of the curves suggests that the zonal motion on the poleward side of the jet is accounted for by lateral mixing with conservation of absolute vorticity. Rossby concludes that complete mixing north of a prescribed latitude would result in the establishment of a constant-vorticity profile with the same total angular momentum as that prior to the mixing. The zonal wind in the southernmost part of the mixed zone would normally be much stronger than in the undisturbed air farther south. The kinetic energy of the jet stream must be derived in part from kinetic energy of the irregular horizontal mixing processes.

Rossby's work shows that lateral mixing north of the jet stream not only equalizes the vorticity but also tends to destroy the horizontal temperature gradients in the zone of mixing and to concentrate the temperature contrast on the southern boundary of the mixing zone, that is, under the jet stream. It is further pointed out, as shown by later work, that the indirect meridional circulation cell of Bergeron is too large; that, in reality, its extent is not more than 5° or 10° of latitude, just south of the front as shown in Palmén's Figure 17.

4. THE SECONDARY CIRCULATIONS—CYCLONES AND ANTICYCLONES

The perturbations in the atmospheric flow are of sufficient size and stability and move sufficiently slowly to be recognized and treated individually. In other words, it is not necessary to treat them statistically as elements of turbulence. Their movement and development are so rapid, however, that they cannot be studied in the detail one would like for accuracy in prediction. If suitable equations could be stated to describe their displacement and development, high-speed computers would be necessary for prediction; and, in fact, satisfactory progress is being made along these lines (see Charney, Fjortoft, and von Neumann, 1950).

Precipitation, strong winds, and other features of stormy weather are associated with the ascent of air in the vicinity of low-level cyclones or low-pressure centers. The anticyclones or high-pressure areas are characterized by descending air and fair weather. The cyclones are the region where potential energy is being converted most actively into kinetic energy and are therefore looked upon as the chief contributors to the whole system of atmospheric perturbations. The cyclones of middle latitudes are associated with the polar front or frontal fragments twisted off from it, in accordance with the now classical theories of Bjerknes and Solberg (1921, 1922). Potential energy is available at the front, where the neighboring cold and warm air masses may get out of equilibrium with each other. (On the rotating planet the air masses are in equilibrium when the boundary between them is sloping rather than horizontal.) Wave-like disturbances of the front are created. The potential energy is convert-ed to kinetic energy through the buoyancy forces of the cold air sliding under the warm air and pushing it upward. Cyclonic circulations develop in the converging currents. The life-cycle of a cyclone at the surface of the earth under idealized frontal-wave conditions is shown in Figure 19.

It is not easy to see how or why the frontal surface gets out of equilibri-um. A large number of theoretical studies in the last twenty-five years

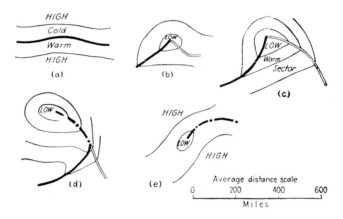

FIG. 19.—Life-cycle of an extra-tropical cyclone of the Northern Hemisphere. Heavy lines are fronts, solid for cold front, double for warm front, and broken for occluded front. Thin lines are idealized isobars. *High* and *Low* refer to relative pressure.

have endeavored to explain this by the development of unstable, originally "infinitesimally small," disturbances. Bjerknes (1951) concludes that the formation of extra-tropical cyclones is due either to unstable frontal-wave action or to unstable growth of an upper wave trough. (Note that the contours of a trough in a constant-pressure surface would follow closely the streamlines.) He finds that the strongest cyclones on record seem to form from a combination of both processes. A theory of "dynamic insta-bility" in the basic westerly current (Solberg, 1936) has appeared to give a suitable explanation of these wavelike disturbances of increasing ampli-tude. The Fultz experiments referred to in the preceding section demon-strate that wavelike perturbations in the upper westerlies are to be ex-pected in a rotating fluid with a heat source. Recently Fuglister and Worthington (1951) have found such perturbations (meanders) in the

Gulf Stream of the North Atlantic Ocean waters. Rossby, Charney, Chaudhury, and others have shown how the flow of air over mountain barriers enhances the development of these perturbations. Another factor in their generation is derived from the alternation of surface heat sources and sinks, in the form of continents and oceans distributed around the earth.

4.1. UPPER WAVES AND CYCLONES

In discussing atmospheric perturbations, there is some logic, as pointed out by Rossby, in starting with the pattern at about the center of the ver-

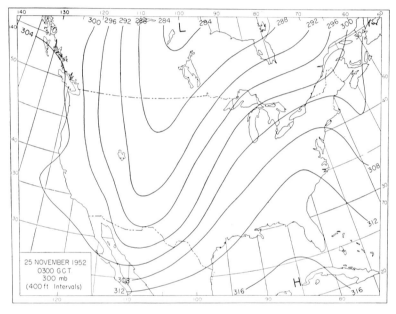

FIG. 20.—Chart of the 300-mb pressure surface over the North American continent at 0300 G.M.T. on November 25, 1952. Lines are height contours at intervals of 400 feet and correspond closely to streamlines, with high values to the right of motion.

tical distribution of mass—the 500-mb pressure surface. From these levels upward into the stratosphere there is very little change in the location of the troughs and ridges. In the lower part of the atmosphere the axes of troughs and ridges have a considerable slope, and at the surface of the earth the flow patterns are much more complicated then those found in the free air. These facts are illustrated by the set of maps in Figures 20–23, showing the contours, which are roughly the streamlines, at the 300-mb, 500-mb, 700-mb, and 1000-mb surfaces.

In the middle tropospheric layer, around 500 mb, the jet stream is a

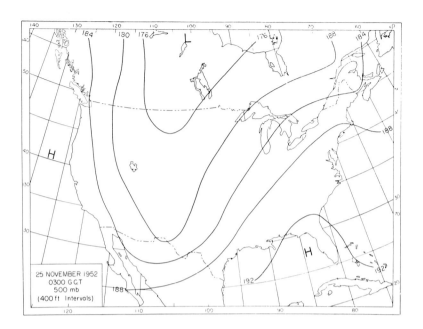

FIG. 21.—Chart of 500-mb pressure surface simultaneous with Fig. 20

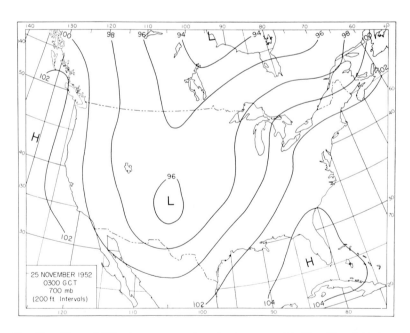

FIG. 22.—Chart of 700-mb pressure surface simultaneous with Figs. 20 and 21, but with contour interval of 200 feet.

dominant feature of the circulation, although its core is at a higher level. Here one also finds, associated with the jet stream, the polar front existing all around the middle latitudes and, as Palmén (1951) points out, more continuous and striking than it is at the surface of the earth. The vertical cross-section in Figure 24, drawn by Palmén for observations at 0300 GMT, November 30, 1946, averaged over several meridians in North America, shows the typical situation. The polar-front zone is represented

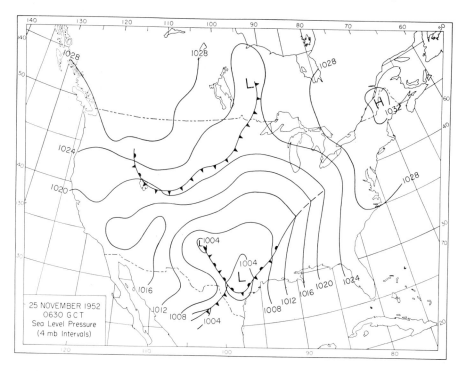

Fig. 23.—Sea-level pressure chart, $3\frac{1}{2}$ hours after those of Figs. 20, 21, and 22. Isobars entered at 4-mb intervals.

by the two heavy lines sloping down to the surface of the earth under the jet stream (*W*). The center of the jet is associated with a typical break in the tropopause, which is here somewhat poorly defined. In this special case, Palmén finds three different tropopauses: a tropical one around 100 mb, a subtropical one between 200 and 250 mb, and a polar one (with multiple structure) over the northern part of the section. In the present discussion no attempt will be made to describe the technical details of how the frontal and tropopause boundaries are located; the reader may be willing to accept the statement that they are well established through

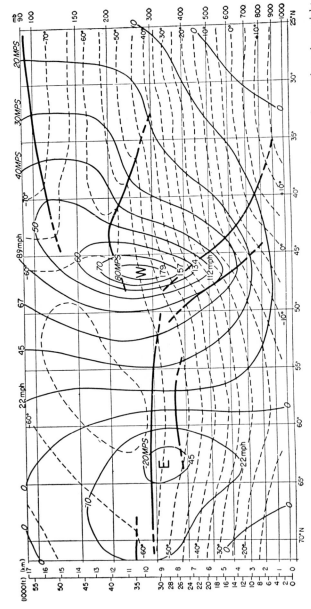

FIG. 24.—Mean cross-section for 0300 G.M.T., November 30, 1946, over North America in a case of approximately straight west-east flow. Heavy lines indicate boundaries of the principal frontal layer (polar front) and tropopauses. Thin solid lines indicate zonal wind velocity, and dashed lines the temperature (° C). From Palmén (1951).

careful analysis procedures. It should suffice to point out that the air north of the polar front at a level such as at 500 mb is 15°–25° C colder than the air to the south of it.

It is important for our discussion to realize that with the meandering of the jet stream comes a series of wavelike displacements of the polar front and its accompanying tropopause perturbation. These wave disturbances in the upper westerlies are therefore linked with the frontal waves, cyclones, and anticyclones observed at the surface of the earth. In terms of pressure, these waves form troughs and ridges in the constant-pressure surfaces, such as the 500-mb surface. And, as pointed out before, it is in these middle-troposphere levels that their action can be followed and understood most easily.

Although there is still no completely satisfactory theory for the initiation of these disturbances of the upper westerlies, there are three recognized causes: (1) waves formed by flow over mountain barriers; (2) disturbances of the general circulation by irregularly distributed heat sources, especially oceans (winter) and continents (summer); (3) the possibility of inherent dynamic instability of the zonal current in a portion of the atmosphere having strong temperature gradients. All three of these effects can be demonstrated in hydrodynamic model experiments.

From a study of synoptic charts, one gains the impression that extratropical cyclones are induced by moving disturbances already in existence. Every disturbance seems to be developed from or affected by a pre-existing one. In the polar-front zone there is a concentration of potential energy between the juxtaposed polar and subtropical air masses. It would seem that a traveling middle-troposphere disturbance can induce there an irreversible process initiating the life-cycle of a cyclone (Fig. 19).

The so-called *long waves* of the middle troposphere, with wave lengths of 45°–90° in longitude, have been studied most extensively in explaining and predicting perturbations in middle latitudes ($30° < \phi < 60°$). Their horizontal dimensions are greater than the dimensions of most polar-front cyclones seen on surface charts. They correspond more in size to the cyclone family as first described by Bjerknes and Solberg. At the 500-mb level the cyclones that are individual members of the cyclone family appear as minor wavelike perturbations within the pattern of the long waves.

Following an approach used by Rossby, many meteorologists have made studies of displacements of these long waves. Rossby's starting point was the principle of conservation of vorticity. In an ideal atmosphere where there is no horizontal density gradient, an air parcel moving horizontally preserves its absolute vorticity about a vertical axis. This vorticity is made up of the vertical component of the vorticity of the earth, given by the Coriolis parameter, f, and the vorticity, Z, of the air relative to the earth. Thus $f + Z = $ Constant. The two terms f and Z are positive in a counterclockwise sense when viewed from above, as on a map, in the Northern Hemisphere. If the motion is not completely horizontal, the vertical components will be expressed by horizontal divergence terms in accordance with the equation of continuity. In applying this simple form of the vorticity equation, it is then necessary to choose a level where the horizontal divergence vanishes. Finding a "level of nondivergence" is an important preoccupation of those who work with this method. Fortunately, such a level often exists in the middle troposphere.

On the basis of these ideal conditions, Rossby introduced a formula for the displacement of the long waves in the upper westerlies. Treating these waves as simple harmonic oscillations in a horizontal current without divergence or shear, he showed that the speed of propagation of the wave, C, is given by

$$C = U - \frac{\beta L^2}{4\pi^2},$$

where U is the speed of the zonal current in which the wave occurs, L is the wave length, and β is the northward rate of increase of the local vertical component of vorticity of the earth ($\beta = \partial f/\partial y$). If L and U are of the usual magnitudes found in the atmosphere (U, 10–100 m sec^{-1}; and L, 1000–5000 km), the wave proceeds eastward at a speed somewhat smaller than U. If $L = 2\pi(U/\beta)^{1/2}$, $C = 0$, and the wave is stationary; if L is larger, $C < 0$, and the wave moves westward. The case of $U = C$ is shown by Rossby to be only transitory in the atmosphere.

Petterssen (1952) improved upon the Rossby equation by taking into account the horizontal shear of the wind, an important factor in most cases. He also considered the asymmetry or tilt of the trough and wedge lines from a meridian and some other terms. In its simplest form, neglecting the tilt and small-scale effects, the wave speed, C, is given by

$$C = \frac{U - \beta\,(L/2\pi)^2}{1 + (L/2\pi B)^2},$$

where the symbols are the same as in Rossby's formula, but with a new term, B, introduced. B is the half-width of the jet stream and can be taken as the mean of the distances from the core of the jet to the points north and south of it, where the speed reaches $U/2$. It is through B that the shear enters into the equation.

Johannessen and Cressman applied this formula to approximately 150 cases, to predict the 24-hour displacements of troughs and ridges on the 500-mb chart. They found that the computed predictions were better than those obtained by linear extrapolation of the motions. In 50 cases selected on the basis of their fulfilling the requirements of the model for which the formula was derived (well-defined sinusoidal pattern and fairly simple and symmetrical velocity profile across the jet), it was found that the error in the computed predictions of 24-hour displacement of troughs and ridges had a mean value of $2°.8$ longitude as against $5°.5$ for an extrapolation forecast. The average observed speed in these 50 cases was $9°.4$ longitude per day; hence the average error in the computated forecast was about 30 per cent.

One is probably justified in assuming that the errors come from oversimplifications in the assumptions of the Rossby and Petterssen formulae. For example, it is assumed that the atmosphere is *barotropic*, that is, has no horizontal density gradients in the region in question. This is far from the true state of affairs, especially in the vicinity of the jet stream, where, on the contrary, the atmosphere is strongly *baroclinic*.

The vorticity relationships have been applied to middle-tropospheric maps to produce a prognostic chart of contours of an isobaric surface. This has been done by Charney *et al.* (1950), using a high-speed digital computor. With a simple barotropic model, a 24-hour forecast requires about two million multiplications for an area slightly larger than the United States. Stated in its simplest form, the computation involves determining and then applying the 500-mb height tendency over the map from some hundreds of points on the basis of vorticity conservation. The success of the prognosis has been encouraging. A baroclinic model has been devised for machine computation, and it promises even greater success.

Riehl *et al.* (1952) have drawn attention to the forecasting value of jet-stream studies. By charting the speeds as they vary along the jet (isotach analysis), one can see the regions of probable horizontal convergence, where the wind decreases downstream, and probable horizontal divergence, where the wind increases downstream. At the jet-stream altitudes these zones of divergence and convergence are associated with vorticity-producing vertical circulations. Riehl finds, as might be expected, that the maximum gradients in wind speed are around the speed maxima. These speed maxima move along the jet, seemingly shot off from perturbations upstream. There often is enough time lag between their appearance and the development of cyclones to make them useful predictors.

4.11. *Influence of other layers.*—Theoretical studies, model experiments, and observed conditions on upper-air charts all seem to justify the emphasis that meteorologists place on the long waves of the middle and upper troposphere. This emphasis implies that atmospheric perturbations are derived from the general circulation which naturally develops in a rotating fluid to which a heat source or sink is applied. The heat inequalities of continent and ocean and the wave-producing effects of mountain ranges modify the pattern. The fact that this type of treatment gives satisfactory results should not be interpreted so as to obscure other causes and effects. Among these are (1) perturbations in the stratosphere and (2) disturbances generated at or near the surface of the earth.

Although the horizontal and vertical temperature distributions in the stratosphere are radically different from those of the troposphere, nevertheless the same types of perturbations can occur in that upper layer as in the lower one, as can also be demonstrated by model experiments. Perturbations of this type, originating from the same cause as those in the troposphere, would be associated with the lower ones, and one would not expect to gain much by concentrating on them. Another possible cause of stratospheric perturbations, however, demands careful attention. That is the distribution of energy sources in the stratosphere derived from direct solar effects. As our knowledge of the sun and its emanations, particularly in connection with solar disturbances, has increased, we have also accumulated more information about the upper atmosphere. Putting the two bodies of knowledge together, we have noted some striking relationships, most of which are detailed in other chapters of this volume. As a possible source of stratospheric disturbances, the variations in the ultraviolet emission from the sun have received the most attention. It is in this part of the spectrum that the ozone layer of the stratosphere absorbs so strongly, and it is argued that the unequal distribution of ozone over the earth guarantees an unequal reaction to the variations in the ultraviolet, and thus heat inequalities. The problem of ozone absorption and ozone balance is not a simple one, and the physical nature of the connection between atmospheric perturbations and ozonosphere processes is not yet understood. An interesting analysis of this connection, mainly negative, has been presented by Wexler. A variety of statistical correlations between weather, climate, and some solar variables, including sunspots, solar flares, etc., has been made. Some of these are about as profound as the correlations between sunspots and economic cycles! Others seem to bear up under the scrutiny of the best statistical minds. Notable recent contributions along these lines are those of Duel and Duel (1948) and of Willett (1950, 1951). These results continue to fan the spark of hope that the physical connection will soon be discovered. Meanwhile, these upper-stratosphere regions are outside the realm of synoptic observations (radio-sondes seldom reach the 20-km height of which they are capable), so that they are left out of consideration in daily meteorological practice.

As has been pointed out, the polar front and similar discontinuities represent zones of concentration of potential energy. Cyclones, other than those of tropical origin, are associated with internal waves on these surfaces of discontinuity between two air masses of different potential temperature. These discontinuities or fronts have slopes of the order of $1:100$. As shown in the discussion of the general circulation, the air currents converge into the belt of lowered pressure existing along these fronts, and the warmer air ascends to levels where, if sufficient water vapor is present, condensation and probably precipitation will occur. These fronts also show, along their lines of intersection with the ground, a wavelike pattern. The cyclones form at the poleward extensions of these waves, where, one sees with a little reflection, the circulation must be cyclonic. These regions become folded valleys in the frontal surface, up which the warm air flows.

These polar-front cyclones may in some cases be low-level disturbances which do not appear distinctly in the middle troposphere. In some cases the polar air mass is so shallow that it does not extend, let us say, to the 500-mb surface except at some great distance poleward from its front at the ground. The treatment of atmospheric perturbations from the middle-tropospheric point of view may overlook these disturbances. As shown in the representation of the life-cycle of the extra-tropical cyclone in Figure 19, there is an initial stage in which the cyclone appears only as a minor wave in the front. It is this stage that sometimes appears at the ground without being reflected aloft. More often, however, it seems to be some upper perturbation that gives the initial impulse to the low-level currents to behave that way.

Cyclones tend to come in families constituted of individuals of different ages of maturity or senility. The death of a cyclone comes after it has been completely surrounded by cold air (occluded), so that no potential energy between air masses of different potential density is left. An "idealized" cyclone family is shown in Figure 25. The family is always associated with a major perturbation of the upper westerlies, with concomitant jet-stream meander, and the breaking-through at the surface of a great mass of polar air pushing equatorward and a poleward flow of tropical air. Advocates of the middle-troposphere approach point out that a study of the long waves in the upper westerlies is the best way to get at these major happenings in the atmosphere.

During the 1920's the Norwegian school of meteorologists, led by V.

Bjerknes, built up the polar-front or air-mass analysis concept. It was based largely on inferential or "indirect" aerology, since aerological observations were then few and infrequent. The treatment of atmospheric perturbations was on the basis of the frontal waves as seen at the surface. Efforts are now directed toward discovering the key to "dynamic instability" leading to unstable waves in the middle and upper troposphere, where the jet stream and polar front mark out their wavy pattern.

Before leaving the subject of extra-tropical cyclones, it is proper to ask whether there are any sources of energy other than that derived from the general circulation or the potential energy of juxtaposition of differing air masses. An important energy source is the latent heat contained in the water vapor, part of which, characteristically, is released by precipitation

FIG. 25.—Idealized cyclone families around the North Pole to the trade-wind belt, showing streamlines, fronts, and pressure centers. From Bjerknes and Solberg (1922).

in cyclones. It is not a difficult matter to compute the energy thus released, for it is exactly proportional to the mass of water precipitated, which, at least over continents, can be fairly well measured and estimated. From wind and related data it is possible to compute or estimate reasonably well the kinetic energy of the cyclone. This latter must be equal to the latent and potential energy released. On the basis of computations of this kind, it is estimated that in the average extra-tropical cyclone the latent heat of condensation accounts for something of the order of 10 per cent or less of the energy. This is not true for tropical cyclones. The occasional development of strong cyclones over continental areas without precipitation or even appreciable cloudiness is an indication that the latent heat of condensation is not necessary. Also it is found that, above about 2 km, most extra-tropical cyclones have lower temperatures in them than in the surrounding areas of higher pressure.

The problem of energy released through heat of condensation has appeared in a different connection recently. Langmuir has put forth the idea that the atmosphere is somehow in such a state that the release of precipitation by artificial nucleation at one point produces profound consequences in the form of great storms and a general upset of the circulation pattern over a whole continent. The idea has met great resistance, since it is backed by a form of statistical analysis in which definite proofs are hard to find.

4.12. *Zones of convergence.*—In addition to the polar front and its derivatives, there are a number of other zones of horizontal convergence in the atmosphere. Most important of these is the *equatorial convergence zone*, the zone of convergence of the trade-wind systems of the two hemispheres. Unlike the polar-front zone, it has no significant, persistent temperature differences across it. The zone is one of weak air currents and, from nautical terminology, also carries the name of the *doldrums*, or belts of calms. A net upward motion and therefore heavy clouds and rain are found there. It migrates seasonally to as far as 15° or more north and south of the equator in some places, reaching its northernmost point in September and southernmost in March, corresponding to the seasons of highest temperatures in the oceans. The reverse Coriolis effect on trade-wind air from one hemisphere moving into the other accentuates the conflict in wind direction on the two sides of the zone. When it is at or near its seasonal maximum displacement, the equatorial convergence zone plays a part in the formation of tropical cyclones (hurricanes and typhoons).

Monsoon-wind systems have convergence zones associated with them. Although monsoons have been defined merely as winds that come in from the sea during summer and from land during winter, the true monsoon amounts to more than that. In the Indian monsoon there is convergence between the very humid air from the Indian Ocean and the westerlies coming from the Mediterranean across Arabia and the Arabian Sea, and the heaviest monsoon rains occur in this convergence zone. Farther east the monsoon is linked with the equatorial convergence zone, the monsoon air being Southern Hemisphere air from the South Indian Ocean. Along the coast of China the summer monsoon blows from the south and southeast, converging against the prevailing middle-latitude westerlies. In Central America the monsoon is tied in with the equatorial convergence zone. Along the Pacific Coast of Mexico a weak southwest monsoon develops in summer, which converges with the trade winds from the Atlantic and the Caribbean. With the aid of the mountains, the moisture is thrust upward to greater heights. The water vapor carried northward in the upper air from this source has an important part in the summer rains of the United States and southern Canada.

Convergence with a diurnal period associated with afternoon sea breezes is noted in some places, particularly on the Florida peninsula, as described by Byers and Rodebush (1948), in Malaya, Java, and possibly other localities.

Vertical motions in mountainous regions are important in producing or increasing clouds and precipitation on windward slopes, as well as aridity (*rain shadow*) on the leeward sides.

5. TROPICAL CYCLONES AND TROPICAL WEATHER

Tropical cyclones, called *typhoons* in the western North Pacific, *hurricanes* in the Atlantic-Caribbean area and elsewhere, are greatly different from the extra-tropical cyclones already discussed. The following distinguishing features are most prominent:

1. They form only at certain seasons.

2. They are found only in certain regions of the tropics.

3. They do not form with any regularity, even in their appropriate season and region. This suggests more or less accidental causes in their origin.

4. They form only in those ocean areas having a high surface temperature, 26° or 27° C being the lowest such temperature observed at the time and place of formation.

5. They form in an atmosphere that is essentially barotropic.

6. They derive their energy from the latent heat of condensation.

7. They are about one-third the size of extra-tropical cyclones.

8. They are many times more intense than extra-tropical cyclones, occasionally having central sea-level pressure of 900 mb (675 mm or 26.55 inches Hg) or lower and surface winds often exceeding 100 knots.

9. They can exist only over the oceans and die out rapidly on reaching land.

10. They have a central core of calm or very light winds. This central region, called the *eye*, has a diameter, on the average, of about 20 km and is largely free of heavy clouds.

11. They have not been observed within 5° of the equator, thus indicating the importance of the Coriolis force in their development and maintenance; but the centrifugal force is greater than the Coriolis force when the circulation has developed (by about 30 times at a radius of curvature of 25 miles and a 100-mph wind at $\phi \simeq 15°$).

The regions of formation and movement of tropical cyclones are represented schematically in Figure 26. They have their maximum frequency in the late summer and early fall of their respective hemispheres. The southwestern North Pacific tropical cyclones greatly exceed in frequency those found in other regions. Those of the North Indian Ocean, the South Indian Ocean, the South Pacific, and the North Atlantic are of about equal frequency, while least frequent are those off the Pacific Coast of Mexico and off northwest Australia. It is interesting to note that there are no tropical cyclones in the South Atlantic or in the eastern South Pacific. A failure of the equatorial convergence zone to be carried noticeably south of the equator in these regions is associated with this lack.

5.1. Lesser Tropical Disturbances

A clear view of processes operating in tropical cyclones can be obtained best by examining, first, the more common, though unspectacular, tropical disturbances. These have been described most completely by Riehl (1945).

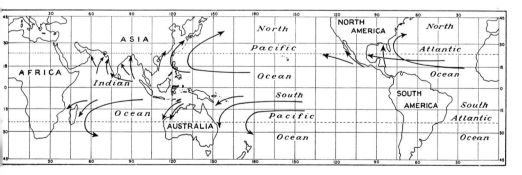

Fig. 26.—Regions of formation and movement of tropical cyclones

They may be of the shear-line type, of which the equatorial convergence zone is the best example, or they may have the character of transverse waves. In addition to the equatorial convergence zone, east-west-oriented shear lines of lesser magnitude are found in the tropics. Often they are the remnants of polar fronts swept into the tropics with the flow still nonuniform, although density differences have disappeared. In other cases they result from some peculiar configuration of the flow imposed by crowding of the subtropical highs by extra-tropical disturbances.

The transverse waves, as described by Riehl, are essentially of two types: (1) waves in the deep easterlies or (2) waves in the upper westerlies over shallow easterlies. While neither of these looks impressive on pressure or streamline charts, the high moisture content of their medium results in the production of copious rains from such minor perturbations. The troughs of these waves appear only as poleward bulges of the isobars or streamlines. In this sense the two types of transverse waves have the same appearance at the surface. Their differences are found aloft and also in their direction of movement. The waves in the easterlies exhibit only perturbed easterlies at all heights. The waves in the upper westerlies are found where westerlies extend aloft equatorward over easterlies, and they progress from west to east against the low-level winds.

Riehl (1951), after examining a prodigious amount of data from the Pacific and Atlantic, concludes that tropical storms never develop spontaneously but always in a pre-existing disturbance. "The combination or superposition of disturbances," he writes, "usually results from motion from different directions or at different rates. Among many possibilities, a common type is westward travel of a wave trough in the easterlies that intersects an ECZ [equatorial convergence zone] extending east-west. At other times such wave troughs become coupled with the southern extensions of eastward-moving troughs in the upper westerlies. . . . The superpositions, therefore, can be horizontal and/or vertical."

Riehl points out that, while most tropical depressions form in consequence of superposition, the great majority of these circulations do not develop beyond a weak wind field with maximum wind speeds of about 25–30 knots. "Sometimes," he states, "such weak centers will persist in steady state up to a week and then suddenly deepen."

These nonviolent storms, however derived, exhibit thermal features radically different from those of true hurricanes and typhoons. The true tropical cyclones have higher temperatures throughout the area of ascending motion and rain than in the undisturbed surroundings. The ordinary disturbances nearly always have lower temperatures aloft than do their surroundings. In this respect they are like extra-tropical cyclones. This cannot be explained except possibly by granting that the disturbances are initially cold for dynamic reasons before the rain begins and then assuming that the precipitation is not great enough to raise the temperature above that of the surroundings. This implies that the disturbances must be created first in the upper air, since in hydrostatic equilibrium a relatively cold region has a more rapid rate of pressure change with height than a warm one.

As was pointed out by Riehl, these circulations, like any heat engine, require an abundance of the working substance, a heat pump or other device for carrying out the energy cycle, and a self-starter. The working substance is the water vapor, the cycling device is provided by a properly directed pattern of air circulation, and the starting mechanism is to be found in superposition. The weak tropical disturbances have an inefficient cycling mechanism, while the true tropical cyclones have an efficient one. To explain the formation of violent storms, one must look for a regular circulation that will produce ascent and precipitation over the greater portion of the storm area. The question is: What happens to weak tropical disturbances on those rare occasions when they suddenly gain in efficiency and develop into hurricanes or typhoons? Theories have centered around some means of accelerating and extending this mass ascent. The most promising theories relate to the mechanism of the upper outflow, which is one link that can control the storm circulation. Riehl has put forth a hypothesis, supported by some observational data, involving a sequence of in-phase superposition of wave troughs and ridges, followed by accelerations of such a character as to bring about horizontal divergence at about 200 mb over the center and convergence at this level east of it. The upper divergence causes the pressure to fall in the low levels, and the convergence to the east accumulates mass and increases the pressure below. Whereas in the minor disturbance each convective cell had its own circulation and area of return settling of the air, as represented by clear spaces, now the ascent and return settling are organized in specified large areas. The great mass ascent now liberates enough heat to keep the circulation self-supporting.

5.2. The "Eye" and Precipitation Bands

The relatively calm, cloudless "eye" in the center of a tropical cyclone has temperatures still higher than those in the rain area. The low humidities in the eye indicate that the high temperatures are caused by sinking and consequent adiabatic compression of the air. The eye is believed to be bounded by a temperature and density discontinuity surface, shaped somewhat like an inverted cone, as shown in Riehl's cross-section in Figure 27. The tropopause is broken above it and takes on a double structure, with the main cyclone tropopause giving way at the center to a higher one. The dynamics of the circulation above and within the eye are not apparent from available data.

The existence of an eye makes it easy to identify and track a tropical cyclone center by means of long-range search radar. The eye appears as a circular vacant spot surrounded by rain-cloud echoes. This is seen from the series of photographs presented in Figure 28, reproduced by the courtesy of the Naval Air Station at Key West, Florida, at which they were taken.

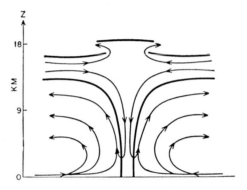

Fig. 27.—Riehl's vertical cross-section through a mature tropical cyclone, showing hypothetical model of the vertical circulation. Heavy solid lines are eye boundaries and tropopauses.

The bright areas are precipitation echoes. The station is in the center, and the range circles are 10 miles apart. It should be borne in mind that the intensity of the echoes varies as r^{-4}. It is surprising to find that these echoes occur in bands, with nonecho-producing areas between. Moreover, the cloud bands have a spiral configuration around the center and move spirally inward in a cyclonic direction (counterclockwise in the Northern Hemisphere). Each band approaches an observer as a heavy rain squall line. Between the bands it is cloudy, with little or no rain, so that no echoes are produced at distant ranges on 10-cm or even 3-cm radar sets at ordinary power settings.

The tendency for convection to occur in bands or lines, often called *squall lines*, is noted in other latitudes. Radar scans in thunderstorm conditions frequently show the thunderstorms forming in lines running more or less along the wind direction of the layers of 1000–2000 m. In an intensive radar study made in Ohio in 1947, Byers and Braham (1949) reported that thunderstorms appeared in lines on 32 out of 56 days on which thun-

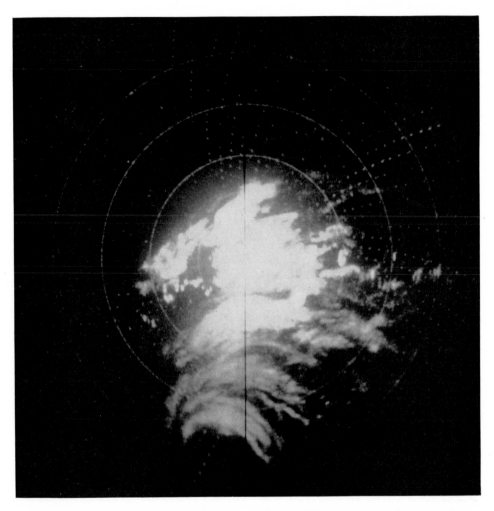

FIG. 28*A*.—Hurricane of Sebtemper 21, 1948, at 0^h40^m E.S.T.; north is up. Explanation in text (U.S. Navy photograph).

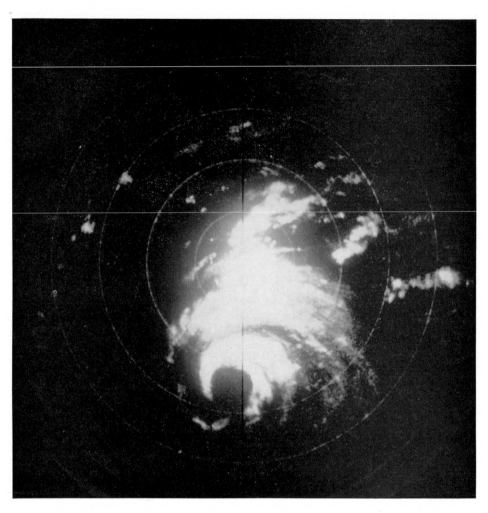

Fig. 28*B*.—Same, at 6^{h}00^m

FIG. 28C.—Same, at 9ʰ00ᵐ

Fig. 28D.—Same, at 11ʰ31ᵐ

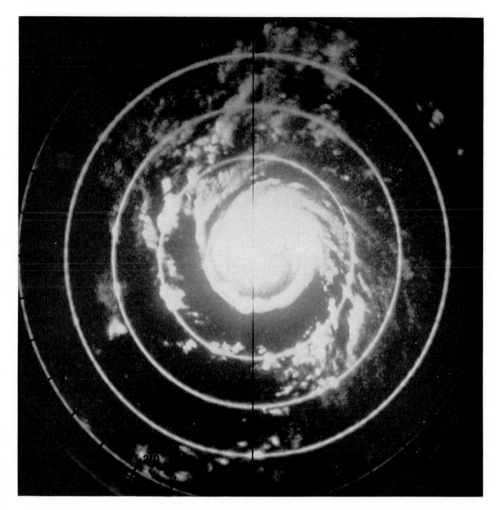

FIG. 28*E*.—Same, at 11ʰ55ᵐ

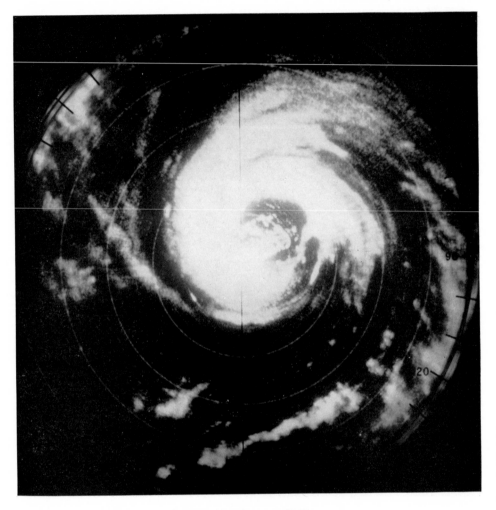

F<small>IG</small>. 28*F*.—Same, at 12^{h}28^m

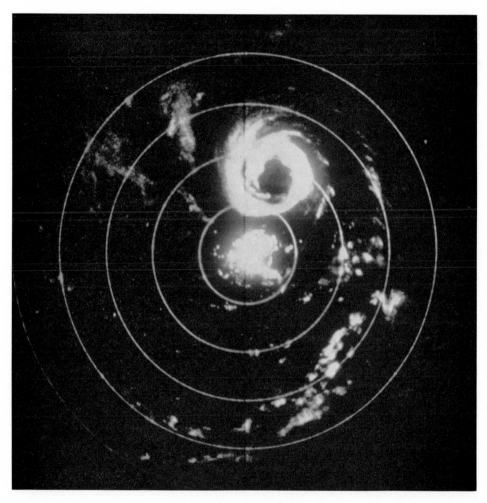

FIG. 28*G.*—Same, at 15ʰ04ᵐ

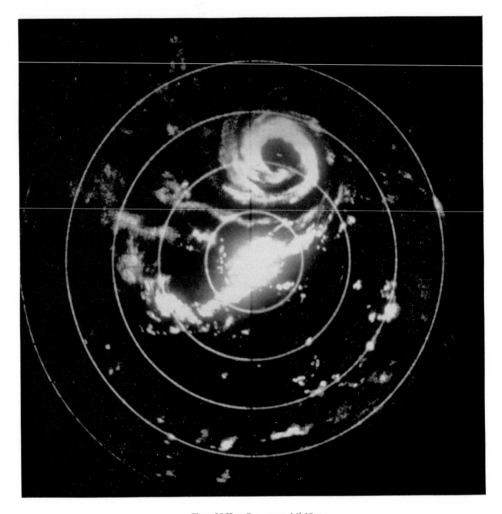

FIG. 28*H*.—Same, at 16ʰ10ᵐ

derstorms were observed by long-range radar. The lines on 6 days occurred along surface fronts, on 19 days they were ahead of surface cold fronts, and on the remaining 7 days they apparently had no connection with surface fronts. An example of a series of squall lines in Ohio is shown in the radarscope photograph reproduced in Figure 29. The explanation of the apparent predisposition toward extreme convection in the atmosphere to occur in lines has yet to be found.

6. ATMOSPHERIC ELECTRICITY

The surface of the earth and the conducting layers of the upper atmosphere may be regarded as the plates of a spherical condenser between which lies the atmosphere. The outer plate has a net positive charge, and the inner one a net negative charge. The condenser leaks, because the atmosphere conducts electricity between the two plates; therefore, they have to be recharged frequently or continuously. Gish (1951) estimates that the leakage current is about 1800 amp. and that the atmosphere has an effective resistance of 200 ohms, thus giving a potential of 360,000 volts. Measurements show that these values are not uniformly distributed throughout the atmosphere. At sea-level the electrical potential gradient is of the order of 100 volts per meter, decreasing with height.

The air conductivity is brought about by the presence of ions. Only the small ions, having mobilities of the order of 1 to 2 cm sec^{-1}/volt cm^{-1}, are of importance as conductors. Large ions, generally considered to be charged condensation nuclei, have such low mobilities (3×10^{-4} to 7×10^{-4} cm sec^{-1}/volt cm^{-1}) that they are not effective conductors.

The small ions are created by cosmic rays and by radioactive gases emanating from the solid earth. At the surface of the earth between 10 and 50 ion pairs are produced per cubic centimeter per second. The rate of formation does not decrease with height as one leaves the source of radioactive gases, because the cosmic-ray activity increases with height; at 12 km the rate of production is usually greater than at the surface of the earth.

Ion formation is balanced by processes of small-ion destruction—recombination between small ions of opposite signs, combination with large ions, and coalescence with neutral condensation nuclei. A balance exists between the rate of ion formation, q, and the rate of destruction, of the form

$$q = a n_+ n_- + \eta_{+-} N_- n_+ + \eta_{+0} N_0 n_+$$

for positive small ions; and a similar equation may be written for negative small ions. Here n_+ and n_- are the number of positive and negative small ions per cubic centimeter, the N's signifying large ions, with the appropri-

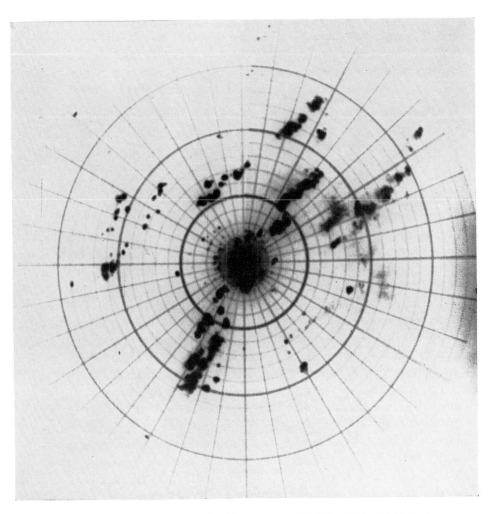

FIG. 29.—Radar picture of squall lines in Ohio on August 14, 1947, 13ʰ42ᵐ E.S.T. Dark areas are precipitation echoes. Heavy range markers are at 50-mile intervals.

ate coefficients of combination and recombination. Over most regions of the earth, at least in the lower layers, the second term—combination of small ions with large ones of opposite sign—is the most important, so that if q remains the same, n_+ is inversely ¦proportional to N_-, and n_- is inversely proportional to N_+.

The electrical conductivity is given by

$$\lambda = e\Sigma k_i n_i \ ,$$

where e is the charge on an electron and n_i represents the various kinds of ions of mobilities k_i. If an ion balance exists, n does not vary appreciably except locally, with the variations in large ions produced by smoke pollution. The atmosphere therefore readily conducts a current. This air-to-

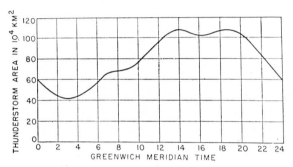

Fig. 30.—Diurnal variation in occurrence of thunderstorms. The ordinate is the average area of thunderstorms estimated to be in progress over all continents. After Whipple and Scrase (1936).

earth or "leakage" current is estimated by Linss (1887) to be sufficient completely to discharge the earth's condenser shell in 100 minutes.

To maintain the electrical balance, there must be some supply current. The generator of this current is believed to be the thunderstorm. First proposed by C. T. R. Wilson (1921), this theory is supported by most workers in the field. Gish (1951) has computed that an average of between 3000 and 6000 centers of lightning activity must be in progress somewhere over the earth at all times in order to account for the supply current. Climatological data compiled by C. E. P. Brooks (1925) indicate 1800 thundery situations, on an average, more or less continuously over the earth. With two or three cells assumed in each situation, Gish's requirement is easily met.

The best indication of a link between thunderstorm activity and the daily regeneration of the earth's electric field was given by Whipple (1936, 1938), whose curve of the diurnal variation of the area covered by thunderstorms on land areas of the earth, reproduced in Figure 30, matches the

diurnal variation of potential gradient on the oceans, Figure 31, showing
a maximum in each case around 18 hours GMT. It seems that at the same
hours of absolute time on the average day the atmospheric condenser is
recharged more vigorously than at other hours; and this effect is easily
recorded over the oceans, where diurnal effects of smoke pollution are
absent. The preponderance of thunderstorms at 14–20 hours is due to the

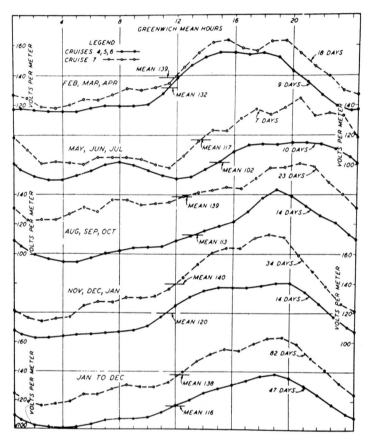

Fig. 31.—Mean diurnal variation of potential gradient for 3-month periods from observations on board the "Carnegie."

great effect of the thunderstorms over equatorial Africa and South
America.

Thunderstorms may be regarded as generators placed between the plates
of the atmospheric condenser. In some manner not yet fully understood,
the precipitation particles, especially those in parts of the cloud where
there is an ice-water mixture, are acted upon by the vertical air currents

in a thunderstorm to produce a charge separation. In the usual thunderstorm there is a positive-charge center in the upper part and a concentration of negative charge in the middle and lower levels. The surface of the earth has a positive charge temporarily induced upon it. A lightning discharge between the cloud and the earth transfers the negative charge to the ground. Thus the average lightning discharge is of the right sign to give the desired effect. Gish and Wait (1950) have measured the current flowing between the tops of thunderstorms and the higher atmosphere. A current carrying positive ions upward from the thunderheads was found to be of the order of 0.3–0.6 amp. for each thunderstorm cell. This supply current from all thunderstorms over the earth must equal the leakage or air-earth current of 1800 amp., thus requiring the more or less constant presence of 3000–6000 thunderstorm cells over the earth. According to observations, this is a reasonable number of storms.

7. CONDENSATION AND PRECIPITATION

As demonstrated by several experimenters toward the end of the last century, condensation of water vapor to the liquid phase occurs on certain available nuclei. Some of these nuclei can serve only if a considerable degree of supersaturation occurs. Such are the small ions and the small particles studied by physicists in cloud chambers. Others, especially if large and composed of substances having a chemical affinity for water, take on water and grow into noticeable droplets even before saturation is reached. Given a variety of particles in an atmosphere containing water vapor, one finds that, as saturation is approached, condensation will occur first on those nuclei that are large and *hygroscopic* or at least not *hydrophobic*. It is an observed fact that in the atmosphere with temperatures favorable for liquid condensation, appreciable supersaturation is not necessary for condensation, and not infrequently it takes place with less than 100 per cent relative humidity. This indicates that there is an ample supply of large and chemically favorable condensation nuclei.

The nucleation process for the passage from vapor to the crystalline phase, or *crystallization*, is not the same as that for condensation; at low temperatures a different set of circumstances prevails, and supersaturation with respect to ice is noted. This indicates that suitable crystallization nuclei are scarce in the atmosphere and that those suitable for condensation are not very suitable for crystallization.

Saturation, or 100 per cent relative humidity, in its ordinary sense and in the sense that it is used in this discussion, refers to a plane surface of pure water and means that if the liquid water and the vapor in the space above it are at the same temperature and in equilibrium, they will have the same (saturation) vapor pressure. If supersaturation is an equilibrium condition over any other kind of surface, then that surface must exert a greater vapor pressure than does a plane surface of pure water at the same temperature.

Fog or cloud droplets depart from exact saturation according to this standard, because they neither are pure water nor have a plane surface. While the curvature causes the vapor pressure at their surfaces to be higher than standard saturation, at the small sizes where this effect is appreciable the impurity introduced in the form of the usual nucleus tends to counteract this effect. If the nucleus is a hygroscopic substance, such as sea salt, the appreciable concentration of salt at small-droplet sizes tends to make the equilibrium vapor pressure less than that of standard saturation.

As nuclei important for condensation in the earth's atmosphere, sea salt and sulphuric acid have been identified most commonly. Sea-salt particles seem to get into the atmosphere where the ocean surface is disturbed by storms or surf and to drift for long distances and at cloud-forming altitudes. Sulphuric acid is known to form from industrial and natural smokes through the oxidation of sulphur dioxide (Aitkin, 1880). Some of these nuclei carry a net charge and thereby may be classed as large ions with diameters of the order of 0.05 μ and ion mobilities of the order of 10^{-4}–10^{-5} cm sec^{-1}/volt cm^{-1}. By the time they are noticeable as cloud or fog droplets, they have grown to diameters of the order of 10–20 μ.

Precipitation occurs when the droplets grow to raindrop size, which is some 100–200 μ in diameter or larger, or when by some process at subfreezing temperatures snowflakes or other solid forms are produced. The critical size is determined by the terminal velocity of fall, which must be fast enough for the precipitating particles to reach the ground in a reasonable time before evaporating. Terminal velocities as determined by Gunn and Kinser (1949) are shown in Figure 32, together with computed rates for small particles given by Stokes's law. Findeisen (1939) has computed the distance of fall of drops before evaporating below a cloud under plausible conditions of relative humidity, etc. The results are shown in Table 4. In most clouds, the radii are of the order of 10^{-3} cm, and it is plain from this computation why most clouds do not produce rain.

The growth to precipitation sizes is not the same process that is involved in the growth of droplets to ordinary cloud size. There seem to be always enough condensation nuclei so that intensification of condensation only produces more small droplets instead of causing growth of those already present. Why 10–20 μ is a limiting diameter is not understood, but it probably has to do with the size, composition, and number of the prevailing nuclei. Occasionally, larger droplets can form in the condensation process, and precipitation may result.

Raindrops can be produced under certain circumstances by coalescence of smaller drops. A probable mechanism for this is found in those cases

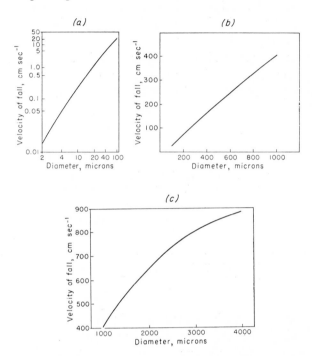

FIG. 32.—Velocity of fall of droplets of various diameters. In a the droplets fall in accordance with Stokes's law. The values in b and c were determined experimentally in still air near normal temperature and pressure by Gunn and Kinzer (1949). The sizes were computed from the mass, to give an equivalent diameter, assuming a spherical mass. At sizes in the upper ranges of curve c it is known that the drops are markedly nonspherical.

TABLE 4*

DISTANCE OF FALL BEFORE EVAPORATION

Radius of Drop (cm)	Distance of Fall before Evaporation	
0.0001	3.3×10^{-4} cm	Cloud particles
.001	3.3 cm	
.01	150 m	
.10	42 km	Raindrops
0.25	280 km	

* For pressure, 900 mb.; temperature, $+5°$ C; relative humidity, 90 per cent.

where some extra-large, let us say droplets 60 μ in diameter, form along with the usual small ones. The larger droplets fall with respect to the smaller ones and grow by accretion through collisions. With the aid of Langmuir's (1948) computed values of collection efficiencies, Houghton (1951) shows, for example, that in a cloud of 20-μ drops containing 1 gm/m^3 liquid water, a 60-μ drop would grow to 100 μ in diameter in 18 minutes during a fall of 160 m. Thus in clouds with a broad spectrum of droplet sizes, the precipitation mechanism can be initiated by this process of gravitational separation. In any event, once drops grow to precipitating sizes, their further growth is primarily by collision.

The Bergeron (1933) or ice-crystal theory of the initiation of precipitation is widely accepted. It is based on the coexistence of water and ice particles in subfreezing portions of the cloud. That supercooling—the maintenance of the liquid form—occurs in clouds at temperatures well be-

TABLE 5

RATIO OF SATURATION VAPOR PRESSURE OVER WATER
TO THAT OVER ICE AT SAME TEMPERATURE

	TEMPERATURE (° C)									
	−50	−45	−40	−35	−30	−25	−20	−15	−10	−5	0
Ratio.....	1.62	1.54	1.47	1.41	1.34	1.28	1.22	1.16	1.10	1.05	1.00

low freezing has been amply demonstrated by repeated observations. Such a state of affairs is the rule rather than the exception. At subfreezing temperatures the saturation vapor pressure over water is higher than that over ice, the ratios of the former to the latter increasing with decreasing temperature, as shown in Table 5. This table indicates that if in a cloud at −10° C there is saturation with respect to liquid water, there is supersaturation with respect to ice, giving a relative humidity of 110 per cent with respect to ice. With the same conditions at − 30° C, the relative humidity with respect to ice would be 134 per cent. The prevalence of supercooled water at these temperatures would indicate that crystallization can occur only with great supersaturations. This suggests that crystallization nuclei are rare or have properties requiring great supersaturation. Experiments of Schaefer (1946, 1948) and others show that supercooling does not occur below about −40° C, at which temperature ice crystals form "spontaneously" without the aid of special nuclei.

The Bergeron theory of precipitation ascribes particle growth to the

vapor-pressure gradients between water and ice particles which exist together in certain subfreezing portions of the cloud. Water evaporates from
the water droplets and condenses on the ice crystals, causing the latter to
grow to precipitation size. In the life-history of a developing cloud, the precipitation mechanism will begin when ice crystals start to form among the
supercooled liquid droplets. Observations show that this seldom occurs at
a temperature higher than $-10°$ C in the natural atmosphere and more
often at about $-20°$ C or less. Sometimes the supercooling proceeds without the presence of ice crystals until the temperature of spontaneous
nucleation is reached, at about $-40°$ C.

Langmuir and Schaefer (1947) were the first to demonstrate on a practical basis that the onset of rain could be hastened in supercooled clouds
by artificial nucleation. They successfully demonstrated two ways of doing
this. One way is to drop very cold particles, such as pellets of dry ice (solid
CO_2) into the clouds. Along the path of fall of the dry ice a momentary
cooling to below that necessary for crystal formation occurs, and narrow
streaks of ice crystals are created in the cloud. Another method is to introduce into the cloud a supply of crystals of another substance which has a
crystalline form similar to that of water. Silver iodide is such a substance,
and it has been used successfully in artificial nucleation. Since it is not
practical to create and handle real ice crystals for this purpose, silver
iodide makes a good substitute. It can be spread into the atmosphere as
an aerosol made by a crude type of smoke generator. Its advantage over the
dry-ice method lies in the fact that it can be spread upward by the air
currents, and, under favorable conditions, clouds may be seeded from
generators located on the ground. While this is more convenient and much
less expensive than flying over or into the clouds, the dependence on the
vagaries of the air currents renders the method less reliable than seeding
from airplanes.

Schaefer (1951) has tested a number of nucleating agents. He finds that
silver iodide begins to become active as a nucleating material at $-4°$ C
and is "completely" active at $-10°$ C. Some natural dusts were tested, in
order to determine the possibilities of natural nucleating agents. Dust
from a loam at Rugby, North Dakota, had its threshold of activity at
about $-8°$ C and became completely active at $-25°$ C. Certain soils,
clays, and sands are slightly active at -10 to $-15°$ C, but many had
thresholds of activity below -15 or $-20°$ C. For spores, the threshold is
at about $-36°$ C.

If the precipitation-release mechanism is to be found at above-freezing
temperatures, then some process favoring the development of out-sized

droplets must presumably be found. These abnormally large droplets (50 μ or larger) could grow to raindrop size by gravitational separation. Woodcock (1950) has measured unusually large sea-salt nuclei in the atmosphere under certain conditions which could lead to unusually large droplets. Cloud droplets collected on Mount Washington, New Hampshire (Staff, 1949–1952), show predominantly narrow size distributions. In only 18 out of 436 cases was 5 per cent of the liquid water found in droplets more than 3 times the volume-median diameter of the distribution. In 11 cases 10 per cent of the water was in this 3 to 1 ratio or more.

As suggested by Langmuir (1950) and demonstrated with fair certainty by Bowen (1952), the precipitation mechanism can be initiated by artificial means in warm clouds by introducing into them a water spray of drops 50–100 μ in diameter. This can be done from an airplane or a mountain peak in the clouds.

Langmuir and Schaefer (1947) showed that the initiating mechanism, whether natural or artificial, sets up what they term a "chain reaction." In the ice-crystal case, the spread of ice crystals through the cloud is extremely rapid, once a few are created. When a dry-ice pellet is dropped into a fogged cold chamber about 10 cubic feet in size, a narrow path of ice crystals in the wake of the pellet spreads so as to transform the entire chamber in about 3 minutes. In atmospheric clouds the process is helped by eddy diffusion.

In warm clouds the "chain reaction" starts as soon as raindrops begin to break up. The largest size that can hold together falling in still air has an equivalent diameter of about 7 mm (it is no longer spherical, but flattened and irregular). Air turbulence presumably splits the raindrops before they reach such sizes. The several drops which split off grow by coalescence with the tiny cloud droplets and in turn split up, and the process continues as long as the cloud has an appreciable liquid content. If all the water could be precipitated out of a cumulus cloud 1 km in vertical thickness containing 1 gm/m^3 of liquid water, there would be a 1-mm rainfall at the ground. It is agreed that the release of this precipitation helps to keep the cloud space warmer than the environment and thus to favor its vertical growth through buoyancy, with accompanying low-level addition of water vapor through convergence.

In the case of ice nucleation, the latent heat of fusion is released. It is argued that this is an important means of releasing new energy for cloud growth and even storm development. Skeptics point out that the ratio of the mass of air to the mass of water is so large that, although the amount of heat released is great, the air is not warmed enough (of the order of 1° C or less) to initiate important buoyancy forces.

In the emphasis on rainmaking, less attention has been attracted to another aspect of artificial nucleation, namely, the artificial dissipation of stratified cloud layers. By dispersing dry ice or silver iodide smoke into a supercooled, stable, stratified cloud layer, the supercooled droplets can be changed to ice crystals, which will settle out and leave a clear area. Dry ice is best, because silver iodide works only at temperatures below $-4°$ C and the atmosphere with stratus clouds is not favorable for vertical transport from the ground by air currents. An airplane flying along the top of such a supercooled cloud layer, dispensing dry-ice pellets at a rate of at least 1 pound per mile, can make a rift in thin clouds that will grow to a width of a mile or more in 20 or 30 minutes, remaining that way for a similar period of time. The usefulness of this technique in clearing airport approach areas in certain winter conditions is obvious.

REFERENCES

AITKIN, J.   1880   *Collected Scientific Papers* (Cambridge: At the University Press, 1923), p. 34.

ALLEN, R. A.; FLETCHER,
    R.; HOLMBOE, J.;
    NAMIAS, J.; and
    WILLETT, H. C.   1940   *MIT–Woods Hole Oceanogr. Inst. Pap. Phys. Oceanogr. Meteorol.*, Vol. **8**, No. 3.

BARRETT, E. W.;
    HERNDON, L. R.; and
    CARTER, H. J.   1950   *Tellus*, **2**, 302.

BAUR, F., and
    PHILIPPS, H.   1934   *Beitr. Geophys.*, **42**, 160.

BERGERON, T.   1930   *Norsk. Vidensk. Akad. Geofys. Pub.*, Vol. **5**, No. 6.
                                             1933   *Proc.-Verb. Assoc. Météorol., Union Géod. et Géophys. Internat.*, **2**, 156.

BJERKNES, J.   1920   *Norsk. Vidensk. Akad. Geofys. Pub.*, Vol. **1**, No. 2.
                                             1951   In *Compendium of Meteorology* (Boston: American Meteorological Society), pp. 577–598.

BJERKNES, J., and
    SOLBERG, H.   1921   *Norsk. Vidensk. Akad. Geofys. Pub.*, Vol. **2**, No. 3.
                                             1922   *Ibid.*, Vol. **3**, No. 1.

BOFFI, J. A.   1949   *Bull. Amer. Meteorol. Soc.*, **30**, 242.
BOLIN, B.   1950   *Tellus*, **2**, 184.
BOLIN, B., and
    CHARNEY, J. G.   1951   *Tellus*, **3**, 248.
BOWEN, E. G.   1952   *Quart. J. R. Meteorol. Soc.*, **78**, 37.
BROOKS, C. E. P.   1925   *Great Britain Meteorol. Off. Geophys. Mem.*, **3**, 145.
                                             1951   In *Compendium of Meteorology* (Boston: American Meteorological Society), pp. 1004–1018.

BYERS, H. R., and
    RODEBUSH, H. R.   1948   *J. Meteorol.*, **5**, 275.

CHAPMAN, S.   1950   *Bull. Amer. Meteorol. Soc.*, **31**, 288.
CHARNEY, J. G.   1951   In *Compendium of Meteorology* (Boston: American
                                        Meteorological Society), pp. 470–482.

CHARNEY, J. G., and
    ELIASSEN, A.   1949   *Tellus*, **1**, 38.
CHARNEY J. G.;
    FJORTOFT, R.; and
    NEUMANN, J. V.   1950   *Tellus*, **2**, 237.
CHAUDHURY, A. M.   1950   *Tellus*, **2**, 56–62.
CRAIG, R. A., and
    WILLETT, H. C.   1951   In *Compendium of Meteorology* (Boston: American
                                        Meteorological Society), pp. 379–390.

DACQUÉ, E.   1915   *Grundlagen und Methoden der Palaeogeographie*
                                        (Jena: G. Fisher), pp 432, 449.

DIEHL, W. S.   1925   *Rept. Nat. Adv. Comm. Aero.*, No. 218.
DUEL, B., and DUEL, G.   1948   *Smithsonian Misc. Coll.*, Vol. **110**, No. 8.
FINDEISEN, W.   1938   *Meteorol. Zs.*, **55**, 121.
                                1939   *Ibid.*, **56**, 453.
FLINT, R. F.   1947   *Glacial Geology and the Pleistocene Epoch* (New
                                        York: John Wiley & Sons).

FRITZ, S.   1951   In *Compendium of Meteorology* (Boston: American
                                        Meteorological Society), pp. 13–33.

FUGLISTER, F. C., and
    WORTHINGTON, V.   1947   *Hydrography of the Western Atlantic; Meanders and
                                        Velocities of the Gulf Stream* ("Woods Hole
                                        Oceanogr. Inst. Technical Report," No. 9).
                                1951   *Tellus*, **3**, 1.
FULTZ, D.   1950   *Proc. Midwest Conf. Flu. Dynam.*
                                1951   In *Compendium of Meterology* (Boston: American
                                        Meteorological Society), pp. 1235–1248.

GISH, O. H.   1951   In *Compendium of Meteorology* (Boston: American
                                        Meteorological Society), pp. 101–119.

GISH, O. H., and
    WAIT, G. H.   1950   *J. Geophys. Res.*, **55**, 473.
GLUECKAUF, E.   1951   In *Compendium of Meteorology* (Boston: American
                                        Meteorological Society), pp. 3–10.

GREGG, W. R.   1922   *Rept. Nat. Adv. Comm. Aero.*, No. 147.
GUNN, R., and
    KINZER, G. D.   1949   *J. Meteorol.*, **6**, 243.
HAURWITZ, B.   1940   *J. Marine Res.*, **3**, 254.
                                1948   *Harvard Obs. Mono.*, **7**, 353.
HOUGHTON, H. G.   1950   *J. Meteorol.*, **7**, 363.
                                1951   In *Compendium of Meteorology* (Boston: American
                                        Meteorological Society), pp. 165–181.

JEFFREYS, H.   1933   *Proc. Verb. Assoc. Météorol. Union Géod. et Géo-
                                        phys. Internat.*, **2**, 219.

JOHANNESSEN, K. R.,
and CRESSMAN, G. P.   1952   *Bull. Amer. Meteorol. Soc.*, **33**, 267.
KIMBALL, H. H.   1927   *Month. Weather Rev.*, **55**, 155.
                          1928   *Ibid.*, **56**, 393.
LANGMUIR, I.   1948   *J. Meteorol.*, **5**, 175.
                          1950   *Bull. Amer. Meteorol. Soc.*, **31**, 386.
LANGMUIR, I.;
SCHAEFER, V. J.; *et al.* 1947   *General Electric Res. Lab., First Quart. Prog. Rept.,
                                   Meteorol. Res.*
LINSS, F.   1887   *Meteorol. Zs.*, **4**, 345.
LIST, R. J. (ed.)   1951   *Smithsonian Meteorological Tables* (6th ed.; Wash-
                                   ington, D.C.: Smithsonian Institution).
MAUCHLEY, S. J.   1923   *Terr. Magn. Atm. Elect.*, **28**, 61.
NAMIAS, J.   1951   In *Compendium of Meteorology* (Boston: American
                                   Meteorological Society), pp. 802–813.
NEIBURGER, M.   1948   *Trans. Amer. Geophys. Union*, **29**, 647.
                          1949   *J. Meteorol.*, **6**, 98.
PALMÉN, E.   1948   *Geophysica*, **3**, 26.
                          1949   *Tellus*, **1**, 22.
                          1951   In *Compendium of Meteorology* (Boston: American
                                   Meteorological Society), pp. 599–620.
                          1951   *Quart. J. R. Meteorol. Soc.*, **77**, 337.
PETTERSSEN, S.   1950   *R. Meteorol. Soc. Centenary Proc.*, pp. 120–155.
                          1952   *Quart. J. R. Meteorol. Soc.*, **78**, 337.
PRIESTLEY, C. H. B.   1950   *Australian J. Sci. Res.*, **3**, 1.
QUÉNÉY, P.   1947   *Univ. Chicago, Dept. Meteorol., Misc. Rept.*, No. 23.
RIEHL, H.   1945   *Univ. Chicago, Dept. Meteorol., Misc. Rept.*, No. 17.
                          1948   *Ibid.*, No. 24, pp. 1–64.
                          1948   *J. Meteorol.*, **5**, 247.
                          1948   *Quart. J. R. Meteorol. Soc.*, **74**, 194.
                          1950   *Tellus*, **2**, 1.
                          1950   *J. Appl. Phys.*, **21**, 917.
                          1951   In *Compendium of Meteorology* (Boston: American
                                   Meteorological Society), pp. 902–913.
RIEHL, H., *et al.*   1952   *Amer. Meteorol. Soc., Meteorol. Mono.*, No. 5.
RIEHL, H., and
JENISTA, C. O.   1952   *J. Meteorol.*, **9**, 159.
RIEHL, H.; NORQUEST,
K. S.; and SUGG, A. L.   1952   *J. Meteorol.*, **9**, 291.
ROSSBY, C.-G.   1940   *Quart. J. R. Meteorol. Soc.*, **66** (Suppl.), 68.
                          1941   "Climate and Man" in *U.S. Dept. Agr. Yearbook of
                                   Agriculture* (Washington: Government Printing
                                   Office), pp. 599–655.
                          1942   *Univ. Chicago, Dept. Meteorol., Misc. Rept.*, No. 5.
                          1947   *Bull. Amer. Meteorol. Soc.*, **28**, 53.
                          1949   In KUIPER, G. P. (ed.), *The Atmospheres of the
                                   Earth and Planets* (Chicago: University of Chica-
                                   go Press), pp. 16–48.

Rossby, C.-G., and
  Collaborators   1939   *J. Marine Res.*, **2**, 38.
Schaefer, V. J.   1946   *Science*, **104**, 457.
                       1948   *Bull. Amer. Meteorol. Soc.*, **29**, 175.
                       1951   In *Compendium of Meteorology* (Boston: American
                               Meteorological Society), pp. 221–234.
Simpson, G. C.   1928   *Mem. R. Meteorol. Soc.*, **3**, 1.
Solberg, H.   1936   *Proc. Verb. Assoc. Météorol., Union Géod. et Géo-
                               phys. Internat.*, **2**, Vol. 66.

Staff Members of the
  Dept. of Meteorolo-
  gy of the University
  of Chicago   1947   *Bull. Amer. Meteorol. Soc.*, **28**, 255.
Staff of Mt. Washing-
  ton Observatory   1949–
                       1952   A series of research reports on the constitution
                               of clouds, Mt. Washington Observatory, Mt.
                               Washington, N. H.

U.S. Air Force, Air
  Materiel Command   1948   *Harvard–Mt. Washington Icing Research Report
                               1946–1947, Air Force Tech. Rept.*, No. 5678.
                               Wright Patterson Air Force Base, Ohio.
U.S Weather Bureau   1949   *The Thunderstorm* (Washington: Government
                               Printing Office).
                       1952   *Normal Weather Charts for the Northern Hemisphere,
                               Tech. Pap.*, No 21. (Washington: Government
                               Printing Office).
Warfield, C. N.   1947   *Nat. Adv. Comm. Aero. Tech. Notes*, No. 1200.
Wexler, H.   1950   *Tellus*, **2**, 262.
                       1950   *J. Meteorol.*, **7**, 370.
Whipple, F. J. W.   1938   *Quart. J. R. Meteorol. Soc.*, **64**, 199.
Whipple, F. J. W., and
  Scrase, F. J.   1936   *Great Britain Meteorol. Off. Geophys. Mem.*, Vol. **7**,
                               No. 68.
Willett, H. C.   1949   *J. Meteorol.*, **6**, 34.
                       1949   *Geog. Ann. Stockholm*, **1–2**, 295.
                       1950   *R. Meteorol. Soc. Centenary Proc.*, pp. 195–206.
                       1951   *J. Meteorol.*, **8**, 1.
Wilson, C. T. R.   1921   *Phil. Trans. R. Soc London, A*, **221**, 73.
Woodcock, A. H.   1950   *J. Meteorol.*, **7**, 161.

The Biochemistry of the Terrestrial Atmosphere

By G. E. HUTCHINSON
Yale University

1. INTRODUCTION

THE present chapter is intended to give an account of such chemical reactions occurring at low levels in the atmosphere as are directly or indirectly brought about by the living matter at the surface of the earth.
Having described as completely as possible such processes, it has seemed
justifiable to consider the possibility of like phenomena occurring on other
planets, notably Mars.

It is obviously impossible to restrict the discussion solely to the permanent gases of the air. One important but most variable constituent of
the lower atmosphere, namely, water vapor, is continually derived from
and returned to the hydrosphere. A considerable interchange of other
materials between the ocean and the air, involving a greater or lesser
amount of chemical transformation, takes place in the cycles of carbon,
nitrogen, and sulphur. Moreover, evaporated sea spray produces saline
dusts, which are probably to be regarded as aerosols, that play an important part in various atmospheric phenomena, some of which are relevant
to the subject of the present chapter. It is therefore necessary to consider
the relationships of the atmosphere and the hydrosphere in any discussion
of the former.

It has long been known that when the average composition of sedimentary rock is compared with that of the primary lithosphere, from which the
main constituents of the sediments are derived, there is an excess of carbon, oxygen, and, to a lesser degree, nitrogen in the sediments. These excesses, which must be derived from the atmosphere and hydrosphere, are

371

usually spoken of as *fossil* gases, following Goldschmidt (1934). It is still uncertain to what extent volcanic gases may truly be regarded as *juvenile*, never having been at the surface of the earth before. A part of the total gaseous output of the lithosphere may presumably be described in such a manner; but another and probably much greater part, however, is certainly *cyclical*, representing the fossil gases of metamorphosed or remelted sediments. In spite of the uncertainties involved, it will be impossible to avoid a consideration of the relationship of the atmosphere both to the sediments and to the primary lithosphere.

Finally, the relationship to the living matter of the earth and to its decomposition products must form the central theme running through the

TABLE 1

COMPOSITION OF DRY ATMOSPHERE

Gas	Volume (Per Cent)	Mass (Per Cent)	Thickness of Gas at S.T.P. above Sea-Level (atm-cm)	gm/cm_e^2	Total Mass (Gg)
N_2	78.09	75.51	624,600	757.4	38.65
O_2	20.95	23.15	167,600	232.2	11.84
A	0.93	1.28	7,440	12.8	0.65
CO_2	0.03	0.046	220	0.46	0.0235
Ne	0.0018	0.00125	14	0.0125	0.00064
He	0.00052	0.000072	4.2	0.00072	0.000037
CH_4	0.00015	0.000094	1.2	0.00094	0.000043
Kr	0.0001	0.00029	0.8	0.0029	0.00015
N_2O	0.00005	0.00008	0.4	0.0008	0.00004
H_2	0.00005	0.0000035	0.4	0.000035	0.0000018
O_3	0.00004	0.000007	0.3	0.00007	0.0000035
Xe	0.000008	0.000036	0.06	0.00036	0.000018
NO_2	0.0000001	0.0000002	0.0008	0.000002	0.0000001
I_2	2×10^{-11}	1×10^{-10}	2×10^{-7}	1×10^{-9}	5×10^{-11}
Rn	6×10^{-18}	5×10^{-17}	4×10^{-14}	5×10^{-16}	2×10^{-18}

chapter, not only by editorial request, but because this relationship is responsible for the most remarkable feature of the atmosphere in contact with the liquid and solid materials at the earth's crust, namely, the fact that the atmospheric gases, in contact with water, do not represent a mixture in thermodynamic equilibrium.

1.1. COMPOSITION OF THE ATMOSPHERE AND HYDROSPHERE

The composition of the atmosphere is given in several different ways in Table 1, while that of the hydrosphere, so far as the constituents of interest in the present work are concerned, is presented in Table 2.[1] In addition

1. In the presentation of total quantities of material at the earth's surface, the *geogram* (Gg) equal to 10^{20} gm (Conway, 1942) is often a convenient unit. Chapman's (1943) terms

to the constituents listed in Table 1, water vapor may form from 0.1 to 1.0 per cent of the air, the quantity being dependent on the site of collection of the sample and on the history of the air mass sampled. The mean amount is about 6.25 gm/cm_e^2 and the total in the atmosphere about 0.13 Gg. The CO_2 content is also fairly variable, in a manner to be discussed at length later. Ozone increases up to a maximum or maxima at heights of

TABLE 2

COMPOSITION OF HYDROSPHERE*

Constituents	Mass (Per Cent)	Mass (Gg)	gm/cm_e^2
Water.	98.3	14,000	274,000
Anions of oxyacids of at-mophile elements:			
F.	0.00013	0.018	0.35
Cl.	1.86	270	5300
Br.	0.0064	0.92	18
I.	0.000004	0.0006	0.012
HCO_3 (incl. CO_3).	0.0137	1.98	38.8
SO_4.	0.260	37.0	730
H_3BO_3 (undissociated). .	0.0026	0.37	7.3
Major cations:			
Na.	1.035	151	2960
K.	0.037	5.40	106
Mg.	0.125	18.2	357
Ca.	0.039	5.7	112
Sr.	0.0008	0.11	2.2
Dissolved gases:			
N_2.	0.00193†	0.26	5.2
O_2.	0.00096‡	0.13	2.6
Inert gases (as A).	0.00007	0.009	0.18
CO_2 (free).	0.0001§	0.014	0.28
Organic compounds of at-mophile elments:‖			
N.	0.00005	0.007	0.14
C.	0.00015	0.02	0.5

* Including the polar caps and inland waters but excluding the water of the sedimentary lithosphere, which probably has a mass of about 2000 Gg.

† An approximate estimate, corresponding to 13 ml/l.

‡ An approximate estimate, corresponding to 5.5 ml/l.

§ Corresponding to a pressure of 4 × 10⁻⁴ atm. at 3° C.

‖ Rough estimates; the quantities are very variable and have not been fully investigated.

20–30 km, while radon and iodine decrease with increasing altitude, owing to decay of the former and removal in rain of the latter. The empirical evi-

"atmo-centimeter" (atm-cm) and "atmo-millimeter" (atm-mm) have been used to designate thicknesses of gases at S.T.P., so avoiding ambiguous statements that might occasionally seem to imply pressure of a certain number of mm Hg. The symbol cm_e^2 (Kalle, 1945) is read as "square centimeter of earth's surface."

dence (Chackett, Paneth, Reasbeck, and Wiborg, 1951) is against any gravitational separation of gases below about 60 km. The presence of minute amounts of the order of 2 mg/ton of Hg in rain water (Stock and Cucuel, 1934) indicates the presence of this volatile metal in the atmosphere in quantitites of the same order of magnitude as that of iodine. A few other carbon compounds, notably CO and CH_2O, also occur, as is indicated later.

All the constituents listed in Table 1 are known to be present in the atmosphere as gases. Certain other atmospheric substances, notably ammonia and sulphur dioxide, have been recorded from the atmosphere by chemical methods but are not detectable spectrographically, though favorable bands occur in their absorption spectra. These substances are presumably present either in solution in water droplets or associated with dust particles or with the moisture films on such particles. Though perhaps strictly not part of the atmosphere, both ammonia and sulphur dioxide in such a suspended form play a considerable part in the chemical events that occur in the air, and these and other materials in a like state will be discussed in greater detail later. It is possible that a small part of the CO_2 of the atmosphere may also be associated with solid particles.

2. THE WATER CYCLE

It will be necessary to use, later in the discussion, an estimate for the total river flow from the land surfaces into the sea. The evaporation from the surfaces of the oceans can be computed by several independent methods and is evidently about 97.5 ± 10 cm (Sverdrup, 1952). The best estimate of the precipitation over the surface of the ocean is 82 cm/year (Jacobs, 1951). From these figures it appears that the runoff from the land surfaces of the earth required to maintain a constant sea-level is 15.5 ± 10 cm. The total river discharge, therefore, apparently is 0.56 ± 0.36 Gg/year.

Various authors have attempted to ascertain the discharge by considering the known runoff from the rivers of the world. The best attempt appears to be that of Henkel, somewhat amplified by Kalle (1945), which results in an estimate of 0.16 Gg/year. There can be little doubt that this estimate is too small, as it neglects the direct discharge of ground water into the ocean and also innumerable minor streams discharging along the coast between the main rivers. Most of the ground water reaching the ocean probably moves through the alluvial filling of river valleys; the discussion given by Halbfass (1934) indicates that it is unlikely that more than 10 per cent of the total runoff is of this kind. The error due to small streams directly discharging into the sea is likely to be small, because their catchment basins are of very limited area. It would seem reasonable, therefore, to adopt a figure of 0.18 Gg as the observed runoff. This result is not inconsistent with the much more uncertain value 0.56 ± 0.36 Gg computed above; a value of 0.20 Gg per year may be adopted.

3. CARBON DIOXIDE AND OTHER CARBON COMPOUNDS

3.1. The CO_2 Content of the Air and Its Geographical Variation

The carbon dioxide content of atmospheric air is commonly given as 0.030 volume per cent or 300 p.p.m. by volume. This figure is a rough approximation for the lower part of the atmosphere in temperate latitudes at the present time, but a more detailed study of the analytical literature indicates variations, in part irregular and in part systematic. The irregular variations are largely, no doubt, due to local artificial derangement of the chemistry of the atmosphere and to technical errors; the systematic variations are of greater interest and may be geographical, altitudinal, seasonal, and secular.

The lowest values observed at ground or sea-level are found in arctic air. Buch (1939*b*, 1942) records a value as low as 0.015 vol. % on the southwestern coast of Spitzbergen and somewhat higher values a little farther north. Meteorological considerations suggested that the air on the southwest of the island, at the time that the observations were made, actually had passed over more arctic sea and had come from higher latitudes than the air containing 0.019–0.029% vol. found in other parts of the western coast of Spitzbergen at the end of August, 1936. The mean content of such air at $\phi \cong 80°$ N. is evidently about 0.022 vol. %, at least at the end of summer. Buch's observations provide considerable evidence for the view that these low CO_2 amounts are primarily determined by the fact that at low temperatures a lower pressure of the gas will be in equilibrium with sea water than at high temperatures. Water carrying pack ice north of Spitzbergen was, in fact, found to be in equilibrium with 0.015 vol. % CO_2. The observations clearly suggest that the equilibrium can be approached very rapidly. Dingle (1954) concludes that, at least in winter, polar *continental* air is relatively high in CO_2 and that this may be of importance in regulating the heat balance of ice sheets.

The normal concentration of CO_2 at ground level in temperate latitudes of the Northern Hemisphere at the present time is about 0.032 vol. %, but during the last century lower values prevailed. The best nineteenth-century values indicating the latitudinal distribution in the temperate and tropical zones are doubtless those of Muntz and Aubin (1886). It is evident

Location	Approx. Latitude	Vol. %
Rural France..........	64° N.	0.0287
West Indies...........	20° N.	.0284
South America........	40° S.	.0272
Cape Horn...........	56° S.	0.0256

from the studies made by the Meteor Expedition (Wattenberg, 1933; Callendar, 1940) that the mean surface water of the tropical Atlantic was, during the 1920's, in equilibrium with 0.0327% vol. CO_2 and the mean water between 40° and 60° S. with 0.0299% vol. It does not necessarily follow that equilibrium was achieved. Buch (1949) regards North and Middle Atlantic air as now typically containing 0.0314–0.0331% vol., and tropical and continental air from 0.0326 to 0.0366% vol.

There is evidently a fairly definite control of the CO_2 content of the air by the cold polar oceans, but probably little other latitudinal variation.

Callendar (1940) has analyzed the best rural western European nineteenth-century data with a view to determining whether the wind direction and origin of the air masses samples have any effect. His results, as *deviations* from the weighted mean, show very slight effects in the direction expected. The high value for continental air at Kew, given in brackets, undoubtedly reflects urban contamination.

	Mean (Vol. %)	Atlantic Air	Polar Air	Continental Air	Tropical Air
Dieppe..........	0.02935	−0.00018	−0.00006	+0.00044	+0.00055
Gembloux.......	0.02938	− .00030	− .00035	+ .00048	+ .00081
Kew............	0.02914	−0.00068	−0.00044	[+0.00173]	+0.00146

Haldane (1936), however, has recorded values of as high as 0.037% vol. for air moving on shore along the Ayrshire coast in August and September, and as low as 0.027% vol. for air moving from the English Channel onto the Isle of Wight in November. The meaning of these variations is unknown.

A slight seasonal effect can also be observed in the nineteenth-century data, the means being:

Spring	0.02971
Summer	.02905
Autumn	.02944
Winter	0.02965

This variation, in so far as it is significant, is doubtless largely of biological origin. Carpenter (1937) gives a number of analyses made in eastern North America which exhibit no seasonal trend; but, as his results are presented only to two significant figures, this is not surprising. Haldane (1936) notes high values at Oxford during a series of barometric lows which conceivably may have enhanced movement of the gas from the soil.

3.2. Vertical Distribution in the Free Atmosphere

The data are wretchedly inadequate but, so far as they go, of considerable interest. The earlier workers found no consistent difference between high mountain air and that from low levels. Lepape and Colange (1935), using balloons, believed that they had detected an irregular increase in the CO_2 content of the air in passing from the ground to heights of 9–16 km. Glückauf (1944) points out that this is probably due to experimental error. Shepherd (1936), in air collected at about 21.5 km during the balloon flight of "Explorer II," found $0.029 \pm 0.002\%$ vol. There is, however, some possibility that this air was not so uncontaminated as might have been supposed. Glückauf himself found the air 4–10 km above southern England to contain significantly less CO_2 than did the air at ground level. His range for the upper air was from 0.024 to 0.030% vol., but the two highest determinations, of 0.028 and 0.030 per cent, are regarded as somewhat suspect. The mean value was 0.025 ± 0.001 and the modal value 0.024. Low values comparable to these are known at ground level in the Northern Hemisphere only in arctic air.

3.3. Effect of Precipitation of Atmospheric Water

The CO_2 content of rain does not seem to have been studied at all extensively; but, owing to the high solubility, it is certain that the gases in rain water will be enriched in CO_2. For the purposes of the present computation, it will be assumed that rain is normally saturated with respect to CO_2. The pH of rain appears to be between 4.0 and 7.7, an acid reaction between 6.1 and 6.8 being usual (Atkins, 1947). The bicarbonate content of rain thus being very low, the solubility for distilled water is appropriately used. This may give a figure slightly too low for saturated rain, but such an error will be counterbalanced by the probability that some rain is not saturated.

At 10° C pure water takes up 2346 mg/kg under a pressure of 1 atm of CO_2, so that in the atmosphere rain saturated at this temperature should contain about 0.7 mg/kg. One meter of rain, therefore, will remove 0.07 mg/cm$_e^2$. Since the total mass of CO_2 is about 460 mg/cm$_e^2$, it is evident that atmospheric precipitation is not likely to play any significant part in regulating the CO_2 content of the air. This is in accord with the statistical results of Kreutz (1941).

3.4. THE UREY EQUILIBRIUM

Urey (1952a) thinks that the general magnitude of the CO_2 content of the atmosphere represents an approximation to the equilibrium pressure in reactions such as the following:

$$MgSiO_3 + CO_2 \, (g) = MgCO_3 + SiO_2$$

or

$$CaSiO_3 + CO_2 \, (g) = CaCO_3 + SiO_2 \, .$$

Such reactions are catalyzed by liquid water and would not be expected on a dry planet. At 25° C the pressure of CO_2 in equilibrium with magnesium carbonate and silicate is $P_{CO_2} = 10^{-5}$ atm, or about one-thirtieth of the observed pressure in the atmosphere. For other possible reactions the equilibrium pressures are lower. It is reasonably certain that the Urey equilibrium, as it may conveniently and appropriately be termed, must account for the general order of magnitude of the CO_2 content of the atmosphere of the earth and presumably also of Mars, at least precluding the existence of large pressures, of the order of 1 atm or more, at the earth's surface. The general mobility of the earth's crust and the existence and structure of the biosphere will, however, give rise to a complex pattern of distribution which will never approach equilibrium at all closely. The places where solution of igneous rock is occurring are likely to be where such rock comes in contact with acid soil extracts or acid stream and bog water, containing far more CO_2 than the equilibrium concentration. It is reasonable to suppose that, if the CO_2 content of the atmosphere were increased several thousand fold, much more solution of silicate would take place and the equilibrium value would be approached from above; but when a fairly low concentration of the gas remained in the air, a great variety of causes, dependent on the prevalent exposure of primary rocks and on the state of the biosphere after so catastrophic an alteration, would operate to produce a new complex steady-state distribution. The consideration of the problem merely as achievement of equilibrium is therefore of little value in the study of the details of terrestrial phenomena.

3.5. PHOTOSYNTHETIC FIXATION OF CO_2

The carbon cycle, as it is commonly understood in biology, consists of the photosynthetic reduction of CO_2 by green plants and a certain number of purple and green bacteria and the subsequent respiratory release by plants, bacteria, and, to a less extent, animals, of CO_2 to the atmosphere. As van Niel (1949 and earlier papers quoted herein) has pointed out, the over-all general photosynthetic reaction is

$$CO_2 + 2H_2A \rightarrow CH_2O + H_2O + 2A \ .$$

Here the hydrogen donator H_2A may be water, hydrogen sulphide, or a variety of organic compounds; and the formaldehyde is to be regarded as a conventional monomer that can be polymerized to whatever carbohydrate is produced. In ordinary photosynthesis by green plants the hydrogen donator is H_2O, and the oxygen produced comes from this water.

The rate of photosynthesis for various plant communities on land has been determined by estimating the total production of organic matter during a growing season and correcting this for the considerable loss of organic compounds lost during the respiratory metabolism of the plant. The best estimates are probably those of Noddack (1937), which are based largely on earlier figures of Schröder (1919) but are corrected and revised in various ways. Schröder gives an admirable account of the earlier work, now only of historic interest.

RATE OF PHOTOSYNTHESIS ON LAND

AREA $(10^{16}$ cm$^2)$	AREAL FIXATION (mg/cm^2 year)		TOTAL FIXATION FOR WHOLE AREA $(10^{15}$ gm/year)	
	C	from CO_2	C	from CO_2
Forest 44........	20	73.3	8.8	32.3
Cultivated 27........	16	58.6	4.3	15.8
Grassland 31........	6	22.0	1.9	7.0
Desert 24........	0.5	1.8	0.1	0.2
Total 126........	Means 12.0	44.0	Total 15.1	55.3

These figures are apparent values, uncorrected for respirations. The total terrestrial photosynthetic rate so corrected is, according to the estimates of error given by Schröder (1919) and of respiration given by Transeau

(1926), to be regarded as $(20 \pm 5) \times 10^{15}$ gm/year of C from $(73 \pm 18) \times 10^{15}$ gm/year of CO_2, while the mean rate on land may be taken as 16 ± 4 mg/cm² year of C from 55 ± 14 mg/cm² year of CO_2. There is, however, little doubt that these figures are too low, as they fail to take into account the very great photosynthetic productivity that must be exhibited in tropical rain forests. Since, however, the areas involved are small compared with the total area of land surfaces, the error may be less serious than might at first be supposed.

For the sea a different method of approach is necessary, as here the photosynthesizing organisms are mainly microscopic unicellular forms that replace one another with great rapidity. The usual methods of study have been based on estimates of uptake of nutrients *in situ* or of oxygen produced in samples brought on board ship. Steemann-Nielsen (1952) has criticized the latter procedure, claiming that the figures given below and based on Riley's (1944) study of all the data available to him are about an order of magnitude too high. Riley (1953) has replied convincingly to this criticism, and, though it is possible that his mean is a little high, the true value must lie within the rather wide limits of uncertainty that he gave. The difference between Steemann-Nielsen's results based on fixation of C^{14} and Riley's largely based on O_2 production is under investigation in several laboratories. It is apparently due to physiological peculiarities of the plankton of nutrient-poor tropical seas, and at present it seems likely that Riley's method of estimation is geochemically the more significant (G. A. Riley, R. R. L. Guillard, *verbal communications*). The figures presented by Riley require no respiratory correction. The total metabolism of the earth may therefore be expressed as follows:

C Fixed

Ocean	$(126 \pm 82) \times 10^{15}$ gm/year
Land	$(20 \pm 5) \times 10^{15}$ gm/year
Whole earth	$(146 \pm 87) \times 10^{15}$ gm/year
Unit area of earth	29 ± 17 mg/cm$_e^2$ year

CO_2 Used

Ocean	$(462 \pm 303) \times 10^{15}$ gm/year
Land	$(73 \pm 18) \times 10^{15}$ gm/year
Whole earth	$(535 \pm 321) \times 10^{15}$ gm/year
Unit area of earth	105 ± 63 mg/cm$_e^2$ year

O_2 Produced

Ocean	$(336 \pm 218) \times 10^{15}$ gm/year
Land	$(53 \pm 13) \times 10^{15}$ gm/year
Whole earth	$(389 \pm 231) \times 10^{15}$ gm/year
Unit area of earth	76 ± 45 mg/cm$_e^2$ year

On land the mean rate of photosynthetic fixation of CO_2, namely, 55 mg/cm² year corresponds to a utilization of the available supply above the vegetation cover once every 8.4 years.

There is much experimental work on the variation in photosynthetic rate with variation in light and in CO_2 content, but most of this work is not relevant to the present discussion. Particularly interesting results have, however, been obtained by considering small variations in CO_2 content under field conditions (Thomas and Hill, 1949). In general, the rate of photosynthesis can be doubled by increasing the CO_2 content of the air by a factor of 2.5–3.0. The best-fitting straight lines relating apparent photosynthesis, uncorrected for respiration, when extrapolated toward the axes, do not converge to the origin but rather imply positive apparent photosynthesis at zero CO_2 concentration. It is therefore evident that in the region below about 0.05 vol. %, the rate of increase of the photosynthetic rate with CO_2 concentration is somewhat greater than at higher concentrations and that, in the region of greatest interest, the rates are nearly proportional to the concentrations. If only the exposed green parts of plants be considered and these are growing in bright light, the equilibrium between photosynthesis and respiration leads to the establishment of a CO_2 concentration much below that found in the atmosphere. In an experiment with sugar beets, equilibrium was established at 0.004 vol. %. Similar results were obtained by Egle (1951) on lower plants.

Various estimates of the total mass of photosynthetic organisms and of unfossilized organic matter have been given. For the purpose of the present discussion, the total organic matter on land, in soils and in vegetation, is a quantity of some interest. Rubey's estimate of 2600×10^{15} gm as the CO_2 equivalent of dead terrestrial organic matter will be used. This figure is based on the area and organic content of the soil types of the world. His figure for total living matter on land, namely, 29×10^{15} gm, which implies a mean turnover of living matter almost twice a year, seems to be too low. A value of the order of 10^{17} gm would be reasonable, most of such organic matter being in forest trees.

3.6. Vertical Distribution near the Ground

Soils ordinarily contain considerable amounts of CO_2. Thus Haldane records 0.1% vol. in air taken 3 cm from below the surface of soil, and other investigators have found similar or higher figures. In most well-vegetated regions, CO_2 near the ground increases markedly at night, often reaching values of 0.06% vol. in both temperate and tropical woodland in early morning (Evans, 1939). At Cloan, Perthshire, Scotland, Haldane and Makgill (Haldane, 1936) in August found a mean diurnal content of 0.0324% vol. and a mean nocturnal content of 0.0386%. This diurnal variation is absent during the winter in temperate regions. Haldane notes that even by day in the grass of a meadow the CO_2 was always somewhat higher than in the free atmosphere. Over bare land Haldane found that the CO_2 content at ground level was, on an average, 0.0058% vol. greater than at a height of 4.5 feet. These results and many others (e.g., Fuller, 1948) in the literature indicate that near the ground, in the relatively less turbulent air among vegetation, there must be a fall in CO_2 content with increasing altitude. Such a gradient implies a steady loss of CO_2 from the soil to the atmosphere. This loss is compensated by day by photosynthesis, so that when the vegetation is active and illuminated, a very slight average rise in CO_2 with altitude must occur as one ascends from some level in the vicinity of the green parts of the plant. This second gradient is probably too feeble and irregular to be detected, but it may be indicated in some of Fuller's data. It obviously must exist if the turbulent movement of the free atmosphere is to bring CO_2 from above to the level of plants that can use it. The over-all rate of return of CO_2 to the atmosphere must, on an average, be about 44 mg/cm² year to compensate apparent photosynthetic fixation; but under special circumstances much more rapid loss may be expected. It should be possible, for instance, to gain some idea of the much faster movement of carbon dioxide from bare soil into the atmosphere by applying the approach used in the study of evaporation from lake surfaces. Assuming a logarithmic fall in CO_2 concentration with height and adopting the semiempirical treatment for water vapor given by Johnsson (1946) to a gas of the density of CO_2 observed at 1 cm and 150 cm (about 4.5 feet) above the ground, we find that

$$R = 5.32 \times 10^{-3} \frac{(r_1 - r_2) V^{0.8}}{\ln 150 - \ln 1}$$

$$= 1.06 \times 10^{-3} (r_1 - r_2) V^{0.8}$$

where R is the rate of transport in grams per centimeter per second, r_1 and r_2 are the volumes of CO_2 per unit volume at heights of 1 cm and 150 cm, respectively, and V is the wind velocity at the standard anemometer height of 6 m. Taking from Haldane $(r_1 - r_2)$ as 5.8×10^{-5} and assuming the very moderate wind velocity of 1 m/sec (i.e., about 2.25 miles/hour), we obtain

$$R = 5.5 \times 10^{-8} \text{ gm/cm}^2 \text{ sec}$$

$$= 4.75 \text{ mg/cm}^2 \text{ day .}$$

It is reasonable to suppose that the rate of removal of CO_2 from the surface of bare earth, which is rougher than water, is lower than over a lake surface. The wind velocity chosen is, however, very moderate, so that it is probable that bare soil surfaces sometimes can lose several milligrams per square centimeter in a day, an amount of the order of 1 per cent of the total CO_2 per square centimeter in the atmosphere.

3.7. PASSAGE OF CO_2 ACROSS THE OCEAN SURFACE

While it has long been supposed (Schloesing, 1880) that the ocean acts as a regulator of the CO_2 content of the air, several modern workers, in spite of the remarkably rapid uptake of CO_2 recorded in the Arctic Sea, have concluded that this effect has been greatly exaggerated. These modern opinions have been based mainly on a qualitative and intuitive examination of the data; but a very rough quantitative treatment may be attempted in the following way. The work of Wattenberg (1933), Buch (1939a, 1942), and a few other investigators indicates that over the greater part of the sea surface the water is in equilibrium with rather more than 0.0003 atm of CO_2. During the summer in the North Atlantic a deficiency of the gas develops in the water, so that, in the area of about 30 million km² north of lat. 30° N., the mean concentration is probably in equilibrium with about 0.00025 atm. Buch himself found at the same time that the air over the sea between Copenhagen and Boston contained 0.00032 atm. In the winter the water and air were in approximate equilibrium. In order to obtain a tentative idea of the exchange, a pressure head across the water surface of 0.00007 atm will be assumed for 6 months of the year.

The rate of passage of a gas across a liquid boundary is given by

$$\frac{dQ}{dt} = a\,A\,(P - p),$$

where $(P - p)$ is the pressure head, A the area of the surface, and a, a constant, the invasion coefficient. Unfortunately, the few determinations of a for CO_2 are discordant, the lowest and highest differing by a factor of 200. The lowest value, namely, 0.033 mg/cm² atm min, was obtained by Becker (1924). Becker's value appears to represent the initial passage across an undisturbed film. Bohr's (1899) older value is about eight times as great as Becker's and perhaps gives an upper limit for the rate of exchange across ordinary natural water surfaces. The very high values for various gases, including CO_2, obtained by Guyer and Tobler (1934) refer to experiments in which the liquid phase was kept in violent motion by means of a propeller; these experiments are probably inapplicable to field conditions. It is evident that a, at least as hitherto determined, is a virtual coefficient, the value of which depends on the condition of the interface in the experiment. Becker's value will be used in computing the minimum expected exchange.

Evaluating for 6 months or 262,800 minutes and for an area of 30,000,-000 km², we obtain

$$\frac{dQ}{dt} = 0.033 \times 30 \times 10^{16} \times 0.00007 \times 262,800 \text{ mg/year}$$

$$= 0.184 \times 10^{15} \text{ gm/year} .$$

In view of Bohr's determination of a, this figure may well be too low by a factor of 10. Some value in the range 0.2–2.0×10^{15} gm/year would seem reasonable for the area of the ocean in which the effect occurs.

Dr. Gordon Riley suggests in conversation that it is not impossible that the characteristic presence of the effect in the North Atlantic is due to a deficiency of nutrients other than CO_2, which might lead, on photosynthesis, to a storage of carbohydrate, which in turn would raise the density—and so the falling speed—of certain members of the phytoplankton. Such falling phytoplankton would continue respiration and ultimately decompose or be eaten. The CO_2 so produced would therefore be returned to the ocean well below the surface.

3.8. PASSAGE OF CO_2 FROM THE ATMOSPHERE TO THE OCEAN IN CHEMICAL EROSION

Carbon dioxide is lost from the atmosphere through the solution of rocks, bicarbonates of the alkaline earths and silica being the main products of this process. We have seen that the equilibrium involved is believed by Urey to determine the general order of magnitude of the CO_2 pressures at the surfaces both of the earth and of Mars. As well as the production of bicarbonate from silicate, the chemical erosion of the lithosphere involves the solution as bicarbonate of a great deal of pre-existing carbonate, which is practically all of sedimentary origin. About one-fourth of the river water flowing to the sea now drains areas of igneous rocks, and three-fourths drains areas of sedimentary rocks. Conway (1942) has estimated the proportions of the different inorganic constituents of the waters from these two types of drainage basin. Considering only the fixed, or carbonate, CO_2 present in the residue left on evaporating the average river water, it appears from Conway's calculations that 100 parts of residue contain the following:

2.0 parts CO_2 derived from formation of new carbonate from igneous rock,
1.4 parts CO_2 derived from formation of new carbonate from sedimentary rock,

22.4 parts CO_2 derived from pre-existing carbonate in sedimentary rock, giving a total of

25.8 parts CO_2 in 100 parts dry residue.

Conway considers that 100 gm/ton of dry residue is the best available estimate for the concentration of inorganic material in the average river water, so that these figures can be regarded as grams of carbonate CO_2 per ton. In order to bring such carbonate into solution, at least as much CO_2 as is present in the carbonate must be added to form bicarbonate.[2] The CO_2 content of 1 ton of average river water may then be considered to consist of

22.4 gm. derived from pre-existing carbonate,
3.4 gm derived from the air[3] and forming new carbonate,
25.8 gm derived from the air and holding carbonate in solution.

Since the total annual runoff has already been estimated as 0.20 Gg or 2×10^{13} tons, these figures represent

44.8×10^{13} gm/year derived from pre-existing carbonate,
6.8×10^{13} gm/year derived from air and forming new carbonate,
51.6×10^{13} gm/year derived from air and holding carbonate in solution.

The 44.8×10^{13} gm/year derived from sediments is returned to sediments and has merely been transferred to the oceanic basins from the continents. The 51.6×10^{13} gm/year derived from the air and forming bicarbonate from carbonate will be returned to the atmosphere; this fraction acts as a conveyor belt. The 6.8×10^{13} gm/year derived from the air in the production of new carbonate from silicate will be lost to the ocean sediments as $CaCO_3$. If a steady state is to be maintained, this loss, which corresponds to 0.013 mg/cm^2 year, must be made up by the liberation of CO_2 from the lithosphere into the atmosphere. Since the values for both runoff and total inorganic matter in solution employed in this calculation are very conservative, the result may be too low. Using older values for river flow and a higher value for residue (Clarke, 1924), a figure about twice the one given would be obtained. However, during most of geological time, both continental emergence and vulcanism have been less than today, so that, in geochemical discussions, the low value that has been given seems reasonable, though it should be remembered that it may be

2. Since the pH of the average river is likely to be between 7 and 8, this is an underestimate for the total CO_2 in river water; but the residue may contain a little $NaHCO_3$, which will tend to compensate for free CO_2 neglected in the computation.

3. In many cases this will come from decaying plant tissue but will be ultimately of atmospheric origin.

too small by a factor of about 2. It seems certain that at the present time there is no region at or near the surface of the earth in which a liberation of CO_2 could take place by the solution of SiO_2, for the CO_2 pressure is always above that indicated by the Urey equilibrium; this condition is likely to have existed throughout most of phanerozoic time. We must evidently look for the origin of the required CO_2 at some deeper level.

3.9. Fossil CO_2

In spite of the indications already given that the partial pressure of CO_2 at the earth's surface is never likely to have been much greater than it is today, the presence of great thicknesses of limestone in the sedimentary column indicates that an enormous quantity of CO_2 has left the atmosphere.

At the present time the chief mechanism of removal of CO_2 is the deposition of calcareous deep-sea sediments. Such sediments are mainly globigerina ooze, formed from the shells of pelagic Foraminifera. Shallow-water coral and lithothamnion reef and various types of shell deposit grow more quickly but cover a much less extensive area of the sea bottom. In practically every case the sedimentation that removes CO_2 involves the deposition of calcium carbonate and is a biological process. Kuenen (1941) points out that before the rise of the pelagic Foraminifera in the Mesozoic, most of the deposition of calcium carbonate must have occurred in shallower water than today, forming great beds of limestone composed of the skeletons of corals, crinoids, and other large multicellular animals. The evolution of the pelagic Foraminifera has thus caused the diversion of calcium and also carbon dioxide, which would have fossilized largely on the continental shelves, to the permanent oceanic basins. Such calcium carbonate is far less likely to be uplifted to form continental sediments than if it had been laid down in relatively shallow water, as in the Paleozoic. The pelagic Foraminifera are, in fact, continuously removing both calcium and CO_2 from the main geochemical cycle, and ultimately their activity will cause a deficiency of calcium in continental sediments and probably of CO_2 in volcanic gases.

Many different estimates of the total mass of carbonate sediments have been made. The most recent and probably much the most careful is that of Rubey (1951), who gives a value of 670 Gg for the entire sedimentary column, corresponding to 13,100 gm/cm_e^2. The oxidized carbon of the calcareous sediments is not the only fossil carbon. Apart from coal and oil deposits which, from the standpoint of planetary circulation, are quite negligible, sedimentary rocks, particularly shales and clays, contain reduced carbon, probably as a very carbonaceous organic matter. It is practically certain that this has been formed biogeochemically and represents carbon originally fixed photosynthetically. The only alternative hypothesis, namely, that a large amount of elementary carbon—derived from the photolysis of methane very early in the history of the earth, as Poole suggests—has undergone continual sedimentation and erosion essentially unchanged, can hardly be entertained seriously. Assuming that the reduced carbon of argillaceous sediments is of biological origin, as it undoubtedly is in such sediments forming today, we must add to the carbon dioxide fossilized as such an equivalent amount corresponding to the fossilized reduced carbon, formed photosynthetically from CO_2, that has been in the atmosphere. Rubey's estimate of 250 Gg will be used for this contribution. Thus we find the entire CO_2 that has passed through the atmosphere is as follows:

Fossilized as carbonate.................	670 Gg or	13,000 gm/cm$_e^2$
Fossilized as reduced carbon...........	250 Gg or	4,900 gm/cm$_e^2$
CO_2 equivalent of total fossil carbon......	920 Gg or	18,000 gm/cm$_e^2$

3.10. VOLCANIC PRODUCTION OF CO_2

Goldschmidt (1934) considered that it is possible to obtain an estimate of the total rate of production of gaseous carbon from volcanoes by dividing the total mass of sedimentary carbon by the age of the earth. Taking the estimate for the total CO_2 fossilized as such or as reduced carbon just given and a time span of 3×10^9 years, the rate of fossilization of carbon, either as photosynthetically reduced CO_2 or as carbonate, would be 3×10^{13} gm/year or 6γ/cm$_e^2$ year ($1\gamma = 10^{-6}$ gm). It is obvious that this estimate is of the same order of magnitude as, though somewhat smaller than, that given earlier for the loss of CO_2 to oceanic sediments. It is reasonable to find that it is somewhat smaller, since it is quite certain that some of the CO_2 discharged from volcanoes is not juvenile in any reasonable sense of the word but has been derived from deeply buried limestones. Borchert (1951), in a paper received as this chapter goes to press, calculates that only 0.1 γ/cm$_e^2$ year of C is truly juvenile. He estimates the metamorphic contributions to the carbon of the atmosphere as about 7.5 γ/cm$_e^2$ year.

The most convincing demonstration of the cyclical nature of much volcanic CO_2 is to be derived from Rittmann's (1936) beautiful study of Vesuvius. The entire history of this volcano through four major cycles of activity has been determined by the assimilation of deep-lying dolomitic limestone, which has led to a progressive change in the chemistry of the lavas produced and which must have supplied enormous quantities of CO_2 to the volcanic gases produced in the major eruptions of the volcano.

Urey (1952a, b) has suggested that the greater part of the circulating carbon of the biosphere and sedimentary lithosphere initially entered the atmosphere, as Poole (1941) and others have also believed, as methane. As oxidizing conditions developed, this methane was slowly oxidized to CO_2, a process doubtless mainly photochemical, though perhaps also biological. The resulting CO_2 could not accumulate on a wet planet, owing to the Urey equilibrium, and so formed vast beds of limestone. This hypothetical early Pre-Cambrian limestone is to be regarded as the source of all the CO_2 that has subsequently entered the atmosphere. From this point of view, juvenile CO_2, in the sense of CO_2 derived from primary magma, may be of no importance. The CO_2 derived from the original limestone would pass into the atmosphere and so to secondary limestones, which could later constitute new secondary sources of CO_2. The rates just given, if Urey's hypothesis be adopted and the figures taken at their face value, suggest that about two cycles in this continuing process have been completed; but no particular significance should be given to such a quantitative estimate. It would evidently be desirable to subject the various Pre-Cambrian limestones to an intense geochemical examination, since it is just possible that their trace-element contents might throw light on the degree of oxidation of the atmosphere at the time when they were formed.

3.11. Carbon Dioxide Produced by the Consumption of Fuels

Values computed for the industrial and domestic production of CO_2 are:

	Whole Earth	mg/cm
Goldschmidt (1934)......	4×10^{15} gm/year	0.8
Callendar (1940).........	4.3×10^{15} gm/year	0.81
Kalle (1945).............	6.1×10^{15} gm/year	1.22

In addition to these figures, Knoche (1938) gives the surprising estimate of 5.75×10^{15} gm/year for the CO_2 produced by grass and forest fires. This, of course, belongs with the respiratory figure in the biological cycle rather than with the combustion of fossil carbon.

3.12. Secular Variation

Callendar (1940) has tabulated the mean values for the best series of determinations made in rural and maritime localities in western Europe and

eastern North America since 1866. Callendar's most recent (1949) estimates are as follows:

	Vol. %		Vol. %
Prior to 1900	.....0.0290	1921–1930	......0.0303
1901–1910	.......0.0293	1931–1940	......0.0310
1911–1920	.......0.0298	1941–1950	.......0.0316

There can be very little doubt that during the first half of the twentieth
century the mean CO_2 content of the air in north temperate latitudes has
increased by 0.0026% vol. or by 9.0% of its late Victorian value.

3.13. SIGNIFICANCE OF THE TWENTIETH-CENTURY INCREASE IN CO_2

The increase in CO_2 of the atmosphere during the present century was
attributed by Callendar to the passive accumulation of the products of
industrial combustion, which he believes are now liberated too rapidly to
permit immediate establishment of equilibrium with the ocean. There is
fair quantitative agreement between the observed rise of 8.9 per cent between about 1900 and 1935, which, if geographically uniform, would imply
the accumulation of 200×10^{15} gm CO_2 in the atmosphere, and the estimated 150×10^{15} gm CO_2 produced by the industrial consumption of fuel
during this period. Callendar explains the discrepancy between the two
figures by supposing that the rise in CO_2 content is not uniform throughout the atmosphere. In spite of the rough agreement between the two figures, Callendar's initial explanation as it stands is very improbable.

The rate of uptake of CO_2 by the Arctic Ocean, as Buch has shown, is
very considerable. The minimum rate of uptake by the North Atlantic in
summer appears to be about 4 per cent of the industrial output, but this
result may be too low by a factor of 10. It is evident that Schloesing's
theory of the regulation of the CO_2 content of the air by the ocean cannot
be dismissed, even if it cannot be quantitatively demonstrated at the
present time.

Industrial production of CO_2 proceeds at a rate that is about 5–7 per
cent that of photosynthetic fixation and respiratory production of CO_2 on
land. It has already been pointed out that slight increases in the CO_2 content of the atmosphere will lead to equivalent increases in photosynthetic
rate and presumably ultimately to like increases in respiratory return of
the gas to the atmosphere. If Rubey's estimate of the total organic carbon
of the terrestrial biosphere be accepted—and it would seem to be very
conservative—and if no exchange with the ocean be postulated, one would
expect any additional carbon dioxide liberated into the air to distribute
itself about equally between the organic matter of organisms and soil and

the gaseous CO_2 of the atmosphere. A rise in CO_2 of 75×10^{15} gm rather than 150×10^{15} gm would thus take place. If some oceanic regulation were permitted, the expected rise would be even less. Some explanation other than the passive accumulation of CO_2 in the terrestrial part of the cycle is evidently required (cf. Hutchinson, 1945; Callendar, 1949).

Such an explanation is readily found in another change that has accompanied increasing industrial output during the last half-century, namely, the changing ratio of agricultural to forest land. If the CO_2 content were maintained constant, such a change would lower photosynthetic efficiency; actually, increasing photosynthesis probably would follow the increase in CO_2. Of greater importance than a reduction of photosynthetic efficiency of the vegetation cover is the far greater opportunity for loss of respiratory CO_2 from soil in arable than in forest land. The somewhat hypothetical quantitative example already given would suggest strongly that an increase in the rate of passage of CO_2 from the soil to the atmosphere has probably set up a new steady-state system, in which a quantity of CO_2 in excess of the industrial output has been added to the atmosphere.

It should be possible, from the variation in C^{14} content of wood of known age, formed at different times during the past century, to distinguish between combusted fuel and the recent carbon of the biosphere as sources of the extra CO_2 in the contemporary atmosphere. The former source would contain no radiocarbon, while the isotope would be present in the latter source. Preliminary studies by Dr. Hans E. Suess (verbal communication) suggest that both sources are about equally important.

3.14. Conditions for the Secular Change of CO_2 Content

Apart from the Urey equilibrium and the artificial liberation of CO_2 by combustion already considered, three pairs of processes may be regarded as determining the CO_2 content of the atmosphere:

a) Volcanic output and oceanic sedimentation of carbonate, the present rate being about $0.03–0.07 \times 10^{15}$ gm/year

b) Transport into and from ocean, the present rate being about $0.7–2.5 \times 10^{15}$ gm/year

c) Photosynthesis and respiration on land, the present rate being about 88×10^{15} gm/year

The first pair of processes, though very important in the geochemistry of calcium and of fossil CO_2, is probably, in view of the cyclical and largely self-regulating aspects of the other two pairs, of little importance in considering changes in the atmosphere.

In the presence of life in the oceans, the processes of *b* involve photosynthesis in the surface waters of the ocean and, in some cases, entry of CO_2 from the air if a deficit develops, sedimentation of dead plankton, formation of CO_2 by decomposition and liberation of CO_2 to the atmosphere wherever upwelling of deep water, supersaturated with respect to the atmosphere, occurs. This process is probably sufficient to maintain the CO_2 of the atmosphere above the Urey equilibrium value, even if the continents were azoic.

In the presence of terrestrial vegetation the third pair of processes tends to keep a quantity of carbon as organic matter on land. In view of the much greater rapidity of photosynthesis and respiration on land than the exchange across the ocean boundary, it is reasonable to suppose that the present concentration represents primarily the steady-state concentration determined by the spatial pattern of photosynthesis and respiration of plants and respiratory metabolism of plant products by soil bacteria and by animals. If we imagine all terrestrial life to be absent, the CO_2 content of the air would presumably be determined by the tendency to achieve the Urey equilibrium on the continents, and the tendency for CO_2 to escape into the atmosphere from upwelling areas. As the pressure determined by the Urey equilibrium is apparently lower than the present pressure and as the oceanic cycle into and out of the atmosphere is much slower than the terrestrial photosynthetic cycle, it seems likely that abolition of terrestrial vegetation would ultimately lead to a steady-state concentration *lower* than that of the present atmosphere. If, starting from such a state, terrestrial vegetation were to develop, CO_2 would at first be drawn from the oceans, but a reservoir of actively respiring carbon would now develop on the continents, and the nocturnal activity of this reservoir, far from the sea, would tend to raise the CO_2 content of the atmosphere to a new steady state, determined by respiration, on the one hand, and the rate at which the thin layer of plants could capture CO_2 from the thick turbulent atmosphere by day, on the other. The slightly greater CO_2 content of continental air as compared with oceanic is in line with this view. If, with Conway (1943), we accept an essentially modern ocean at the opening of the Paleozoic, the development of a terrestrial plant cover at some time prior to the close of the Silurian is likely to have been accompanied by a rise in the CO_2 content of the air. No information permitting computation of the initial Early Paleozoic concentration, dependent on the distribution of upwelling, exists, but even if it was of the order of 0.01 per cent vol., it is evident from Conway's treatment that the pH of the ocean surface would have been very little higher than today.

Subsequent changes could have resulted only from major disturbances of the terrestrial vegetation cover. Variations of importance, if they occurred, are likely to have been due to changes in the total available precipitation. Initially, any widespread destruction of vegetation would raise the CO_2 content because of enhanced diffusion of respiratory CO_2 from unprotected soils, as seems to be occurring today. If the aridity or other unfavorable circumstance were widespread enough and were sufficiently long continued, the CO_2 content might fall because of the reduction in area of rapidly respiring soil. Destruction of vegetation at the glacial maxima may well have had a like effect, enhanced by the widespread low oceanic temperatures at such times. It is evident that since we are dealing with more than one interrelated steady-state system, deductive predictions are likely to be extraordinarily difficult. All that one can say is that there is a good possibility that slight variations have occurred. The limits within which such variations could have taken place might be from well below the modern value, up to about 0.06% vol., which would be achieved if 90 per cent of the terrestrial organic matter, according to Rubey's estimate, were oxidized rapidly enough to prevent equilibration with the ocean. On the whole, it would seem that values below, rather than above, those at present observed are more likely in the past; but the twentieth-century rise by about 9 per cent indicates that positive variation is possible in some circumstances. The consequences of such variation to the heat balance of the atmosphere are beyond the scope of the present chapter but may prove to be of interest.

3.15. METHANE

The presence of this gas as a normal atmospheric constituent was discovered by Migeotte (1948). The quantity present has been carefully determined, the most recent and accurate estimate (Goldberg, 1951) being 1.2 atm-cm, or 0.00084 gm/cm_e^2. The absolute concentration appears to fall off vertically in an exponential manner with the permanent gases of the atmosphere; cf. also chapter 9. The total quantity of methane in the atmosphere would therefore seem to be 4.3×10^{15} gm.

Hutchinson and Setlow (Hutchinson, 1948, 1949) computed, from the known rate of production of methane by domestic animals and from the known or estimated numbers of large ungulates that might produce methane by enteric fermentation, that 45×10^{12} gm of the gas are produced annually from this source. Conger (1943), studying a productive fresh-water pond, 2 m deep, draining into Chesapeake Bay, estimates that during the late summer the lake produces 90 cubic feet of methane per acre per day or 0.063 cm^3/cm^2 day. It is most unlikely that such a rate of production would last for any great part of the year; an estimate of $3 \text{ cm}^3/\text{cm}^2$ year is probably generous for this locality, which is obviously rather exceptional. The fresh-water lakes of the world have an area of about $2.5 \times 10^{16} \text{ cm}^2$. Methane is produced in significant amounts only in the very small fraction of the lakes and swamps that are quite shallow and rich in decomposing vegetation. For the bodies of water that do produce methane, Conger's data suggest that $3 \text{ cm}^3/\text{cm}^2$ year would be a liberal estimate for the production rate. If about one-thousandth of the whole of the area of inland waters of the world produced the gas at this rate, $7.5 \times 10^{13} \text{ cm}^3/\text{year}$ or 54×10^9 gm would be added to the atmosphere. This is so much less than the estimate for enteric fermentation that even if the adopted proportion of lakes producing methane were ten times too low and the amount produced by them likewise was underestimated by the same amount, the corrected value would only increase the enteric estimate by 10 per cent. It is probable that, although methane is popularly called "marsh gas," stagnant water is not the major source of the gas. Some methane may be produced in ordinary soils. For the purposes of the present work, it is probably safe to suppose that the rate of production is between 45×10^{12} gm/year and 90×10^{12} gm/year. This implies a rate of replacement of once in 47–95 years.

The region where the oxidation of this methane occurs is uncertain. Photochemical oxidation can take place under radiation of wave length < 1450 A. Kuiper (1952) points out that such photochemical oxidation can occur only above 90 km and involves passage of the unaltered gas through the quiet zone of the atmosphere from 30 to 50 km. The replacement rates then would imply that all the methane in this zone can be transmitted from 30 to 50 km in 0.4–0.8 years. Oxidation at lower levels by HO_2 and other transitory products of photochemical reactions may, however, also occur; see chapter 12.

Further, it is possible that biological oxidation at the earth's surface is of importance. *Methanomonas* is a chemoautotrophic bacterium isolated from soils. Nothing, however, is known of its role in nature, and unless certain environments constitute methane sinks, it is difficult to see how such bacteria are of any importance in oxidation of gas that has already escaped into the atmosphere. It is just possible that methane may be oxidized at the surface of the ocean.

3.16. OTHER ATMOSPHERIC CARBON COMPOUNDS

Migeotte (1949) has found evidence of a small and possibly variable quantity of CO in the atmosphere. This problem is more fully discussed by Dr. Goldberg in chapter 9, section 5.2; he concludes that the most probable amount derived from his measures at Mount Wilson, California, is 0.06 atm cm. Various observers at different times have found amounts varying between 0.02 and 0.16 atm cm, and 0.10 atm cm appears to be a good average. This small quantity of CO may well be largely of industrial origin.

Dhar and Ram (1933) found 0.15–1.2 mg/liter of formaldehyde in rain water. Though they suspect a photochemical origin, it is more likely that this is derived from some biological source. Groth and Suess (1938), however, have indicated that the photochemical synthesis of this compound might be expected at high altitudes.

4. OXYGEN

In view of the suboxidized state of the earth's crust, the occurrence of molecular oxygen in the terrestrial atmosphere is remarkable. The quantity present appears to be very constant. This, however, is not unexpected, since the diurnal variation of CO_2 content is seldom likely to exceed $\pm 0.02\%$ vol., so that the maximum variation in oxygen content due to photosynthesis and respiration is unlikely to be greater than one part in a thousand. Other causes of variation in nature are likely to be even less effective. A few cases of oxygen-deficient air have been recorded in polar regions. Lockhart and Court (1942), for example, record from 20.48 to 20.73% vol. at Little America. This deficiency is supposed to be due to local oxidation of the lithosphere, but it is not quite certain that technical errors were entirely excluded.

Three major and several minor sources of the oxygen of the terrestrial atmosphere have been suggested. Tammann (1924) believed that an initial supply of the order of magnitude of that now present would be produced by thermal dissociation of water at a temperature of about 1000° C, with subsequent escape of hydrogen to space. If this occurred, it can have happened only when much reduced material was present in the hot aqueous atmosphere. None of such oxygen is therefore likely to have survived (cf. Urey, 1952a). The photolytic decomposition of water vapor has been considered by several authors, notably Harteck and Jensen (1948), to be a major source of O_2 in the atmosphere. These authors concluded that about 50 times the present supply of atmospheric oxygen may have been produced in this way. Kuiper (1952) has re-examined the problem, finding that 0.38 γ/cm_e^2 year or 1.15 kg/cm_e^2 in the course of the 3×10^9 years of geological time is the most reasonable estimate.

We have already seen that photosynthesis produces from 30 to 122 mg/cm$_e^2$ year, an amount vastly greater than that produced by photolysis, even if the highest published values for the yield of the latter process be accepted. Most of the oxygen actually present in the atmosphere must be of photosynthetic origin. Photosynthesis, however, also provides a store of reduced carbon that can consume this oxygen in respiration, while photolysis in the stratosphere followed by loss of hydrogen to space is an acyclic process which actually increases the average oxidation of the earth as a whole.

Several minor sources of oxygen have been suggested (Nichols, 1941). The only one that can be quantitatively examined is the production of oxygen in biological nitrogen fixation. The net effect of this process may be regarded as the replacement of H^- in an organic compound by NH_2^-. The over-all reaction, therefore, is

$$2\,N_2 + 2\,H_2O + 4\,H^- \rightarrow 4\,NH_2^- + O_2 \,.$$

The rate of biological nitrogen fixation, as is shown later (p. 414), lies between 12×10^{12} gm/year and 105×10^{12} gm/year. The corresponding limits for oxygen production are 7×10^{12} gm/year and 60×10^{12} gm/year. No other minor process is likely to be so important as this.

In view of the much greater solubility of CO_2 than O_2 in the dilute bicarbonate solution that constitutes sea water, a far greater quantity of CO_2 and of bicarbonate that can provide CO_2 in photosynthesis is present below the average sea surface than above it; whereas in the case of oxygen the reverse is true (cf. Tables 1 and 2). The results of photosynthesis in the ocean are, therefore, more likely to produce marked supersaturation of oxygen than respiration and decomposition marked supersaturation of CO_2. Passage in and out of the sea surface is therefore likely to be of considerable importance. Redfield (1949) has shown that the process is in accord with what is known of the invasion coefficient for the gas under laboratory conditions. It is probably safe to conclude that a large part of the oxygen present in the air has been produced by photosynthesis by the marine phytoplankton, which for this reason may be the most important type of economic plant. The only difficulty of any importance that the hypothesis of the biological origin of atmospheric oxygen has had to meet concerns the isotopic constitution of this oxygen, in which O^{18} is appreciably concentrated over that in the H_2O of the ocean. Dole (1949) has given much attention to this problem, and Roake and Dole (1950) have recently obtained experimental evidence that the excess is due to isotope exchange with CO_2 in the stratosphere.

4.1. FOSSIL OXYGEN

The total organic carbon of the sediments is estimated by Rubey (1951) as 68 Gg, which would correspond to the photosynthetic liberation of 181 Gg oxygen. Some oxygen is certainly present in the organic matter of which the main constituent is organic carbon; but, since it is apparently less than the equivalent of the hydrogen, it need not be subtracted from the supposed photosynthetic production. No reasonable explanation of the organic carbon of sediments other than a biological origin has been proposed, so that we may assume 182 Gg of oxygen should have been liberated into the atmosphere by photosynthesis and not returned to the cycle in respiration. In addition, the photolytic decomposition of water vapor should have produced 59 Gg, and the nitrogen associated with reduced carbon implies a liberation of 1.8–2.9 Gg. The total estimated production of oxygen is therefore:

	Gg
By photosynthesis in excess of respiration	181
By photolysis of water vapor	59
By nitrogen fixation	2
Total	242

The quantity of atmospheric and fossil oxygen that can be recognized is much less than this amount. Rubey (1951) gives the most recent estimate. Assuming that all the sulphate of the sea and the sediment represents oxidized sulphide and that oxygen has been fossilized in the production of ferric from ferrous iron, the total free and fossil oxygen appears to be:

	Gg
Free in atmosphere	12
As sulphate in sea and sediments	47
As ferric iron derived from ferrous	14
Total	73

Rubey, who has not considered photolytic production of oxygen, examines several possible additions to and subtractions from this balance sheet, none of which, at present, can be estimated satisfactorily. He believes that the most probable explanation of the discrepancy between the observed fossil oxygen and the computed quantity of oxygen produced is that an appreciable amount of the oxidized carbon is liberated from volcanoes as CO rather than as CO_2, though, of course, other reduced gases, such as CH_4 and H_2, are also possible (Cotton, 1944). If Urey's hypothesis that the CO_2 of the biosphere and sediments was derived from methane, oxidized to carbonate in the early Pre-Cambrian, proves acceptable, Rubey's interpretation implies that for every molecule of CO liberated, an atom of oxygen has been fossilized by oxidation of magmatic rather than sedimentary ferrous iron. Such an idea is by no means unreasonable.

4.2. POSSIBILITY OF CHANGE OF OXYGEN CONTENT IN PHANEROZOIC TIME

The oxygen content of the air is to be regarded as determined by a steady state between photolysis and deposition of reduced carbon, on the one hand, and fossilization, on the other. Taking the 242 Gg of oxygen at its face value, the rate of fossilization is about 0.8 Gg in 10,000,000 years. If periods of intense loss of oxygen, owing to volcanic output of reduced gases and great erosion of elevated continents, lasted for such a time and doubled the rate of fossilization, the oxygen content of the air would be reduced only to 19.50% vol. At the same time, any additional CO_2, liberated from the volcanoes, either as such or as CO that was oxidized, would probably raise the over-all photosynthetic rate of the earth and slightly increase the deposition of reduced carbon. It is therefore very unlikely, at least during phanerozoic time, that any very significant changes in the oxygen content of the atmosphere have taken place.

5. NITROGEN AND ITS COMPOUNDS IN THE EARTH'S ATMOSPHERE

5.1. GEOCHEMICAL DISTRIBUTION OF NITROGEN

Nitrogen occurs in igneous rocks; according to Rayleigh (1939), the quantity present is remarkably constant, averaging 0.04 cc N_2/gm, or 0.005 per cent by weight. Quantities of the same order are found in stony meteorites (Lipman, 1932; Buddhue, 1942). An appreciable quantity of the nitrogen in terrestrial igneous rocks was found by Rayleigh to be in combination. If the powdered rock be heated with soda lime, such nitrogen is driven off as a compound that gives the Nessler reaction. Urey (1952a) takes the nitrogen of igneous rocks to be present as NH_4Cl, though he quotes a suggestion of Suess that the rare meteoritic mineral, osbornite, TiN, may also be present. A small amount of diadodic substitution of NH_4^+ for K^+ may be possible. Urey's suggestion, which is largely based on the conditions of stability of ammonia, requires experimental verification. Assuming that the silicate mantle represents 55 per cent of the mass of the earth and that the mantle uniformly contains 0.005 per cent N, the nitrogen content of primary rock is about 32,000 gm/cm_e^2. The ratio of C to N in ordinary argillaceous sediments appears to be about 100:8.1 (Miller,

1903; Hall and Miller, 1908). Recently Arrhenius (1950) has concluded that the relationship of carbon to nitrogen in a sediment is given by

$$C = 46.8 \ N^{1.26} \ .$$

This relationship, of course, cannot strictly be used where only the arithmetic-mean carbon content is available, though if the actual distribution around the mean be fairly close, it doubtless permits a good approximation. Taking the mean carbon content of argillaceous rock as analyzed by Miller (1903), Hall and Miller (1908), and Clarke (1904) as 0.81 per cent, the application of the equation gives a content of 0.040 per cent N and a ratio C to N of 100:5. Goldschmidt (1938) earlier took a ratio of 100:3, which is certainly too low. Rubey takes the total reduced carbon of the sediments as 68.2 Gg. This, with a ratio of $C:N = 100:8.1$, gives 5.5 Gg or 108 gm/cm_e^2 of N; or with a ratio $C:N = 100:5$, one finds 3.4 Gg or 67 gm/cm_e^2 of N. The final estimates for the distribution of nitrogen will therefore be:

	gm/cm_e^2
In primary rock...	32,000
In atmosphere...	755
Fossil N associated with reduced C of sediments.............	67–108
N as nitrate in superficial deposits (p. 417)................	2×10^{-5}

Of the fossil nitrogen, about 8 gm/cm_e^2 appear to be derived from igneous rock, so that only about 60–100 gm/cm_e^2 are to be regarded as lost from the atmosphere. Rubin (1954) points out that the nitrogen of the atmosphere and sediments has a mass of the same order of magnitude as the stoichiometric equivalent of the chloride of the sea, though somewhat less than the latter. He supposes both to be derived from an original supply of NH_4Cl; this hypothesis probably implies an excessive nitrogen content in deep-sea sediments.

5.2. MOLECULAR NITROGEN

From the small positive free energy of the formation of nitric acid from water, nitrogen, and oxygen,

$$\tfrac{1}{2}H_2O + \tfrac{1}{2}N_2 + O_2 = HNO_3 \qquad \Delta F = 1,780 \ cal \ ,$$

we should expect the two major atmospheric gases to be in equilibrium with an appreciable concentration of nitric acid. Owing to the extreme stability of the $N:N$ bond, the difficulty of the initial rupture of the molecule prevents a detectable production of nitric acid at any ordinary temperature or pressure. There are, however, processes, such as bacterial fixation of nitrogen, ammonia production by the fixing organisms, and subsequent nitrification, which, though consuming energy, do actually produce a continual supply of nitrate in the biosphere. It is obviously thermodynamically possible for a not inconsiderable quantity of nitrate to accumulate in the biosphere. Actually, circumstances do exist under which this can happen.

It is also evident that if such circumstances prevailed widely enough and for a long-enough time, the oxygen content of the atmosphere would be depleted. It is evident from the very small amount of nitrate that probably has collected at the earth's surface that there are mechanisms continually returning nitrogen and, if this nitrogen should come from nitrate, oxygen also, into the atmosphere. The whole series of processes by which that molecular nitrogen of the air enters into other compounds and is finally returned again to the atmosphere constitutes the *nitrogen cycle*.

5.3. Nitrogen in Organisms

In living organisms the most important nitrogen compounds are amino acids ($R \cdot CHNH_2$–COOH) polymerized to form proteins. Amines are produced by some heterotrophic bacteria, and amine nitrogen plays some part in metabolism. Imino-nitrogen ($=NH$) is of less importance. Several heterocyclic N compounds are known biochemically, the tetrapyrrol ring of chlorophyll, hemoglobin, and various respiratory enzymes being of extraordinary importance. A few nitriles and isonitriles are known. Oxynitrogen compounds are practically absent from the living world, the only well-established exception to their absence being the well-known antibiotic chloromycetin.

In view of the great preponderance of amino nitrogen in living matter, it is reasonable to find that all organisms capable of obtaining their nitrogen from inorganic compounds can use ammonia. Where other forms of nitrogen, such as molecular nitrogen or nitrate, are used by such autotrophic organisms, they invariably convert the compound taken up into ammonia. This is true of both green plants and of chemoautotrophic bacteria. In some cases nitrate may be a more convenient source of nitrogen than is ammonia. At high pH values, when most of the ammonia is present as undissociated NH_4OH, which may be toxic, nitrate may well be a better nitrogen source, as Österlind (1949) found for the unicellular alga *Scenedesmus*. This convenience of nitrate does not alter the fact that ammonia is evidently the essential form of nitrogen when living matter is being synthesized from simple inorganic compounds.

As well as being the fundamental form in which nitrogen enters living matter, ammonia is the most widespread nitrogenous product of metabolism. The higher animals may elaborate other compounds for special reasons, but in the bacteria and in the lower animals ammonia is the dominant end-product of the biological part of the cycle. If only N_2 and NH_3 could occur in the inorganic world, life would be able to operate perfectly well.

5.4. AMMONIA

Ammonia is stable relative to its elements at the ordinary pressures and temperatures existing at the surface of the earth. At a pressure of 1 atm the gas is about half-dissociated at 700° K, and at higher pressures correspondingly less dissociated. These results, although of cosmochemical importance (Urey, 1952*a*), are, in general, of no particular interest at the earth's surface today. In all parts of the earth's mantle, nitrogen and hydrogen would be in equilibrium with a considerable excess of ammonia. The occurrence of ammonia in igneous rocks is therefore reasonable.

In the absence of excess hydrogen, ammonia is decomposed photochemically under light of wave length <2200 A; but in an atmosphere containing oxygen it is unlikely that any of the gas could reach levels at which this might happen. The reaction

$$NH_4^+ + OH^- + \tfrac{3}{2}O_2 = H^+ + NO_2^- + 2H_2O; \qquad \Delta F = -59,400 \text{ cal},$$

being accompanied by a large decrease in free energy, can proceed practically to completion if suitably activated. Cooper (1937) suspects that the air-water interfaces of bubbles at the disturbed surface of the sea may provide conditions in which ammonia can be spontaneously oxidized to nitrate. In general, however, the reaction, which is undoubtedly of some importance in the economy of the biosphere, is activated by light in the presence of certain oxides, notably SiO_2 (Rao and Dhar, 1931). Ordinary sunlight is effective in the process, and natural sea water contains a photosensitizer (ZoBell, 1933; Rakestraw and Hollaender, 1937) which is destroyed on autoclaving and is possibly colloidal silica.

Earlier investigators, notably Brown (1870), believed that they had detected ammonia in the atmosphere by chemical methods. In view of the normal occurrence of ammonia in rain water, it is reasonable to suppose that such records are valid, but it is improbable that they refer to gaseous NH_3. Though Mohler, Goldberg, and McMath (1948) thought that they had detected ammonia in the air by infrared spectrography, Migeotte and Chapman (1949), using the particularly favorable band at 10.5 μ, were unable to confirm this. Their method permitted the detection of 10 cm NH_3 at a pressure of 1 mm Hg. Disregarding pressure effects, this amount, equivalent to 0.132 atm-mm, may be regarded as giving a rough upper limit to the gaseous ammonia in the atmosphere. If such a quantity were uniformly distributed, it would correspond to 1.65×10^{-8} parts of ammonia by volume, or a pressure of 1.25×10^{-5} mm Hg at sea-level.

Ammonia in equilibrium with an aqueous solution does not obey Henry's law, but the data of de Wijs (Dorsey, 1940) indicate that at very low pressures, p, the pressure of the gas in mm Hg is satisfactorily given by

$$p = 0.0129\,C ,$$

where C is the concentration in solution in millimols. We therefore find that 1.25×10^{-5} mm Hg of gaseous ammonia will be in equilibrium with about 10^{-3} millimols/liter in solution. Rain water may occasionally contain as little ammonia as this, but more usually the concentration is of the order of 0.4 mg/liter or 0.03 millimols/liter and not infrequently considerably more. The assumption that the ammonia that has entered the rain was originally present in the air mainly in *solid* form is therefore reasonable.

In London air, which is hardly a fair sample of the atmosphere, Reynolds (1930) found 90 per cent of the ammonia could be removed in filtration through cotton. The quantity present is approximately equivalent stoichiometrically to the chloride, and Reynolds therefore supposed that the ammonia is present as an NH_4Cl aerosol. In unpolluted air one may suppose with Russell and Richards (1919) that the ammonia is associated with fine air-borne dust derived from soil. Finnell and Houghton (1931) obtained evidence of the correlation of the ammonia content of rain and the dustiness of the air at Hopewell, Oklahoma, and concluded that such an origin would be quantitatively possible. Shutt and Dorrance (1917) found near Ottawa rather a greater proportion of the total nitrogen to be present in organic form (liberated by permanganate in alkaline solution, the albuminoid ammonia of water analysis) in snow than in rain:

NITROGEN COMPOUNDS IN mg/liter
CONTAINED IN SNOW AND RAIN

	$N \cdot NH_3$	Organic N	$N \cdot (NO_2 + NO_3)$
Snow.........	0.240	0.097	0.160
Rain.........	0.541	0.151	0.342

DISTRIBUTION OF N (PER CENT) AMONG
NITROGEN COMPOUNDS CONTAINED
IN SNOW AND RAIN

	$N \cdot NH_3$	Organic N	$N \cdot (NO_2 + NO_3)$
Snow.........	48	20	32
Rain.........	53	14	33

They supposed that snow removed dust particles more efficiently than rain did and that the organic nitrogen was more closely associated with such particles than were the other forms. It is, however, quite possible that the results are due to more rapid decomposition of organic nitrogen compounds in summer than in winter, the ammonia produced remaining associated with the dust.

The probable presence of ammonia in dust particles or in the liquid films that surround such particles recalls Cooper's (1948) conclusion that much ammonia in the surface of the sea is associated with the surface film or with substances adsorbed thereto. Such a mode of occurrence probably provides the best conditions for photoxidation, and it is just conceivable that a little biological nitrification may also occur in the atmosphere.

6. OXIDES AND OXYACIDS OF NITROGEN IN AIR AND RAIN

6.1. NITROUS OXIDE

The existence of a small stationary concentration of nitrous oxide in the atmosphere was implied by the results of Corbet (1935; see also Waksman and Madhok, 1937) in a paper, overlooked by most investigators other than biochemists, in which the production of the gas by soil microörganisms and its subsequent photochemical decomposition were pointed out.

Adel (1939, 1941), on the basis of an absorption-band doublet at 7.6 and 7.8 μ in the spectrum of the sun, as observed at Flagstaff, Arizona, inferred the presence of the gas in the terrestrial atmosphere; and Price (1943) computed from Adel's data that the quantity present corresponds to about 0.8 atm-cm. Shaw, Sutherland, and Wormell (1948), working at the much lower altitude of Cambridge, England, were unable to observe Adel's original bands, owing to interference by water vapor; but they recognized several other absorption bands which allowed them to estimate the quantity present at 1.0 atm-cm. More recently an improved determination at the McMath-Hulbert Observatory gave a value of 0.4 atm-cm (McMath, and Goldberg, 1949); this value is probably superior to the earlier estimates. Slobod and Krogh (1950), moreover, have isolated the gas from air at ground level and have estimated, by the mass spectrometer, that the quantity present is $0.00005 \pm 0.00001\%$ vol. This quantity, assuming an even vertical distribution, corresponds to 0.4 atm-cm, in excellent agreement with the best determination from the infrared absorption spectrum of the atmosphere. The vertical distribution and the abundance are discussed in chapter 9.

Adel (1950) concludes from measurements of emissivity and of the radiation intensity at 7.8 μ that the effective radiation temperatures implied by the infrared absorption of the gas lie between 0° and 10° C—if anything, nearer the latter than the former temperature. He also indicates that recent studies of the infrared solar spectrum, as observed at high altitudes, indicate no concentration of the gas in the upper atmosphere.

When the existence of infrared absorption due to N_2O in the solar spectrum was first announced, several rather improbable hypotheses implying the photochemical formation of the gas at high altitudes were put forward. In view of the presence of considerable amounts of the gas in samples of soil gases studied by the mass spectrometer by various investigators (Kriegel, 1944; Taylor, Brown, Young, and Headington, 1948) interested in the presence of hydrocarbons, in geochemical prospecting for petroleum, Adel (1946, 1951) concluded that such photochemical hypotheses were unnecessary. His view that the atmospheric N_2O is derived from the soil is, moreover, in accord with the distribution of the gas and with Corbet's discovery of soil bacteria, which actually produce considerable quantities of N_2O. Corbet showed that hyponitrite is formed in the oxidation of ammonia to nitrite in soil. It is reasonable to suppose that, under acid conditions, free hyponitrous acid is produced and that this, being less stable than hyponitrite in neutral or slightly alkaline solutions, decomposes to produce nitrous oxide:

$$H_2N_2O_2 \rightarrow N_2O + H_2O .$$

It is evidently desirable for bacteriologists interested in denitrification to pay more attention to the gases commonly regarded as N_2 which are produced by denitrifying bacteria; for part of the gas that has hitherto been identified as molecular nitrogen may well prove to be nitrous oxide.

Nitrous oxide is an extremely stable substance at ordinary temperatures and is not likely to react with any atmospheric constituent at low altitudes. When irradiated with ultraviolet in the region 1860–1990 A (Macdonald, 1928; Noyes, 1937) it decomposes thus:

$$N_2O + h\nu \rightarrow N_2 + O^*, \qquad N_2O + h\nu \rightarrow NO + N^* .$$

If oxygen atoms are present, they may react with N_2O:

$$N_2O + O \rightarrow 2 NO , \qquad N_2O + O \rightarrow N_2 + O_2 .$$

It is evident that such nitrous oxide as enters the atmosphere will, when it reaches the appropriate level, be decomposed to give either atomic or molecular oxygen or nitrogen; or nitric oxide, which itself will undergo decomposition. The concentration observed in the atmosphere may, as Adel has urged, be regarded as a steady state between the biological production in the soil and the direct or indirect photochemical decomposition of the gas in the upper atmosphere. Goody and Walshaw (1953) come to a like conclusion; not so Harteck and Dondes (*Phys. Rev.*, **95**, 320, 1954).

6.2. NITRIC OXIDE

Nitric oxide should be formed not merely from nitrous oxide, according to the equations just given, but also from nitrogen peroxide, which is known to be an atmospheric constituent at least under some conditions. The balanced reaction,

$$2\,NO_2 \rightleftharpoons 2\,NO + O_2\ ,$$

which in elementary laboratory demonstrations is made to proceed from right to left, involves a bimolecular reaction on the left and a termolecular reaction on the right. It will therefore be pressure-dependent, proceeding to the right at low pressures. Moreover, a photochemical decomposition of the over-all nature of

$$2\,NO_2 + h\nu \rightarrow 2\,NO + O_2$$

occurs under light of wave length <4300 A and so may proceed by day at any level of the atmosphere.

The photolysis of nitric oxide,

$$NO + h\nu \rightarrow N + O\ ,$$

takes place under wave lengths <1832 A; and, in the presence of oxygen, some oxidation of NO, produced photochemically in excess of the quantity in equilibrium with NO_2, will take place. It is evident that a small stationary concentration of NO would be expected, at least in the upper atmosphere, determined by the rate of production from N_2O and such NO_2 as may be present and by the rate of photolysis to oxygen and nitrogen atoms. Moreover, it is commonly believed, with some justification, that NO is formed by the combination of N_2 and O_2 at high temperatures in lightning flashes; near the ground this may be expected, at least by day, to form NO_2.

In spite of the theoretical probability that NO is a minor constituent of the atmosphere, it has not been detected. The best infrared band, at 5.3 μ, is obscured by water vapor except at very high altitudes. On dry days at the Jungfraujoch in Switzerland (alt. 3580 m) Migeotte (1952) has been able to observe this region and has derived 0.02 atm-cm as the upper limit for the total content in a vertical column. Pearse (1943) lists a number of weak bands of the β-system of NO that might be identifiable in the spectrum of the night sky; but the few coincidences are probably accidental (see chap. 11), and the strong double-headed band of the γ-system at 2997 and 3009 A lies just outside the region that has proved practical for investigation. The disappearance of NO_2 during bright warm weather and its reappearance under an overcast sky, recorded by Edgar and Paneth, may perhaps imply photochemical production of NO at ground level.

6.3. Nitrogen Peroxide

Nitrogen peroxide, which at the low partial pressures present in the atmosphere will be almost entirely present as NO_2, is a minor and inadequately studied atmospheric constituent. No good quantitative work on its occurrence, done in areas remote from industrial contamination, has been published. Masson (1917) made a number of determinations in Australia, but the full account promised seems never to have appeared. The oxides of nitrogen, the relative distribution of which was studied by Hayhurst and Pring (1910), were presumably mainly NO_2; these investigators claimed an increasing concentration with altitude, but the interpretation of their results is far from clear. Most modern determinations have been made in or near metropolitan areas. Thus Edgar and Paneth (1941) found from 0.05 to 2.0×10^{-6} % vol. in air collected in South Kensington, the mean being 0.75×10^{-6} % vol. Two determinations at Kew gave 0.05 and 0.3×10^{-6} % vol. Reynolds (1930) found from 0.3 to 0.8×10^{-6} % vol. in air collected in Plaistow in the London suburbs, while at Upminster only about one-sixth of this amount occurred. Francis and Parsons (1925), using liquid air prepared within the urban area of London, found higher values than those of Reynolds at Plaistow. It is evident that the mean quantity of NO_2 in uncontaminated air is unlikely to exceed 10^{-7} % vol. or one five-hundredth of the quantity of N_2O.

There seems to be very great temporal variation in the NO_2 content of city air. Reynolds, whose results are not published in full, concluded that NH_3, Cl^-, SO_2, and NO_2 varied concomitantly and that all were derived from the combustion of fuels. The observations of Edgar and Paneth, however, suggest that the problem is more complex. These observers recorded a reduction to an undetectable amount after a fall of snow, and, more remarkably, they were unable to find the gas in the atmosphere for a whole week during fine warm spring weather. When the sky subsequently became very overcast, the gas returned. As has already been noted, it is conceivable that photochemical decomposition lowered the concentration of the gas during the fine spell. If regulation of this kind really occurs, there should be, as Price (1943) points out, a diurnal cycle in the concentration. An extensive study of the NO_2 content of the air in localities remote from industrial pollution would be most valuable.

6.4. Nitrogen Pentoxide

Both NO_2 and NO may be oxidized by ozone to form nitrogen pent-oxide. Adel originally believed that the infrared solar spectrum gave evidence of the presence of N_2O_5 in the intensification of the 7.6 μ band of N_2O, but later withdrew the suggestion when Migeotte and others pointed out that the absorptions were caused by the ν_4 band of CH_4 (cf. chap. 9). Nitrogen pentoxide undergoes photolytic decomposition to nitrogen peroxide and oxygen; and the same reaction occurs spontaneously but slowly in the dark at ordinary temperatures and more rapidly at 40° C. It is just possible that NO_3 might also be produced by the action of ozone on NO_2.

6.5. The Electrical Production of Nitrate in the Atmosphere

The idea that the nitrate in rain is produced by electrical discharges in the atmosphere was apparently first advanced by Liebig (1827). It was enthusiastically adopted by Dumas and Boussingault (1841) and has been reaffirmed on countless later occasions by other expositors. Some recent investigators, notably Finnell and Houghton (1931, 1932), have supposed that their data support the hypothesis, while others (Shutt and Dorrance, 1917; Hansen, 1931; Dhar and Ram, 1933), have failed to observe the correlation. The reasonableness of the hypothesis is obviously increased by a consideration of the analogous industrial processes for the production of oxides of nitrogen; but, in view of the results of different students of rain water, it is obviously desirable to go beyond industrial analogy and to attempt to discover what really happens in the atmosphere. The best available modern data appear to be those of Finnell and Houghton (1931, 1932). These investigators give the nitrate nitrogen per unit volume of precipitation and the total nitrate nitrogen delivered per unit area during each rain and snowfall at Hopewell, Oklahoma, during 1925, 1930, and 1931. The recording of the 1931 data differs from that used in the two earlier years. For 1925 and 1930 no nitrite figures are given, and the nitrate recorded presumably includes nitrite. It is not clear whether or not the 1931 figures are corrected for nitrite: either interpretation leads to inconsistencies. For the present, the 1931 data therefore will not be used. The other two years appear to differ somewhat in the distribution of storms and of nitrate. For the present purposes, only the 1925 data are satisfactory and will be used; while on p. 410 the 1931 nitrite data are considered.

Finnell and Houghton supposed that their data indicated categorically an association of high nitrate per rain with severe thunder. Since the mean *concentrations* show no such relationship, an equally satisfactory conclusion would be that the heavy rain, associated with thunder, washes more oxidized nitrogen from the air than does light rain. Moreover, since heavy rains accompanied by thunder occur mostly in summer, a seasonal factor may also be involved. Omitting for the present any consideration of such a possible seasonal effect, since the 1925 data seem inadequate to isolate it, if it exists, it is possible to submit the relationship of nitrate to rainfall and lightning to statistical analysis. If the lightning intensity were recorded quantitatively, the obvious method would be partial correlation. It is, however, most improbable that the four categories—none, mild, medium, and severe—used in recording the electrical discharge can be given numerical ratings. The removal of the effect of total rainfall by considering concentrations is, moreover, certain'y unsound, because severe storms delivering much nitrate may often be accompanied by rain which has a very low mean nitrate concentration, presumably because most of the nitrate was removed early in the storm. The following method, therefore, was employed.

The nitrate delivered per storm was plotted against the precipitation falling during that storm on ordinary graph paper; snowfalls were excluded, as not certainly comparable with rainfalls. The resulting scatter diagram clearly implies nonlinear regression; but, since the use of a logarithmic scale for rain, which might seem reasonable on account of a washing-out effect, was no improvement in this respect, the simpler linear plot was preferred. A curve (Fig. 1) was then drawn by eye to fit as well as possible the six mean points obtained by grouping the forty-two available observations by sevens. The expected nitrate for the rainfall corresponding to each point was read off from the curve, and the differences from this value and the observed value were tabulated. There is a tendency for the points corresponding to "no lightning" on to "mild lightning" to fall below the curve and those associated with "medium" or "severe lightning" to fall above it, as would be expected on the basis of the hypothesis being considered. The differences were tabulated in ascending order from the largest negative to the largest positive and were marked as to whether they corresponded to the two lower or two higher categories of lightning. The association of storms with mild discharge and those with no lightning seems justified, because in the spring, when both these types of rainstorm occur, there is no difference in the mean nitrate delivered by either type. The distribution was then examined by means of the Willcoxon sum (Bliss and Calhoun, 1954). The observed tendency for the points corresponding to the lower lightning category to lie below the curve leads to a value of the

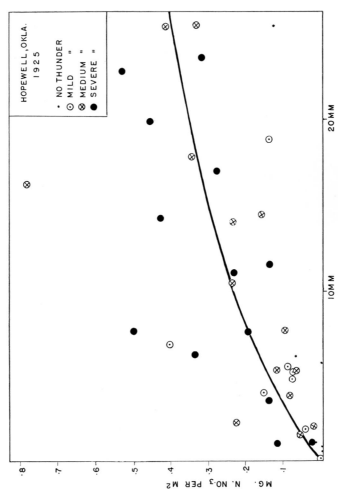

FIG. 1.—Nitrate nitrogen delivered per unit area of surface per storm at Hopewell, Oklahoma, plotted against depth of rain precipitated, from the data of Finnell and Houghton. The presence and intensity of thunder is indicated by the symbols listed at the top right-hand corner of the diagram.

Willcoxon sum of 243, while the expected random value is 322.5. Such a deviation would be expected to occur by chance once in twenty times, so that the distribution may be regarded as moderately significant. Addition of 0.65 mg of $N \cdot NO_3/m^2$ to each rain in the low-lightning group would bring the Willcoxon sum up to expected random value. This figure may be taken as the best estimate of the contribution made by medium or severe electrical discharges to the nitrate delivered per rain. Since the mean value of the nitrate nitrogen delivered by rains accompanied by medium or severe lightning was 2.58 mg/m², approximately one-quarter of this nitrate may reasonably be attributed to lightning, though it must be remembered that there is a small, but not negligible, chance that the *whole effect is due to random variation* or that a greater quantity was actually involved. An estimate of 0.65 mg/m² in each of the 26 medium or severe storms adds up to 16.9 mg/m² year and corresponds to about 21 per cent of the total 80.7 mg/m² year nitrogen delivered as nitrate during the course of 1925 at Hopewell. An earlier, but less convincing, calculation (Hutchinson, 1944) suggested limits between 14 and 35 mg/m² year for the nitrate associated with lightning precipitated at this locality. Bearing in mind the uncertainties already indicated, it is probably quite safe to conclude that over half the nitrate falling at Hopewell must come from sources other than oxidation in lightning flashes. Since Hopewell probably is a more fulminant locality than the average but receives rather less nitrate in precipitation than most humid localities, it is reasonable to conclude that, in general, the greater part of the nitrate falling in rain is *not* derived from the direct oxidation of N_2 in the atmosphere during thunderstorms. Dhar and Ram's hypothesis of the *photochemical oxidation of ammonia* seems to be the only reasonable explanation of the presence of most of the nitrate in rain. It is important to note that such nitrate, unlike that newly fixed in lightning flashes, does not add any combined nitrogen to the quantity circulating in the biosphere.

Ångström and Högberg (1952, *a, b*) have recently considered the relationship of nitrate to ammonia in Swedish rain. They find a strong tendency for the ammonia nitrogen to be twice the nitrate nitrogen. They reject the hypothesis of electrical fixation but suggest a direct *photochemical fixation of N_2* to give equal quantities of ammonia and ammonium nitrate. The reaction suggested seems rather unlikely and is not in accord with the recorded variation in the ratio of nitrate to ammonia; Eriksson (1952*a*) is skeptical, however, that the ratio is really higher in the tropics than in temperate latitudes.

6.6. The Significance of Nitrite in Rain Water

The reactions leading to the production of nitrate when oxygen and nitrogen are passed through an electric arc and then are led into water are:

$$O_2 + N_2 \rightarrow 2\,NO \;,$$

$$2\,NO + O_2 \rightarrow 2\,NO_2 \;,$$

$$2\,NO_2 + H_2O \rightarrow HNO_2 + HNO_3 \;,$$

$$HNO_2 + \tfrac{1}{2}O_2 \rightarrow HNO_3 \;.$$

The final reaction proceeds relatively slowly, compared to the others, and is very sensitive to pH and temperature changes (Corbet, 1934, 1935). We should therefore expect, as Anderson (1915) has pointed out, that newly fixed nitrite and nitrate would be present initially in equal quantities in rain falling in thunderstorms.

The distribution of nitrite, though less well known than that of nitrate, has been studied in a number of localities. Wherever studied, nitrite appears to vary seasonally, but sometimes the maximum amount is present in summer and sometimes in winter rain. At Hopewell (Finnell and Houghton, 1932) there is a marked winter maximum; the total nitrite and nitrate delivered in the rains for which these ions were both determined are as follows:

Subgroup and Dates (1931)	$N \cdot NO_3$ (mg/m²)	$N \cdot NO_2$ (mg/m²)	Ratio
Sum of first 5 rains without lightning, Feb. 19–Apr. 18....	45.8	35.5	1.4
Sum of first 4 rains with lightning, Feb. 19–Apr. 18.....	21.2	17.4	1.2
Sum of next 4 rains with lightning, Apr. 18–May 30.....	63.3	2.2	29
Sum of last 4 rains with lightning, June 1–Sept. 1.......	83.7	1.1	76

It is evident from these sums, as well as from the individual and more variable data given by Finnell and Houghton, that in the winter the nitrite and nitrate are present in approximately equal amounts, whether the rain is accompanied by lightning or not, while in the summer the rain falling in thunderstorms is practically free from nitrite.

These findings are difficult to reconcile with the hypothesis that any large quantity of nitrate is produced from NO, newly fixed in lightning flashes. It is most unlikely that even in slightly acid rain nearly all the nitrite would disappear at summer temperatures in a few minutes, as would seem to be implied by the data if one accepts the hypothesis of fixation in thunderstorms. If, however, the greater part of the nitrate is ultimately derived from the photochemical oxidation of ammonia to nitrite and the further oxidation of nitrite to nitrate over a period of several days (possibly in moisture films on dust particles or in minute droplets of water), the observed phenomena are reasonable. The oxidation of nitrite to nitrate is catalyzed by the hydrogen ion and takes place appreciably and spontaneously below pH 5, a value not exceeded in some rain-water samples; but because it takes place slowly its marked temperature dependence should be expressed as a seasonal difference in nitrite content. Where there is evidence of a summer maximum in nitrite, perhaps one may suppose that, under special conditions, the effect that has just been considered is obscured by the photochemical reduction of nitrate to nitrite, which Corbet (1934) finds can occur at ground level in sunlight. It is, moreover, obviously desirable for subsequent investigators to consider the possibility that the small concentration of NO_2, which probably is normally present in the atmosphere, is actually formed from nitric acid rather than being a precursor of the latter.

6.7. BIOLOGICAL FIXATION OF NITROGEN

Though several earlier workers had suspected that atmospheric nitrogen can be metabolized by various organisms, the first definite indications of specific organisms capable of fixing nitrogen was the demonstration by Hellriegel (1887) that legumes with root nodules could take up N_2 and were independent of other sources of nitrogen. Later, Winogradsky (1893) discovered the anaerobic fixation of nitrogen in soils by bacteria, now referred to the genus *Clostridium;* and Beijerinck (1901) discovered the aerobic bacteria of the genus *Azotobacter*, which fix nitrogen in both soil and water. For many years these three groups of organisms—the leguminous plants in symbiosis with the root-nodule bacterium *Rhizobium;* certain species of the anaerobic free-living *Clostridium butyricum, C. pasteurianum*, and other allied and doubtfully separable species; and the three or four known species of *Azotobacter*—were the only certainly established biological fixers of molecular nitrogen. More recently a number of species of blue-green algae and most of the purple photosynthetic bacteria that have been studied have proved to have the capacity; and it is quite possible that these groups are quantitatively as important as the better-known organisms just listed in the nitrogen economy of the earth. Among the blue-green algae of the family Nostocaceae, species of *Nostoc* (Burris, Epling, Wahlin, and Wilson, 1943), of *Anabaena* (De, 1939), and of *Cylindrospermum* (Bortels, 1940) certainly fix nitrogen. Moreover, Watanabe, Nishigaki, and Konishi (1951) report that *Tolypothrix tenuis* of the family Scytonemataceae and *Calothrix brevissima* of the Rivulariaceae possess the capacity. Odintsova (1941) likewise reports nitrogen fixation by *Gloeocapsa minor* of the family Chroococcaceae. It is, however, desirable, particularly in view of many erroneous claims in the past, that all these claims of nitrogen fixation outside the Nostocaceae be confirmed. Apart from Odintsova's record for *Gloeocapsa*, all the blue-green algae supposed to fix nitrogen are filamentous forms belonging to the Hormogoneales. Nitrogen fixation by purple photosynthetic bacteria was first (Kamen and Gest, 1949) observed in *Rhodospirillum rubrum*. It is now known to occur in most strains of at least three species of *Rhodopseudomonas* and also (Lindstrom, Lewis, and Pinsky, 1951) in *Rhodomicrobium vannielii*. These organisms all belong to the Athiorhodaceae, a peculiar group which uses organic matter as the hydrogen donator in photosynthesis; but there is indirect evidence, from the inhibition of production of hydrogen by illuminated cells of *Chromatium* by molecular nitrogen (Bregoff and Kamen, 1951) that at least one member of the purple sulphur bacteria is likely to behave in the same way.

A few other claims of nitrogen fixation exist unrefuted in the literature, but it is reasonable to suppose that the symbiotic root-nodule bacteria in leguminous and a few other plants, the two or three nitrogen-fixing members of *Closterium*, the species of *Azotobacter*, many Nostocaceae and probably some other blue-green algae, and the majority of the purple photosynthetic bacteria are the main agents introducing molecular nitrogen into more reactive forms at the surface of the earth.

The mechanism of nitrogen fixation has been intensively studied during the last two or three decades but has proved extremely difficult to unravel. It is reasonably certain that ammonia is an intermediate between the molecular nitrogen of the air and the NH_2^- groups of the amino acids formed from the newly fixed nitrogen. In anaerobic fixation by *Clostridium* there is, in fact, no experimental evidence of any other intermediate (Rosenblum and Wilson, 1951). Most European workers (Clemo and Swan, 1949; Virtanen and Rautanen, 1952, give reviews) seem to believe that the aerobic process proceeds as follows:

$$N_2 \rightarrow 2N \rightarrow 2N^+ \rightarrow N_2O \rightarrow (NOH)_2 \rightarrow NH_2OH \rightarrow NH_3 \; ;$$

but this is not entirely reconcilable with the fact that hydroxylamine or oxime nitrogen cannot be used (Novak and Wilson, 1948; Segal and Wilson, 1949) as a nitrogen source by *Azotobacter*, though it may be urged that the compound added to the culture medium does not enter the cells until a toxic concentration is reached. It is, however, noteworthy that N_2O inhibits fixation in *Azotobacter* (Molnar, Burns, and Wilson, 1948) but not in *Clostridium*, which observations are consistent with the scheme given earlier. A hydrogenase can usually be identified in the enzyme systems of the nitrogen-fixing organisms, but this is apparently not true of the root-nodule *Rhizobium* complex. In the latter case the presence of a hemo-globin, which gives the pink color to the nodules that can easily be seen when a clover plant is pulled from soft soil, is evidently of great impor-tance. In all cases it seems clear that an enzyme system containing molyb-denum is involved. It is unlikely that the details of the mechanisms in-volved within the cell are likely to have much influence in determining the biogeochemical cycle of nitrogen outside the organism, but it is perhaps of some cosmochemical interest that there are likely to be some broad simi-larities between the reductive fixation of nitrogen and the photosynthetic reduction of CO_2.

The rate of nitrogen fixation at the surface of the earth can be estimated in several ways, though the results are not very concordant. If one may assume that no significant combined nitrogen moves from the ocean to land surfaces, it is evident that the total rate of discharge of combined nitrogen in river water into the ocean gives a minimum value for the rate of fixation on land and of denitrification in the ocean. The assumption that an appreciable gain of nitrogen compounds by the land from the ocean does not occur is justified by the observations that rain falling from Atlan-tic air in the Hebrides is low in ammonia (Russell and Richards, 1919). In view of the fact that as much air must pass from the land surfaces to the ocean as passes from the ocean to the land surfaces, it is quite likely that ammonia carried on terrestrial dust from land to sea greatly overcompen-sates for any possible movement of marine ammonia through the atmos-phere to the land.

Clarke (1924) computes that the dry inorganic residue of the average river contains 0.2 per cent of $N \cdot NO_3$. There is about 10 per cent as much organic as inorganic matter in such water, and this organic matter will contain about 3 per cent N (Birge and Juday, 1934). The data available on ammonia contents are less satisfactory. It is unlikely that the ammonia nitrogen content will exceed that of nitrate nitrogen and also unlikely that ammonia nitrogen will be absent. The best estimate of combined nitrogen in river water is, therefore, about 0.6 per cent of the inorganic residue. Conway (1942) considers a value of 100 mg/liter to be the best value for the concentration of such inorganic matter in river water, so that the nitrogen content would be about 0.6 mg/liter. Using the estimate of the total annual discharge of 20×10^{18} gm of water given above, the total combined nitrogen entering the ocean will be 12×10^{12} gm/year, corresponding to annual fixation of 8 γ/cm^2 of land surface. My previous minimal estimate (Hutchinson, 1944) was larger, being based on the concentration of inorganic material and volume of total discharge given by Clarke, both of which figures now appear to be too high. The new figure is certainly a minimal estimate, as it is in no way corrected for the denitrification that is known to take place in soils and inland waters. Cases are known where the total runoff from an area removes less nitrogen than is delivered in precipitation (Roelofsen, 1941), in spite of the fact that fixation must be occurring to some extent in all but the coldest and most arid regions.

In an elaborate study of the nutrient budget of the land surface of the United States, Lipman and Conybeare (1936) estimate from lysimeter experiments and from other sources that the mean rate of fixation by nonsymbiotic bacteria is about 67.4 γ/cm^2. The intense fixation in root nodules of legumes in a limited part of the total area is believed almost to double this estimate when averaged over the whole country. The estimate for nonsymbiotic fixation is apparently regarded as conservative by other workers in this field; but it is improbable that leguminous fixation for the earth as a whole is likely to be nearly as great as in the cultivated part of temperate North America. Allowing a small contribution from this source, a rate of fixation of 70 γ per square centimeter would seem reasonable. Hutchinson (1944), using a somewhat involved argument, obtained a like figure from the ratio of N to P in lake waters. The main difficulty in accepting such estimates is that laboratory studies indicate that about 100 gm of carbohydrate are metabolized in the fixation of 1 gm of nitrogen. Since it would appear that the mean rate of carbohydrate production is 30 mg/cm^2 year, the fixation of 70 γ of N/cm^2 year would use about 23.3 per cent of the carbohydrate annually produced by photosynthesis. This seems an impossibly high figure. It is, however, conceivable that under natural ecological conditions the very low efficiencies observed in nitrogen fixation might be somewhat improved.

At present it is evident that the rate of nitrogen fixation must lie between 8 and 70 γ/cm^2 year when referred to the land surfaces of the earth. These limits correspond to 12–105 $\times$ 10^{12} gm/year for the whole atmosphere and to a cycle length of between 36.6 and 320 million years, or very roughly of the order of 10^8 years.

6.8. The Formation of Nitrate

As was indicated earlier, oxygen and nitrogen at ordinary temperatures and pressures are, in the presence of water, in equilibrium with an appreciable concentration of nitric acid. It is therefore not unexpected to find that under certain circumstances nitrates occur in considerable quantity at the surface of the earth.

Nine mineral species containing NO_3 are recorded by Palache, Berman, and Frondel (1951). Of these, two—namely, gerhardtite, $Cu_2(NO_3)(OH)_3$, and buttgenbachite, $Cu_{19}(NO_3)_2 \cdot Cl_4(OH)_{32} \cdot 3H_2O$—are known to occur, the former at several localities, the latter only at Likasi in the Belgian Congo, as the result of the alteration of copper minerals. Nitrobarite, $Ba(NO_3)_2$, once recorded from Chile, and ammonia niter, $NH_4(NO_3)$, once doubtfully recorded from a cave in Tennessee, are likewise of little geochemical importance, while nitromagnesite, $Mg(NO_3)_2 \cdot 6H_2O$, though apparently less rare than the minerals just mentioned, is of no great quantitative significance. The remaining nitrate minerals—soda niter, $NaNO_3$; niter, KNO_3; nitrocalcite, $Ca(NO_3)_2 \cdot 4H_2O$; and darapskite, $Na_3(NO_3)$-$SO_4 \cdot H_2O$—are often associated and are the main natural sources of nitrate. Any or all of them may be formed when certain kinds of biological activity occur in regions of low and intermittent rainfall.

The normal products of bacterial metabolism of proteins are water, carbon dioxide, and ammonia. It is reasonably certain that most of the nitrogen present in the bodies of animals and plants is ultimately destined to form ammonia. The oxidation of ammonia to nitrite,

$$NH_4^+ + OH^- + \tfrac{3}{2}O_2 = H^+ + NO_2^- + 2H_2O ; \qquad \Delta F = -59,400 \text{ cal} ,$$

and of nitrite to nitrate,

$$NO_2^- + \tfrac{1}{2}O_2 (g) = NO_3^- ; \qquad \Delta F = -18,000 \text{ cal} ,$$

involves falls in free energy and can potentially be energy sources to organisms. It has been known since the studies of Winogradsky (1890) that soil bacteria exist that can use these reactions in chemoautotrophic nutrition, utilizing the energy derived from the oxidation of ammonia to reduce CO_2 and to form all the organic compounds of their cells. The two stages of the reaction are performed by different bacteria, *Nitrosomonas* oxidizing ammonia to nitrite; and *Nitrobacter*, nitrite to nitrate. Soils also contain species of *Achromobacter* and *Corynebacterium*, which can oxidize pyruvic oxime and oxalacetic oxime to nitrite (Quastel, Scholefield, and Stevenson, 1950). Hydroxyamine (Lees, 1952) is probably formed as an intermediate in the oxidation, and hyponitrite may also be involved. The efficiency of the ammonia-oxidizing organisms is not great, and very special techniques are needed in their cultivation (Lees, 1950). It is, however, probable that they have a special relationship in soils to ammonium ions held in the ionic atmospheres of soil colloids and that the structure of a soil provides them with niches in which they can flourish in spite of competition from other bacteria for oxygen and other nutrients.

In spite of the difficulty of working with the nitrifying organisms, they can be extremely effective biogeochemical agents in nature. An enormous literature exists on nitrification in soils. For the purposes of the present chapter it is only necessary to mention that in some circumstances up to 0.5 gm of nitrate nitrogen per kilogram of soil can be formed in relatively short periods, as in barren Uganda soil at the onset of the rainy season (e.g., Griffith and Manning, 1950). The conditions for the accumulation of nitrate are probably imitated by the traditional method of making niter in Europe. Soil and manure were mixed together and piled in heaps. Niter-containing soil solution, drawn to the surface by capillarity, evaporated on the windward side, and the crust of KNO_3 so formed could be collected. In nature a falling organic content, which probably means a falling population of denitrifying heterotrophic bacteria, certainly encourages the production of nitrate. Hutchinson (1950) points out that in the deposits of bat caves the ratio of nitrate to total nitrogen rises as the organic matter falls. The formation of considerable beds of nitrate may be expected when ammonia is liberated in an appropriate oxidizing medium and when the nitrate so formed is removed and deposited in a solid form rapidly enough so that there is no time for it to be taken up by green plants or to be reduced by the numerous heterotrophic bacteria that can use nitrate as a hydrogen acceptor instead of oxygen in their metabolism.

The origin of the great deposits of soda niter in Chile and of the smaller beds elsewhere has been endlessly debated. A tabular summary of all the theories, reasonable and unreasonable, that had been put forward before 1932 is given by Wetzel (1932). In view of the fact that nitrate deposition develops to some extent whenever the right climatic conditions are present, it is obvious that some general explanation dependent on these climatic conditions must be involved, though it is equally certain that the climatic factors operate much more advantageously under some conditions than under others. It is evident that two or three different processes have to be considered, namely, the fixation of the nitrogen, its nitrification, and its concentration into discrete deposits. The discovery that blue-green algae and purple bacteria are very effective nitrogen fixers probably provides the most satisfactory explanation of the initial fixation process, as Odintsova first pointed out with reference to the former group. The only reasonable explanation of the nitrification is that it is bacterial and that it has proceeded, probably at the time of very brief rainy seasons, under conditions that were subsequently too dry to permit much denitrification, though very short rains might be effective in permitting the concentration of the nitrate in shallow pools or by capillary water.

The total quantity of nitrogen that has been deposited in the upland deserts of Chile is estimated by Wetzel (1932) as the equivalent of about 327,000,000 tons of $NaNO_3$. This would correspond to 54×10^{12} gm of nitrogen. One may presumably set the total nitrate nitrogen in superficial deposits of the earth as about 10^{14} gm. The total quantity of nitrogen contained in guano deposits, now mostly exhausted, was evidently of the order of 10^{11} gm (Hutchinson, 1950).

6.9. DENITRIFICATION

A great variety of facultative anaerobic bacteria can use both nitrate and nitrite instead of oxygen in the respiratory oxidation of organic matter. This capacity is paralleled by the similar reduction of sulphate, selenate, and apparently even phosphate by other species. Such denitrifying bacteria are probably mainly responsible for the return of molecular nitrogen to the atmosphere. Molecular nitrogen is produced only when ammonia or organic amino nitrogen exists in the presence of undissociated nitrous acid. The process, therefore, can proceed only at pH ≤ 5. The liberation of N_2O likewise presumably demands the formation of free hyponitrous acid. Nothing is known at present of the relative importance of the production of N_2 and N_2O, but it would not be surprising if the latter substance turned out to be almost as important as the former.

7. THE HALOGENS IN THE ATMOSPHERE

Since it is not impossible that organisms participate in the cycles of the halogens and of sulphur in the atmosphere, it may be useful to devote a little space to these elements.

Chlorine, bromine, and iodine are all known to occur in rain water.[4] The only simultaneous determinations and, indeed, the only analyses giving the bromine contents are those of Selivanov (1939, 1946), who found in the vicinity of Moscow, the following mean values.

Precipitation	Cl	Br	I
From maritime air......	0.5 mg/liter	0.03 mg/liter	0.002 mg/liter
From continental air.....	0.04 mg/liter	0.002 mg/liter	0.0002 mg/liter

4. The whole of the material on the cycle of bromine and iodine in the biosphere will be reviewed in detail in a forthcoming monograph by Dr. Eva M. Low and the writer. Dr. Low has most kindly made her notes available for the present contribution.

The ratios Cl:Br:I are 100:6:0.4 for maritime air and 100:5:0.5 for continental air. The corresponding ratios for sea water are 100:0.34: 0.00021. There is a moderate enrichment of bromine and an enormous enrichment of iodine in atmosphere precipitation. Some slight doubt about the general enrichment of bromine may exist, as Selivanov's chloride contents are very low. Of the enrichment in iodine there can be no doubt whatever.

The chlorine of the atmosphere is undoubtedly all present as chloride in suspension. The matter has received considerable attention, on account of the widespread belief, largely elaborated by Köhler, that salt nuclei derived from sea spray are the main condensation nuclei around which cloud droplets form. The history of this idea has been reviewed in a masterly fashion by Simpson (1941a), who in a later paper (1941b) has shown that at least in one well-studied case the evidence clearly indicates that coastal mist, far from industrial contamination, cannot have condensed around sea-salt particles.

An admirable review of the composition of rain (Eriksson, 1952b) appeared after the present account had been completed. Moyerman and Shuler (1953) have also reviewed the data on the presence of sodium and chloride in air; they conclude that, remote from the sea coast, inland air contains, on the average, 1.15×10^{11} atoms of sodium/cm^3, mainly as chloride.

Early in the present century a good deal of attention was devoted to the establishment of isochlor maps for unpolluted natural waters in eastern North America, in order to have standards for recognition of sewage pollution, which ordinarily leads to enrichment in chloride of urinary origin. Conway (1942), from a study of such maps, concluded that the mean concentration (c) of chloride in atmospheric precipitation falling at any locality can be expressed by

$$c = 5.7 \, e^{-0.059x} + 0.55 \, e^{-0.0024x}$$

where x is the distance from the coast in kilometers. The two terms on the right of the equation were regarded as representing two different types of virtual diffusion with different virtual diffusion coefficients. Drischel (1940) has studied the matter, using the available and largely European data for chloride in rain rather than in uncontaminated surface water. He finds the same rapid fall on leaving the coast that led Conway to adopt the equation given above; but the absolute values at any distance from the sea are greater in Drischel's table than are those given by evaluating Conway's expression. This is probably due to the fact that less rain falls in eastern North America from air that has moved onshore directly perpendicular to the coast than in Europe. It is therefore doubtful whether Conway's analysis of the processes involved is valid, though it would seem reasonable to suppose that aerial transportation of chloride from the ocean inland is a multiple process. Larger particles would fall out of the air more rapidly than smaller, and the latter might be regarded as forming an aerosol and be capable of dispersal over immense distances.

The iodine of the air evidently has a history quite different from that of atmospheric chloride. Atmospheric iodine was first investigated by Chatin (1851). These early results are probably not very reliable, but during the present century a number of studies of the element have been made. Fellenberg (1926) obtained evidence that iodine might be present in adsorbed or combined form, associated with dust particles, as well as free in the atmosphere.

Some evidence (Fellenberg, 1926; Cauer, 1932) exists that air near the ground is generally richer in iodine than it is in the free atmosphere and that less iodine is present in cold weather than in warm, owing to the lower vapor pressure at low temperatures. It is reasonable to suppose that these effects are due to a balance between removal by atmospheric precipitation, which would keep the turbulent atmosphere as a whole relatively low, and diffusion from the soil, which would maintain a higher concentration in the less turbulent region near the ground.

Fellenberg (1926) concluded that in Switzerland 560 γ/m^2 year is deposited by rain, but this was at a time when the iodine content of the air was high. During the last two decades very remarkable changes in the iodine content of the air of Continental Europe have been recorded by Cauer (1939) and by Jesser and Thomae (1943). The absolute values of the latter workers are about ten times greater than those of Cauer, but in both investigations a great decline is reported during the 1930's. In 1932 Cauer found about 0.3 γ/m^3 of air in most nonindustrial regions in Europe, while in 1939 the mean value was 0.002 γ. Jesser and Thomae found a less marked and rather later fall at Stuttgart, where there may conceivably be more local contamination than in Cauer's localities. This marked reduction is believed to be due to the collapse of the European iodine industry during the decade in which the fall occurred.

Kalle assumed that about 0.2 mm of sea surface forms sea spray annually and so carries 3600 tons of iodine into the atmosphere. Such iodine, returning evenly in rain, would give an annual contribution of 7 γ/m^2 year. The contribution from combustion of coal and oil is greater. Assuming about 6 mg/kg of iodine in fuels, the total liberation in the burning of

5×10^9 tons will be 30,000 tons or about 60 γ/m^2 year. Up to 1934, Cauer believed that about 90–230 tons of iodine escaped from European industrial production of iodine into the air. After this date the industry collapsed, and most iodine then came from Chile, at least up to 1939. It is probable that, so far as nonindustrial parts of Europe are concerned, the decline of the iodine industry has been a major factor in reducing the iodine of the atmosphere. Taking the latest of Cauer's average values, of 0.002 γ/m^3 or 1.1×10^{-10} per cent as a mean value for the natural iodine content of the atmosphere, the total amount present will be about 5000 tons and the circulation time presumably of the order of a few decades. The process of liberation of iodine from soils into the atmosphere apparently involves the production of iodine from iodide. It has been claimed (Scharrer and Schwaibold, 1928) that this process is biochemical, but such an interpretation is denied by Fellenberg (1926, 1927) and by Hercus, Benson, and Carter (1925). It will be evident from the discussion already given that the iodine cycle in the atmosphere is dependent at least as much on artificial, anthropogeochemical activities as on natural events.

8. THE SULPHUR CYCLE IN THE ATMOSPHERE

No sulphur compounds have been identified spectrographically in the terrestrial atmosphere. Price (1943) sets the upper spectrographic limit of SO_2 for the whole atmosphere as of the order of $0.00n$ atm-cm. It seems probable that such sulphur compounds as are present in unpolluted air are associated with water droplets or dry aerosols. The local presence of SO_2 in industrially polluted air is well known.

Coste and Wright (1935) found that a small amount of sulphate, of the order of 1 per cent of the total SO_2, accompanied the latter gas. They conclude that the oxidation of SO_2 produced by combustion of sulphur-containing fuels cannot be very rapid. Aitken (1911) obtained some evidence that this oxidation involves a photochemical process taking place under visible and long-wave ultraviolet at ground level. The oxidation of SO_2 to SO_3 and the subsequent formation of hygroscopic nuclei of H_2SO_4 are believed by Aitken to produce characteristic mists, which obscure bright mornings in industrial regions. Whatever the mechanism of the oxidation and whatever its speed, the rapid fall in sulphate content of rain in passing from an industrial town into the country (MacIntire and Young, 1923) suggests that industrial oxides of sulphur are of little importance in the economy of the atmosphere as a whole, however distressing their effects may be in the immediate neighborhood of their production. The most important information as to the existence of sulphur compounds in the atmosphere is derived from a study of the chemistry of cloud and rain. Köhler (1937), examining rime formed by the freezing of mist at Hallde in northern Norway, found 3.56 mg/liter of Cl and 0.57 mg/liter of SO_4, the ratio SO_4:Cl of 0.16 being hardly higher than in sea water. Houghton (in Rankama and Sahama, 1950), however, found a definite enrichment in fog from the coast of Nova Scotia and Massachusetts and in clouds from Mount Washington, the SO_4:Cl ratio being 0.51–1.73. Except for a few samples obviously contaminated by sea spray, all analyses of rain and snow give ratios well in excess of 0.14, which is characteristic of the ocean.

Sugawara (1948), who collected the sulphate and chloride that could be filtered from air and compared his value with the local rain, concluded that rain falling near the Japanese coast, though richer in sulphate relative to chloride than in sea water, has a lower relative SO_4 content than the air from which it falls.

Three explanations of the high sulphate content of rain have been given. The first, which was applied by MacIntire and Young primarily to urban rain, is from industrial combustion of sulphur-containing fuels. Conway has shown that such a source is quantitatively inadequate.

The second, that the sulphate is derived from the oxidation of H_2S produced during organic decomposition, was first put forward by Smith (1870). He supposed the decomposing organic matter to be situated in the soil. Conway (1942) has more recently suggested that the main source of the H_2S is the blue mud of shallow marine sediments.

The third hypothesis, developed by Sugawara, Oana, and Koyama (1949), is that sea spray, in drying, tends to produce two types of particle, one mainly $CaSO_4 \cdot 2H_2O$, which is not hygroscopic, the other mainly NaCl with some $MgCl_2$, which is hygroscopic. The hygroscopic salt particles will form nuclei in oceanic and coastal rains and will be returned to the sea; the calcium sulphate particles will form a more stable aerosol and so be distributed over the surface of the earth. Such calcium sulphate as is washed out of the air over the continents will therefore be accompanied by less chloride than over the oceans. Dr. A. H. Woodcock, who has recently given great attention to the study of salt nuclei (Woodcock, 1950, 1954) has expressed verbally some skepticism as to the efficacy of this supposed mechanism. The analytic data on which the hypothesis was put forward deserve the most serious attention. Since there is a detectable shift in the isotopic ratio when sulphate and sulphide come into equilibrium, the isotopic constitution of sulphate in rain should throw light on the matter.

9. COSMOCHEMICAL CONSIDERATIONS

9.1. The Earth

It would seem universally admitted that the earth's atmosphere is secondary, as is indicated by the extremely low content of the heavy rare gases (Brown, 1949), if by nothing else. It would also seem clear that the first atmosphere could not have contained much CO_2, since the Urey equilibrium should be established in the presence of water. It is also reasonably certain that, initially, it could not have contained free oxygen. The most likely constituents are ammonia, giving rise to nitrogen as hydrogen is lost, and methane, which would be fairly stable in the absence of oxygen. Such an atmosphere is accepted by Urey and has obvious cosmochemical analogues. The primary questions to be solved concern the times at which the various processes, notably the appearance of oxygen and of living organisms characteristic of the modern biosphere, appeared. The data available for the empirical treatment of the question are wretchedly inadequate, but so far as they go may be summarized as follows:

1. The oldest sediments, found in the Archean of both the New and the Old World, are lithologically comparable to later sediments (Eskola, 1932; Pettijohn, 1943), though they are mainly of the kind that fill geosynclines early in orogenesis.

2. The finer-grained Archaean sediments contain an amount of carbon of the same order of magnitude as is found in comparable modern sediments. In the latter, such carbon is certainly organic.

3. There is a macroscopic carbonaceous structure, consisting of a cylindrical wall with rounded ends, like a sausage, found in Archaean rocks of Finland and estimated to be 1.4×10^9 years old, which is reasonably interpreted (Rankama, 1948, 1950) as a fossil, *Corycium enigmaticum* Sederholm. No plausible inorganic explanation of *Corycium* is available, and the interpretation as the cell wall of a large unicellular alga, like a single cell of *Hydrodictyon*, is plausible. Tyler and Barghoorn (1954) have recently described well-defined microscopic plant fossils of supposedly somewhat greater age from North America.

4. When the continuous fossil record opens in the Cambrian, all the major phyla of invertebrate animals are present. It is difficult to avoid the conclusion that well-organized many-celled animals with an ordinary aerobic metabolism had existed for a long period of time. All guesses are risky; the extraordinarily rapid development of certain mammalian stocks, including that of man himself, in the late Tertiary indicates that great complexity can be evolved with great rapidity. As a rough guess,

however, it would be reasonable to suppose that as much time was needed for the evolution of the Cambrian arthropods, mollusks, brachiopods, and echinoderms as has elapsed in the subsequent evolution of the vertebrates. One might therefore consider speculatively that the Metazoa arose around 10^9 years ago.

5. The almost complete absence of fossils prior to the Cambrian has puzzled most investigators who have paid attention to the matter. It may be that this lack is merely due to the rarity of unmetamorphosed sediments of the kind that might contain good fossils. The sediments that have been preserved are largely clastics, graywackes, and the like, or are associated with continental shields; or, at best, in the Algonkian, are algal reefs which throw little light on the organisms that supposedly produced them. Good argillaceous shallow-water marine deposits formed on the margins of the continents may simply not have survived. Alternative hypotheses, involving various geochemical possibilities, have been put forward. All are patently deficient, and, in spite of the eminence of the sponsors of some of them, it hardly seems worth while to point out their defects here.

6. The well-oxidized ironstones appear only in the later Pre-Cambrian, an observation used by Lane (1917, 1945) and by MacGregor (1927) as an argument in favor of the late appearance of molecular oxygen. Dr. A. E. J. Engel, however, has expressed in conversation great skepticism as to such conclusions.

7. The isotopic ratios $S^{36}:S^{32}$ and $S^{34}:S^{32}$ increase in sulphates and decrease in sulphides from the Cambrian to the present. In the late Pre-Cambrian, isotopic separation of this sort seems to have been absent (Thode, in Urey, 1952a, b). Thode seems to think the fractionation involves aerobic metabolism, beginning about 8×10^8 years ago.

8. There is apparently a difference in the C^{13} content of Pre-Cambrian and phanerozoic limestones (Mars, 1951), suggesting less regular fractionation of isotopes between oxidized and reduced carbon in the Pre-Cambrian.

The most recent consideration of the significance of such facts is that of Urey (1952a, b), whose discussion develops and amplifies earlier works of many investigators, notably Chamberlin (1908), Wildt (1939), and Poole (1941). Urey first considers a prebiological stage, when the earth's atmosphere consisted of water vapor, hydrogen, methane, and ammonia, all of these substances being derived from solids incorporated at a low temperature in the forming earth. The quantities involved are unknown; but since most of the water is likely to have been dissolved in silicate magma or present in crystalline rock, considerably less than, and perhaps but 5–10 per cent of, the present water of the oceans may have been present. The other possible atmospheric constituents may well have been present also in relative small amounts. Oxygen would form photochemically, oxidizing ammonia, methane, and sulphide present. No free oxygen could be formed until the distribution of these reduced compounds insured a more rapid rate of oxygen production than oxidation. A bewildering variety of photo-chemical reactions would take place, and their products would dissolve in rain and so be transferred to the shallow oceans. Here surface reactions on solids, probably aluminosilicate clays (Bernal, 1949), might provide further opportunities not only for organic synthesis but also for incipient biological organization. Miller (1953) has succeeded in imitating the initial stages in laboratory models, producing a great variety of organic compounds from water, methane, and ammonia in an electric discharge, provided that oxygen is entirely absent. At the surface of the newly formed earth, the energy source would presumably have been ultraviolet solar radiation, but the effect of the discharge should be similar, and it is more easily handled in the laboratory.

It is evident that practically the whole of the methane originally present must have gone through one cycle of the sort just described to produce the CO_2 of the order of 18 atm that has apparently passed through the atmosphere. Part of this methane may have been liberated throughout geological time, and the oxidation may account for the fossilization of excess oxygen. If it be assumed that no carbon dioxide is primary and that all the CO_2 of the lithosphere is derived from methane, then about 54 atm of oxygen or about 270 times the present quantity in the air appear to have been needed in the course of geological time. It is therefore possible that initially the photolytic mechanism was much more active than today. Dr. Harrison Brown points out in conversation that the kinetics of the processes involved make such a conclusion reasonable.

Urey suggested that the prebiological period was succeeded by a period in which metabolism was anaerobic. The fundamental energy source could have been solar, as today, but would depend on the photochemical production of hydrogen. Photosynthesis of a fairly normal type, using hydrogen as the oxygen acceptor, could have evolved at this time. As soon as CO_2 appeared in the atmosphere, the cycle of erosion would be comparable to that now observed. The Archean sediments studied by Pettijohn could have been formed under anaerobic conditions without betraying the nature of the environment. There is no way of telling whether *Corycium*, if it lived, lived in a still anaerobic environment. Thode's ideas about the sulphur isotopes are likely to provide information of the greatest importance, but the available data are still very meager and, to the present writer, unconvincing. In the present state of knowledge one can hardly reconcile a date for the appearance of oxygen as late as 8×10^8 years ago, which Urey tends to accept on the basis of these studies, with a time of 10^9 years for the evolution of the Metazoa. The problem of the absence of calcareous skeletons in the Pre-Cambrian is not solved by speculations as to what happened in the anaerobic biological phase, if such existed, because one would hardly expect the organisms then living to produce such skeletons. The problem concerns not the existence of calcareous unicellular anaerobes but of the amphineuran mollusks and perhaps the precursors of the echinoderms and brachiopods in the later Pre-Cambrian. Since the opening of the Cambrian there has evidently been little change in the atmosphere, as has already been pointed out.

9.2. VENUS

Urey's conclusions seem unescapable, that the large amount of CO_2 can have been formed only by the oxidation of methane by photolytically produced oxygen but that the continued presence of the gas is due to the modern absence of free water on the planet. This conclusion, however, involves a very critical arrangement of times and concentrations and, though inevitable in the present stage of knowledge, leaves something to be desired.

9.3. MARS

The Martian atmosphere presumably consists of nitrogen with argon, with a small amount of CO_2, and a very minute amount of water vapor. Kuiper[5] (1952) computes from observations on the scattering power of the Martian atmosphere that one volume of its gas consists of about 0.96 N_2, 0.04 A, and 0.003 CO_2. The thickness (440 atm-cm) of the CO_2 is about twice that on earth. Since gravity is of the order of 0.4 of the value at the earth's surface, the partial pressure at the surface of the planet will be about 0.8 that at the earth's surface. In so far as the partial pressure required for the Urey equilibrium is known, the Martian value, like the terrestrial, appears to exceed the equilibrium pressure. Kuiper concludes that the maximum amount of water that can be condensed from the Martian atmosphere would be about 0.02 mm. Most of this is present as vapor but a part as ice haze.

Less than 0.05 atm-cm of ozone must be present. In the absence of large amounts of oxygen, the ozonosphere, if present, should be at a low level, so that the absence of detectable ozone is clear evidence of an extremely small amount of oxygen.

5. I am greatly obliged to Dr. Kuiper for an opportunity to consult his paper in proof.

The great interest of the planet lies in the possibility that it has, like the earth, developed living organisms. Kuiper has recently considered the whole problem with great care, and his ideas may be summarized as the most probable conclusions at the present time. The green areas do not exhibit a reflection spectrum like that of a green leaf; the rather featureless infrared reflection spectrum can, however, be matched by that from xerophytic lower plants, particularly lichens. The colored areas change in hue, apparently with changing humidity. Several kinds of colored objects must be present, because the changes are very diverse. Antoniadi's (1930) map of such changes indicates a broken zonal distribution of the types of color change, which to the biologist looks extraordinarily like a vegetation map. Öpik (1950) has pointed out—and the present writer had independently come to a like conclusion—that the colored material must have the capacity to grow if it is to remain visible in the presence of the dust storms that are continually occurring at the surface of the planet. Death and decomposition probably would occur beneath the dust, returning CO_2 and H_2O to the atmosphere.

Three major difficulties may be urged against a flora of several species of the general complexity of the lichens or mosses underlying the phenomenon. The first is the extremely low water content of the atmosphere. The only possible water source would appear to be precipitated ice. This would limit the rate of photosynthesis very greatly. The second objection that may be raised is the difficulty with which life could develop, unprotected by a layer either of oxygen or of water, in the ultraviolet radiation that must reach the planet. Kuiper concludes that an appreciable amount of ultraviolet of wave length greater than 1900 A must reach the surface of the planet. This would disrupt any nucleic acids present and would probably make difficult any kind of organization remotely like terrestrial life. The outer layer of the Martian organisms must be very opaque to ultraviolet. It is possible that some fluorescence will ultimately be detected.

The third difficulty involves metabolism at a very low temperature, of the order of $-30°$ C. The cell contents must be saturated with some quite soluble material which permits a liquid state at such a temperature. The absence of oxygen in the atmosphere may imply merely a very slow photosynthetic metabolism and a loss of oxygen to space, since oxygen atoms can probably be lost from Mars. It seems unlikely that such a situation would lead to a steady-state concentration of O_2 in the atmosphere that is entirely undetectable. It is more likely that an oxygen acceptor exists in the organisms. Peroxides have been suggested. A more stable and therefore perhaps more likely poising system is the nitrite-nitrate system. This, as we have seen, is easily used as an oxygen source in oxidative metabolism. It is, moreover, not at all unlikely that if Mars once had a better supply of water and oxygen than it has today, the final fate of such oxygen as did not leave the planet would be to become nitrified. The ultra-xerophytic flora which is presumably now developed may well have come to depend on such nitrate for its oxygen supply by night; and it is just possible that magnesium nitrate, which has a eutectic temperature of $-29°$ C, is involved in lowering the freezing point of the liquid contents of the organisms. Beyond this at present one cannot go.

REFERENCES

Adel, A.	1939	*Ap. J.*, **90**, 627.
	1941	*Ibid.*, **93**, 509.
	1946	*Science*, **103**, 280.
	1950	*A.J.*, **55**, 69.
	1951	*Ibid.*, **56**, 33.
Aitken, J.	1911	*Proc. R. Soc. Edinburgh*, **32**, 183.
Anderson, V. G.	1915	*Quart. J. R. Meteorol. Soc. London*, **41**, 99.
Ångström, A., and Högberg, L.	1952a	*Tellus*, **4**, 31.
	1952b	*Ibid.*, p. 271.
Antoniadi, E. M.	1930	*La Planète Mars* (Paris: Hermann & Cie).
Arrhenius, G.	1950	*Geochim. et Cosmochim. Acta*, **1**, 15.
Atkins, W. R. G.	1947	*Nature*, **159**, 674.
Becker, H. G.	1924	*Ind. Eng. Chem.*, **16**, 1220.
Beijerinck, M. W.	1901	*Zentralbl. Bakt. f. Parasitenk.*, Abt. 11, **7**, 561.
Bernal, J. D.	1949	*Proc. Phys. Soc. London, A*, **62**, 537.
Birge, E. A., and Juday, C.	1934	*Ecol. Mono.*, **4**, 440.
Bliss, C. I., and Calhoun, D. W.	1954	*An Outline of Biometry* (New Haven: Yale Co-op.).
Bohr, C.	1899	*Ann. d. Phys.*, **68**, 500.
Borchert, H.	1951	*Geochim. et Cosmochim. Acta*, **2**, 62.
Bortels, H.	1940	*Arch. f. Mikrobiol.*, **11**, 155.
Bregoff, H. M., and Kamen, M. D.	1951	*J. Bact.*, **63**, 147.
Brown, Harrison	1949	*The Atmospheres of the Earth and Planets*, ed. G. P. Kuiper (Chicago: University of Chicago Press), chap. 9.
Brown, H. T.	1870	*Proc. R. Soc. London*, **18**, 286.
Buch, K.	1939a	*Acta Acad. Aboensis, Math.-phys. Kl.*, Vol. **11**, No. 9.
	1939b	*Ibid.*, No. 12.
	1942	*Ann. Hydrog. Marit. Meteorol.*, 1942, p. 193.

BUDDHUE, J. D.   1942   *Pop. Astr.*, **50**, 560.
BURRIS, R. H.; EPLING,
   F. J.; WAHLIN, H.;
   and WILSON, P. W.   1943   *J. Biol. Chem.*, **148**, 349.
CALLENDAR, G. S.   1940   *Quart. J. R. Meteorol. Soc. London*, **66**, 395.
                          1949   *Weather*, **4**, 310.
CARPENTER, T. M.   1937   *J. Amer. Chem. Soc.*, **59**, 358.
CAUER, H.   1939   *Zs. f. angew. Chem.*, **52**, 625.
CHACKETT, K. F.;
   PANETH, F. A.;
   REASBECK, P.; and
   WIBORG, B. S.   1951   *Nature*, **168**, 358.
CHAMBERLIN, R. T.   1908   *Pub. Carnegie Inst. Washington*, No. 106.
CHAPMAN, R. M.; SHAW,
   J. H.; and WILLIAMS,
   D.   1950   *Phys. Rev.*, **78**, 332.
CHAPMAN, S.   1943   *Rept. Prog. Physics* (Phys. Soc. London), **9**, 92.
CHATIN, E. A.   1851   *C.R. Acad. Sci. Paris*, **32**, 669.
CLARKE, F. W.   1904   *U.S. Geol. Surv. Bull.*, No. 228.
                          1924   *Ibid.*, No. 770.
CLEMO, G. R., and
   SWAN, G. A.   1949   *Nature*, **164**, 811.
CONGER, P. S.   1943   *Ebullition of Gases from Marsh and Lake Waters*
                                  ("Publications of the Maryland Board of
                                  Natural Resources," No. 59).
CONWAY, E. J.   1942   *Proc. R. Irish Acad.*, *B*, **48**, 119.
                          1943   *Ibid.*, p. 161.
COOPER, L. H. N.   1937   *J. Marine Biol. Assoc.*, **22**, 183.
                          1948   *Ibid.*, **27**, 322.
CORBET, A. S.   1934   *Biochem. J.*, **28**, 1575.
                          1935   *Ibid.*, **29**, 1080.
COSTE, J. H., and
   WRIGHT, H. L.   1935   *Phil. Mag.*, ser. 7, **20**, 209.
COTTON, C. A.   1944   *Nature*, **154**, 399.
DE, P. K.   1939   *Proc. R. Soc. London*, *B*, **127**, 121.
DHAR, N. R., and
   RAM, A.   1933   *J. Indian Chem. Soc.*, **10**, 125.
DINGLE, A. N.   1954   *Bull. Amer. Meteorol. Soc.*, **35**, 89.
DOLE, M.   1949   *Science*, **109**, 77.
DORSEY, N. E.   1940   *Properties of Ordinary Water Substance* ("A.C.S.
                                  Mono. Ser.," No. 81).
DRISCHEL, H.   1940   *Balneologe*, **7**, 321.
DUMAS, J. B. A., and
   BOUSSINGAULT, J. B.   1841   *Leçon sur la statique chimique des êtres organisés*
                                  (Paris: Fortin, Masson et Cie); see also *Phil.
                                  Mag.*, ser. 3, **19**, 337.

EDGAR, J. L., and
    PANETH, F. A.   1941   *J. Chem. Soc. London*, **144**, p. 519.
EGLE, K.   1951   *Naturwiss.*, **38**, 350.
ERIKSSON, E.   1952a   *Tellus*, **4**, 215.
                             1952b   *Ibid.*, p. 280.
ESKOLA, P.   1932   *Ann. Acad. Sci. Fenn.*, *A*, **36**, 1.
EVANS, G. C.   1939   *J. Ecol.*, **27**, 436.
FELLENBERG, T. VON   1926   *Ergebn. d. Physiol.*, **25**, 176.
                             1927   *Biochem. Zs.*, **187**, 4.
FINNELL, H. H., and
    HOUGHTON, H. W.   1931–32   *Panhandle Bull. Panhandle Agr. Exper. Stat.*
                                (Goodwell, Okla.), **23**, 1; **34**, 3.

FRANCIS, A. G., and
    PARSONS, A. T.   1925   *Analyst*, **50**, 262.
FULLER, H. J.   1948   *Amer. Midland Naturalist*, **39**, 247.
GLÜCKAUF, E.   1944   *Nature*, **153**, 620.
GOLDBERG, L.   1951   *Ap. J.*, **113**, 567.
GOLDSCHMIDT, V. M.   1934   *Geol. Fören. Stockholm Förh.*, **56**, 385.
                             1938   *Skr. Norsk. Vidensk. Akad. Oslo. Mat. Nat. Kl.*,
                                     1937, No. 4.

GOODY, R. M., and
    WALSHAW, G. D.   1953   *Quart. J. R. Meteorol. Soc. London*, **79**, 496.
GRIFFITH, G. AP, and
    MANNING, H. L.   1950   *Nature*, **165**, 571.
GROTH, W., and
    SUESS, H. E.   1938   *Naturwiss.*, **26**, 77.
GUYER, A., and
    TOBLER, B.   1934   *Helvet. chem. acta*, **17**, 257.
HALBFASS, W.   1934   *Petermann's Mitt.*, **80**, 137, 177.
HALDANE, J. B. S.   1936   *Nature*, **137**, 575.
HALL, A. D., and
    MILLER, N. H. J.   1908   *J. Agr. Sci.*, **2**, 343.
HANSEN, F.   1931   *Tidsskr. Planteavl.*, **37**, 123 (not seen: *Exper. Stat.*
                                     Rec., **66**, 312).

HARTECK, P., and
    JENSEN, J. H. D.   1948   *Zs. f. Naturforsch.*, **3a**, 591.
HAYHURST, W., and
    PRING, J. N.   1910   *J. Chem. Soc. London*, **97**, 868.
HELLRIEGEL, H.   1887   *Landw. Vers. Stat.*, **33**, 464.
HUTCHINSON, G. E.   1944   *Amer. Sci.*, **32**, 178.
                             1948   *Ann. New York Acad. Sci.*, **50**, 221.
                             1949   *Amer. J. Sci.*, **247**, 27.
                             1950   *Bull. Amer. Mus. Nat. Hist.*, **96**, 1.
JACOBS, W. C.   1951   *Bull. Scripps Oceanogr. Inst.*, **6**, 27.
JESSER, H., and
    THOMAE, E.   1943   *Zs. f. anal. Chem.*, **125**, 89.
JOHNSSON, H.   1946   *Geografisk. Ann.*, **28**, 1.

430 G. E. HUTCHINSON

KALLE, K.	1945	*Der Stoffhaushalt des Meeres* ("Probleme der kosmischen Physik," Vol. XXIII [Leipzig: Akad. Verlagsgesellschaft, Becker & Erler]).
KAMEN, M. D., and		
GEST, H.	1949	*Science*, **109**, 560.
KNOCHE, W.	1938	*Ann. Soc. cient. Argentina*, **126**, 41.
KÖHLER, H.	1937	*Bull. Geol. Inst.-Univ. Upsala*, **26**, 279.
KREUTZ, W.	1941	*Angew. Bot.*, **23**, 89.
KRIEGEL, M. W.	1944	*Geophysics*, **9**, 447.
KUENEN, P. H.	1941	*Amer. J. Sci.*, **239**, 161.
KUIPER, G. P.	1952	*The Atmospheres of the Earth and Planets* (2d. ed.; Chicago: University of Chicago Press), chap. 12.
LANE, A. C.	1917	*Amer. J. Sci.*, 4th ser., **43**, 42.
	1945	*Ibid.*, **343A**, B93.
LEES, H.	1950	*Nature*, **167**, 355.
	1952	*Ibid.*, **169**, 156.
LEPAPE, A., and		
COLANGE, G.	1935	*C.R. Acad. Sci. Paris*, **200**, 2109.
LIEBIG, J. VON	1827	*Ann. Chem. Phys.*, **35**, 329.
LINDSTROM, E. S.;		
LEWIS, S. M.; and		
PINSKY, J. M.	1951	*J. Bact.*, **61**, 481.
LIPMAN, C. B.	1932	*Amer. Mus. Nov.*, **598**, 1.
LIPMAN, J. G., and		
CONYBEARE, A. B.	1936	*New Jersey Agr. Exper. Stat. Bull.*, No. 607.
LOCKHART, E. E., and		
COURT, A.	1942	*Month. Weather Rev.*, **70**, 93.
MACDONALD, J. Y.	1928	*J. Chem. Soc. London*, **131**, 1.
MACGREGOR, A.	1927	*South African J. Sci.*, **24**, 155.
MACINTIRE, W. H., and		
YOUNG, J. B.	1923	*Soil Sci.*, **15**, 205.
McMATH, R. R.	1949	*A.J.*, **54**, 212.
McMATH, R. R., and		
GOLDBERG, L.	1949	*Proc. Amer. Phys. Soc.*, **93**, 362.
McMATH, R. R.;		
MOHLER, O. C.; and		
GOLDBERG, L.	1948	*Phys. Rev.*, **73**, 1203.
MARS, C. E.	1951	*J. Geol.*, **59**, 131.
MASSON, O.	1917	*Rept. Brit. Assoc. Adv. Sci.*, 1916, p. 128.
MIGEOTTE, M. V.	1948	*Phys. Rev.*, **73**, 519; see also *Ap. J.*, **107**, 400.
	1949	*Phys. Rev.*, **75**, 1108.
	1952	*The Atmospheres of the Earth and Planets*, ed. G. P. KUIPER (2d ed.; Chicago: University of Chicago Press), p. 287.
MIGEOTTE, M. V., and		
CHAPMAN, R. M.	1949	*Phys. Rev.*, **75**, 1611.

MILLER, N. H. J.	1903	*Quart. J. Geol. Soc. London,* **59,** 133.
	1905	*J. Agr. Sci.,* **1,** 280.
MILLER, S. L.	1953	*Science,* **117,** 528.
MOLNAR, D. M.; BURR, R. H.; and WILSON, P. W.	1948	*J. Amer. Chem. Soc.,* **70,** 1713.
MOYERMAN, R. M., and SHULER, K. E.	1953	*Science,* **118,** 612.
MUNTZ, A., and AUBIN, E.	1886	*Recherches sur la constitution chimique de l'atmosphère, Mission scient. du Cap Horn,* Vol. **3,** Fasc. 2 (Paris: Gauthier Villars).
NICHOLS, R. L.	1941	*Trans. Amer. Geophys. Union,* 1941 (II), 505.
NODDACK, W.	1937	*Zs. f. angew. Chem.,* **50,** 505.
NOVAK, R., and WILSON, P. W.	1948	*J. Bact.,* **55,** 517.
NOYES, W. A.	1937	*J. Chem. Phys.,* **5,** 807.
ODINTSOVA, S. V.	1941	*C.R. (Doklady) Acad. Sci. U.R.S.S.,* **32,** 578.
ÖPIK, E.	1950	*Irish A.J.,* **1,** 45.
OSTERLIND, S.	1949	*Symb. Bot. Upsal.,* Vol. **10,** No. 3.
PALACHE, C.; BERMAN, H.; and FRONDEL, C.	1951	*Dana's System of Mineralogy* (7th ed.; New York: John Wiley & Sons), Vol. **2.**
PEARSE, R. W. B.	1943	*Rept. Prog. Physics* (Phys. Soc. London), **9,** 42.
PETTIJOHN, F. J.	1943	*Bull. Geol. Soc. Amer.,* **54,** 925.
POOLE, J. H. J.	1941	*Proc. R. Dublin Soc.,* N.S., **22,** 345.
PRICE, W. C.	1943	*Rept. Prog. Physics* (Phys. Soc. London), **9,** 10.
QUASTEL, J. H.; SCHOLEFIELD, P. G.; and STEVENSON, J. W.	1950	*Nature,* **166,** 940.
RAKESTRAW, N. W., and HOLLAENDER, A.	1936	*Science,* **84,** 442.
RANKAMA, K.	1948	*Bull. Geol. Soc. Amer.,* **59,** 389.
	1950	*J. Geol.,* **58,** 75.
RANKAMA, K., and SAHAMA, T. G.	1950	*Geochemistry* (Chicago: University of Chicago Press).
RAO, G. G., and DHAR, N. R.	1931	*Zs. f. anorg. allg. Chem.,* **199,** 422.
REDFIELD, A. C.	1948	*J. Marine Res.,* **7,** 347.
REYNOLDS, W. C.	1930	*J. Soc. Chem. Indust.,* **49,** 168T.
RILEY, G. A.	1944	*Amer. Sci.,* **32,** 129.
	1953	*J. Cons. Internat. Explor. de la Mer,* **19,** 85.
RITTMANN, A.	1936	*Vulkane und ihre Tätigkeit* (Stuttgart: F. Enke).
ROAKE, W. E., and DOLE, M.	1950	*J. Amer. Chem. Soc.,* **72,** 36.

ROELOFSEN, P. A.   1941   *Natuurw. Tijdschr. Nederland. Indie*, **101**, 179 (not seen: *Chem. Abstr.*, **36**, 1824).

ROSENBLUM, E. D., and
  WILSON, P. W.   1951   *J. Bact.*, **61**, 475.
RUBEY, W. W.   1951   *Bull. Geol. Soc. Amer.*, **62**, 1111.
RUBIN, T.   1954   *Science*, **119**, 66.
RUSSELL, E. J., and
  RICHARDS, E. H.   1944   *J. Agr. Sci.*, **9**, 309.
SCHARRER, K., and
  SCHWAIBOLD, J.   1928   *Biochem. Zs.*, **200**, 258.
SCHLOESING, T.   1880   *C.R. Acad. Sci. Paris*, **90**, 1410.
SCHRÖDER, H.   1919   *Naturwiss.*, **7**, 8.
SEGAL, W., and
  WILSON, P. W.   1949   *J. Bact.*, **57**, 55.
SELIVANOV, L. S.   1939   *Trav. (Trud.) Lab. Biogeochem. Acad. Sci. U.R.S.S.*, **5**, 113.
                              1946   *Ibid.*, **8**, 5.

SHAW, J. H.; SUTHER-
  LAND, G. B. B. M.;
  and WORMELL, T. W.   1948   *Phys. Rev.*, **74**, 978.
SHEPHERD, M.   1936   *Nat. Geog. Soc. Contr. Tech. Pap. Stratosphere Ser.*, **2**, 117.
SHUTT, F. T., and
  DORRANCE, R. L.   1917   *Trans. R. Soc. Canada*, **11**, 63.
SIMPSON, G. C.   1941a   *Quart. J. R. Meteorol. Soc. London*, **67**, 99.
                              1941b   *Ibid.*, p. 163.
SLOBOD, R. L., and
  KROGH, M. E.   1950   *J. Amer. Chem. Soc.*, **72**, 1175.
SMITH, R. A.   1870   *J. Scottish Meteorol. Soc.*, **3**, 2.
STEEMANN NIELSEN, E.   1952   *J. Cons. Internat. Explor. de la Mer*, **18**, 117.
STOCK, A., and
  CUCUEL, F.   1934   *Naturwiss.*, **22**, 390.
SUGAWARA, K.   1948   *Kagahu no Ryoiki*, **2**, 341 (not seen: *Chem. Abstr.*, **45**, 1449).

SUGAWARA, K.;
  OANA, S.; and
  KOYAMA, T.   1949   *Bull. Chem. Soc. Japan*, **22**, 47.
SUTHERLAND, G. B. B. M.,
  and CALLENDAR, G. S.   1943   *Rept. Prog. Physics* (Phys. Soc. London), **9**, 18.
SVERDRUP, H.   1952   MS on file in Bingham Oceanographic Laboratory, Yale University.

TAMMANN, G.   1924   *Zs. f. phys. Chem.*, **110**, 17.
TAYLOR, R. C.;
  BROWN, R. A.;
  YOUNG, W. A.; and
  HEADINGTON, C. E.   1948   *Anal. Chem.*, **20**, 396.

THOMAS, M. D., and
  HILL, G. R.   1949   *Photosynthesis in Plants*, ed. J. FRANCK and W. E.
                                      LOOMIS (Ames: Iowa State College Press),
                                      chap. 2.
TRANSEAU, E. N.   1926   *Ohio J. Sci.*, **26**, 1.
TYLER, S. A., and
  BARGHOORN, E. S.   1954   *Science*, **119**, 606.
UREY, H. C.   1952a   *The Planets: Their Origin and Development* (New
                                      Haven: Yale University Press).
                            1952b   *Proc. Nat. Acad. Sci.*, **38**, 351.
VAN NIEL, C. B.   1949   *Photosynthesis in Plants*, ed. J. FRANCK and W. E.
                                      LOOMIS (Ames: Iowa State College Press),
                                      chap. 22.
VIRTANAN, A. I., and
  RAUTANEN, N.   1952   *The Enzymes*, ed. J. B. SUMNER and K. MYRBACK
                                      (New York: Academic Press), Vol. **2**, Part 2,
                                      chap. 76.
WAKSMAN, S. A., and
  MADHOK, M. R.   1937   *Soil Sci.*, **44**, 361.
WATANABE, A.;
  NISHIGAKI, S.; and
  KONISHI, C.   1951   *Nature*, **168**, 748.
WATTENBERG, H.   1933   *Wiss. Ergebn. Atlant. Exped. Meteor.*, Vol. **8**.
WETZEL, W.   1932   In O. STUTZER and W. WETZEL, *Phosphat-Nitrat*
                                      (*Die wichtigsten Lagerstatten der "Nicht-Erze"*)
                                      (Berlin: Gebrüder Borntraeger).
WILDT, R.   1939   *Proc. Amer. Philos. Soc.*, **81**, 135.
WINOGRADSKY, S.   1890   *Ann. Inst. Pasteur*, **4**, 213.
WOODCOCK, A. H.   1950   *J. Meteorol.*, **7**, 161.
                            1954   *J. Amer. Meteorol. Soc.*, **35**, 88.
ZOBELL, C. A.   1893   *Science*, **77**, 27.

CHAPTER 9

The Absorption Spectrum of the Atmosphere

By LEO GOLDBERG

Director, University of Michigan Observatory

1. INTRODUCTION

Before the radiation from an extra-terrestrial light-source reaches the surface of the earth, it is attenuated by the earth's atmosphere. The attenuation is caused by two processes, namely, (1) *scattering* by molecules, haze, fog, and dust and (2) *absorption* by atoms and molecules. The spectrum that results from the scattering process is continuous, whereas the absorption spectrum is both discrete and continuous, since it includes both line absorption and continuous absorption beyond the ionization and dissociation limits of atoms and molecules. The subject of scattering by atmospheric particles has recently been thoroughly discussed in an excellent article by van de Hulst (1952). The scope of the present chapter will therefore be limited to a discussion of the atomic and molecular absorption.

Detailed knowledge of the absorption spectrum of the earth's atmosphere (telluric spectrum) is required both for the interpretation of the spectra of celestial objects and for the information it can give on the composition and physical state of the earth's atmosphere. Although important work has been done with artificial sources (Gebbie, Harding, Hilsum, and Roberts, 1949; Benesch, Elder, and Strong, 1950), the most common method of observing the absorption spectrum is to employ the sun as a light-source. The atmosphere then serves as an absorption tube, the length of the path varying with the altitude of the sun. Since the intensities of atmospheric absorption lines vary with solar altitude, they are readily distinguishable from the solar lines. The total mass of the atmosphere per unit cross-section through the zenith is defined as 1 air mass. For solar altitudes greater than about 5°–10°, the number of air masses is proportional to the secant of the sun's zenith distance (plane-parallel approximation), regardless of the vertical distribution of the absorbing gases. For very low solar altitudes, the curvature of the atmosphere causes the path length to depend on the vertical distribution. For a sea-level station, the number of air masses traversed by sunlight in the horizontal direction is about 38. It is useful to define the *reduced height*, H (van de Hulst, 1952), of the atmosphere as the total mass of air contained in a vertical column of unit cross-section above the point of observation divided by the density at sea-level. At sea-level, H is about 8 km. Values of H for different altitudes up to 220 km are given in Table 1. For altitudes 0–30 km, H was

TABLE 1

REDUCED HEIGHT, H, OF ATMOSPHERE ABOVE ALTITUDE h

h (km)	H (cm)	h (km)	H (cm)	h (km)	H (cm)
0	804,000	50	790	140	0.0074
5	430,000	60	220	150	.0032
10	211,000	70	57	160	.0021
15	90,000	80	10	170	.0016
20	45,000	90	2.0	180	.0013
25	21,000	100	0.44	190	.0008
30	10,000	110	0.13	200	.0006
35	4,700	120	0.037	210	.0004
40	2,500	130	0.016	220	0.0002

taken from the tables of Link (1940), averaged between winter and summer. For the higher altitudes, the values were computed from the pressure measurements of Havens, Koll, and LaGow (1952) by the formula

$$H = \frac{p_h d_{\mathrm{Hg}}}{d_0},\qquad (1)$$

where p_h is the pressure at altitude h in cm Hg, $d_{\mathrm{Hg}} = 13.60 \; \mathrm{gm/cm^3}$ is the density of mercury at 0° C temperature, and $d_0 = 1.293 \times 10^{-3} \; \mathrm{gm/cm^3}$ is the density of dry air at sea-level and at 0° C.

Table 2 lists the various gases that are known to be present in the telluric spectrum, together with their abundances (see Sec. 5.2). Many different types of transitions, both atomic and molecular, are represented in the spectrum. The bulk of the absorption takes place below 100 km, where it is caused almost entirely by the molecules N_2, O_2, O_3, H_2O, and CO_2. Above 100 km, the oxygen and perhaps also the nitrogen molecules

are completely dissociated into atoms, which absorb strongly in the far
ultraviolet beyond 1000 A.

The molecular absorption results from three types of transitions (see
G. Herzberg, 1950) involving (1) changes in rotational energy, (2) simultaneous changes in rotational and vibrational energy, and (3) simultaneous changes in rotational, vibrational, and electronic energy. The first type
gives rise to rotational lines in the spectral region from about 10 μ to about
10 cm whereas the second results in vibration-rotation bands, chiefly in
the region between 1 and 20 μ. The third type, usually referred to as electronic transitions, produces systems of rotation-vibration bands in the
visible and ultraviolet. Just as an atomic series of lines converges to a limit

TABLE 2

MOLECULES IDENTIFIED IN EARTH'S ATMOSPHERE

Molecule	Molecu-lar Weight	cm(NTP)	Notes*	Molecule	Molecu-lar Weight	cm(NTP)	Notes*
N_2........	28.1	624,600	1	$C^{12}O^{16}O^{18}$...	46.0	0.67	3
O_2........	32.0	167,600	1	N_2O.......	44.0	0.4	3
$O^{16}O^{18}$.....	34.0	659	2	O_3........	48.0	0.3	
$C^{12}O_2^{16}$.....	44.0	320	3	CO........	28.0	0.06–0.15	3
$O^{16}O^{17}$.....	33.0	134	2	H_2O.......	18.0	10^3–10^4	
$C^{13}O_2^{16}$.....	45.0	1.5	3	HDO......	19.0	0.4–4	4
CH_4.......	16.0	1.2	3				

* Notes: (1) chemical determination for dry atmosphere (Paneth, 1937); (2) mass spectrograph (Birge, 1941);
3) spectroscopic (see Sec. 5.2); (4) calculated from H_2O values on assumption D:H ratio = 1:5000.

beyond which continuous absorption occurs, so there are systems of bands
that merge into strong continua resulting from the absorption by the
molecule of energy greater than that required for dissociation or ionization. In the earth's atmosphere, absorption in molecular dissociation and
ionization continua plays a major role in impeding the passage of ultraviolet radiation.

Absorption by atoms of oxygen and nitrogen is important at altitudes
above 100 km and for wave lengths less than about 900 A. The absorption
takes place both in the resonance lines of O and N and in the bound-free
ionization continua corresponding to the removal of inner-shell (X-ray)
and outer-shell (optical) electrons.

Although the sun emits radiation at all wave lengths, from X-rays to
radio radiation, the solar spectrum observed from sea-level shows numerous gaps produced by complete absorption in the earth's atmosphere. The
region from 0 to 3000 A is totally obscured, as are numerous other regions

centered approximately at 1.3, 1.9, 2.7, 4.2, and 6.0 μ, and from 14 μ to the region of millimeter waves. Between 14 and 24 μ there is a region of limited transparency, which opens up with increased altitude and decreased water content. At longer wave lengths, the atmosphere is made completely opaque from 24 to about 1000 μ by the pure rotational spectrum of H_2O. The long-wave end of the ultraviolet absorption, from λ 3000 to λ 2200, is produced entirely by ozone. From λ 2400 to λ 1300, radiation is absorbed by discrete bands and by continua of O_2. From λ 1300 to about λ 300 are found similar bands and continua of both N_2 and O_2. Beginning at about λ 900 the bound-free continua of atomic nitrogen and oxygen absorb strongly to about λ 200. Below λ 200 energy is absorbed by the K and L X-ray continua of atomic nitrogen and oxygen. Very little absorption takes place in the visible region of the spectrum apart from the red electronic bands of O_2. In the near infrared, on the short-wave-length side of the photographic limit at 1.35 μ, are found relatively weak rotation-vibration bands of H_2O and electronic bands of O_2 at 1.06 μ and 1.27 μ. The regions of 100 per cent absorption in the infrared are caused entirely by H_2O and CO_2. Many intervening regions are partially obscured by weaker bands of H_2O, CO_2, CH_4, N_2O, CO, and O_3. In the radio-frequency region the atmosphere is semitransparent between wave lengths of a few millimeters and about 10 cm and almost completely transparent at longer wave lengths. The absorption of millimeter and centimeter waves is caused mostly by a rotational line of H_2O centered at 1.35 cm and by a series of lines of O_2 at about 5 mm and 2.5 mm that result from changes in the orientation of the spin vector in the ground electronic state.

2. REGION $0-0.3\,\mu$

The most abundant constituents of the atmosphere, oxygen and nitrogen, form homonuclear molecules, and therefore their rotational and vibrational transitions involving electric dipole radiation are rigorously forbidden. Consequently, apart from the weak, forbidden electronic bands of O_2 at λ 10600 and λ 12700, these molecules do not absorb infrared radiation. Their presence, however, is almost entirely responsible for the absorption by the atmosphere of wave lengths shorter than λ 3000. Absorption by O_2 and N_2 occurs more or less throughout the region $\lambda\lambda$ 2600–200. A fraction of the O_2 and of the N_2 molecules is photodissociated, and this process has two important consequences. First, the oxygen and the nitrogen exist at high altitudes in the form of atoms, which absorb wave lengths short of λ 900 by bound-free transitions. Second, a portion of the oxygen atoms combines with O_2 to produce ozone (O_3), which forms a layer at an altitude of about 25 km and which strongly absorbs ultraviolet radiation in the region λλ 2200–2900.

2.1. OZONE

The apparently sharp cutoff of the ultraviolet solar spectrum at about λ 3000 appears to have been first attributed to atmospheric ozone by Hartley (1881), following his discovery of the Hartley bands of ozone in the laboratory. The Hartley band system consists of a series of diffuse bands extending from λ 3200 to λ 2340, followed by strong continuous absorption to about λ 2100. Hartley's suggestion was strongly supported by Fowler and Strutt's (1917) investigation of the so-called "Huggins bands," which were first observed in the spectrum of Sirius by Sir William Huggins (1890) in the region λλ 3200–3400. The Huggins bands, which are extremely weak, were found by Fowler and Strutt in the low-sun spectrum and also in the laboratory spectrum of ozone. Final proof that atmospheric ozone was responsible for the disappearance of the ultraviolet spectra of the sun and stars was given by Fabry and Buisson (1921a), who measured the variation of absorption coefficient with wave length near the ultraviolet limit of the solar spectrum and obtained close agreement with their measurements on the laboratory spectrum of ozone.

2.11. *Abundance and vertical distribution.*—The abundance and vertical distribution of ozone have been the subject of numerous observational and theoretical investigations. Good summaries have been written by Mitra (1948), Chapman (1943), Fabry (1950), Regener (1952), and others. Fabry and Buisson (1921b) first showed how the equivalent thickness of the ozone layer could be determined from spectrophotometric measurements of the sun's ultraviolet spectrum for different values of the solar zenith distance. After refinements by Dobson and Harrison (1926), which took account of scattering by large particles, Dobson (1931) adapted the principle of Fabry and Buisson's method to photoelectric spectrophotometry. Following a suggestion by Götz (1931), Dobson's photoelectric photometer was applied to the determination of the abundance and vertical distribution of ozone from the so-called *Umkehr effect*, by observation of the intensity of scattered sunlight at the zenith during sunrise or sunset (Götz, Meetham, and Dobson, 1934). The vertical distribution has also been determined from spectrographic observations made from sounding balloons (E. and V. H. Regener, 1934; V. H. Regener, 1951) and from V-2 rockets (Johnson, Purcell, Tousey, and Watanabe, 1952).

The total quantity of ozone is variable from 0.2 to 0.4 cm NTP. Dobson (1930) finds a remarkable annual and latitude variation in the ozone abundance (see Fig. 3, chap. 12). At the equator the abundance is constant, but away from the equator the quantity varies periodically with the seasons, the amplitude increasing with the latitude. Both north and south of the equator the maximum abundance occurs during the local spring and the minimum during the local autumn.

Ozone is not distributed uniformly through the atmosphere but is mostly concentrated between 10 and 40 km above the earth's surface, with a fairly sharp peak in the distribution at about 20–30 km. The variation of ozone content with height is shown in Figure 1, as determined from three

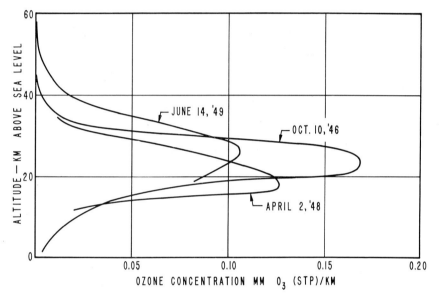

FIG. 1.—Vertical distribution of O₃ from three NRL rocket flights (Johnson, Purcell, Watanabe, and Tousey, 1952).

V-2 rocket flights. The ordinates are altitudes in kilometers, and the abscissae are centimeters NTP per kilometer of altitude. The shapes of the distribution-curves and the heights of the maxima are remarkably dissimilar.

2.12. *Absorption coefficients.*—The ultraviolet absorption coefficients for ozone have been measured in the laboratory, first by Fabry and Buisson (1913), later by Tsi-Zé and Shin-Piaw (1933), and very recently by Vigroux (1952) (see Fig. 2). The absorption coefficients are defined in terms of Beer's law of absorption, viz.,

$$I = I_0 e^{-kx} \tag{2}$$

where I_0 is the intensity of the incident radiation and I is its intensity after traversal of a column of gas equivalent to x cm at NTP. The absorption coefficient k, which is plotted against wave length in Figure 2, is in units of cm^{-1} and has been measured at a temperature of 18° C. From λ 2100 to λ 2340, the absorption is by the dissociation continuum of the Hartley bands, which occupy the region $\lambda\lambda$ 2340–3200. At $\lambda = 3000$, k is about 5 cm^{-1}, which means that, for a layer thickness of 0.3 cm, the intensity of sunlight is reduced by the factor $e^{1.5}$, or about 4.5. The absorption coefficient reaches a maximum value of 126 cm^{-1} at λ 2550.

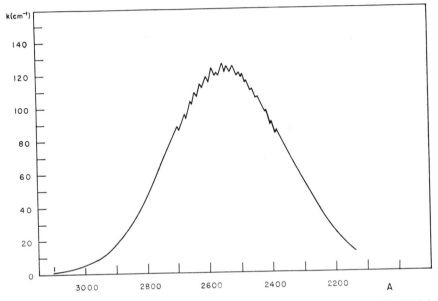

F$_{IG}$. 2.—Continuous absorption per centimeter NTP of ozone. Region 3100–2300 A (Vigroux, 1952); region 2300–2150 A (Ny Tsi-Zé and Choong Shin-Piaw, 1933).

Absorption coefficients derived by the application of Beer's law may frequently be in error by large factors. Beer's law holds only for monochromatic radiation or, more generally, when the variation of absorption coefficient over the slit-width is small. Owing to the fine structure of molecular bands, this condition is usually satisfied only in the continuum. In the region of discrete bands the measured coefficients will depend on the instrumental resolving power and on the pressure. Changes in temperature will also affect the intensity distribution in the bands. According to Vigroux (1952), however, the absorption coefficient at λ 3000 is reduced by only 10 per cent when the temperature is lowered to −92° C. The change at shorter wave lengths is even less.

2.2. Molecular Oxygen

Ultraviolet absorption by molecular oxygen becomes appreciable, beginning at about λ 2600, with the appearance of the Herzberg forbidden bands,

$$^3\Sigma_u^+ \leftarrow {}^3\Sigma_g^- ,$$

followed by a continuum beginning at λ 2400 (Herzberg, 1932, 1952). The bands are extremely weak and are of little importance in absorbing extra-terrestrial radiation, owing to the much stronger absorption by ozone in the same spectral region. It is possible, however, as suggested by Herzberg (1932), that the bands play a key role in the formation of ozone (see chap. 12).

Absorption by molecular oxygen becomes very strong in the region of the Schumann-Runge bands,

$$^3\Sigma_u^- \leftarrow {}^3\Sigma_g^- ,$$

which begin at λ 1925 and converge to a limit, recently redetermined by Herzberg (1953) at λ 1752. Beyond this dissociation limit, continuous absorption sets in and extends to about λ 1300. Absorption in the continuum is very much greater than in the bands, the maximum absorption coefficient occurring at λ 1450. The absorption coefficients for the continuum have been measured by Ladenburg and van Voorhis (1933) and are shown in Figure 3. Herzberg (1953) believes that a weak continuum, joining onto the near-ultraviolet bands, underlies the Schumann-Runge bands.

The spectrum of O_2 at wave lengths shorter than λ 1300 has been studied in detail by Price and Collins (1935), by Tanaka and Takamine (1942), and by Tanaka (1952). In the region $\lambda\lambda$ 1300–1000, Price and Collins find a series of strong, diffuse absorption bands that form an electronic Rydberg series, converging to a limit near 1000 A, which corresponds to the first ionization potential of O_2, 12.2 eV. No continuous absorption has been detected beyond the series limit. The region $\lambda\lambda$ 1000–680 is occupied by the strongest bands of O_2, the so-called "Hopfield bands" (1930a). The Hopfield bands form three Rydberg series that converge to the second, third, and fourth ionization limits of O_2 at $\lambda\lambda$ 770, 730, and 680 (16.1, 16.9, and 18.2 eV). An additional Rydberg series, converging to λ 610, was found by Tanaka and Takamine (1942). It will be seen below that O_2 has a strong continuous absorption in this region that extends to λ 300 and which may be identified with the continua beyond the foregoing three ionization limits.

Absorption coefficients for O_2 in the far ultraviolet have been measured by Weissler and Po Lee (1952) between λ 1300 and λ 300, and by

Clark (1948) between λ 1025 and λ 855 and for the helium lines at 584.3 A and 537.0 A. Schneider (1940) has made measurements in air for the region λλ 1600–380, and Williams (1940) and Preston (1940) have obtained the coefficients of the hydrogen Lyman-α line λ 1215.7 for air and its component gases. No good source of continuous radiation is available at these wave lengths, and hence the measurements have been based on the atten-

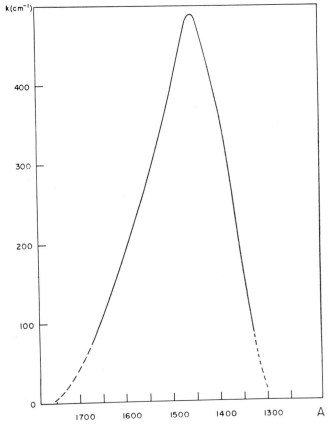

Fig. 3.—Absorption per centimeter NTP by Schumann continuum of O_2 (Ladenburg and van Voorhis, 1933).

uation, according to Beer's law, of discrete emission lines excited in the spark. This procedure should yield accurate results for absorption continua. As pointed out by Weissler and Lee, however, the physical significance of the measures within absorption bands is ambiguous, without detailed knowledge of the fine structure of each band (Elsasser, 1938). An additional uncertainty arises from the dependence of the molecular line widths on the pressure.

The results of Weissler and Lee (1952) may be summarized as follows: The measurements show clearly the presence of the several strong Rydberg band series between λ 1300 and λ 610. Within the bands, k values as high as 900 cm^{-1} were found. By selecting the smallest observed k values in each spectral region, Weissler and Lee were able to derive a reasonable approximation to the continuous absorption (see Fig. 4). Between λ 1300 and λ 1200, the continuous-absorption coefficient was found to be less than 10 cm^{-1}. In the region λλ 1200–1000, the k value is of the order of 50–100

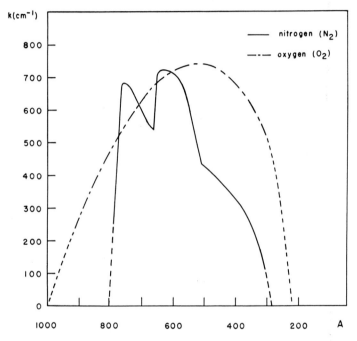

Fig. 4.—Continuous absorption by N_2 (Weissler, Lee, and Mohr, 1952) and by O_2 (Weissler and Lee, 1952). The dotted extensions of the two curves are extrapolated.

cm^{-1}. No strong continuous absorption was detected between λ 1000 and λ 740, the region of the Hopfield bands, but at wave lengths shorter than λ 740, in the overlapping ionization continua, the continuous k values exceed 700 cm^{-1}. The absorption-curve of Figure 4 is reasonably accurate below λ 740 but may be uncertain at longer wave lengths, owing to the presence of diffuse, unclassified bands. It should be remarked that the authors attach low weight to small k values of the order of 50 cm^{-1} or less. Absorption by molecular oxygen ceases to be of importance below about λ 200.

Very recently, a new series of measurements of the ultraviolet absorption coefficients of ten atmospheric gases by photoelectric methods has been undertaken at the Air Force Cambridge Research Center. The results obtained for the Schumann continuum of O_2 (Watanabe, Inn, and Zelikoff, 1952) differ considerably from those of Ladenburg and van Voorhis (1932), in that the maximum value is 380 cm^{-1} at λ 1420 as compared with 490 cm^{-1} at λ 1450 and the intensity distribution is relatively asymmetric.

2.3. MOLECULAR NITROGEN

The absorption spectrum of N_2 has been investigated in detail to an ultraviolet limit of about λ 600 (Lyman, 1911; Birge and Hopfield, 1928; Hopfield, 1930b; Watson and Koontz, 1934; Takamine, Suga, and Tanaka, 1938; Worley, 1943; and Setlow, 1948). Molecular nitrogen is practically transparent at all wave lengths longer than about λ 1450, which corresponds to the origin of the fundamental electronic transition

$$X^1\Sigma_g^+ \leftarrow a^1\Pi_g .$$

Unlike molecular oxygen, no dissociation continua have been found for N_2, but the far-ultraviolet spectrum shows very intense ionization continua (Chapman and Price, 1936). The region $\lambda\lambda$ 1450–1000 contains a series of narrow, discrete bands, first identified by Lyman (1911) and further analyzed by Birge and Hopfield (1928). These are the well-known Lyman-Birge-Hopfield bands. Between λ 1000 and λ 800 the spectrum consists of a large number of strong, discrete bands forming numerous progressions, together with a molecular Rydberg series (Worley and Jenkins, 1938) that converges to a limit at λ 796, corresponding to the first ionization potential of N_2 (15.58 eV). The region $\lambda\lambda$ 800–650 (Hopfield, 1930b) also shows very strong band progressions and the Hopfield-Rydberg series converging to the first excited state $B^2\Sigma_u^+$ of N_2^+ at λ 661.

Absorption measurements for N_2, similar to those described above for O_2, have been carried out by Weissler, Lee, and Mohr (1952) in the region $\lambda\lambda$ 1300–300. The results indicate that, in the region from λ 1300 to λ 800, the continuous absorption does not exceed 150 cm^{-1}, even though the measured k values in the neighborhood of bands in the same region were as high as 860 cm^{-1}. The absorption coefficients measured in the non-Rydberg bands were much higher than in the Worley-Jenkins and Rydberg series, attaining values greater than 2500 cm^{-1} near λ 770. From λ 800 to λ 300, the discrete band absorption appeared to be superimposed on a background of continuous absorption, the nature of which is shown in Figure 4. The curve appears to be composed of two parts: (1) the ionization continuum adjoining the Worley-Jenkins series limit at λ 796 and (2) a much weaker ionization continuum beyond the limit of the Hopfield series at λ 661.

2.4. ATOMIC OXYGEN AND NITROGEN

The very intense Schumann-Runge continuum in the ultraviolet spectrum of O_2 is evidence that oxygen molecules are very easily photodissociated by ultraviolet radiation. At λ 1450, the absorption coefficient is 490 cm^{-1}, which means that a layer of O_2 approximately 0.002 cm NTP thick will reduce the intensity of radiation by $1/e$. Since the equivalent thickness of the atmosphere above 100 km is 0.44 cm, it is clear that all the oxygen at high altitudes will be in the atomic form (Chapman, 1930; Penndorf, 1949). The emission of the forbidden lines of O I in the spectrum of the night sky is direct evidence for the presence of atomic oxygen in the upper atmosphere. Hence atomic oxygen must contribute to the absorption spectrum of the atmosphere.

The role played by atomic nitrogen is not so clear. The laboratory evidence is unmistakable that molecular nitrogen is not readily photodissociated, since dissociation continua have not been found in the spectrum. It seems definite, however (see chap. 12), that N_2 can become pre-dissociated following absorption of radiation in the wave-length range λλ 1200–1250, for which the absorption coefficient is low (Herzberg and Herzberg, 1948). There is direct observational evidence for the presence in the atmosphere of atomic nitrogen, but the amount and vertical distribution are uncertain (Swings and Meinel, 1952; Nicolet and Pastiels, 1952).

Absorption by atomic oxygen and nitrogen will occur both in the discrete lines, which are unimportant, and in the continuous bound-free transitions beyond the various ionization limits. The continuous-absorption coefficients for removal of the optical $2p$ electrons have been calculated by Bates and Seaton (1949) and are reproduced in Figure 5. The absorption by O begins at about λ 910, where its value is about 70 cm^{-1}, and attains a maximum value of about 350 cm^{-1} near λ 500, after which it slowly decreases. The absorption-curve for atomic nitrogen is similar but has been calculated only for the first ionization limit. Since the total number of oxygen atoms above 100 km is equivalent to about 0.19 cm NTP, it is clear that oxygen atoms are the chief absorbers of solar radiation in the wave-length region from λ 900 to λ 300.

At wave lengths shorter than about 200A, atomic absorption of a different type takes place. Whereas the absorption by O I of radiation of wave length shorter than about λ 900 can remove a $2p$ electron, the absorption of X-rays of wave length shorter than certain critical values can eject both the inner $1s$ and $2s$ electrons. This process gives rise to sharp absorption edges, in analogy with the series limits that characterize bound-free continua in optical spectra. The limit corresponding to the energy just required to remove a $1s$ electron is known as the K-limit, and similarly the L_I-limit refers to the energy of removal of a $2s$ electron. On the long-wave-length side of each limit, the continuous absorption is zero,

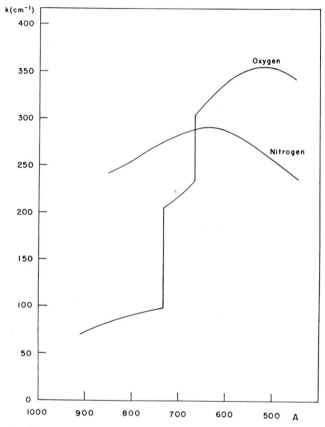

Fig. 5.—Continuous absorption beyond series limits of N and O (Bates and Seaton, 1949).

and on the short-wave side it decreases with decreasing wave length (see Fig. 6).

2.5. Other Constituents

Several of the polyatomic constituents of the atmosphere—H_2O, CO_2, CH_4, and N_2O—are known to absorb strongly in the region between 2000 and 700 A (Nicolet, 1952; Price, 1943). Because of the low abundances of these molecules relative to oxygen and nitrogen, it is probable that they are of little importance as ultraviolet absorbers, especially since they are concentrated at low altitudes (see Sec. 5). The ultraviolet absorption of CH_4, NO, and NH_3 at wave lengths shorter than λ 1300 has recently been measured by Weissler and Sun (1952).

2.6. Transparency at Higher Altitudes

It was clear from the earliest estimates of absorption coefficients in the laboratory that the ultraviolet barrier presented by the atmosphere could

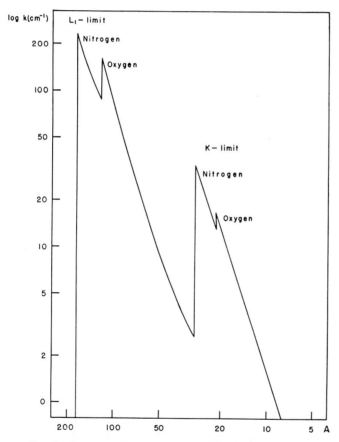

Fig. 6.—Continuous X-ray absorption by N and O (Nicolet, 1952)

not be penetrated from the ground, even from the highest mountain tops. Interesting attempts to extend the ultraviolet limit of the solar spectrum by automatic photography from balloons were made by E. and V. H. Regener (1934). On a plate taken with an exposure of 10 minutes from an altitude of 29.3 km, the spectrum was extended to λ 2875; but equally good results were obtained from mountain sites with spectrographs of large aperture and exposures of several hours (Götz, 1931b; Chiplonkar, 1939). The recent introduction of the rocket as a tool for high-altitude research has finally lifted the curtain on the ultraviolet solar spectrum, and it is probably only a matter of time before observations of the ultraviolet radiation from other stars are also undertaken. The first substantial extension of the solar spectrum, to a limit of about λ 2100, was accomplished by the Naval Research Laboratory as a result of a V-2 rocket flight on October 10, 1946. Subsequent flights have led to the recording of solar radiation at various shorter wave lengths as small as 8 A.

Before we describe the results obtained from these flights, it will be instructive to make use of existing data on continuous-absorption coefficients to estimate the degree to which the transparency of the atmosphere improves with altitude. Figure 7 gives, as a function of wave length, the altitude at which the atmosphere becomes 50 per cent transparent. Similar calculations have been made by Tousey, Watanabe, and Purcell (1951) to an ultraviolet limit of λ 800.

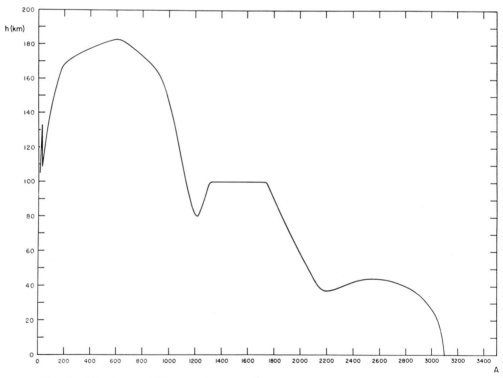

FIG. 7.—Altitudes at which atmosphere is 50 per cent transparent as function of wave length.

Between λ 3000 and λ 2100, the absorption was assumed to be due entirely to ozone, and from λ 2000 to λ 1300 to the Schumann-Runge bands and continuum. Precise data on the continuous absorption in the spaces between the Schumann-Runge bands are not available, and hence the points at λ 2100 and λ 1760 have simply been connected by a smooth curve. In the region from λ 1300 to shorter wave lengths, the continuous-absorption coefficients for molecular and atomic oxygen and nitrogen were employed, according to Figures 4–6, except that at λ 1216 Preston's (1940) value for O_2, $k = 0.28$ cm^{-1}, was used.

The transparency was calculated by Beer's law. At all altitudes below 100 km it was assumed that the atmosphere was composed entirely of molecular nitrogen and oxygen, in the proportion 78 per cent N_2 to 22 per cent O_2. Both the oxygen and the nitrogen were assumed to be completely

TABLE 3

ASSUMED ABUNDANCE OF N AND O IN cm NTP ABOVE ALTITUDE h

h (km)	N	O	h (km)	N	O
100	0.70	0.19	170	0.0025	0.0007
110	.20	.054	180	.0020	.0005
120	.06	.016	190	.0013	.0004
130	.025	.007	200	.0009	.00025
140	.012	.003	210	.0006	.00016
150	.005	.0014	220	0.0003	0.00009
160	0.003	0.0009			

dissociated above 100 km, but with the same relative concentrations as at lower altitudes. Table 3 lists the assumed equivalent thicknesses in centimeters NTP of O and N for various altitudes above 100 km. Figure 7 is very preliminary in nature, in view of the uncertainties in the high-altitude concentrations of atomic oxygen and nitrogen and in the continuous absorption between λ 1300 and λ 900. It nevertheless shows the broad features of the dependence of atmospheric transmission on wave length, including the well-known absorption minima at λ 2100 and λ 1200. The plateau from λ 1300 to λ 1750 results from the assumption of complete dissociation above 100 km. The peak at λ 600 would undoubtedly extend toward shorter wave lengths if all three series limits of atomic nitrogen were included instead of the single one shown in Figure 5. The sharp maximum near 30 A is due to K-limit absorption by N and O.

Hopfield (1946) photographed the laboratory absorption spectrum of air in the region λλ 600–2000, using a constant path length of 100 cm and various pressures from 1 atm to very low values. The equivalent air path varied from 100 to 0.0019 cm NTP. These air paths, neglecting dissociation, correspond to the total quantities of air above altitudes of about 68 and 165 km, according to Table 1. Hopfield's spectra, which are reproduced in Figure 8, are in excellent agreement with the calculated transmission-curve in Figure 7. The Schumann-Runge bands of O_2 at λ 1800 are clearly shown, as is the strong dissociation continuum extending to λ 1300. The region $\lambda\lambda$ 1300–1000 is seen to be relatively transparent, the absorption taking place chiefly in discrete bands of O_2 and N_2 rather than in continua. Below λ 1000, the spectrum is again veiled by a small fraction of a centimeter of air, first by strong, discrete bands of O_2 and N_2 and then, below λ 800, by ionization continua of O_2 and N_2. Hopfield's chief conclusions, prior to the first successful photography of the solar spectrum from V-2 rockets, were that the solar spectrum might be extended to λ 1800 from a height of 86 km and that above 96 km a window might appear between λ 1100 and λ 1200. It should be noted that the apparent agreement between Figures 7 and 8 below λ 1000 is illusory, owing to the expected dissociation of O_2 and N_2 at high altitudes.

The ultraviolet solar spectrum has been photographed from rockets at various altitudes up to about 150 km, both by the Naval Research Laboratory and by the Applied Physics Laboratory of Johns Hopkins University (Hopfield and Clearman, 1948). A series of spectrograms obtained by NRL, which are reproduced in Figure 9 (Johnson, Purcell, Tousey, and Watanabe, 1952), show how the ozone layer was penetrated on June 11, 1949, beginning at an altitude of 29.0 km. Since the flight was made near sunset, the ozone absorption could be detected to an altitude of 70 km. By means of similar experiments the solar spectrum has been extended to nearly λ 1800 (Tousey, 1952). Most of the ultraviolet absorption structure can be identified with solar atomic lines, but the structure between 2200 and 2280 A appears to be molecular in origin. It has been suggested (Durand, Oberly, and Tousey, 1949) that this structure may be due to electronic bands of atmospheric nitric oxide, NO, concentrated in a layer at an altitude of about 60 km. From infrared observations in the region of the fundamental vibration-rotation band at 5.3 μ, Migeotte and Neven (1952a) state that the abundance of telluric NO must be less than 0.02 cm NTP. It is also possible, if not probable, that the absorption at λ 2200 is produced by NO in the solar atmosphere. The absorption by solar CO in the 2.3 μ region of the spectrum is equivalent to that by a layer about 1 cm thick at NTP. According to a calculation by Russell (1934), based on the known solar concentrations of C, N, and O, the abundance of NO

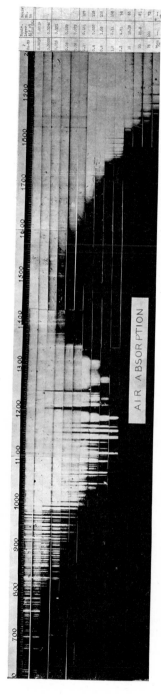

Fig. 8.—Absorption spectra of air λλ 600–2000 (Hopfield, 1946). Path length, 100 cm; pressure in centimeters Hg indicated to right of each spectrum.

in the sun should be as great as that of CO. Leifson (1926) finds that an NO concentration of 1 cm NTP produces very intense series of bands, beginning at λ 2264 and extending to wave lengths below λ 1300. Because of the high temperature of the sun, the excited vibrational states of NO would be highly populated, and the resulting spectrum would be more complex than the laboratory spectrum and would also extend to longer wave lengths. The solar NO bands are probably strong enough to depress the intensity of the continuous spectrum to that of a black body at the boundary temperature, $T = 4500°$ K.

The NRL observers have also been successful in recording solar radiation at various wave lengths shorter than λ 1800, including soft X-rays. Burnight (1949) used Schumann photographic plates in conjunction with Al and Be filters to detect X-radiation at high altitudes. Tousey, Watanabe, and Purcell (1951) used a thermoluminescent phosphor with CaF_2, LiF, and Be filters to isolate and detect radiation in the wave-length bands 0–8, 1050–1340, and 1230–1340 A. Friedman, Lichtman, and Byram (1951) employed photon counter tubes and Be, LiF, sapphire, and quartz filters to record continuously the intensity of solar radiation in the four wave-

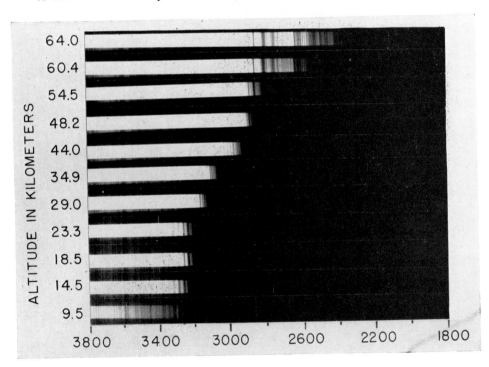

FIG. 9.—Solar spectra photographed from V-2 rocket, June 14, 1949. (Johnson et al., 1952)

length bands, 0–10, 1100–1350, 1425–1650, and 1725–2100 A throughout a rocket flight that reached a height of 150 km. In the 2000 A region the intensity rose sharply at 7-km altitude and became too great to record above 20 km.

The results obtained for the other three regions are consistent with existing data on absorption coefficients and with reasonable assumptions concerning the vertical distribution and state of dissociation of oxygen and nitrogen. Radiation in the band 1100–1350 A penetrated to a height of 70 km. Fifty per cent transmission occurred at 85 km. For the region 1425–1650 A, the very rapid rate of change of transmission in the neighborhood of 100 km suggests that molecular oxygen suffers complete dissociation above this altitude, as assumed in Figure 7. The observed transmission of soft X-rays is also in satisfactory agreement with the calculated transmission. The X-radiation penetrated to 87 km, and 50 per cent transmission occurred at almost precisely 100 km. The NRL experiments should lead eventually to the derivation of the vertical distribution of both molecular and atomic nitrogen and oxygen.

3. THE SPECTRUM BETWEEN 0.3 AND 24 μ

The telluric spectrum at wave lengths greater than 0.3 μ exhibits interesting differences from that at shorter wave lengths. First, the absorption bands and continua in the ultraviolet are all of the electronic type, but, in the visible and infrared, vibration-rotation and pure rotation bands dominate the spectrum. Second, inasmuch as vibration-rotation and pure rotation spectra are forbidden to oxygen and nitrogen, the absorption spectrum above 0.3 μ is produced mainly by the minor constituents of the atmosphere, especially by water vapor and carbon dioxide. Finally, since the abundances of air molecules other than nitrogen and oxygen are low and the absorption coefficients of vibrational and rotational transitions are much smaller than those of electronic transitions, the visible and infrared regions of the telluric spectrum are relatively transparent. Although many of the infrared bands are strongly saturated and therefore show no structure, dozens of other bands are developed to just the right degree to furnish valuable information on the structure and composition of the atmosphere.

The absorption spectrum of the atmosphere from 0.3 to 24 μ has been most thoroughly studied, with the sun employed as a light-source. The famous A and B bands in the solar spectrum, which are now recognized as resulting from the 0–0 and 1–0 transitions in O_2, respectively, were conspicuous features of the first visual map of the solar spectrum (Fraunhofer,

1815). Photography has made possible the detailed mapping of the spectrum from 0.3 to an infrared limit of 1.35 μ. The first great photographic map of the solar spectrum (Rowland, 1895–1897) extended from λ 2975 to λ 7331 and resulted from Rowland's development of the concave grating. Mapping of the photographic spectrum has been improved and extended at the Mount Wilson Observatory and has resulted in the publication of tables of accurate wave lengths and eye-estimates of intensity for both the ultraviolet and visual regions of the spectrum (St. John, Moore, Ware, Adams, and Babcock, 1928) and the near infrared region $\lambda\lambda$ 6600–13495 (Babcock and Moore, 1947). The tables contain both solar and telluric lines, but more than half the lines in the infrared section originate in the earth's atmosphere. Direct-intensity tracings of high-dispersion Mount Wilson solar spectrograms, embracing the region $\lambda\lambda$ 3300–8700, may be found in the Utrecht atlas (Minnaert, Mulders, and Houtgast, 1940).

The spectrum beyond the infrared photographic limit has been explored with prisms and gratings and with phosphors, bolometers, thermocouples, thermopiles, photoconductive cells, and Golay detectors. The great pioneer in this field was S. P. Langley (1881 ff.), who succeeded, by 1900, in mapping the infrared solar spectrum to about 5.5 μ (see Fig. 10). Langley was able to identify the most conspicuous absorption features with known bands of water vapor and carbon dioxide, but his remarkable map also shows clearly the presence of CH_4 and N_2O, gases that have only recently been identified spectroscopically as atmospheric constituents. Langley's studies were made with prisms and bolometers, as were those of his successors, Fowle (1917), who extended the solar spectrum to 13 μ, and Abbot and Freeman (1929). The next important advance in this field resulted from improvements in the design and manufacture of gratings and thermocouples, which were applied by Adel to the extension of the prismatic solar spectrum from 14 to 24 μ (1942) and to the mapping (1941c) of the grating spectrum from 2 to 14 μ, with a theoretical resolving power of 10,000. In the very modern period, since 1945, new progress in infrared solar spectroscopy has resulted from the introduction of photoconductive cells and from new gains in the sensitivity of thermocouples and thermopiles. As a result of very intensive work during the past few years, primarily at the Ohio State University, at the University of Michigan, at Johns Hopkins University, and at the University of Liége (Belgium), the telluric spectrum between 1.4 and 24 μ has been mapped in very great detail. Nearly all the rotational band structures have been resolved, except in totally obscured regions, and nearly all lines have been identified with

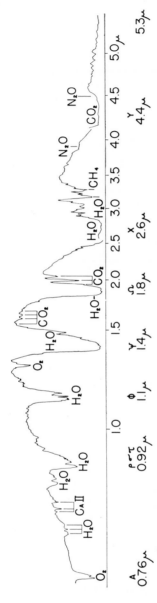

FIG. 10.—The infrared solar spectrum 0.76–5.3 μ, after Langley (1900). In addition to the labeled bands, the 3.7 μ band of HDO appears also to be present.

known atmospheric constituents. A complete record of the midday infrared solar spectrum from 0.8 to 13 μ is contained in the tracings published by Mohler, Pierce, McMath, and Goldberg (1951) for the region 0.8–2.5 μ; by Shaw, Chapman, Howard, and Oxholm (1951) for the region 3.0–5.2 μ; and by Shaw, Oxholm, and Claassen (1951) for the region 7–13 μ. The region 2.8–24 μ has also been mapped in its entirety by Migeotte and Neven (1952a) at the Jungfraujoch (Switzerland) in an atmosphere of very low water-vapor content, and the tracings are soon to be published in atlas form.

Table 4 lists, in order of increasing wave length, the molecular bands that are known to appear in the telluric spectrum between 0.3 and 24 μ. The data have been compiled from many different sources. The basic reference is G. Herzberg (1945), but a great many additions and corrections have been taken from the literature subsequent to 1945. Also included in Table 4 are eight bands of H_2O recently identified by W. S. Benedict, of Johns Hopkins University. The writer is indebted to Dr. Benedict for releasing this important material in advance of publication.

The first and second columns give the approximate band positions in cm^{-1} and microns, respectively, while the third column identifies the responsible molecule. Superscripts denoting the atomic weights have ordinarily been omitted except where necessary to distinguish the rare isotopic forms of oxygen and carbon dioxide. The fourth column contains the band designation, if known. The infrared O_2 bands at λ 10600 and at λ 12700 belong to the electronic system

$$^1\Delta_g \leftarrow {}^3\Sigma_g^-.$$

All the other O_2 bands, including the different isotopic forms, are associated with the electronic transition

$$^1\Sigma_g^+ \leftarrow {}^3\Sigma_g^-.$$

The fifth column of Table 4 carries a rough description of the band intensity. The intensity designations, which are similar to those employed by Herzberg (1945) for laboratory bands, have the following meaning:

Very strong—produces 100 per cent absorption over wide interval of spectrum. Rotational structure not observable even with highest resolving power.
Strong—strongest band lines are saturated but separable under high resolving power.
Medium—band structure well developed for path length of 1 air mass.
Weak—band structure just detectable for path length of 1 air mass.
Very weak—band structure detectable only for path lengths greater than 1 air mass.

TABLE 4

Molecular Bands in the Telluric Spectrum
between 0.3 and 24 μ

Wave Number (cm^{-1})	Wave Length (μ)	Molecule	Band Designation	Intensity
29400..........	0.3400	O_2	Huggins	vw
20940..........	0.4774	O_4	....	vw
18394..........	0.5436	H_2O	000–411	w
17495..........	0.5714	H_2O	000–203	vw
17384..........	0.5750	O_3	Chappuis	vw
17324..........	0.5770	O_4	....	vw
17248..........	0.5796	O_2	3–0	m
17023..........	0.5872	O_3	Chappuis	vw
16899..........	0.5915	H_2O	000–401	m
16898..........	0.5918	H_2O	000–302	w
16822..........	0.5942	H_2O	000–321	w
16605..........	0.6020	O_3	Chappuis	vw
15900..........	0.6288	O_2	2–0	m
15892..........	0.6290	O_4	....	vw
15832..........	0.6314	H_2O	000–113	w
15671..........	0.6379	O_2	3–1	m
15348..........	0.6513	H_2O	000–311	vw
14523..........	0.6884	O_2	1–0	s
14494..........	0.6897	$O^{16}O^{17}$	1–0	vw
14486..........	0.6901	$O^{16}O^{18}$	1–0	w
14343..........	0.6970	O_2	2–1	w
14319..........	0.6981	H_2O	000–103	m
14221..........	0.7032	H_2O	000–400	w
13831..........	0.7227	H_2O	000–301	m
13828..........	0.7232	H_2O	000–202	w
13653..........	0.7324	H_2O	000–221	m
13120..........	0.7620	$O^{16}O^{18}$	0–0	m
13119..........	0.7620	$O^{16}O^{17}$	0–0	w
13118..........	0.7621	O_2	0–0	s
12966..........	0.7710	O_2	1–1	w
12565..........	0.7955	H_2O	000–013	m
12408..........	0.8059	H_2O	000–112	w
12151..........	0.8226	H_2O	000–211	m
12140..........	0.8237	H_2O	000–310	w
11813..........	0.8465	H_2O	000–131	w
11032..........	0.9061	H_2O	000–003	m
10869..........	0.9200	H_2O	000–102	m
10613..........	0.9419	H_2O	000–201	s
10600..........	0.9434	H_2O	000–300	m
10329..........	0.9681	H_2O	000–121	m
10284..........	0.9724	H_2O	000–220	w
9834..........	1.017	H_2O	000–041	w
9366..........	1.067	O_2	1–0	w
9000..........	1.111	H_2O	000–012	m
8807..........	1.135	H_2O	000–111	s
8762..........	1.141	H_2O	000–210	m
8273.9.........	1.209	H_2O	000–130	m
8273.7.........	1.209	H_2O	000–031	m
7882..........	1.268	O_2	0–0	m
7445..........	1.343	H_2O	000–002	s
7250..........	1.379	H_2O	000–101	vs
7201..........	1.388	H_2O	000–200	s
6973..........	1.434	CO_2	$00_00–00_03$	s
6871..........	1.455	H_2O	000–021	s
6775..........	1.475	H_2O	000–120	m

TABLE 4—*Continued*

Wave Number (cm⁻¹)	Wave Length (μ)	Molecule	Band Designation	Intensity
6503	1.54	CO_2	06_01	w
6350	1.57	CO_2	00_00- 14_01	m
6228	1.61	CO_2	22_01	m
6076	1.64	CO_2	30_01	w
6005	1.67	CH_4	$2\nu_3$	m
5861	1.71	CH_4	$\nu_1+\nu_2+\nu_4$	vw
5775	1.73	CH_4	$\nu_2+\nu_3+\nu_4$	vw
5331	1.87	H_2O	000–011	vs
5235	1.91	H_2O	000–110	s
5100	1.96	CO_2	04_01	s
4978	2.01	CO_2	00_00- 12_01	s
4853	2.06	CO_2	20_01	s
5132	1.95	CO_2	05_11	m
4965	2.02	CO_2	01_10- 13_11	m
4808	2.08	CO_2	21_11	m
5046	1.98	$C^{13}O_2^{16}$	04_01	w
4887	2.05	$C^{13}O_2^{16}$	00_00- 12_01	m
4748	2.10	$C^{13}O_2^{16}$	20_01	vw
5042	1.98	$C^{12}O^{16}O^{18}$	04_01	vw
4905	2.04	$C^{12}O^{16}O^{18}$	00_00- 12_01	w
4791	2.09	$C^{12}O^{16}O^{18}$	20_01	vw
4735	2.11	N_2O	00_00-20_01	vw
4667	2.14	H_2O	000–030	m
4630	2.16	N_2O	00_00-12_01	vw
4546	2.20	CH_4	$\nu_2+\nu_3$	m
4420	2.26	N_2O	00_00-00_02	w
4390	2.28	N_2O	?	vw
4313	2.32	CH_4	$\nu_3+\nu_4$	m
4260	2.35	CO	2–0	vw
4216	2.37	CH_4	$\nu_1+\nu_4$	m
4123	2.43	CH_4	$\nu_2+2\nu_4$	m
3756	2.66	H_2O	000–001	vs
3657	2.74	H_2O	000–100	s
3714	2.69	CO_2	00_00- 10_01	vs
3613	2.77	CO_2	02_01	vs
3481	2.87	N_2O	00_00-10_01	m
3366	2.97	N_2O	00_00-02_01	m
3151	3.17	H_2O	000–020	s
3019	3.31	CH_4	ν_3	s
2823	3.55	CH_4	$\nu_2+\nu_4$	m
2798	3.57	N_2O	00_00-01_11	m
2724	3.67	HDO	000–100	m
2600	3.85	CH_4	$2\nu_4$	m
2564	3.91	N_2O	00_00-20_00	m
2462	4.06	N_2O	00_00-12_00	m
2349	4.26	CO_2	00_00-00_01	vs
2283	4.38	$C^{13}O_2^{16}$	00_00-00_01	m
2260	4.42	N_2O	$\pi-\pi$	w
2224	4.51	N_2O	00_00-00_01	s
2161	4.63	H_2O	010–001	s
2143	4.67	CO	1–0	m
2130	4.69	CO_2	01_10-20_00	m
2105	4.75	O_3	$2\nu_1(3\nu_2)(A_1)$	m
2093	4.79	CO_2	01_10-12_20	m

TABLE 4—*Continued*

Wave Number (cm⁻¹)	Wave Length (μ)	Molecule	Band Designation	Intensity
2057.........	4.87	H_2O	010–100	m
2077.........	4.81	CO_2	$00_00-\begin{Bmatrix} 03_10 \\ 11_10 \end{Bmatrix}$	s
1933.........	5.18	CO_2		m
1595.........	6.27	H_2O	000–010	vs
1556.........	6.43	H_2O	010–020	m
1403.........	7.14	HDO	000–010	s
1306.........	7.66	CH_4	ν_4	s
1285.........	7.78	N_2O	00_00-100	s
1167.........	8.54	N_2O	00_00-02_00	m
1064.........	9.39	CO_2	$\left.\begin{matrix} 02_00 \\ 10_00 \end{matrix}\right\}-001$	m
961.........	10.4	CO_2		m
1043.........	9.6	O_3	ν_1	s
792.........	12.6	CO_2	02_00-11_10	m
741.........	13.5	CO_2	02_20-11_10	m
720.........	13.9	CO_2	01_10-10_00	m
667.........	15.0	CO_2	00_00-01_10	vs
618.........	16.2	CO_2	01_10-02_00	m
589.........	17.0	N_2O	00_00-01_10	m

3.1. REGION 0.3–1.3 μ

The boundaries of the photographic region of the telluric spectrum are the ozone cutoff at 0.3 μ and the Ψ band of H_2O at 1.38 μ. The Huggins bands of O_3 form a tail from λ 3200 to λ 3600 on the long-wave-length side of the Hartley bands. The bands can be seen only for very long path lengths, the absorption coefficient at λ 3400 being about 0.02 cm⁻¹ NTP (Chalonge and Lefebvre, 1933). In fact, the bands in the entire region λλ 3200–5700 are so weak that atmospheric band absorption can be detected only in the spectrum of the setting sun. The absorption between λ 4600 and λ 6900 has been summarized by Dufay (1942). Evidence for the presence of O_4 in the low atmosphere comes from the appearance of the band at λ 4774 at a zenith distance of about 85°, and its rapid strengthening as the sun sets. The other two O_4 bands at λ 5770 and λ 6290, although probably present, are blended with stronger bands of O_2. The Chappuis bands of O_3 are difficult to observe because of their diffuse character and absence of distinct band structure. According to Vassy (1938) the maximum absorption coefficient for the Chappuis bands is about 0.07 cm⁻¹.

The very extensive literature on the red atmospheric bands of oxygen has been summarized by van de Hulst (1945a), who has also developed an accurate theory of the intensities of the atmospheric lines. All the red bands are produced by the same electronic transition

$$^1\Sigma_g^+ \leftarrow {}^3\Sigma_g^- .$$

Since this is both a magnetic dipole and an intersystem transition, the transition probability is very low compared with the ultraviolet bands, of the order of 10^{-1} sec^{-1} (Childs and Mecke, 1931). The wave lengths of the red band system have recently been remeasured (Babcock and Herzberg, 1948) with extremely high accuracy—about one part in seven million—and the molecular constants of the molecules O_2^{16}, $O^{16}O^{18}$, and $O^{16}O^{17}$ have been re-evaluated with great precision.

The red oxygen bands are of special interest, because their study led to the discovery of the isotopes O^{18} and O^{17} of oxygen. From their measurements of the oxygen bands, Dieke and Babcock (1927) isolated a faint A' band, which was intermingled with, but apparently independent of, the A band. The A' band was identified with $O^{16}O^{18}$ by Giauque and Johnston (1929a), who also (1929b) established the presence of $O^{16}O^{17}$ from additional measurements of still another faint companion band by Babcock (1929). The locations and designations of the several isotope bands are shown in Table 4.

The fine structure of the infrared oxygen bands has been analyzed in detail on photographic plates by Herzberg and Herzberg (1947). The bands at 1.27 (see Fig. 11) and 1.07 μ are, respectively, the 0–0 and 1–0 components of the

$$^1\Delta_g \leftarrow {}^3\Sigma_g^-$$

system. Like the red bands, the infrared system arises from an intersystem magnetic dipole transition, but, in addition, it violates the rule that Δ–Σ transitions are forbidden, and it is therefore relatively weak.

The first water-vapor bands of any consequence in the photographic region of the spectrum begin to make their appearance in the red just short of λ 7000. They become stronger with increasing wave length, dominate the regions $\lambda\lambda$ 8100–8400, $\lambda\lambda$ 8900–9900, $\lambda\lambda$ 10950–12800, and finally obscure the spectrum entirely at 1.4 μ. The width of the obscured region varies with humidity and also depends on the altitude of the observer. Except under exceptionally dry conditions, however, very little radiation between λ 13500 and λ 14300 penetrates the atmosphere to ground level. The number of known H_2O bands in the region $\lambda\lambda$ 6600–13495 has recently been nearly doubled by the identification of ten new bands from analysis of solar data (Benedict, 1948).

3.2. Region 1.4–2.5 μ

The photographic region of the spectrum is a transition region in which only relatively weak electronic bands and overtone and combination vibration-rotation bands are found. Beginning at 1.4 μ, no further electronic

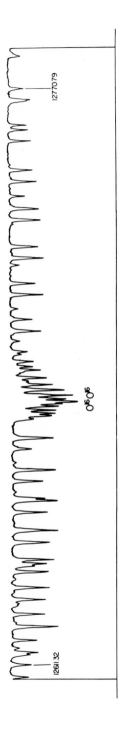

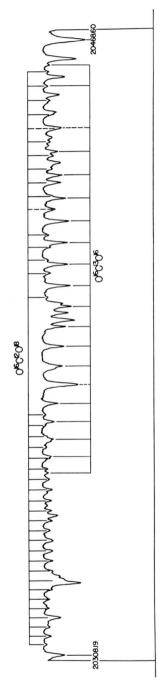

Fig. 11.—The infrared oxygen band at 1.27 μ (*upper*) and isotope bands of $C^{12}O^{16}O^{18}$ and $C^{13}O_2^{16}$ at 2.04 μ. Photographs of original tracings by McMath-Hulbert Observatory.

transitions are encountered until the region of millimeter waves. Also, between 1.4 and 2.5 μ, the vibration-rotation bands are all of the overtone
and combination variety. The first fundamental band to appear at longer
wave lengths is ν_3 of H_2O at 2.66 μ. The comparative weakness of the band
structures in the 1.4–2.5 μ region makes them well suited for intensity
analysis, since the usual difficulties in the interpretation of the intensities
of strong lines may be avoided. Because of the great sensitivity of the lead
sulphide detector, this region of the spectrum may be studied with a resolving power of more than 50,000, which begins to be comparable with
that which can be attained with the photographic plate. All the bands in
the 1.4–2.5 μ region, except those labeled "very weak" in Table 4, appear
in the McMath-Hulbert atlas (Mohler, Pierce, McMath, and Goldberg,
1951) of the near infrared solar spectrum, which was recorded at the
Mount Wilson Observatory (altitude 1742 m) with a high-dispersion grating spectrometer and Cashman PbS cell.

The absorption of sunlight in the region 1.34–1.42 μ is caused by the
(101) band of H_2O. Analysis of solar tracings by Mohler and Benedict
(1948) and of new laboratory data by Nelson and Benedict (1948) shows
that the well-known bands (101) and (021) are accompanied by the newly
identified bands (200) and (120) and that, together, the four bands account for practically all the strongest water-vapor lines in the region 1.42–
1.54 μ. Absorption between 1.82 and 1.97 μ is caused by the strong (011)
band of H_2O at 1.87 μ accompanied by the much weaker band (110) at
1.91 μ (Nelson and Benedict, 1948). Additional relatively weak lines between 2.00 μ and 2.22 μ have been assigned to (030) of H_2O (Mohler an
Benedict, 1948). The third overtone of ν_2, (040), is expected to appear in
the relatively clear region 1.54–1.64 μ but has not yet been identified.
Many individual resolved lines of the positive branch of (001), which
causes complete obscuration beyond 2.5 μ, have been found between
2.22 and 2.50 μ.

Seventeen bands of carbon dioxide and its two isotopic forms, $C^{13}O_2^{16}$
and $C^{12}O^{16}O^{18}$, are expected to occur in the region 1.4–2.5 μ, of which six-
teen have been observed in the solar spectrum (Goldberg, Mohler,
McMath, and Pierce, 1949). Two of the isotope bands, at 2.04 μ, are shown
in Figure 11. The second overtone $3\nu_3$ at 1.435 μ is overlapped by neighboring H_2O bands but is observable on days of low humidity. The upper
levels of the other bands occur in resonating groups of three and four, the
related levels being indicated by the braces in Table 4. The resonating
triad of CO_2 bands at 2 μ and the tetrad at 1.6 μ were known from the early

solar observations of Langley (1900), Adel and Lampland (1938), and the laboratory observations of Barker and Wu (1934). The most recent observations of the solar spectrum with the lead sulphide cell have resulted not only in the complete resolution of the 1.6 and 2 μ bands, but also in the discovery of five of six expected bands of $C^{13}O_2^{16}$ and $C^{12}O^{16}O^{18}$ (Goldberg, Mohler, and McMath, 1948) and of a triad of difference bands originating from the excited vibrational level 01_10 (Mohler, McMath, and Goldberg, 1949). The difference bands result from a II–II transition and therefore provide an interesting example of combined resonance interaction and l-type doubling (de Heer and Nielsen, 1952).

Following Migeotte's (1948) recognition of methane in the telluric spectrum by his observation of the fundamental band ν_3 at 3.3 μ, seven weaker bands of CH_4 have been found at shorter wave lengths (McMath, Mohler, Pierce, and Goldberg, 1949). The overtone band $2\nu_3$ at 1.66 μ and the combination bands at 2.20, 2.32, and 2.37 μ show prominent Q-branches, which, however, are absent in the resonating pair at 1.71 and 1.73 μ and in $\nu_2 + \nu_4$ at 2.43 μ. The rotational structure of $2\nu_3$ is extremely regular and amenable to rotational analysis (Nelson, Plyler, and Benedict, 1948; McMath, Mohler, and Goldberg, 1949); but the combination bands are strongly perturbed, and their rotational structures are complicated and irregular (Nielsen and Nielsen, 1935). About 50 per cent of all telluric lines in the region 2.15–2.45 μ are due to the combination bands of CH_4.

Very minor contributions to the telluric spectrum between 2.1 and 2.3 μ are made by nitrous oxide and carbon monoxide. The former is represented by four faint bands (McMath, Pierce, Mohler, Goldberg, and Donovan, 1950), only one of which, $2\nu_3$ at 2.26 μ, appears weakly in the spectrum of the noonday sun. The 2.11 μ band becomes visible at path lengths of 2 or 3 air masses, but the 2.16 μ band can be seen only when the sun is at the horizon. The unclassified band at 2.28 μ is probably a difference band. The faint overtone band of carbon monoxide at 2.28 μ is overlapped in the solar spectrum by lines of telluric CH_4 and H_2O and solar CO. The band appears definitely to be present, however (Howard and Shaw, 1952), although few, if any, of the lines are unblended and the intensities are uncertain (see Sec. 5).

The total absorption of sunlight between 2.5 and 2.9 μ is produced by the ν_1 and ν_3 fundamentals of H_2O at 2.74 and 2.66 μ, and by two combination bands of CO_2 at 2.69 and 2.77 μ. The rotational structure of this spectral region has recently been studied in detail by Benedict and Plyler (1951).

3.3. REGION 2.9–5.5 μ

Following the very early prismatic investigations of Langley, this region, or part of it, has been explored with high resolution by Adel (1952a) at Flagstaff, Arizona, in 1940 and in still finer detail by Migeotte at Columbus, Ohio, Liége, Belgium, and the Jungfraujoch, Switzerland; by Shaw, Chapman, Howard, and Oxholm at Columbus, Ohio; by Strong and Benesch (1950) at Baltimore, Maryland; and by Mohler and Pierce (1949) at Pontiac, Michigan, and Mount Wilson, California (Mohler, 1951). Improved prismatic spectra have also been obtained at the Solar Physics Observatory, Cambridge, England. The gases that contribute prominent bands in this region are H_2O, HDO, CO_2, CH_4, N_2O, and CO. Between 2.9 and 3.4 μ, the spectrum is depressed by $2\nu_2$ of H_2O, centered at 3.17 μ. Following a relatively clear stretch between 3.4 and 4.0 μ, the spectrum is again cut off completely by the ν_3 fundamental of $C^{12}O_2^{16}$ at 4.26 μ and of $C^{13}O_2^{16}$ at 4.38 μ, and only partially recovers between 4.6 and 5.0 μ before it is again obliterated by the very powerful ν_2 fundamental of H_2O centered at 6.27 μ.

A detailed description of the region 2.9–5.5 μ, based on both solar and laboratory observations, has been given by Shaw, Chapman, Howard, and Oxholm (1951). A careful related analysis of the rotational structure of the laboratory spectrum of H_2O has also been carried out by Benedict, Claassen, and Shaw (1951) for the region 4.5–13 μ. Although centered at 6.27 μ, the ν_2 fundamental of H_2O contributes many strong lines at shorter wave lengths. This band and the two difference bands $\nu_3-\nu_2$ at 4.63 μ and $\nu_1-\nu_2$ at 4.87 μ account for most of the strong H_2O lines between 4.5 and 5.5 μ. In addition to the strong ν_3 fundamental, carbon dioxide is represented by four weaker, but still prominent, bands at 4.68, 4.79, 4.81, and 5.18 μ. The fundamental ν_3 of methane, discovered in the solar spectrum by Migeotte (1948), shares the region 3.1–3.5 μ with $2\nu_2$ of H_2O. Many weaker lines of methane, belonging to $\nu_2 + \nu_4$ at 3.55 μ and $2\nu_4$ at 3.85 μ, have been identified with the aid of laboratory spectra by Shaw, Chapman, Howard, and Oxholm (1951). Very striking records of the ν_3 band have been obtained by Migeotte and Neven (1952a) in the dry air over the Jungfraujoch.

Six bands of nitrous oxide have been identified in the region 2.9–5.5 μ. Following Adel's (1939) discovery of the 7.8 μ fundamental in the solar spectrum, other bands at 3.9 (see Fig. 12) and 4.5 μ were detected by Migeotte (1948) and by Shaw, Sutherland, and Wormell (1948). Weaker combination bands have since been observed at 2.97 μ (McMath and Goldberg, 1949), at 3.57 μ (Strong and Benesch, 1950), and at 4.06 μ (Shaw, Chapman, Howard, and Oxholm, 1951). Migeotte and Neven

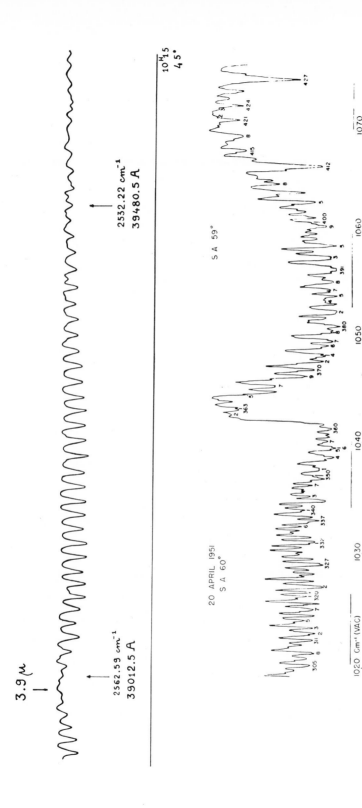

Fig. 12.—*Upper:* negative branch of the 3.9 μ band of N₂O in the solar spectrum observed on the Jungfraujoch (Migeotte and Neven, 1952*a*). *Lower:* ozone at 9.6 μ in the solar spectrum (Shaw, Oxholm, and Claassen, 1951).

(1952*a*), at the Jungfraujoch, have succeeded in tracing the band at 2.87 μ under very dry conditions.

Following the discovery by Migeotte (1949) at Columbus of the fundamental band of carbon monoxide at 4.67 μ, it has since been observed further at Columbus (Shaw, Chapman, Howard, Oxholm, *et al.*, 1951), at the Jungfraujoch (Migeotte and Neven, 1952*a*); by Mohler (1952) at the McMath-Hulbert Observatory at Pontiac, Michigan, and at Mount Wilson, California; and by Locke and Herzberg (1953) at Ottawa, Canada. The band has also been found by Adel (1952*a*) on tracings made at Flagstaff in 1940.

The fundamental ν_1 of HDO at 3.67 μ was first detected in the earth's atmosphere by observation of an artificial light-source through more than a mile of sea-level air (Gebbie, Harding, Hilsum, and Roberts, 1949). Individual rotational details of this band have been identified in the solar spectrum by comparison with laboratory spectra (Chapman and Shaw, 1950; Benesch, Strong, and Benedict, 1950).

The ozone band at 4.75 μ has been included in Table 4, although overlapping lines of H_2O, CO_2, and CO have thus far prevented its positive identification in the solar spectrum. According to J. H. Shaw (1953), however, the envelope of the band can be seen on published tracings from Ohio State University, and improved resolution of the 4.7–4.8 μ region shows a large number of new telluric lines probably due to O_3. M. Migeotte (1953) reports that the general appearance of the solar spectrum at 4.75 μ follows that of the laboratory spectrum of O_3 (Vigroux, Migeotte, and Neven, 1953) but that the crowding of lines in the solar spectrum makes difficult the identification of individual lines of O_3. Numerous attempts have been made to establish the presence in the high atmosphere of NO, on theoretical as well as on observational grounds. Unfortunately, the fundamental vibration-rotation band of NO falls at 5.32 μ in a region of strong water-vapor absorption. Migeotte and Neven (1952*a*), however, have taken advantage of the low H_2O content above the Jungfraujoch to search for the Q-branch of the NO fundamental. No trace of the band could be found, even when the sun's altitude was as low as 6°, from which they conclude that the abundance of telluric NO can be no greater than 0.02 cm NTP. From similar considerations they assign an upper limit of 0.2 cm NTP to the abundance of C_2H_2.

3.4. REGION 7–13 μ

Following the extension of the solar spectrum to 13 μ (Fowle, 1917), the region 7–13 μ was explored with a prism spectrometer at Flagstaff, Arizona (Adel and Lampland, 1938), and with a high-dispersion grating instrument (Adel, 1941c). Very recently, improved spectra have been secured at the Ohio State University (Shaw, Oxholm, and Claassen, 1951), which, with the aid of new laboratory spectra, have resulted in the identification of all but relatively few details of the spectrum. This region has also been investigated at high altitudes by Migeotte and Neven (1952a), but the detailed results have not yet been published.

A low-dispersion prismatic spectrum of the sun in the 7–13 μ region, made at Cambridge, England, is shown in Figure 13. The transparency between 7 and 8 μ is highly variable, depending on the water-vapor content. The absorption at 7.8 μ is due also to the fundamentals ν_4 of CH_4 and ν_1 of N_2O. The powerful ozone absorption at 9.6 μ is flanked on either side by difference bands of CO_2 at 9.4 and 10.4 μ. Water-vapor lines and CO_2 bands at 12.6 and 13.5 μ lead to the complete extinction of the spectrum beyond about 13.5 μ.

The identifications of water-vapor lines by Shaw, Oxholm, and Claassen are taken from the new laboratory investigation of Benedict, Claassen, and Shaw (1951). At wave lengths longer than about 11.5 μ, the water-vapor spectrum consists almost entirely of pure rotational transitions within the ground vibrational level. Between 10 and 7 μ the ν_2 fundamental centered at 6.27 μ predominates, together with weaker lines of the difference band at 6.43 μ. At 10 μ there is a region of minimum absorption by H_2O; the pure rotational lines begin to appear beyond 10 μ. Adel (1941a) attributed a small depression in the 7.2 μ region of the prismatic solar spectrum to the 7.14 μ band of HDO. It is probable, however, that this feature is due entirely to H_2O (Benedict, Claassen, and Shaw, 1951), although a few individual lines of the 7.14 μ band may appear near 8 μ, where the H_2O absorption is relatively weak.

The carbon dioxide bands between 9 and 13 μ were identified in the solar spectrum by Adel (1941b) and observed in the laboratory by Martin and Barker (1932) and Barker and Adel (1933). The bands are all of the difference variety, and, since four of the five bands have lower excitation potentials of about $\frac{1}{6}$ eV, they should exhibit pronounced seasonable variations in intensity. The carbon dioxide bands in the 9–13 μ region have recently been reinvestigated in both the solar spectrum and the laboratory by Shaw, Oxholm, and Claassen (1951). The P-branch of the 9.4 μ band falls in the region of the intense ozone absorption band at 9.6 μ. But the R-branch and the 10.4 μ band lie in a clear region relatively free of water-vapor lines. The CO_2 band structure in the neighborhood of 13 μ is complicated by the presence of three bands, at 12.6, 13.5, and 13.9 μ. It

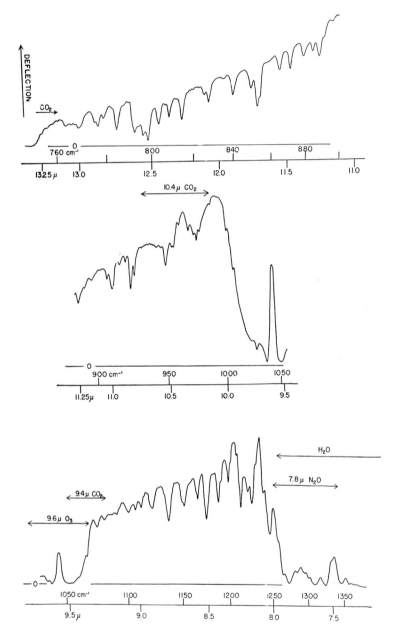

FIG. 13.—The prismatic solar spectrum 13.5–7.5 μ observed at the Solar Physics Observatory, Cambridge, England (Shaw, Oxholm, and Claassen, 1951).

appears, however, that most of the structure can be accounted for by lines of the 12.6 μ band.

The ozone band ν_1 at 9.6 μ (Fig. 12) was first resolved by Adel (1941c) and studied with improved resolution in solar and laboratory spectra by Shaw, Oxholm, and Claassen (1951) and by Migeotte, Neven, and Vigroux (1952). Most of the structure in the solar spectrum between 9.4 and 10.1 μ can be attributed to O_3, the remainder being due to weak lines of CO_2 and H_2O. High-dispersion laboratory studies of the fine structure of the infrared bands of O_3, including the very faint ones at 9, 3.59, and 3.27 μ, have recently been made by Vigroux, Migeotte, and Neven (1953). Individual lines of the 9 μ band have been identified in the solar spectrum by Migeotte (1953).

The remaining identified bands in the 7–13 μ region are due to CH_4 and N_2O. The ν_4 fundamental of methane at 7.66 μ exhibits an intense Q-branch in the solar spectrum at 1306 cm^{-1}. According to Migeotte and Neven (1951), solar spectra made from the Jungfraujoch show 115 lines of CH_4 between 7.21 and 8.29 μ. In addition to the ν_1 fundamental at 7.8 μ (Adel, 1939), a weaker overtone band, $2\nu_2$, of nitrous oxide was also identified by Migeotte (1950) at 8.6 μ and studied further by Shaw, Oxholm, and Claassen (1951). Very few strong lines in the 7–13 μ region of the spectrum remain unidentified. As a result of comparisons with laboratory spectra, the Ohio State group find no indication of appreciable absorption in the telluric spectrum by C_2H_6(11.9 μ band), C_2H_4(10.5 μ), NH_3(10.74 μ), C_2N_2(4.6 μ), SO_2(8.6 μ), and NO_2(3.4 μ).

3.5. REGION 15–24 μ

The existence of a semitransparent window in this region of the spectrum was first established by Adel (1942) at Flagstaff, Arizona, from low-disperson observations. The existence of the window has been confirmed by Anthony (1952), also from prismatic observations. High-dispersion spectrograms between 15 and 24 μ have been obtained from the Jungfraujoch by Migeotte and Neven (1952b). About 145 rotational lines were found between 15.90 and 23.73 μ. At shorter wave lengths, the spectrum is totally obscured by the ν_2 band of CO_2 at 15 μ. Water-vapor absorption terminates the spectrum at 23.73 μ. Nearly all the observed lines have been identified with either the 16.2 μ band of CO_2, the ν_2 fundamental of N_2O at 17.0 μ, or pure rotational lines of H_2O. The unresolved P-, Q-, and R-branches of the N_2O fundamental have also been detected by Adel (1952b).

4. MILLIMETER AND CENTIMETER WAVES

The absorption of millimeter and centimeter waves in the earth's atmosphere is caused chiefly by electronic transitions in O_2 and by pure rotational transitions in H_2O. Although the pure rotational spectra of molecules might be expected to extend well into the microwave region, they are forbidden to the major permanent constituents of the atmosphere, namely, oxygen, nitrogen, and carbon dioxide. The microwave absorption of O_2 and H_2O has been investigated both experimentally (Beringer, 1946; Dicke, Beringer, Kyhl, and Vane, 1946) and theoretically (van Vleck, 1947). Because of the interaction between the magnetic moment and rotation of the oxygen molecule, each state of rotational quantum number, K, has associated with it three components with resultant inner quantum numbers $J = K - 1$, K, and $K + 1$. Magnetic dipole transitions are permitted between level K and either $K - 1$ or $K + 1$. The transition $J = 0$ to $J = 1$ gives a line at 2.5 mm. All the remaining transitions are very nearly coincident at about 5 mm. In addition to the two strong resonance maxima, there is also a much weaker nonresonant absorption extending to long wave lengths.

The absorption spectrum of H_2O in the region from about 1 mm to 10 cm consists of three strong rotational lines at 1.35 cm, 1.63 mm, and 0.94 mm, together with a continuum formed of the overlapping wings of lines on the short-wave-length side of the 1.35-cm line.

The microwave absorption coefficients of oxygen and water vapor have been calculated from quantum mechanics by van Vleck (1947) and are shown in Figures 14 and 15. The dotted curve gives the attenuation in decibels per kilometer, due to oxygen, of dry air at 300° K, and atmospheric pressure. Since the peak at $\frac{1}{2}$ cm is produced by many overlapping lines, the calculated absorption coefficient is critically dependent on the damping constant. Beringer's (1946) experimental data are best fitted by a value of 0.02 cm^{-1} for the half-width at half-intensity. The solid curve gives the absorption by H_2O in an atmosphere containing 1 per cent uncondensed water by volume (density $= 7.5$ gm/m^3). It is based on a half-width of 0.10 cm^{-1} for H_2O.

Van Vleck's calculations suggest that the atmosphere is relatively transparent to microwaves longer than about 2 cm; and, indeed, observations of solar and galactic radio noise at those wave lengths are not seriously affected by atmospheric absorption. The relative transparency of the region between the two H_2O lines at 0.9 and 1.6 mm has been confirmed by Sinton (1952), who has observed millimeter-wave solar radiation with a Golay detector.

5. ANALYSES OF LINE SPECTRA

The abundances of atmospheric molecules may be derived from their absorption lines in the solar spectrum if the absolute line-absorption coefficients are known. The spectroscopic method is most profitably applied to the minor constituents of the atmosphere, inasmuch as the nitrogen spectrum is not observable from the ground and the proportions of both

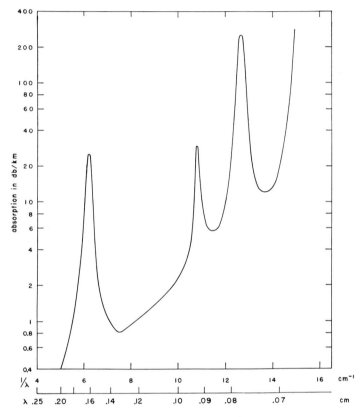

FIG. 14.—Millimeter wave absorption by H_2O in db/km (van Vleck, 1947)

nitrogen and oxygen may be determined with high precision by chemical methods (Paneth, 1937). Information on the vertical distribution of gases may also be inferred from observations of the intensities of telluric lines when the sun is close to the horizon.

5.1. LINE-ABSORPTION COEFFICIENTS

Until recently, very few accurate determinations of absorption coefficients have been made for infrared atmospheric bands, because of inade-

quate instrumental resolving power. Two developments have served to re-
vive interest in infrared intensity measurements. First, Wilson and Wells
(1946) have shown that the integrated absorption coefficient of an entire
vibrational band may be measured accurately with a spectrograph of
relatively low resolving power. Briefly, the method is to eliminate the
rotational fine structure by introduction of a foreign gas at high pressure
and to extrapolate the apparent, integrated absorption coefficient to zero
partial pressure of the absorbing gas, to obtain the true absorption coefficient. Second, the introduction of high-dispersion infrared spectrometers
employing photoconductive cells makes possible the measurement of individual rotational line intensities (Goldberg, Mohler, and Donovan,
1952; Benedict and Silverman, 1953) and their reduction to absorption
coefficients by the curve-of-growth method.

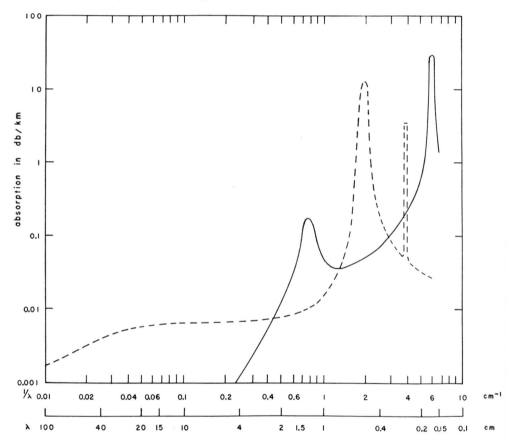

Fig. 15.—Centimeter wave absorption by H₂O (*solid line*) and by O₂ (*dotted line*) in db/km (van Vleck,
1947).

Existing measures of infrared absorption coefficients are summarized in Table 5 for H_2O, CO_2, N_2O, CH_4, CO, and NO. The first column gives the wave number of the band center, the second column the absorption coefficient in cm^{-1} per cm NTP, and the third column the reference. Where more than one reference is given for a band, the tabulated value is aver-

TABLE 5

INTEGRATED ABSORPTION COEFFICIENTS OF
INFRARED ATMOSPHERIC BANDS

Band Center (cm^{-1})	Absorption Coefficient (cm^{-1} per cm NTP)	Reference*	Band Center (cm^{-1})	Absorption Coefficient (cm^{-1} per cm NTP)	Reference*
H_2O........	....	......	H_2O...........	....	......
1595.........	300	10	16899.........	0.01	10
3151.........	1	10	17495.........	0.002	10
3657.........	8	10	18394.........	0.0005	10
3756.........	180	10			
4667.........	0.008	10	CO_2..........	....	......
5235.........	1	10	667.........	173	1, 2, 3
5331.........	30	10	1933.........	0.011	9
6775.........	0.03	10	2077.........	0.104	9
6871.........	1.4	10	2093.........	0.007	9
7201.........	2.0	10	2130.........	0.0037	9
7250.........	20	10	2349.........	2480	9
7445.........	0.15	10	3613.........	28	2, 3, 9
8273.7.......	0.02	10	3714.........	35	9
8273.9.......	0.005	10	4853.........	0.27	3
8762.........	0.01	10	4978.........	1.0	3
8807.........	0.6	10	5100.........	0.43	3
9000.........	0.02	10	6228.........	0.0077	4
9834.........	0.002	10	6973.........	0.023	9
10284.........	<0.001	10			
10329.........	0.06	10	N_2O.........	....	......
10600.........	0.015	10	589.........	21	2
10613.........	0.3	10	1167.........	8.5	2
10869.........	0.01	10	1285.........	245	2
11032.........	0.05	10	1868.........	0.41	2
11813.........	0.003	10	2224.........	1633	2, 5
12140.........	0.0015	10	2798.........	2.4	2
12151.........	0.15	10			
12408.........	0.002	10	CH_4..........	....	......
12565.........	0.02	10	1306.........	150	1
13653.........	0.015	10	3019.........	300	1
13828.........	<0.0005	10	6005.........	0.96	6
13831.........	0.08	10			
14221.........	0.002	10	CO.........	....	......
14319.........	0.02	10	2143.........	259	7
15348.........	0.005	10	4260.........	1.80	7
15832.........	0.0005	10			
16822.........	0.005	10	NO.........	....	......
16898.........	0.001	10	1875.........	143	8

* References are as follows:
1. Thorndike (1947).
2. Eggers and Crawford (1951).
3. Weber, Holm, and Penner (1952).
4. Goldberg (1954).
5. Callamon, McKean, and Thompson (1951).
6. Goldberg, Mohler, and Donovan (1952).
7. Penner and Weber (1951a).
8. Crawford and Dinsmore (1950).
9. Benedict and Silverman (1953).
10. Benedict (1953).

aged from two or more determinations. Formulae relating the absorption coefficients of individual band lines to the integrated values in Table 5 have been given for diatomic and linear triatomic molecules by Crawford and Dinsmore (1950), Penner and Weber (1951b), and Eggers and Crawford (1951). The absorption coefficients obtained by Benedict (1953), by Benedict and Silverman (1953), by Goldberg (1954), and by Goldberg, Mohler, and Donovan (1952) were derived from measurements on individual lines of the various bands. All the other values were obtained by the method of Wilson and Wells (1946). Benedict regards his values for H_2O as estimates, some of which may be in error by as much as 100 per cent.

For the 6005 cm^{-1} band of CH_4, the intensity was calculated in the following way. Let $S_{JJ'}$ be the absorption coefficient per molecule in level J for a transition between lower-level J and upper-level J'. In general, there will be three transitions originating from level J, corresponding to lines in the P-, Q-, and R-branches. According to Childs and Jahn (1939), the sum of $S_{JJ'}$ for each group of three transitions is a constant for the band and is, in fact, equal to the integrated band-absorption coefficient per molecule in the ground vibrational state. Values of $S_{JJ'}$ have been given for the individual lines in the R- and P-branches only (Goldberg, Mohler, and Donovan, 1952). However, inasmuch as only the positive branch is permitted for a line originating from $J = 0$, the coefficient S_{01} is also the integrated band-absorption coefficient. Its value is 1.07×10^{-9} cm^2/sec per molecule or 0.96 cm^{-1} per cm NTP.

5.2. ABUNDANCES

Ideally, the abundance of an atmospheric gas could be found from the analysis of individual line profiles; however, true line profiles can rarely be observed with existing instrumentation. On the other hand, the area under the line, called the *total absorption* or *equivalent width*, is usually independent of resolving power (Dennison, 1928). The relation between the equivalent width of an absorption line and the abundance and physical state of the absorbing gas is embodied in the theory of the curve of growth, which has been widely employed as a tool of analysis in astrophysics. The curve of growth is the functional relationship between the equivalent width of an absorption line and the line-absorption coefficient. Numerous investigators (see Unsöld, 1938) have developed the theory for a homogeneous atmosphere of constant pressure and temperature. It turns out that the shape of the curve depends on a parameter a, which is the ratio between $\gamma/2\pi$, the collisional width at half-intensity, and b_D, the Doppler displacement corresponding to the most probable velocity. Curves of growth for various values of a are reproduced in Figure 16. The ordinates are log $A/2b_D$, where A is the equivalent width; and the abscissae are log $N_J S/ 2b_D$, where S is the absorption coefficient per molecule and N_J is the number of molecules per square centimeter cross-section in level J. All three quantities, A, b_D, and $N_J S$, may be expressed either in wave length, wave number, or frequency units, but the units must be the same for each quantity. For example, if A is in sec^{-1}, b_D is also in sec $^{-1}$, and the units of S are cm^2 sec^{-1}.

The formation of telluric absorption lines is complicated by the nonhomogeneity of the earth's atmosphere—the total pressure, the temperature, and the density of the absorbing gas all vary with altitude. The complications may be taken into account, however, and the line intensities calculated with the aid of atmospheric models based upon observational data on pressures and temperatures. Calculations of this type have been performed for molecular oxygen (Childs, 1933; Allen, 1937; van de Hulst, 1945a) and for methane (Goldberg, 1951). Van de Hulst's calculations are

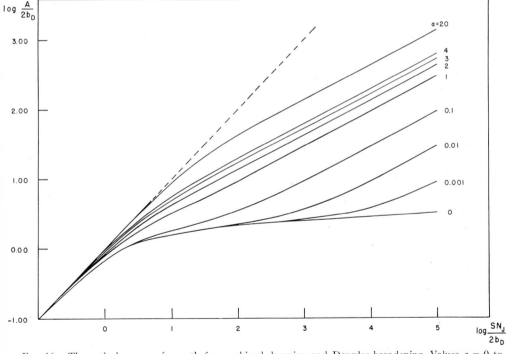

FIG. 16.—Theoretical curves of growth for combined damping and Doppler broadening. Values $a = 0$ to $a = 2$ after van der Held (1931). Values $a = 3$ to $a = 20$ after Penner and Kavanagh (1952).

generally applicable to diatomic and linear triatomic molecules (CO_2, N_2O), whereas the methane results are valid for spherical and symmetric-top molecules. A number of general conclusions may be stated which are independent of the type of molecule. First, the line intensities follow a curve of growth, which is very nearly identical with that for pure collisional broadening. Second, the damping constant increases slowly with increasing excitation potential, but for lines of low excitation energy, the damping constant is very nearly equal to half its value at the ground level. Van de Hulst finds that for O_2 the ratio γ_{eff}/γ_0 increases from 0.48 for lines of low energy to 0.73 for those with energy about 2000 cm^{-1}. Similar results were obtained for methane. Finally, for energies less than about 600 cm^{-1}, the populations of the various rotational levels, integrated through the atmosphere, may be represented accurately by the Boltzmann formula, with an effective temperature about 20 per cent lower than the ground temperature.

If an observational curve of growth can be constructed from measurements of equivalent widths, application of the theory may lead to the determination of the abundance, the effective temperature, and the effective damping constant. Or the abundance may be assumed, and the absolute transition probabilities derived (van de Hulst, 1945a). The curve of growth of a telluric line may be obtained from a plot of the logarithm of its equivalent width against the logarithm of the secant of the sun's zenith distance. Inasmuch as the proportionality between air mass and sec z breaks down when sec z is greater than about 10, the complete curve of growth cannot usually be obtained from a single line. If different lines are used, their curves will be displaced horizontally by $\Delta \log N_J S$. The individual curves will usually overlap sufficiently in equivalent width so that they may be superposed by lateral displacement, and the amounts of the shifts used to determine the effective excitation temperature from the Boltzmann formula. A curve of growth obtained in this fashion for the 1.6 μ band of CO_2 in the earth's atmosphere is shown in Figure 17 (Goldberg, 1954). The excitation temperature derived from combining the separate curves is 246° K. The ground temperature during the times of observation averaged 290° K; hence the ratio is 1.18, in good agreement with theory. The solid line drawn through the observed points is a theoretical curve of growth for pure collisional broadening with $\gamma/2\pi = 1.7 \times 10^9$ sec^{-1}. Van de Hulst (1945b) obtained $\gamma/2\pi = 1.2 \times 10^9$ sec^{-1} for O_2 molecules observed from sea-level, and Goldberg (1951) found 2.4×10^9 sec^{-1} for CH_4, also from sea-level. The latter value is consistent with other CH_4 values of 2.0×10^9 sec^{-1} for Mount Wilson (Goldberg, 1951) and 1.6 $\times$

10^9 sec^{-1} for the Jungfraujoch (Nielsen and Migeotte, 1952). The CO_2 observations were made at Mount Wilson, and hence the effective $\gamma/2\pi$ corrected to sea-level is 2.0×10^9 sec^{-1}.

From the absolute absorption coefficient of the 1.6 μ band (see Table 5), the number of CO_2 molecules through the zenith air over Mount Wilson is 7.4×10^{21} cm^{-2}. If the CO_2 is assumed to be uniformly mixed, the abundance corrected to sea-level is 8.7×10^{21} cm^{-2}, which is equivalent to 320 cm NTP. The percentage volume abundance is therefore 0.040, which is in reasonably good agreement with chemical determinations. The observa-

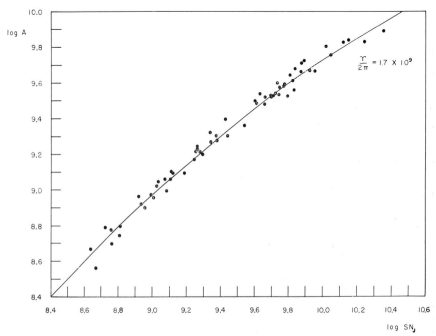

Fig. 17.—Empirical curve of growth for 1.6 μ band of CO_2 in earth's atmosphere

tions of the CO_2 line intensities were made in early January, 1951. It would be of great interest to look for possible seasonal variations in the abundance.

Simultaneously with the CO_2 observations, tracings were made of the 2.05 and 2.04 μ bands of $C^{13}O_2^{16}$ and $C^{12}O^{16}O^{18}$, respectively. The abundances found (corrected to sea-level) were 1.54 cm NTP for $C^{13}O_2^{16}$ and 0.67 cm NTP for $C^{12}O^{16}O^{18}$. In the calculation of the abundances it was assumed that the absorption coefficients of the isotope bands were identical with that for the corresponding band of $C^{12}O_2^{16}$ at 2.02 μ (see Table 5). The results are consistent with abundance ratios for C^{12}/C^{13} and O^{16}/O^{18}

of 210 and 1000, respectively. Both ratios are too great by about a factor of 2, as compared with other terrestrial determinations. This suggests possible systematic errors in the relative values of the absorption coefficients of the 1.6 and 2.0 μ bands of CO_2. It is also possible that the absorption coefficients of the isotope bands may differ appreciably from those of the ordinary 2 μ bands.[1]

Evidence on the abundance of carbon monoxide has been conflicting, owing chiefly to uncertain knowledge of the damping constant. However, the correct procedure for determining the abundance from the fundamental band has recently been given by Locke and Herzberg (1953). According to van de Hulst (1945a), absorption lines are formed in the earth's atmosphere with an effective damping constant equal to half the value at ground level. Locke and Herzberg have therefore used the curve-of-growth method to measure the damping of CO molecules by air at $\frac{1}{2}$ atm pressure. The measured damping constant, $\gamma/2\pi = 1.4 \times 10^9 \text{ sec}^{-1}$, has been applied to the calculation of the abundance from measurements of the equivalent width of the R3 line in the fundamental band. The result is that on 14 days between June 2, 1952, and October 24, 1952, the amount of CO over Ottawa, Canada, was found to vary between 0.08 and 0.16 cm NTP.

The results of Locke and Herzberg appear to confirm earlier reports of the variability of the CO content (Migeotte, 1949; Migeotte and Neven, 1952a). Shaw and Howard (1952) found the abundance at Columbus, Ohio, to be 0.09 cm NTP from observations of the fundamental R2 line in February, 1952. The damping constant was derived from laboratory measurements on CO pressure broadened by N_2 at atmospheric pressure and is therefore too high by about a factor of 2. Very recently, Benesch, Migeotte, and Neven (1953) have reported measurements of the R3 fundamental line which indicate that the CO content over the Jungfraujoch may vary by a factor of up to 5 and that it may undergo large fluctuations within the period of 1 hour.

A different approach to the determination of the CO content is by the measurement of overtone lines, which are very weak and therefore independent of the damping. Unfortunately, no overtone line is entirely free of blending with other solar and telluric lines. For example, the P6 line, employed by Howard and Shaw (1952) in deriving the value 0.10 cm-atm at Columbus on March 6 and 8, 1952, is coincident with the line R30 of the solar 4–2 band of CO. The solar contribution was allowed for by How-

---

1. After this manuscript was sent to press, Dr. W. S. Benedict kindly supplied the writer with the results of his measurements of absorption coefficients of isotope bands of CO_2 at wave lengths longer than 2 μ. These results strongly suggest that the absorption coefficients of the isotope bands can differ greatly from those of the corresponding ordinary bands.

ard and Shaw, but the possibility of blending with a weak telluric line of H_2O or CH_4 is not ruled out.

Lower values of the CO abundance have been obtained from measurements of the overtone lines observed at Mount Wilson (Goldberg and Müller, 1953a). Four lines were measured, namely, R3, R10, P7, and P9. Each line gave a different value of the abundance, ranging from 0.03 cm NTP for R3 to 0.10 cm NTP for R10. Since no two lines were observed on the same day, the apparent variations in abundance may be real. On the other hand, the differences may be caused by blending, which can serve either to raise or to lower the observed intensity. When the coincidence with the blended line is nearly exact, the measured intensity is increased. But even when there is no obvious blending, the wings of neighboring lines may depress the continuous background and thus decrease the line intensity. This appears to be the case for the R3 overtone line.

For the present, the Mount Wilson data suggest a CO abundance, reduced to sea-level, of 0.06 cm NTP; but the reality of the apparent variation in abundance will be open to question until based upon nearly simultaneous observations of at least two lines. Otherwise, there is danger that the variation in CO content may turn out to be correlated with humidity. The remaining discrepancy of about a factor of 2 between the Ottawa and Columbus results, on the one hand, and the Mount Wilson data, on the other, is not excessive in view of the many possibilities for systematic errors.

The methane abundance has been accurately determined from observations (Goldberg, 1951) at Lake Angelus, Michigan (elevation 296 m); Mount Wilson, California (elevation 1742 m); and most recently (Nielsen and Migeotte, 1952) at the Jungfraujoch (elevation 3580 m). The abundance of CH_4 over each station is consistent with the belief that the gas is uniformly distributed throughout the world and that its density decreases exponentially with height at the same rate as the main body of the atmosphere. The number of molecules per square centimeter through the zenith from sea-level is 3.2×10^{19}, corresponding to 1.2 cm NTP.

The spectroscopically determined abundances are summarized in Table 2. The value for nitrous oxide is only approximate, since accurate absorption coefficients have not yet been measured for the weak band at 2.16 μ on which the abundance is based (McMath and Goldberg, 1949).

5.3. VERTICAL DISTRIBUTION

The vertical distribution of minor atmospheric constituents can provide important clues to their origin and chemistry (Bates and Witherspoon,

1952). It may be inferred by direct sampling from high-altitude vehicles, from chemical and spectroscopic analyses of the lower atmosphere (Slobad and Krogh, 1950; Gebbie, Harding, Hilsum, Fryce, and Roberts, 1951), by comparison of abundances determined spectroscopically from sites at different altitudes (Sec. 5.2), and, by a method to be described here, from the intensities of telluric lines in the low-sun spectrum.

It is well known that at very low solar altitudes the rate at which the intensity of a telluric line increases with zenith distance depends on the vertical distribution of the absorbing gas. The total number of molecules traversed by a light-ray passing through the atmosphere is, neglecting refraction,

$$\int n_h \, dl \; ,$$

where n_h is the number density at altitude h, and l is the slant height. The increment of path length, dl, is given by (Goldberg, 1951),

$$dl = \frac{(1 + h/R)}{(\cos^2 z + 2h/R + h^2/R^2)^{1/2}} \, dh \; ,$$

where z is the sun's zenith distance and R is the radius of the earth. In the plane-parallel approximation,

$$\cos^2 z \gg \frac{2h}{R} + \frac{h^2}{R^2} \; ,$$

and the familiar secant law holds:

$$dl = dh \times \sec z \; .$$

It is clear that the plane-parallel approximation is valid closer to the horizon for the low-lying layers than for the higher layers and also that when the altitude of the absorbing layer is high, the path length of a ray near the horizon increases relatively slowly with zenith distance.

Link (1940) has made very accurate calculations of the total number of air masses traversed by a light-ray originating at any apparent zenith distance, taking account of refraction and of the true density distribution in the atmosphere. Link's tables also permit similar relations to be drawn for absorbing layers of various thicknesses lying at various altitudes up to, say, 50 km. The tables have been employed (Goldberg and Müller, 1953b) in studying the vertical distribution of CH_4 and N_2O over Mount Wilson. The intensities of four lines (P25, 26, 27, 29) of N_2O in the negative branch of the 2.16 μ band and of the 5–6 line in the 1.67 μ band of CH_4 were measured in the low-sun spectrum. In each case the equivalent width was plotted against the path length, the latter being calculated from the apparent zenith distance on four different assumptions as to the vertical distribution, namely, that the absorbing gas is concentrated in a relatively thin layer at altitudes of (1) 15 km, (2) 25 km, (3) 50 km, and (4) that the gas is uniformly mixed in the atmosphere (exponential density distribution). The results are shown in Figures 18 and 19, in which L_0 and L_z are the total amounts of absorbing gas through the zenith and at zenith angle z, respectively. The solid lines represent segments of theoretical curves of growth, the weak N_2O lines lying on the linear branch of the curve and the strong CH_4 line on the square-root branch.

Some caution must be exercised in interpreting Figures 18 and 19. The

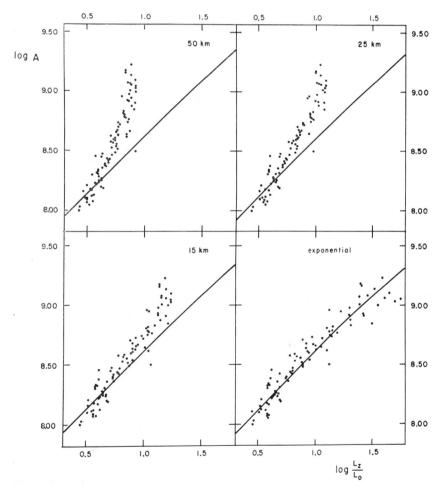

Fig. 18.—Empirical curves of growth for N_2O on four different assumptions as to vertical distribution in atmosphere. *Upper left:* thin layer at 50-km altitude. *Upper right:* thin layer at 25-km altitude. *Lower left:* thin layer at 15-km altitude. *Lower right:* exponential distribution.

method employed does not give a definitive determination of the vertical distribution, but rather it enables a choice to be made between different assumptions as to the vertical distribution. In Figures 18 and 19 there is no question but that the exponential distribution fits the observations and that the thin-layer distributions do not. On the other hand, other possible vertical distributions are not ruled out. It should also be mentioned that the measurement of equivalent widths on low-sun tracings is difficult, because of uncertainty in the location of the continuous background. Nevertheless, it seems safe to conclude that the bulk of both the N_2O and the

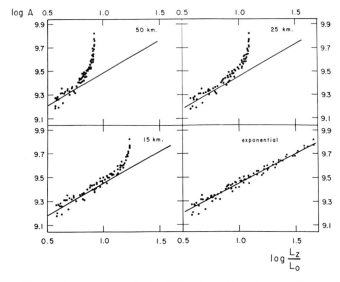

Fig. 19.—Empirical curves of growth for CH_4 on four different assumptions as to vertical distribution in atmosphere. *Upper left:* thin layer at 50-km altitude. *Upper right:* thin layer at 25-km altitude. *Lower left:* thin layer at 15-km altitude. *Lower right:* exponential distribution.

CH_4 occurs at low levels in the atmosphere. Slobad and Krogh (1950) find that the fractional volume concentration of N_2O at ground level is 5×10^{-7}, which agrees exactly with that derived spectroscopically for the entire atmosphere. However, the CH_4 concentration near the ground was found to be only one-fifteenth as great as that derived for the whole atmosphere.

Note added May 1, 1954.—Since the completion of this manuscript, important new laboratory measurements of the ultraviolet absorption coefficients of known and suspected atmospheric gases have been carried out at the Air Force Cambridge Research Center (Watanabe, Zelikoff, and Inn, 1953). Photoelectric measurements of high accuracy in the spectral region λλ 1050–2500 have been made on the gases O_2, O_3, CO, CO_2, NO, N_2O, N_2, H_2O, H_2, CH_4, and NH_3. The earlier work in this spectral region (Sec. 2) has been greatly extended and improved. Of special interest are the results for the Lyman-α region. Preston's (1940) value for O_2 of $k = 0.28$ cm^{-1} at the position of the Lyman-α line is confirmed; and it is also found that the absorption coefficient has several additional minima of the same order of magnitude between λ 1100 and λ 1300. Following the first successful photograph of the Lyman-α emission line in the solar spectrum from an Aerobee rocket (Pietenpol, Rense, Walz, Stacey, and Jackson, 1953), an improved series of spectra have been obtained by Johnson, Purcell, and Tousey (1954). At the maximum altitude of 104 km, the rocket was apparently not completely above the molecular oxygen atmosphere; but, in addition to the strong Lyman-α emission line, traces of the solar continuum can be seen at the wave lengths of the O_2 absorption minima. Photon-counter measurements interpreted in the light of the very narrow absorption minimum at Lyman-α by Byram, Chubb, Friedman, and Gailar (1953) suggest that the solar emission line is less than 1 A in width.

The writer wishes to acknowledge the valuable assistance of Dr. Edith A. Müller in making computations, of Mr. Gordon Grant in drawing the figures, and of Mrs. Kathryn K. Weddell in the preparation of the manuscript.

REFERENCES

ABBOT, C. G., and
   FREEMAN, H. B.   1929   *Smithsonian Misc. Coll.*, Vol. **82**, No. 1.
ADEL, A.   1939   *Ap. J.*, **90**, 627.
     1941a   *Ibid.*, **93**, 506.
     1941b   *Ibid.*, **94**, 375, 379.
     1941c   *Ibid.*, **94**, 451; also, *Phys. Rev.*, **59**, 915.
     1942   *Ibid.*, **96**, 239.
     1952a   *Scientific Rept. HA-2*, Contract No. AF19(122)-198, Arizona State College.
     1952b   *Phys. Rev.*, **88**, 128; also, *Ap. J.*, **116**, 442.
ADEL, A., and LAMP-
   LAND, C. O.   1938   *Ap. J.*, **87**, 198.
ALLEN, C. W.   1937   *Ap. J.*, **85**, 156.
ANTHONY, R.   1952   *Phys. Rev.*, **85**, 674.
BABCOCK, H. D.   1929   *Proc. Nat. Acad. Sci.*, **15**, 471.
BABCOCK, H. D., and
   HERZBERG, L.   1948   *Ap. J.*, **108**, 167.
BABCOCK, H. D., and
   MOORE, C. E.   1947   *Pub. Carnegie Inst. Washington*, No. 579.

BARKER, E. F., and
    ADEL, A.   1933   *Phys. Rev.*, **44**, 185.
BARKER, E. F., and
    WU, T. Y.   1934   *Phys. Rev.*, **45**, 1.
BATES, D. R., and
    SEATON, M. J.   1949   *M.N.*, **109**, 698.
BATES, D. R., and
    WITHERSPOON, A. E.   1952   *M.N.*, **112**, 101.
BENEDICT, W. S.   1948   *Phys. Rev.*, **74**, 1246.
                                1953   To be published.
BENEDICT, W. S.; CLAAS-
    SEN, H. H.; and SHAW,
    J. H.   1951   *Scientific Report 1A-3*, Contract No. AF19(122)65, Ohio State University; also, *J. Res. Nat. Bur. Standards*, **49**, 91, 1952.
BENEDICT, W. S.;
    HERMAN, R. C.; and
    SILVERMAN, S.   1953   To be published.
BENEDICT, W. S., and
    PLYLER, E. K.   1951   *J. Res. Nat. Bur. Stand.*, **46**, 246.
BENESCH, W.; ELDER, T.;
    and STRONG, J.   1950   *Progress Report on Absorption Spectrum of Lower Atmosphere*, Contract No. N5ori-166V.
BENESCH, W.;
    MIGEOTTE, M.; and
    NEVEN, L.   1953   *J. Opt. Soc. Amer.*, **43**, 1119.
BENESH, W.; STRONG J.;
    and BENEDICT, W. S.   1950   *Progress Report to ONR*, Contract No. N5ori-166.
BERINGER, R.   1946   *Phys. Rev.*, **70**, 53.
BIRGE, R. T., and
    HOPFIELD, J. J.   1928   *Ap. J.*, **68**, 257.
BURNIGHT, T. R.   1949   *Phys. Rev.*, **76**, 165.
BYRAM, E. T.; CHUBB,
    T.; FRIEDMAN, H.;
    and GAILAR, N.   1953   *Phys. Rev.*, **91**, 1278.
CALLAMON, H. J.;
    McKEAN, D. C.; and
    THOMPSON, H. W.   1951   *Proc. R. Soc. London*, *A*, **208**, 332.
CHALONGE, D., and
    LEFEBVRE, L.   1933   *C.R.*, **197**, 444.
CHAPMAN, R. M., and
    SHAW, J. H.   1950   *Phys. Rev.*, **78**, 71.
CHAPMAN, S.   1930   *Phil. Mag.*, **10**, 369.
                                    1943   *Rept. Prog. Physics*, **9**, 92.
CHAPMAN, S., and
    PRICE, W. C.   1936   *Rept. Prog. Physics*, **3**, 56.
CHILDS, W. H. J.   1933   *Ap. J.*, **77**, 212.

CHILDS, W. H. J., and
  JAHN, H. A.   1939   *Proc. R. Soc. London, A*, **169**, 451.
CHILDS, W. H. J., and
  MECKE, R.   1931   *Zs. f. Phys.*, **68**, 344.
CHIPLONKAR, M. W.   1939   *Current Sci.* (Bangalore), **8**, 312.
CLARK, K. C.   1948   *Phys. Rev.*, **73**, 1250.
CRAWFORD, B. L., JR.,
  and DINSMORE, H. L. 1950   *J. Chem. Phys.*, **983**, 1682.
DE HEER, J., and   1952   *J. Chem. Phys.*, **20**, 101.
  NIELSEN, H. H.
DENNISON, D. M.   1928   *Phys. Rev.*, **31**, 503.
DICKE, R. H.; BERIN-
  GER, R.; KYHL, R. L.;
  and VANE, A. B.   1946   *Phys. Rev.*, **70**, 340.
DIEKE, G. H., and
  BABCOCK, H. D.   1927   *Proc. Nat. Acad. Sci.*, **13**, 670.
DOBSON, G. M. B.   1930   *Proc. R. Soc. London, A*, **129**, 411.
                    1931   *Proc. Phys. Soc. London*, **43**, 324.
DOBSON, G. M. B., and
  HARRISON, D. N.   1926   *Proc. R. Soc. London, A*, **110**, 660.
DUFAY, J.   1942   *Ann. d'ap.*, **5**, 93.
DURAND, E.; OBERLY,
  J. J.; and TOUSEY, R. 1949   *Ap. J.*, **109**, 1.
EGGERS, D. F., JR., and
  CRAWFORD, B. L., JR. 1951   *J. Chem. Phys.*, **19**, 1556.
ELSASSER, W. M.   1938   *Phys. Rev.*, **54**, 126.
FABRY, C.   1950   *L'Ozone atmosphérique* (Paris: Centre Nat. de la
                              Recherche Scientifique, 13 quai Anatole France).
FABRY, C., and BUIS-
  SON, H.   1913   *J. de phys.*, **3**, 196.
                    1921*a* *Ap. J.*, **54**, 297.
                    1921*b* *J. de phys.*, **2**, 297.
FLORY, P. J.   1936   *J. Chem. Phys.*, **4**, 23.
FOWLE, F. E.   1917   *Smithsonian Misc. Coll.*, Vol. **68**, No. 8.
FOWLER, A., and STRUTT,
  R. J. (LORD RAY-
  LEIGH)   1917   *Proc. R. Soc. London, A*, **93**, 577.
FRAUNHOFER, J.   1815   *Denkschr. d. Münch. Akad.*, **5**, 193.
FRIEDMAN, H.; LICHT-
  MAN, S. W.; and
  BYRAM, E. T.   1951   *Phys. Rev.*, **83**, 1025.
GEBBIE, H. A.; HARD-
  ING, W. R.; HILSUM,
  C.; PRYCE, A. W.; and
  ROBERTS, V.   1951   *Proc. R. Soc. London, A*, **206**, 87.
GEBBIE, H. A.; HARD-
  ING, W. R.; HILSUM,
  C.; and ROBERTS V. 1949   *Phys. Rev.*, **76**, 1534.

GIAUQUE, W. F., and
JOHNSTON, H. L.   1929a   *J. Amer. Chem. Soc.*, **51**, 1436.
     1929b   *Ibid.*, p. 3528.
GÖTZ, F. W. P.   1931a   *Gerland's Beitr. z. Geophys.*, **31**, 119.
     1931b   *Strahlentherapie*, **40**, 690.
     1944   *Vierteljahrschr. d. naturforsch. Gesellsch.* (Zurich), **89**, 250.

GÖTZ, F. W. P.; MEE-
THAM, A. R.; and
DOBSON, G. M. B.   1934   *Proc. R. Soc. London, A*, **145**, 414.
GOLDBERG, L.   1951   *Ap. J.*, **113**, 567.
     1954   *Vistas in Astronomy*, ed. ARTHUR BEER (London: Pergamon Press, Ltd.).

GOLDBERG, L.; MOHLER,
O. C.; and DONOVAN,
R. A.   1952   *J. Opt. Soc. Amer.*, **42**, 1.
GOLDBERG, L.; MOHLER,
O. C.; and McMATH,
R. R.   1948   *Phys. Rev.*, **74**, 1881.
GOLDBERG, L.; MOHLER,
O. C.; McMATH,
R. R.; and PIERCE,
A. K.   1949   *Phys. Rev.*, **76**, 1848.
GOLDBERG, L., and MÜL-
LER, E. A.   1953a   Unpublished.
     1953b   *J. Opt. Soc. Amer.*, **43**, 1033.
HAVENS, R. J.; KOLL,
R. T.; and LaGOW,
H. E.   1952   *J. Geophys. Res.*, **57**, 59.
HARTLEY, W. N.   1881   *J. Chem. Soc.*, **39**, 57, 111.
HERZBERG, G.   1932   *Naturwiss.*, **20**, 577.
     1945   *Infra-red and Raman Spectra* (New York: D. Van Nostrand Co.).
     1950   *Spectra of Diatomic Molecules* (New York: D. Van Nostrand Co.).
     1952   *Canadian J. Phys.*, **30**, 185.
     1953   Private communication.
HERZBERG, G., and
HERZBERG, L.   1948   *Nature*, **161**, 283.
HERZBERG, L., and
HERZBERG, G.   1947   *Ap. J.*, **105**, 353.
HOPFIELD, J. J.   1930a   *Ap. J.*, **72**, 133.
     1930b   *Phys. Rev.*, **35**, 1133; **36**, 789.
     1946   *Ap. J.*, **104**, 208.
HOPFIELD, J. J., and
CLEARMAN, H. E.   1948   *Phys. Rev.*, **73**, 877.
HOWARD, J. N., and
SHAW, J. H.   1952   *Phys. Rev.*, **87**, 679; also, SHAW, J. H., and HOW-
ARD, J. N., *Scientific Report 1A-7*, Contract No. AF19(122)65, Ohio State University.

HUGGINS, WILLIAM	1890	*Proc. R. Soc. London*, **48**, 216.
JOHNSON, F. S.; PUR-CELL, J. D.; and TOUSEY, R.	1954	*Bull. Amer. Phys. Soc.*, **29**, 33.
JOHNSON, F. S.; PUR-CELL, J. D.; TOUSEY, R.; and WATANABE, K.	1952	*J. Geophys. Res.*, **57**, 157.
LADENBURG, R., and VAN VOORHIS, C. C.	1933	*Phys. Rev.*, **43**, 315.
LANGLEY, S. P.	1881	*Proc. Amer. Acad. Sci.*, **16**, 342.
	1900	*Ann. Smithsonian Inst.*, Vol. **1**.
LEIFSON, S. W.	1926	*Ap. J.*, **63**, 73.
LINK, F.	1940	*Pub. Obs. Nat. Prague*, Vol. **14**.
	1947	*Ibid.*, Vol. **18**.
LOCKE, J. L., and HERZ-BERG, L.	1952	*A.J.*, **57**, 161.
	1953	*Canad. J. Phys.*, **31**, 504.
LYMAN, T.	1911	*Ap. J.*, **33**, 98.
McMATH, R. R., and GOLDBERG, L.	1949	*Proc. Amer. Phil. Soc.*, **93**, 362.
McMATH, R. R.; MOH-LER, O. C.; and GOLD-BERG, L.	1949	*Ap. J.*, **109**, 17.
McMATH, R. R.; MOH-LER, O. C.; PIERCE, A. K.; and GOLD-BERG, L.	1949	*Phys. Rev.*, **76**, 1533.
McMATH, R. R.; PIERCE, A. K.; MOH-LER, O. C.; GOLD-BERG, L.; and DONO-VAN, R. A.	1950	*Phys. Rev.*, **78**, 65.
MARTIN, P. E., and BARKER, E. F.	1932	*Phys. Rev.*, **41**, 291.
MIGEOTTE, M.	1948	*Phys. Rev.*, **73**, 519; also *Ap. J.*, **107**, 400.
	1949	*Phys. Rev.*, **75**, 1108.
	1953	Private communication.
MIGEOTTE, M., and NEVEN, L.	1951	*Ann. d'ap.*, **14**, 315.
	1952a	*Mém. Soc. R. Sci. Liége*, 4th ser., **12**, 165.
	1952b	*Ap. J.*, **115**, 326.
MIGEOTTE, M.; NEVEN, L.; and VIGROUX, E.	1952	*Physica*, **18**, 981.
MINNAERT, M.; MUL-DERS, G. F. W.; and HOUTGAST, J.	1940	*A Photometric Atlas of the Solar Spectrum* (Amsterdam: Schnabel, Kampert & Helm).

MITRA, S. K.   1948   *The Upper Atmosphere* ("R. Asiatic Soc. of Bengal Monograph Series," Vol. **5** [Calcutta]).

MOHLER, O. C.   1951   *Phys. Rev.*, **83**, 464.

     1952   Unpublished.

MOHLER, O. C., and
BENEDICT, W. S.   1948   *Phys. Rev.*, **74**, 702.

MOHLER, O. C.; Mc-
MATH, R. R.; and
GOLDBERG, L.   1949   *Phys. Rev.*, **75**, 520.

MOHLER, O. C., and
PIERCE, A. K.   1949   *Pub. A.S.P.*, **61**, 221.

MOHLER, O. C.; PIERCE,
A. K.; McMATH, R. R.;
and GOLDBERG, L.   1951   *Photometric Atlas of the Near Infra-red Solar Spectrum* (Ann Arbor: University of Michigan Press).

NELSON, R. C., and
BENEDICT, W. S.   1948   *Phys. Rev.*, **74**, 703.

NELSON, R. C.; PLYLER,
E. K.; and BENEDICT,
W. S.   1948   *J. Res. Nat. Bur. Stand.*, **41**, 615.

NICOLET, M.   1952   *Physics and Medicine of the Upper Atmosphere* (Albuquerque: University of New Mexico Press), chap. xii.

NICOLET, M., and
PASTIELS, R.   1952   "The Optical Study of the Earth's Atmosphere," *Mém. Soc. R. Sci. Liége*, 4th ser., **12**, 147.

NIELSEN, A. H., and
MIGEOTTE, M.   1952   *Ann d'ap.*, **15**, 134.

NIELSEN, A. H., and
NIELSEN, H. H.   1935   *Phys. Rev.*, **48**, 864.

PANETH, F. A.   1937   *Quart. J. R. Meteorol. Soc.*, **63**, 433.

PENNDORF, R.   1949   *J. Geophys. Res.*, **54**, 7.

PENNER, S. S., and
KAVANAGH, R. W.   1952   *Tech. Rept. No. 6*, Contract Nonr-220(03), NR-015-210 (California Institute of Technology).

PENNER, S. S., and
WEBER, D.   1951*a*   *J. Chem. Phys.*, **19**, 807.

     1951*b*   *Ibid.*, p. 1351.

PIETENPOL, W. B.;
RENSE, W. A.; WALZ,
F. C.; STACEY, D. S.;
and JACKSON, J. M.   1953   *Phys. Rev.*, **90**, 156.

PRESTON, W. M.   1940   *Phys. Rev.*, **57**, 887.

PRICE, W. C.   1943   *Rept. Prog. Physics*, **9**, 10.

PRICE, W. C., and
COLLINS, G.   1935   *Phys. Rev.*, **48**, 714.

REGENER, E., and
   REGENER, V. H.   1934   *Zs. f. Phys.*, **35**, 788.
REGENER, V. H.   1951   *Nature*, **167**, 276.
                   1952   *Physics and Medicine of the Upper Atmosphere*
                                 (Albuquerque: University of New Mexico Press),
                                 chap. viii, p. 109.
ROWLAND, H. A.   1895–
                   1897   *Ap. J.*, Vols. **1–6**.
RUSSELL, H. N.   1934   *Ap. J.*, **79**, 317.
ST. JOHN, C. E.; MOORE,
   C. E.; WARE, L. M.;
   ADAMS, E. F.; and
   BABCOCK, H. D.   1928   *Pub. Carnegie Inst. Washington*, No. 396.
SCHNEIDER, E. G.   1940   *J. Opt. Soc. Amer.*, **30**, 128.
SETLOW, R. B.   1948   *Phys. Rev.*, **74**, 153.
SHAW, J. H.; CHAPMAN,
   R. M.; HOWARD, J. N.;
   and OXHOLM, M. L.   1951   *Ap. J.*, **113**, 268.
SHAW, J. H.; OXHOLM,
   M. L.; and CLAASSEN,
   H. H.   1951   *Scientific Report 1A-4*, Contract No. AF19(122)65,
                                   Ohio State University.
SHAW, J. H.; SUTHER-
   LAND, G. B. B. M.; and
   WORMELL, T. W.   1948   *Phys. Rev.*, **74**, 978.
SINTON, W. M.   1952   *Phys. Rev.*, **86**, 424.
SLOBAD, R. L., and
   KROGH, M. E.   1950   *J. Amer. Chem. Soc.*, **72**, 1175.
STRONG, J., and
   BENESCH, W.   1950   *Progress Report Aug. 1*, Contract N5ori-166, Johns
                                   Hopkins University.
SWINGS, P., and MEINEL,
   A. B.   1952   *The Atmospheres of the Earth and Planets*, ed. G. P.
                                   KUIPER (rev. ed.; Chicago: University of Chi-
                                   cago Press), chap. 6.
TAKAMINE, T.; SUGA, T.;
   and TANAKA, Y.   1938   *Scient. Papers Inst. Phys. Chem. Res. Tokyo*, **34**,
                                   854.
TANAKA, Y.   1952   *J. Chem. Phys.*, **20**, 1728.
TANAKA, Y., and
   TAKAMINE, T.   1942   *Scient. Papers Inst. Phys. Chem. Res. Tokyo*, **39**,
                                   437.
THORNDIKE, A. M.   1947   *J. Chem. Phys.*, **15**, 868.
THORNDIKE, A. M.;
   WELLS, A. J.; and
   WILSON, E. B., JR.   1947   *J. Chem. Phys.*, **15**, 157.
TOUSEY, R.   1952   Private communication.

TOUSEY, R.; WATANABE,
K.; and PURCELL,
J. D.   1951   *Phys. Rev.*, **83**, 792.
TSI-ZÉ, NY, and SHIN-
PIAW, CHOONG   1933   *C.R.*, **196**, 916.
UNSÖLD, A.   1938   *Physik der Sternatmosphären* (Berlin: Julius Spring-
                                   er).
VAN DE HULST, H. C.   1945a   *Ann. d'ap.*, **8**, 1, 12.
                           1945b   *B.A.N.*, **10**, 77.
                           1952   *The Atmospheres of the Earth and Planets*, ed. G. P.
                                   KUIPER (rev. ed.; Chicago: University of Chi-
                                   cago Press), chap. 3.
VAN DER HELD, E. M. F.   1931   *Zs. f. Phys.*, **70**, 508.
VAN VLECK, J. H.   1947   *Phys. Rev.*, **71**, 413.
VASSY, A.   1938   *C.R.*, **206**, 1838.
VIGROUX, E.   1952   *C.R.*, **234**, 2351, 2439, 2529, 2592.
VIGROUX, E.; MIGEOTTE,
M.; and NEVEN, L.   1953   *Physica*, Vol. **19**, No. 1.
WATANABE, K.; INN,
E. C. Y.; and ZELI-
KOFF, M.   1952   *J. Chem. Phys.*, **20**, 1969.
WATANABE, K.; ZELI-
KOFF, M.; and INN,
E. C. Y.   1953   *Geophys. Res. Papers*, No. 21 (Cambridge, Mass.:
                                   Geophys. Research Directorate, AF Cambridge
                                   Research Center).
WATANABE, K.; ZELI-
KOFF, M.; INN,
E. C. Y.; and
TANAKA, Y.   1953   *J. Chem. Phys.*, **21**, 1026, 1643, 1648, 1651.
WATSON, W. W., and
KOONTZ, P. G.   1934   *Phys. Rev.*, **46**, 32.
WEBER, D.; HOLM, R. J.;
and PENNER, S. S.   1952   *J. Chem. Phys.*, **20**, 1820.
WEISSLER, G. L., and
LEE, PO   1952   *J. Opt. Soc. Amer.*, **42**, 200.
WEISSLER, G. L.; LEE,
PO; and MOHR, E. I.   1952   *J. Opt. Soc. Amer.*, **42**, 84.
WEISSLER, G. L., and
SUN, H.   1952   Paper presented at Pasadena meeting of the Ameri-
                                   can Physical Society, December 29.
WILLIAMS, S. E.   1940   *Nature*, **145**, 68.
WILSON, E. B., JR., and
WELLS, A. J.   1946   *J. Chem. Phys.*, **14**, 578.
WORLEY, R. E.   1943   *Phys. Rev.*, **64**, 207.
WORLEY, R. E., and
JENKINS, F. A.   1938   *Phys. Rev.*, **54**, 305.

CHAPTER 10

Density, Pressure, and Temperature Data above 30 Kilometers

By FRED L. WHIPPLE

Harvard College Observatory

1. INTRODUCTION

DURING the interval since World War II, the rate of increase of our precise knowledge concerning densities, pressures, and temperatures in the upper atmosphere has become so rapid that any review of the subject is highly dated and can remain authoritative for only a year or two. The postwar data are based primarily upon the extensive rocket program carried out by the United States Army Ordnance at the White Sands Proving Ground at Las Cruces, New Mexico, and by the Air Force at Holloman Air Force Base, Alamogordo, New Mexico, with the aid of a number of research groups who have instrumented the rockets. These results have proved so definitive with regard to conditions in the upper atmosphere that the older estimates based upon less substantial information have largely become of historical interest only. The results from the double photography of meteors have continued to accumulate and have supplemented the rocket data, particularly with regard to seasonal effects and effects dependent upon geographical latitude. Furthermore, more recent studies of the anomalous propagation of sound, coupled with careful determinations of the wind fields, have provided considerably more satisfactory information than previous studies.

Hence it is the intent of the present paper to present the best results available at the present time on density, pressure, and temperature in the upper atmosphere *without* a historical summary of the previous work on the subject. The qualitative nature of the variation of temperature, pressure, and density with height was firmly established a number of years ago and has not been changed in essence, although the quantitative agreement of the other estimates with the more recent rocket measures is rather poor. Many summary articles of the earlier work on the subject have been presented, and a repetition of this material in the present paper would not add distinctly to its value. The general tendency of the newer results is to depress the prerocket temperature-curve at altitudes above about 40 km. The "Tentative Standard Atmosphere" of the National Advisory Committee for Aeronautics[1] or the Rand "atmosphere"[2] are good examples of the earlier estimates.

The rocket research in the United States has been guided by an unofficial scientific group called "The Upper Atmosphere Rocket Research Panel," established early in 1946. At that time the program concerned the firing of a number of German V-2 rockets. The early instrumentation was severely hampered by an understanding that the rockets would deteriorate below a usable level within approximately a year. As the general research program continued, the United States Aerobee and Viking rockets were developed, while the deterioration of the V-2 rockets was counteracted by the replacements of many delicate parts. Hence the instrumentation of the upper-atmospheric sounding rockets became progressively more leisurely and more thorough, comprising many extremely complicated mechanisms of great scientific perfection. By August, 1954, some 67 V-2 rockets, 120 Aerobees, 11 Vikings, and 27 Deacons had been fired in this program, and most of these carried instrumentation for upper-atmospheric measurements. The Deacon rockets were launched from balloons, to extend their operational ceiling.

The results of the present paper depend primarily upon the combined rocket results presented by the Rocket Panel.[3] At the time this compilation was made, during the first part of 1952, this panel consisted of the following members: Chairman, Dr. J. A. Van Allen, State University of Iowa; Secretary, Mr. G. Megerian, General Electric Company; Dr. L. A. Delsasso, Ballistics Research Laboratory; Professor W. G. Dow, University of Michigan; Dr. M. Ference, Jr., Signal Corps Engineering Laboratory; Dr. C. F. Green, General Electric Company; Dr. H. E. Newell, Jr., Naval Research Laboratory; Dr. M. D. O'Day, Air Force Cambridge Research Center; Dr. W. H. Pickering, California Institute of Technology; and Dr. F. L. Whipple, Harvard College Observatory.

1. C. N. Warfield, *Tech. Note, Nat. Adv. Comm. Aero.*, No. 1200 (1947).

2. G. Grimminger, *Report No. 105* (Santa Monica, Calif.: Rand Corporation, 1948).

3. Rocket Panel, "Pressures, Densities and Temperatures in the Upper Atmosphere," *Phys. Rev.*, **88**, 1027, 1952.

Several of the groups, specifically the Naval Research Laboratory group, through the courtesy of R. J. Havens, and the University of Michigan group, under a contract with the United States Air Force, through the courtesy of H. S. Sicinski, have permitted the writer to make use of certain of their data in advance of publication. In addition, L. J. Jacchia, of the Massachusetts Institute of Technology, has made available tentative reductions of the meteor data obtained in New Mexico by the Harvard Meteor Project under the auspices of the United States Naval Bureau of Ordnance and the United States Office of Naval Research. Otherwise the data of the present paper are from relatively recent publications in the general literature.

It is difficult to appreciate the huge amount of effort that has been expended in the instrumentation and firing of these upper-atmospheric research vehicles. The extremely expensive "overhead" of the program has been carried by the three branches of the United States Department of Defense, and almost all the funds for the special instrumentation and analysis have been government funds allotted to academic research groups, commercial research groups, and the research laboratories of the three services.

2. PRINCIPLES AND BACKGROUND DATA
OF ROCKET RESEARCH

The trajectory of each rocket is determined with rather high precision by optical, photographic, and electronic techniques. From these observations it is possible to deduce the velocity and position of the rocket at any given instant during flight with acceptable accuracy. However, all rockets tend to roll about their major axis with a period of only a few seconds, and in many cases they "tumble" about a minor axis. Recently it has become possible to determine the aspect of the rocket itself, in terms of the Eulerian angles as functions of the time. While both legs of the flight were usually recorded, in many cases only the upward flight has been evaluated, being of greater interest to the research groups involved. The techniques for determining aspect use either a solar or a terrestrial reference frame. They are of four types: (1) external photography of the earth's surface and horizon including the sun; (2) photoelectric sensing of the sun; (3) use of free gyroscopes; and (4) geomagnetic-field angular orientation.

The actual physical measurements in the upper atmosphere have most commonly been made by extremely sensitive pressure gauges placed at various positions on the rocket, but in one case by probes placed near the nose of the rocket to establish the shock-wave angle. The various gauges are read mechanically at short intervals of time, usually several times a second, and the results telemetered by radio means to the ground, where they are recorded for future analysis. Sometimes missile-borne cameras photograph equipment during the flight. In approximately five firings, explosive grenades have been released at various altitudes along the trajectory, and the velocity of sound at the various layers was determined by the instant of reception of the sounds from the explosions at a number of stations on the ground. Recently, falling spheres dropped from rockets have also been used.

At a selected position on the surface of the rocket near the base, the measured pressure equals the ambient pressure when the rocket is in steady flight along its major axis. Such measures have been made in approximately 9 firings by R. Havens, R. Koll, and H. LaGow, of the Naval Research Laboratory.[4] These investigators have, in addition, determined the ram pressure in the nose of the rocket. From this ram pressure, by means of a series expansion, they have shown that the measured pressure can be combined with the known velocity of the rocket to derive a measurement of the ambient atmospheric density. Since the ram pressure normally exceeds the ambient air pressure, the latter method can be utilized at greater altitudes than the former and is particularly valuable at extreme altitudes, where the pressure arising from degassing of the rocket greatly exceeds the ambient air pressure. This unfortunate circumstance begins before an altitude of 100 km is reached and becomes quite excessive at the maximum altitude so far obtained—219 km by the Naval Research Laboratory with a Viking rocket. Under these circumstances the combination of rocket motion and roll has made it possible for the "ambient-pressure measures" near the base of the rocket to provide information on rocket orientation, in addition to determinations of ambient atmospheric density.

Investigators H. S. Sicinski, N. W. Spencer, and W. G. Dow, of the University of Michigan, under a contract with the United States Air Force,[5] have applied similar techniques with extremely sensitive pressure gauges. They locate the pressure gauges on a special conical nose of the rocket at the tip and a short distance from the tip. By applying the Taylor-Maccoll theory for conical flow regimes as tabulated by Z. Kopal, they have been able to determine the Mach number, M, of the rocket by direct measures. This method becomes difficult when the yaw angle of the rocket

4. *J. Geophys. Res.*, **57**, 59, 1952.

5. H. S. Sicinski *et al.*, *J. Appl. Phys.*, **25**, 161, 1954.

is greater than the cone angle. The probable errors with this technique are about $\pm 5°$ K. The same group is using the flow properties about a circular cone, being recorded through a pair of small metal flags placed near the cone, combined with position and aspect data of the rocket. This method, proposed by Sicinski, avoids the degassing and conductance problems affecting gauges and also avoids the need for high-vacuum calibrations.

A second group at the University of Michigan, consisting of F. L. Bartman, V. C. Liu, and E. J. Schaefer,[6] under a contract with the United States Army Signal Corps, have, in one V-2 firing, established an array of recording probes near the nose of the rocket, in order to measure the Mach angle of the shock wave and hence the Mach number at various intervals during flight. In another method developed under the same contract, densities have been calculated from the drag of falling spheres. Four-foot inflated nylon spheres were dropped from rockets and tracked by Doppler radar during their descent.[7]

An entirely different technique has been used by the Signal Corps Engineering Laboratories of the United States Army, as reported by M. Ference.[3] In 5 night firings, extremely sensitive sound-recording equipment at the ground has determined the instants of arrival of explosions from grenades at various heights near Aerobee rockets. The differential time lags and the directions of arrival of the sounds at the ground have enabled them not only to measure the velocity of sound for intervals of 5–12 km in altitude but also to determine the mean directions of the winds in these intervals. Corrections for wind velocity were then applied to the observed velocities of sound. This last method appears to be very free from systematic errors, including the effects of averaging in height, and leads to estimates of systematic errors amounting to only about $4°$ K in the temperatures at altitudes below 70 km.

It will be seen, then, that the rocket instrumentation has measured the ambient air pressure, p, the ambient air density, ρ, the Mach number, M, or the velocity of sound, vs, as functions of the time and the altitude, during the course of various rocket firings. When combined with the true air

6. "An Aerodynamic Method of Measuring the Ambient Temperature of Air at High Altitudes," *Eng. Res. Inst., U. Michigan* (July, 1950); "Final Progress Report, Signal Corps Contract W-36-039 sc-32307," *Eng. Res. Inst., U. Michigan* (October, 1950); "Final Progress Report, Signal Corps Contract DA-36-039 sc-125," *Eng. Res. Inst., U. Michigan* (February, 1952).

7. F. L. Bartman *et al.*, "Falling Sphere Method for Upper Air Density and Temperature," *Rocket Exploration of the Upper Atmosphere*, ed. R. L. F. Boyd and M. J. Seaton (London: Pergamon Press, 1954).

velocity of the vehicle, the Mach number gives immediately the ambient velocity of sound.

Since descriptions of the upper-atmospheric conditions most often involve the temperature, T, as a parameter, it is important to note the relationship between the measured quantities and the true value of the ambient temperature as defined by the laws of a perfect gas. A series of measurements of ambient *pressure* as a function of height, h, leads to a determination of temperature through the following equation:

$$\frac{d \ln p}{dh} = -\frac{1}{H} = -\frac{g\mu}{RT},$$ (1)

where g is the local acceleration of gravity, μ the mean molecular weight of the atmosphere, R the gas constant, and H the scale height.

In case a series of measurements of ambient *density* as a function of height is available, the temperature can be derived from Boyle's law:

$$\rho = \frac{\mu p}{RT},$$ (2)

which, when combined with equation (1), yields, after integration,

$$T = \frac{\mu}{R\rho} \int_\infty^h g\rho dh.$$ (3)

When the *velocity of sound* is known, either directly or by means of the Mach number, then the temperature is given by

$$v_s^2 = \frac{\gamma RT}{\mu} = \frac{\gamma p}{\rho},$$ (4)

where γ is the ratio of specific heats for the atmosphere.

Thus we see that, regardless of whether p, ρ, or v_s is measured, the atmospheric temperature can be expressed as a known function of one of these quantities multiplied by the mean molecular weight, μ. In case M or v_s is measured, the temperature also involves the ratio of specific heats. Since γ varies so slowly with most characteristics of likely atmospheric gases, there is little hope that it can be determined by the intercomparison of measured values of v_s, p, and ρ. In all rocket measures to date, the temperature depends linearly upon an arbitrarily assumed value of the mean molecular weight in or near the region in question.

It is obviously important, then, to examine present knowledge concerning the mean molecular weight in the upper atmosphere. Few facts are known beyond an altitude of about 70 km. The University of Michigan workers, L. M. Jones and colleagues, under an Army Signal Corps contract, have set up and recovered a number of sampling bottles, which have been analyzed for a change in mean molecular weight with altitude. In the altitude region from 64 to 70 km they were particularly successful with the air samples taken directly from the steel sampling bottles used in flight—without intermediate storage in glass bottles, as had been done previously. The air samples so obtained have been analyzed by K. F. Chackett, F. A. Paneth, P. Reasbeck, and B. S. Wiborg. They found that near the highest altitude the He/N_2 ratio is increased by about a factor of 2, while there is a correspondingly small increase in the Ne/N_2 ratio and a decrease in the A/N_2 ratio. More recent samples, taken between 60 and 93 km, have on the whole confirmed this result; there is no change in composition up to 60 km, where an apparent change sets in that seems to increase with elevation. However, the Michigan group found evidence that the sampling technique itself might lead to diffusive separation, and the atmospheric results are considered uncertain pending further research.[8]

Previous efforts to discover true variations in the mean molecular weight of the upper atmosphere at somewhat lower altitudes showed no change whatsoever from the mean ground values for dry air.[9] Thus we must conclude that the change in mean molecular weight is exceedingly small to an altitude of at least 70 km and that it may change slowly beyond. Above 80 km it is possible that the change in mean molecular weight takes place more rapidly, not only because of the possible dissociation of O_2 in these regions during daylight hours, but also because the temperature gradient in the atmosphere appears definitely to be positive with altitude and might permit more diffusion by reducing vertical circulation. On the other hand, it is well known that the winds in the upper atmosphere from this level to 100 km are fairly strong, as measured by the motions of persistent meteor trains in the analysis of C. P. Olivier.[10] Furthermore, the winds appear to increase in violence with greater altitude, as evidenced by the investigation of A. Maxwell and C. G. Little.[11] By establishing from moment to moment the time variations in absorption by the F-layer of 80-Mc radiation from radio star fluctuations at several stations, these investigators find that the average horizontal velocity is of

8. L. M. Jones, "The Measurement of Diffusive Separation in the Upper Atmosphere," *Rocket Exploration of the Upper Atmosphere*, ed. R. L. F. Boyd and M. J. Seaton (London: Pergamon Press, 1954).

9. K. F. Chackett, F. A. Paneth, and E. J. Wilson, *J. Atm. and Terr. Phys.*, 1, 49, 1950.

10. "Long Enduring Meteor Trains," *Proc. Amer. Phil. Soc.*, 85, 93, 1941–1942; "Long Enduring Meteor Trains: Second Paper," *ibid.*, 91, 315, 1947.

11. *Nature*, 169, 746, 1952.

the order of 350 km/hour; they record velocities up to 1400 km/hour. The meteor-train velocities average 203 km/hour in the altitude region from 80 to 104 km (night trains) and 173 km/hour from 27 to 77 km (twilight and daytime trains). See also chapter 13.

At the moment, then, there is no complete theory or reliable measures of the variation of mean molecular weight with altitude in the upper atmosphere. The Rocket Panel chose arbitrarily to carry out most of their analysis on the basis of a constant mean molecular weight of 28.966. They have included, however, estimates of the mean molecular weight based upon the assumption of a linear dissociation of O_2 in the altitude range from 80 to 120 km and a linear dissociation of N_2 from 120 km to 220 km. The uncertainty in the mean molecular weight becomes progressively greater with altitude. Since estimates of the diffusion effects depend markedly upon circulation patterns as well as temperature, it is extremely difficult to make any reliable estimate at altitudes much above 100 km. We shall therefore follow the pattern of the Rocket Panel in treating temperature and mean molecular weight in the upper atmosphere and discuss the problem largely in terms of "T_{29}," defined as the temperature calculated from p, ρ, or v_s on the basis of an assumed $\mu = 28.966$ gm mol^{-1}.

It is unfortunate that no intercomparison of the presently observed quantities in the upper atmosphere can lead to a determination of the mean molecular weight. When measurements of kinetic temperatures by molecular radiations of the atmosphere lead to reliable values at known heights, these temperatures can be combined with the observed rocket data to provide accurate information concerning the mean molecular weight as a function of altitude. At the moment we must await more complete analysis of the observed molecular radiations of the night sky before such calculations can be trusted. For a discussion of these problems, see chapter 11, Sections 3.4 and 4.4.

3. THE ROCKET DATA

The results of this section are taken directly from the Rocket Panel report[3] through the courtesy of the *Physical Review*. Although any investigator who might choose to set up mean values of the atmospheric parameters as a function of height might adopt a different mean curve than that presented here, it would appear that the combined judgment of the actual investigators who obtained the fundamental data should, at the moment at least, be given the highest weight with regard to the mean values. The observed data averaged for each investigation group separately were transformed into temperatures ($T_{29}°$ K) and presented as the observed

T_{29} in Table 1 as a function of height at 5-km intervals to 100 km and at 10-km intervals to 160 km. A weight of 4 for each independent method and a weight of 1 for each firing were used in combining the observed temperatures from the various groups. The significance of the weights decreases with increasing altitude; above 80 km the results depend almost entirely upon the Naval Research Laboratory (NRL) determinations of density from ram pressure. Four firings provide the data to 156 km, and the single

TABLE 1*

OBSERVED AND ADOPTED TEMPERATURES (° K, $\mu = 28.966$)

Height h (km)	NRL	SCEL	UMAF	UMSC	Weighted Mean	Adopted
30.....	232(12)	235(9)	230(6)	227(5)	231.7(32)	231.7
35.....	249(12)	249(9)	238(6)	234(5)	244.6(32)	244.5
40.....	264(12)	260(9)	271(6)	253(5)	262.5(32)	262.5
45.....	273(12)	264(9)	272(6)	278(5)	271.1(32)	271.3
50.....	280(12)	260(9)	268(6)	....	270.7(27)	270.8
55.....	278(12)	252(9)	258(5)	....	265.2(26)	265.8
60.....	262(12)	243(9)	238(5)	....	250.8(26)	252.8
65.....	248(12)	238(9)	209(5)	....	237.0(26)	235.0
70.....	228(12)	218(9)	189(5)	....	217.0(26)	218.0
75.....	208(12)	227(9)	185(5)	....	210.2(26)	209.1
80.....	200 (8)	213(5)	....	....	205.0(13)	205.0
85.....	205	....	....	....	205	208.9
90.....	216	....	....	....	216	217.0
95.....	229	....	....	....	229	227.5
100.....	240	....	....	....	240	240.0
110.....	270	....	....	....	270	270.0
120.....	330	....	....	....	330	330.0
130.....	390	....	....	....	390	390.0
140.....	450	....	....	....	450	447.0
150.....	500	....	....	....	500	503.0
160.....	560	....	....	....	560	560.0
219.....	†	....	....	....	900†	900.9†

* Abbreviations in second to fifth columns are as follows: NRL = Naval Research Laboratory, R. Havens, R. Koll, and H. LaGow; SCEL = Signal Corps Engineering Laboratories, U.S. Army, M. Ference; UMAF = University of Michigan, Air Force, H. S. Sicinski, N. W. Spencer, and W. G. Dow; and UMSC = University of Michigan, Signal Corps. Figures in () are weights.
† See text for basis.

firing on August 7, 1951, provides a density measure at 219 km. The adopted temperature at 219 km is highly arbitrary and was obtained on the basis of a constant rate of increase in the scale height above 160 km. The weighted mean values of T_{29} in the sixth column of Table 1 were arbitrarily smoothed to provide the adopted values of T_{29} in the last column. The smoothing was done to expedite numerical integration of the upper-atmospheric parameters and should not be confused with true accuracy.

For the purposes of such numerical integration the adopted values of

T_{29}, $\log_{10} p$, and $\log_{10} \rho$ are given in Table 2 as functions of altitude at 2-km steps to 110 km, at 5-km steps to 160 km, and at 10-km steps to 220 km. The table begins at the sea-level altitude of the White Sands Proving Ground, and the values of the parameters below 30 km were adopted from radio sound-balloon measures made from the White Sands Proving Ground by Detachment 19-14L of the United States 19th Weather Squadron and by the United States Army Signal Corps. Apparently, a mean yearly ground pressure was used in establishing this table, and the

TABLE 2*

ADOPTED ATMOSPHERIC DATA

Height (Sea-Level) (km)	Tem-perature ($\mu = $ 28.966) ° K	Pressure ($\log_{10}$) (dynes/cm²)	Density ($\log_{10}$) (gm/cm³)	Height (Sea-Level) (km)	Tem-perature ($\mu = $ 28.966) ° K	Pressure ($\log_{10}$) (dynes/cm²)	Density ($\log_{10}$) (gm/cm³)
1.216..	291.0	5.945	− 2.977	72......	213.6	1.650	− 7.138
2......	282.0	5.905	− 3.003	74......	210.5	1.513	− 7.268
4......	272.6	5.799	− 3.095	76......	207.9	1.375	− 7.401
6......	260.0	5.688	− 3.185	78......	205.8	1.235	− 7.536
8......	245.0	5.571	− 3.276	80......	205.0	1.094	− 7.676
10......	230.8	5.446	− 3.375	82......	205.8	0.953	− 7.818
12......	219.5	5.315	− 3.484	84......	207.7	0.814	− 7.962
14......	211.6	5.178	− 3.606	86......	210.3	0.675	− 8.105
16......	208.0	5.037	− 3.739	88......	213.5	0.539	− 8.248
18......	209.0	4.895	− 3.883	90......	217.0	0.405	− 8.389
20......	212.8	4.755	− 4.030	92......	220.7	0.274	− 8.528
22......	216.7	4.618	− 4.176	94......	225.0	0.144	− 8.666
24......	220.9	4.484	− 4.318	96......	230.0	0.018	− 8.802
26......	225.1	4.352	− 4.458	98......	235.0	−0.106	− 8.935
28......	228.5	4.222	− 4.594	100......	240.0	−0.227	− 9.065
30......	231.7	4.095	− 4.728	102......	245.0	−0.345	− 9.192
32......	235.7	3.969	− 4.861	104......	250.0	−0.461	− 9.317
34......	241.2	3.846	− 4.994	106......	255.0	−0.575	− 9.440
36......	248.1	3.726	− 5.126	108......	261.0	−0.686	− 9.561
38......	255.6	3.610	− 5.256	110......	270.0	−0.794	− 9.684
40......	262.5	3.497	− 5.380	115......	300.0	−1.045	− 9.981
42......	267.6	3.386	− 5.499	120......	330.0	−1.273	−10.249
44......	270.5	3.278	− 5.612	125......	360.0	−1.480	−10.495
46......	271.7	3.170	− 5.722	130......	390.0	−1.670	−10.720
48......	271.6	3.062	− 5.829	135......	419.0	−1.845	−10.927
50......	270.8	2.955	− 5.936	140......	447.0	−2.009	−11.119
52......	269.7	2.847	− 6.042	145......	475.0	−2.163	−11.299
54......	267.6	2.738	− 6.147	150......	503.0	−2.308	−11.468
56......	263.7	2.629	− 6.250	155......	531.0	−2.445	−11.629
58......	258.6	2.517	− 6.353	160......	560.0	−2.574	−11.781
60......	252.8	2.404	− 6.457	170......	618.7	−2.813	−12.062
62......	246.5	2.287	− 6.563	180......	676.9	−3.030	−12.318
64......	239.0	2.167	− 6.669	190......	734.9	−3.228	−12.552
66......	231.0	2.044	− 6.778	200......	792.5	−3.411	−12.768
68......	223.2	1.916	− 6.891	210......	849.8	−3.580	−12.968
70......	218.0	1.784	− 7.012	220......	906.6	−3.738	−13.154

*The empirical data are p, ρ, and T/μ. The smoothing of all these was done in T/μ, from which p and ρ were then recomputed.

values of T_{29} and $\log_{10} \rho$ are consistent with these values but do not represent mean temperatures or mean densities near the ground.

In Tables 1 and 2, the observed data are uncorrected for the time of year in which they occur, in case seasonal effects are present, and they depend, as stated above, upon the assumed value of the mean molecular weight equal to 28.966 gm mol^{-1}. The interrelations among the quantities in Tables 1 and 2 were based upon equations (1), (2), and (4), with the gravity taken as 979.15 cm/sec^2 at the altitude of the White Sands Proving Ground, 1.2165 km above mean sea-level and varying inversely as the square of the distance from the earth's center. The gas constant, R, was adopted as 8.31436×10^7 ergs/deg mol; the absolute temperature as $273°16$ at $0°$ C; and the mean pressure at the altitude of the White Sands Proving Ground as 0.881×10^6 dynes/cm^2. The rocket firing range is roughly at latitude $33°$ N. and longitude $106°$ W.

Figures 1, 2, and 3 were also taken from the Rocket Panel report and present, respectively, the observed and derived temperatures (T_{29}) as a function of the height in kilometers, the $\log_{10} p$ (dynes/cm^2), and $\log_{10} \rho$ (gm/cm^3), all as functions of the height in kilometers. The figures stop at a height of 160 km, since the results already become somewhat uncertain at this altitude.

An inspection of the adopted data in Tables 1 and 2 and Figures 1, 2, and 3 shows that the mean temperature in the atmosphere rises rather uniformly from about 17 km to 48 km, reaching a maximum of about $0°$ C. The curve then falls off smoothly to a minimum at about 80 km, where $T_{29} = 205°$ K; the temperature rises with a continuing acceleration to $T_{29} = 560°$ K at 160 km. The densities and pressures are roughly 10^{-6} times the sea-level values at 100 km and $10^{-10} \times$ at 220 km.

A comparison of the observed and adopted values in the figures shows that there are appreciable systematic differences among the various methods of determining temperature (T_{29}) which are probably greater than the combined errors expected from the internal consistencies and actual variations in the atmosphere from time to time. It is difficult to appraise the significance of these deviations in methodology and instrumentation. Presumably, a more complete analysis by the Rocket Panel will be required to establish the nature of the systematic deviations that have crept into the results.

The Rocket Panel points out that no clear-cut seasonal effects are indicated from the rocket data but that marked variations within a few hours are known to occur in the atmospheric temperatures around the 70-km level. These were definitely established by the Signal Corps Engineering

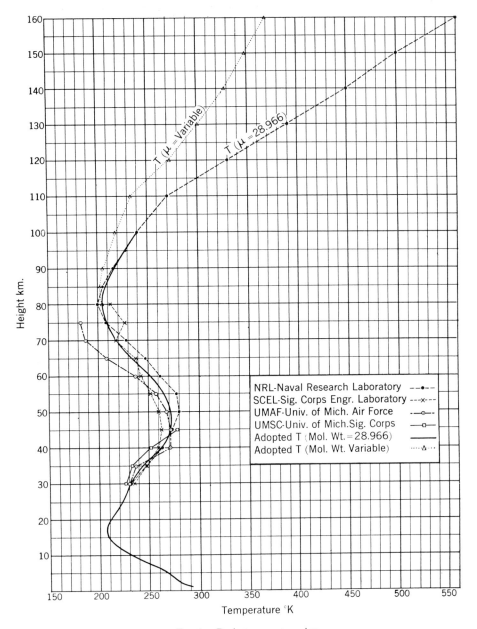

Fig. 1.—Basic temperature data

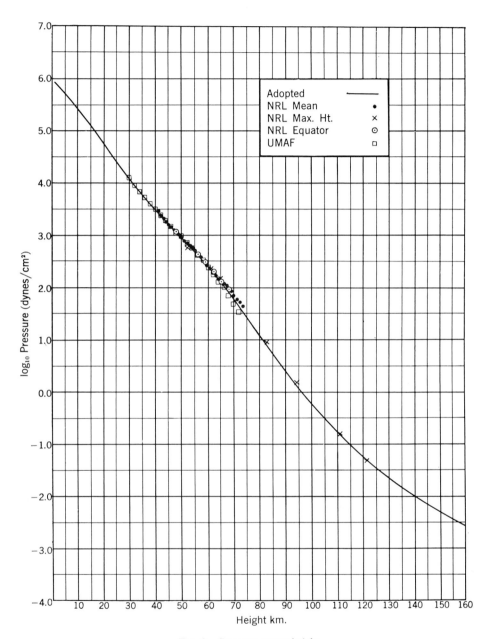

FIG. 2.—Pressure versus height

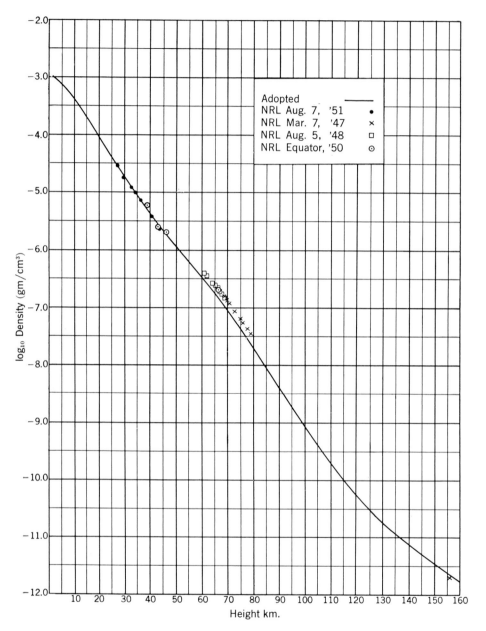

FIG. 3.—Density versus height

Laboratories group between two firings made on a single night in December, 1950. It is the opinion of the Rocket Panel that the adopted mean curve of T_{29} versus h is far smoother and represents much less range in temperature between the maximum at 47 km and the minimum at 80 km than is true at any instant chosen at random. They express the belief that the actual curve relating T_{29} with h probably shows at any given moment a much sharper peak near the 50-km level and that the height of the peak may range over 10 or more km. Similarly, the minimum at 80 km at any given instant is also probably sharper and ranges in height by a comparable amount. They suggest that a double maximum is quite possible and that the curve is probably irregular and serrated at any given instant.

Derived atmospheric data from the Rocket Panel report are presented in Table 3. Here μ is assumed to vary as described above, allowing for dissociation of O_2 in the range 80–120 km and N_2 in the range 120–220 km. The table gives in successive columns the height (sea-level) to 220 km, the adopted values of μ, the derived values of the temperature on the basis of the adopted values of T_{29} and μ, the scale height defined by equation (1) (which is independent of the assumed value of μ), the acceleration of gravity used in the previous calculations, and the mean free path. This last quantity is calculated from an adopted value of 7.37×10^{-6} cm in a standard sea-level atmosphere and is assumed to vary inversely as the number of particles per unit volume. The calculations neglect all effects of ionization. The temperature with variable molecular weight is plotted in Figure 1.

Perhaps the most interesting data given in Table 3 are those of mean free path, which reaches 1 cm at about 85 km, 1 m near 140 km, and almost 1 km at 220 km.

The temperatures in Table 3 are, of course, directly proportional to the assumed mean molecular weight; the true values may vary markedly from the derived ones, particularly at altitudes above 120 km. The mean free path will depend upon the density divided by the mean molecular weight, so long as one neglects the variation in cross-sectional area depending upon the natures of the individual atmospheric particles.

4. VARIATIONS WITH TIME AND PLACE

4.1. DIURNAL EFFECTS

Figure 1 shows that the upper-atmospheric temperatures obtained by the Naval Research Laboratory tend to lie systematically above those obtained by the Signal Corps Engineering Laboratories. The differences between these two sets of measures may arise from systematic effects introduced by the difference in methodology, but it is worth while to note that the NRL data were all obtained in the daytime, while those of the SCEL were all obtained at night. Possibly, therefore, a diurnal effect may exist, in the sense that the upper-atmospheric temperatures are greater in the daytime than at night. Probably, however, the effect is very much smaller than the systematic difference between these two sets of measures. From

TABLE 3

ATMOSPHERIC DATA FOR μ VARIABLE*

Height (Sea-Level) (km)	Adopted Mol. Wt. (gm/mol)	Temperature (° K)	Scale Height (km)	Accel. Gravity (cm/sec²)	Mean Free Path (cm)
1.216	28.97	291.0	8.53	979.2	8.6×10^{-6}
5	28.97	276.8	7.83	978.0	1.2×10^{-5}
10	28.97	230.8	6.78	976.5	2.1×10^{-5}
15	28.97	209.1	6.16	974.9	4.2×10^{-5}
20	28.97	212.8	6.28	973.4	9.7×10^{-5}
25	28.97	223.0	6.59	971.9	2.2×10^{-4}
30	28.97	231.7	6.85	970.4	4.8×10^{-4}
35	28.97	244.5	7.24	968.9	1.0×10^{-3}
40	28.97	262.5	7.79	967.3	2.2×10^{-3}
45	28.97	271.3	8.06	965.8	4.2×10^{-3}
50	28.97	270.8	8.06	964.3	7.8×10^{-3}
55	28.97	265.8	7.93	962.8	1.4×10^{-2}
60	28.97	252.8	7.55	961.3	2.6×10^{-2}
65	28.97	235.0	7.03	959.8	4.8×10^{-2}
70	28.97	218.0	6.53	958.4	9.3×10^{-2}
75	28.97	209.1	6.27	956.9	2.0×10^{-1}
80	28.97	205.0	6.16	955.4	4.3×10^{-1}
85	28.23	203.6	6.29	953.9	9.5×10^{-1}
90	27.52	206.2	6.54	952.4	2.1
95	26.86	210.9	6.87	951.0	4.5
100	26.22	217.3	7.26	949.5	9.5
110	25.03	233.3	8.19	946.6	3.8×10^1
120	23.95	272.8	10.04	943.6	1.3×10^2
130	22.50	302.9	11.90	940.7	3.7×10^2
140	21.21	327.3	13.68	937.9	8.7×10^2
150	20.06	348.4	15.44	935.0	1.8×10^3
160	19.34	368.0	17.24	932.1	3.6×10^3
170	18.10	386.7	19.11	929.3	6.1×10^3
180	17.26	403.4	20.97	926.4	1.0×10^4
190	16.50	418.5	22.84	923.6	1.8×10^4
200	15.79	432.1	24.70	920.8	3.0×10^4
210	15.15	444.4	26.57	918.0	5.1×10^4
220	14.55	455.5	28.43	915.2	8.7×10^4

* The p and ρ data of Table 2 are not changed, since T/μ remains the same.

no other source is there clear-cut evidence of an appreciable night-day effect.

The results of the Harvard photographic meteor program[12] show no

12. F. L. Whipple, L. Jacchia, and Z. Kopal, "Seasonal Variations in the Density of the Upper Atmosphere," *The Atmospheres of the Earth and Planets*, ed. G. P. Kuiper (Chicago: University of Chicago Press, 1949), pp. 149–158; L. Jacchia, "Atmospheric Density Profile

indication of a systematic variation in upper-atmospheric density as a function of hours after sunset. C. L. Pekeris,[13] however, has recently predicted second-order atmospheric oscillations with a period of 6 hours around the 80–100-km level. The density measurements by photographic meteors suggest (vaguely) the reality of the effect, with the phase of minimum density near local midnight; but many more data are required to establish the effect as a reality.

4.2. SEASONAL EFFECTS

The rocket data show no clear-cut seasonal effects in pressure, density, or temperature. The NRL data[14] of Figure 4 indicate the random seasonal character of the NRL measures of pressure by rockets. On the other hand, the SCEL temperature measurements made in the summer and winter seasons suggest that the temperatures in the 60-km zone may be higher in summer than in winter.

The photographic meteor data, on the other hand, show clearly that over Massachusetts the upper-atmospheric densities are greater in summer than in winter.[12] The correlation is made in terms of the residuals in $\log_{10} \rho$ between the meteoric observations and a standard atmosphere. Such residuals, within the accuracy of measurement, plot linearly against the ground temperature at Boston, as shown in Figure 5. The average height of the meteors in Figure 5 is 78 km. In a more detailed analysis of the photographic meteor data over Massachusetts (42°5 N.), L. Jacchia[12] finds that the effect decreases with height in such a fashion that the total yearly mean amplitude in $\log_{10} \rho$ is 0.43 at a mean height of 64 km; 0.29 at 77 km; 0.14 at 87 km; and 0.12 at 95 km. Since the probable error in the amplitude is of the order of 0.1, the derived seasonal variation above 80 km has little statistical significance.

Another independent method of investigating the seasonal effects in the upper atmosphere has been reported upon by A. P. Crary.[15] Here the anomalous propagation of sound has been measured from a large number of explosions produced by bombs dropped from aircraft. The method was applied in the Canal Zone, near Bermuda, and in Alaska. The method is of

---

and Variations from the Study of Meteor Trajectories," *Technical Report*, No. 2 ("Harvard Reprint Series," (Vol. **2**, No. 26 [1948]); L. Jacchia, "Atmospheric Density Profile and Gradients from Early Parts of Photographic Meteor Trails," *Tech. Report*, No. 4 ("Harvard Reprint Series," Vol. **2**, No. 32 [1949]).

13. *Tech. Note, Nat. Adv. Comm. Aero.*, No. 2314 (March, 1951).

14. R. Havens, R. Koll, and H. LaGow, *Pressures and Temperatures in the Earth's Upper Atmosphere* (reprint; Naval Research Laboratory, March, 1950).

15. *J. Meteorol.*, **7**, 233, 1950.

particular interest because of the great attention that was given to the
determination of upper-atmosphere wind fields, which so markedly affect
the results of anomalous propagation experiments. Winter-summer values
were compared only in Alaska during the winter of 1948 and the summer
of 1949. The resultant curves of T_{29} versus h are shown in Figure 6. It will
be seen that a marked increase in the temperature is shown at all altitudes
studied during the summer, as compared to the winter. This would pro-

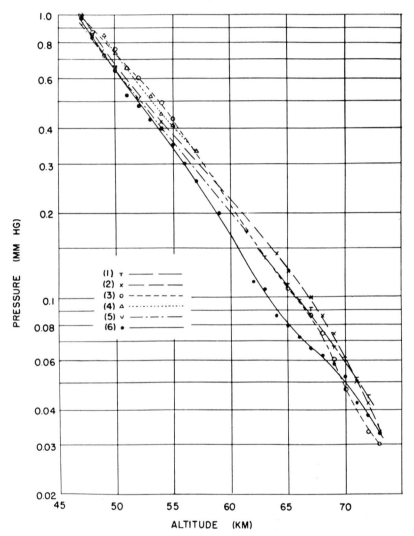

FIG. 4.—Results of Naval Research rocket firings. Dates: (*1*) October 10, 1946, 1102
M.S.T.; (*2*) March 7, 1947, 1123 M.S.T.; (*3*) January 22, 1948, 1313 M.S.T.; (*4*) August 5,
1948, 1837 M.S.T.; (*5*) January 28, 1949, 1020 M.S.T.; (*6*) May 3, 1949, 0914 M.S.T.

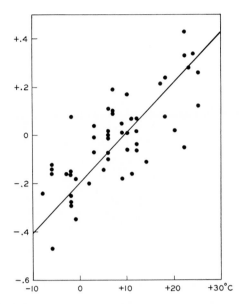

FIG. 5.—Combined residual-temperature data for meteors. *Abscissae: T° C* at ground; *ordinates:* Δ log ρ.

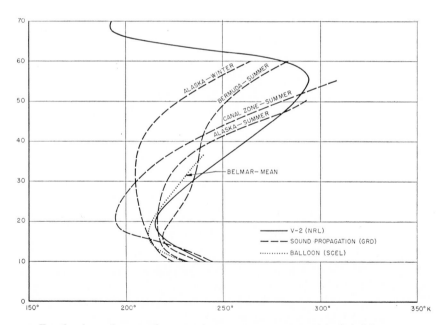

FIG. 6.—Anomolous sound-propagation temperatures versus altitude in kilometers

duce seasonal variations of density in the upper atmosphere above the 60-km level, in the sense indicated by the meteor results.

It is interesting to note that in unpublished results made near the White Sands Proving Ground (33° N.) by the Harvard Meteor Expedition under the auspices of the United States Naval Bureau of Ordnance and the Office of Naval Research, L. Jacchia has found more evidence confirming the seasonal effects, of much the same character as that over Massachusetts. Furthermore, H. Wexler predicts that an effect of the same order and sense as indicated by the meteor data would be expected on theoretical grounds.[16]

Summarizing, we note that although the rocket data are not specific with regard to seasonal effects, the meteor observations indicate such effects over New Mexico and over Massachusetts, while the measures by the anomalous propagation of sound indicate a similar effect over Alaska. The atmospheric densities at the 60–80-km level are greater in summer than in winter; the atmospheric-temperature increase in summer to produce this effect appears to occur at lower altitudes. As yet no clear-cut indication of the temperature changes above 60 km is available.

4.3. Variations Dependent upon Geographic Position

Unpublished tentative results of the Harvard Meteor Expedition by L. Jacchia indicate that the mean densities in the upper atmosphere from 60 to 90 km are lower by roughly 0.15 in $\log_{10} \rho$ over New Mexico (33° N.) than over Massachusetts (42°.5 N.). On the other hand, as seen in Figure 2, equatorial measures of upper-atmospheric pressures by the Naval Research Laboratory indicate no systematic effect between the equator and the area of White Sands. But over the latitude range of the Canal Zone (9° N.), Bermuda (33° N.), and Alaska (65° N.), Crary finds, from studies of the anomalous propagation of sound, that there is an appreciable dependence on latitude during the summer months. From his measures of atmospheric temperature, the atmospheric densities above 60 km would increase with increasing northerly latitude (see Fig. 6). Unfortunately, he finds that the Bermuda data are not entirely consistent internally, and the comparison rests largely upon the data of the Canal Zone and Alaska.

We see, then, that there is no evidence of a change in upper-atmospheric temperatures between the equator and latitude 33° N. but that the meteoric and acoustic data do indicate increasing temperatures above 40 km with increasing northerly latitude and concomitant increasing densities

16. *Tellus*, **2**, 262, 1950.

above 40–60 km. No other homogeneous data dependent upon latitude are at present available.

It should be noted that the effects suggested above are not necessarily dependent solely upon latitude but also may be affected by the nature of the geographic surfaces beneath. The difficulties that Crary mentions in investigations over Bermuda may arise from the absence of a continental mass in the neighborhood. At this early stage it would be unwise to ascribe the geographical variations discussed here entirely to latitude effects.

4.4. Nonperiodic Variations

Because of the difficulties of the observations of upper-atmospheric parameters, little is known precisely about their nonperiodic variations from moment to moment. The results of the United States Signal Corps Engineering Laboratories during one night of December, 1950, indicate that around the 60-km level changes of the order of 20° in temperature are not at all impossible over an interval of a few hours. The individual meteoric data include such large random variations intrinsic to the meteoroid itself that one cannot as yet deduce from them any information about random changes in the upper atmosphere. Similarly, the acoustic studies are so dependent upon the wind fields, which are known to be quite variable with time, that it again is not quite possible to be certain of variations in temperature or other upper-atmospheric parameters from moment to moment. Figure 4 shows variations in *pressure* versus *altitude* during 6 rocket firings by the Naval Research Laboratory. The corresponding derived variations in *temperature* versus *altitude* are shown in Figure 7. The indicated variations in temperature are so extremely sensitive to the precise slopes of the pressure-altitude curves that it is very difficult to decide as to the reality of the variations in temperature so derived.

In spite of the large uncertainties in the measurements, most upper-atmosphere investigators are convinced that large variations in atmospheric temperature occur at altitudes above about 40–50 km over relatively short intervals of time. The true nature of these variations must depend upon changes in the energy absorption at the various levels, as well as upon turbulence. Energy absorption will depend upon changes in the energy sources, as well as changes in the relative abundances of the absorbing molecules or atoms. Energy sources of a variable character include the diurnal and seasonal changes in the sun's general radiation, abrupt changes in the solar ultraviolet radiation, and variations in the corpuscular radiation from the sun, which is generally believed to produce the aurora.

On the basis of energy considerations, then, one would expect the largest variations in the upper atmosphere to occur where (1) absorption of solar energy (particularly in the far ultraviolet) is largest per unit mass of atmosphere; (2) the abundances of absorbing particles are most variable; and (3) corpuscular energy from the sun is most effective in heating.

Clearly, the variations at very high altitudes (> 100 km) must be quite large, as usually observed in ionospheric activities, in variations of the earth's magnetic field, and in auroral activity.

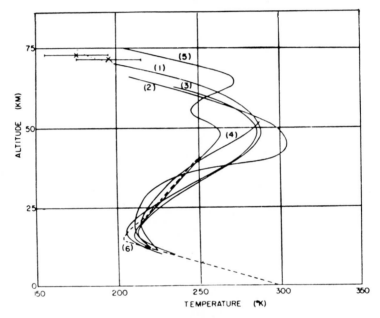

Fig. 7.—Curves of T versus h by the Naval Research Laboratory. Dates: (*1*) March 7, 1947, 1123 M.S.T.; (*2*) January 22, 1948, 1313 M.S.T.; (*3*) August 5, 1948, 1837 M.S.T.; (*4*) January 28, 1949, 1020 M.S.T.; (*5*) May 3, 1949, 0914 M.S.T.; (*6*) balloon flight, September 28, 1948.

At altitudes below 100 km one should expect considerable variation at the upper limit of the ozone layer, from 40 to 60 km, since the abundance of ozone here must be variable. The effects of all such variation on upper-atmospheric temperatures may not increase very rapidly with height below the E-region, since near 80 km there appears to be a minimum of heat absorption directly from the sun. In the region where upper-atmospheric density, pressure, or temperature is most directly measured (30–80 km) it is probable that variations in ozone content and the resultant turbulence are primarily responsible for short-term nonperiodic variations.

Such changes in ozone content may depend upon variations in the ultraviolet solar radiation or opacity fluctuations in the upper atmosphere (cf. chaps. 12 and 13).

The meteoric data so far have shown no significant correlations with synoptic weather fronts, atmospheric temperatures in the stratosphere, sunspot numbers, lunar hour angle, or solar hour angle. Correlations with other types of solar activity will be sought in the near future as the data accumulate.

The physical and dynamic properties of the layers here considered are developed in chapters 11, 12, and 13. These discussions include the uppermost layers, for which no direct measurements have been made. The reader is further referred to the Rand report[2] and to a discussion by L. Spitzer.[17] General works on the earth's upper atmosphere are the book by S. K. Mitra[18] and the *Compendium of Meteorology*, edited by T. F. Malone.[19]

Notes added in page proof.—In the two years since this manuscript was written, the discovery of peculiarities in the physical characteristics of meteoroids in certain streams reduces the significance of the seasonal effects in upper-atmospheric densities as derived from photographic meteor data. Specifically, the Geminid meteoroids tend to give atmospheric densities that are systematically small. Since the Geminids are numerous and occur near the winter solstice, the seasonal ranges in atmospheric density have been overestimated.

With a Bennett-type mass spectrometer J. W. Townsend of the Naval Research Laboratory has found no evidence of the diffusive separation of argon relative to nitrogen up to an altitude of about 130 km.

17. "The Terrestrial Atmosphere above 300 km," *The Atmospheres of the Earth and Planets*, ed. G. P. Kuiper (Chicago: University of Chicago Press, 1949), pp. 211–247.

18. *The Upper Atmosphere* (Calcutta: Royal Asiatic Society of Bengal, 1948).

19. Published by the American Meteorological Society, Boston, Massachusetts, 1951.

CHAPTER 11

Emission Spectra of Twilight, Night Sky, and Aurorae

By J. W. CHAMBERLAIN AND A. B. MEINEL

Yerkes Observatory, University of Chicago

1. INTRODUCTION

1.1. THE BASIC PROBLEMS

THE airglow and the aurorae are phenomena that are potentially important in the understanding of the physical and chemical properties of the upper atmosphere. Unfortunately, the interpretation of these phenomena has proved so complex that we are still in doubt with regard to many of the questions that investigators have struggled with. To begin with, both phenomena are difficult to study. The airglow is very weak, necessitating the use of the fastest possible spectrographs. Even so, a single exposure may require all the dark hours for several months. The strong airglow green line, λ 5577, has a brightness of about 3×10^8 quanta/cm²-column · sec. Although the aurora is sometimes 10,000 times brighter, it is a transient phenomenon both in time and in space, sometimes lasting an entire night but more frequently only a few minutes. Quite often the lifetimes of the most interesting features are measured in tenths of a second. Whereas newly developed photoelectric techniques offer hope in attacking such problems, we must at this time be content to review the work already completed and point out the areas in which the major questions still lie.

For some years the major airglow problem has been one of the *identifications* of the emissions. Now that this problem is largely solved, the major questions remaining are the *heights* of the emissions and the *excitation mechanisms*. In nearly all cases a satisfactory simultaneous solution has not yet been attained.

As to the aurorae, the chief current problem is the determination of the

514

detailed role played by the *protons* and *electrons* in producing the auroral emissions. This is closely allied to the question of the origin of these particles. A parallel problem is the determination of *changes* in the auroral spectrum with time and height. The presence of diurnal, seasonal, and latitude variations forms a complex synoptic problem that greatly increases the difficulty of interpretation.

There have been recent attempts to observe a daytime airglow, the presence of which can be anticipated from radiative processes that must occur under the influence of solar radiation. To date, however, there has been no conclusive daytime observation of the airglow, although it has been suspected several times. The twilight airglow, which is merely the dayglow observed from the dark hemisphere, has been studied extensively. The differences between the dayglow and the nightglow are of considerable interest.

On many problems the observational data are still quite incomplete. Often interpretations are hampered by the lack of reliable quantitative data on the structure of the atmosphere or on the physical and chemical processes believed to be operating. Hence some of the interpretations of the airglow and aurora are still speculative.

In Section 2 we review some of the instruments adapted to auroral and airglow work. Sections 3 and 4 discuss the observations and some of the conclusions on aurorae and the airglow, respectively. For both these phenomena we examine first the spectral identifications (Secs. 3.1 and 4.1), then the spectral variations (Secs. 3.2 and 4.2), the heights and other data on the emitting regions (Secs. 3.3 and 4.3), and the important topic of spectroscopic temperatures and their relation to kinetic temperatures (Secs. 3.4 and 4.4). In Sections 3.5 and 4.5 we include a few remarks on the interpretation of the data in terms of excitation processes. Auroral theories and the observational data they must explain are discussed briefly in Section 3.6.

1.2. NOMENCLATURE AND NOTATION

Following the custom of the past few years, we use the term *airglow* to indicate radiation emitted by the earth's upper atmosphere. The airglow is often subdivided into *nightglow, dayglow,* and *twilight airglow.* The older term, *light of the night sky,* includes the zodiacal light, starlight, etc., as well as the nightglow.

In this chapter we have many occasions to refer to the atomic and molecular transitions producing the auroral and airglow spectra. Unfortunately, the usual spectroscopic terminology is somewhat confusing, especially when one is dealing with both atomic and molecular spectra.

Therefore, we emphasize that for *atomic* transitions the lower level is always written first, and for *molecular* transitions the upper level. These conventions are independent of whether absorption or emission is represented, but in this chapter we are invariably concerned with emission transitions.

In discussing *molecular* spectra we consider a *band system* as consisting of all the transitions between two *states*, e.g., $B\,^3\Pi \rightarrow A\,^3\Sigma$. The word *level* may apply to either vibrational or rotational levels.

In *atomic* spectra we adopt the conventional, but often violated, terminology: A *transition array* consists of all jumps between two *configurations:* 3s—4p. A *multiplet* includes all transitions between two *terms:* $3s\,^2P - 4p\,^2S^0$. A *line* arises from a transition between two *levels:* $3s\,^2P_{3/2} - 4p\,^2S^0_{1/2}$. (In addition, one usually considers the levels to consist of $2J + 1$ atomic *states* which give rise to *Zeeman components.* In atmospheric spectra we are not concerned with magnetic splitting.) For further details on spectroscopic terminology the reader is referred to Aller's (1953) textbook.

The forbidden lines of N I, N II, O I, and O II are quite important to our subject. Each of these atoms and ions contains three terms in its ground configuration (see Fig. 9); hence to denote forbidden radiation from the low-lying terms, we propose the following extension to the usual [ ].

$^3_2[\ ]$ indicates a transition between the upper and middle terms; e.g., $^1D - {}^1S$ produces λ 5577 $^3_2$[O I]. These transitions are often called *auroral transitions,* since $^3_2$[O I] produces the strongest feature in the visible auroral spectrum.

$^2_1[\ ]$ indicates a transition between the middle and lower terms; e.g., $^3P - {}^1D$ producing $\lambda\lambda$ 6300 and 6364 $^2_1$[O I]. In gaseous nebulae $^2_1[\ ]$ transitions predominate; hence the term *nebular transitions.*

$^3_1[\ ]$ indicates a transition between the upper and lower terms; e.g., $^3P - {}^1S$ producing λ 2972 $^3_1$[O I]. By analogy with the foregoing cases, $^3_1[\ ]$ is called a *transauroral transition.*

2. INSTRUMENTATION

2.1. PHOTOGRAPHIC TECHNIQUES

2.11. *Parallactic photography.*—The use by Størmer (1910) and subsequently by others of precision pairs of direct photographs, simultaneously taken from two points on a base line greater than 30 km, has clearly established the region of the upper atmosphere in which the aurorae are located. Figure 11 shows the results for the lower and upper boundaries of aurorae.

Direct photography cannot be used in the study of the airglow, since the angular scale is too large and the patchiness has too low contrast for the photographic technique. Only photoelectric techniques are likely to give reliable parallactic heights.

2.12. *Sequence photography.*—Sequence-camera records, also introduced by Størmer, are of considerable value in studying the development of an auroral display. A significant advance has resulted from the use of the Henyey-Greenstein wide-angle camera (Osterbrock and Sharpless, 1951). These cameras will photograph nearly the entire celestial sphere with negligible optical aberrations and, at an aperture of $F/2.0$, will record aurorae in a few seconds. The advantage of these cameras is that one can see the entire auroral display together. The records obtained by Meinel and Schulte (1953) have shown interesting systematic drifts of auroral features, correlated with local time. A different type of instrument was used by Harang (1951, p. 12), who recorded the intensity of aurorae on film moving slowly under an aperture and exposed by the unfocused auroral light.

2.13. *Interference photography.*—The interferometer is a highly specialized instrument using direct photography. It is of distinct historical interest, since it enabled McLennan and Shrum (1925) to identify the green line, λ 5577—previously measured in the airglow by Babcock (1923) with an interferometer—as the forbidden $^3_2[\mathrm{O\ I}]$ transition. Later, Vegard and Harang (1934) showed that the auroral green line was also the $^3_2[\mathrm{O\ I}]$ emission.

In principle, the interferometer should yield the *temperature* of the O I atoms, from the thermal broadening of the green line. So far no successful determination has been made, since an interference order of at least 500,-000 would be required. The difficulty is that no spectral line is sharp enough for a laboratory alignment of the interferometer plates, so that an error in alignment cannot be separated from a temperature broadening. More promising is to replace the Fabry-Perot interferometer with an *échelle* and to analyze the line profile by electronic methods. The use of low-order interferometers appears to be particularly advantageous for a study of large-scale distributions of transient features like Hα in aurorae. An interferometer of low-order (say, 50) coupled with a filter and plate combination to isolate a region of about 300 A centered on Hα, not only would show the regions in which Hα was present, but the fringe profile would give accurate information of the velocities of the hydrogen atoms.

2.14. *Spectroscopic photography.*—Spectrographic equipment for auroral studies has developed rapidly in the last two decades. Whereas the early spectra had dispersions measured in thousands of angstroms per millimeter, spectrographs are now in use with dispersions as high as 7 A/mm and cameras operating around $F/1$. The spectrograph has proved invaluable in providing precise information on the spectrum of the time-integrated auroral light. Even the fastest spectrographs of moderate dispersion require exposure times of the order of 10–30 minutes, whereas accurate wave lengths for identification purposes require exposures of several nights.

The most serious drawback of the spectrograph is that it cannot tell us very much about *rapid* changes in the auroral spectrum; however, Vegard, Tønsberg, and Kvifte (1950) and Meinel (1952) were able to show that striking changes do occur in short times. The eye, of course, can detect many interesting auroral forms. Quite often these forms last for seconds or even less. We have no information whatever on their spectra and thus on the mechanisms producing these transient features.

Recently, *échelle* spectrographs have been developed for auroral studies. The *échelle* grating, designed by Harrison (1949), enables one to obtain extremely high dispersion without sacrificing camera speed and still record a large range of the spectrum on a fairly small plate. In these spectrographs the *échelle* grating is mounted in series with a prism (or another grating) which disperses the spectrum in a direction normal to the *échelle* dispersion. The resulting spectrum is in the form of a mosaic, with successive *échelle* orders (e.g., 44th, 45th, 46th, etc.) separated on the plate by the prism's dispersion. Such high dispersion may be used to advantage on aurorae for a study of the sharp atomic lines or bands that are easily resolved into their rotational structure. Sharp lines are particularly suitable because the effective speed of the spectrograph is not greatly dependent on the dispersion when the true width of the emission is small compared with the width of the slit projected onto the plate.

2.2. Electronic Techniques

2.21. *Filter photometry.*—The much greater speed of modern photoelectric equipment compared with photography is making the former method increasingly important for certain types of observation. Photoelectric photometers combined with suitable filters for measuring the intensity of airglow emission over a small wave-length interval have been widely used by several observers, principally in France and the United States. These data are important not only for determining the absolute intensity of the emissions but also for deriving emission heights—from variations of intensity with zenith angle—and diurnal, seasonal, and latitude variations. Recently these observations have disclosed that the intensity of the green line (λ 5577, $\frac{3}{2}$[O I]) is not uniform over the sky, and studies of the *motions* of the green-line emission patches are providing data on ionospheric winds and emission heights.

Roach and his associates at Cactus Peak, California, employ four photometers that simultaneously scan the sky in the red, yellow, and green lines and in a spectral region relatively free from airglow emission. Similar instruments will soon be in operation on the aurora, which should fill some serious gaps in our knowledge of intensity fluctuations in various auroral emissions.

Interpretation of the photometric data has been hampered by the fairly wide band of wave lengths covered by the filters; even a good interference filter might have a half-width of 100 A. In order to isolate atmospheric emissions from the background radiation and from neighboring emissions, it would be desirable to use band widths of the order of 1 A. The use of spectrometers or birefringent filters of the Lyot type, although expensive, may be the best solution. Further, Blamont (1953) has announced a new Na filter that might be useful for airglow work.

2.22. *Photoelectric spectrometry.*—Hunten (1953) has developed a rapid-scanning auroral spectrometer equipped with a 1P21 photomultiplier tube. The entire visible spectrum is traced in about 10 seconds with 10 A resolution. Although this resolution is not so good as one can obtain photographically with an exposure of several hours, the spectrometer is extremely useful for studying rapid variations in the spectra. Traces of auroral spectra made by Hunten are shown in Figure 10.

Photoelectric techniques have also been applied to the infrared airglow and aurora, which cannot yet be conveniently recorded photographically longward of 9000 A. Stebbins, Whitford, and Swings (1944, 1945) recorded a strong airglow emission around 10,400 A with a photoelectric cell and various infrared filters. A similar investigation on the aurora was made by Rodionov and Fishkova (1950). Later Kron (1950) observed the infrared airglow spectrum with a photocell attached to a quartz monochromator. Krassovsky (1949, 1950) and his associates in the U.S.S.R. have applied an electron image-converter to the study of the airglow spectrum. So far these techniques have yielded only very low resolution.

2.23. *Photoconductive spectrometry.*—Jones and Gush (1953) have reported successful preliminary measurements of the airglow and aurora for $\lambda > 9000$ A, by means of a grating spectrometer equipped with a photoconductive PbS cell as a detector (see Fig. 13). For $\lambda > 11,000$ A, telluric absorption bands restrict the amount of observable emission.

2.24. *Radio probing.*—During recent years radar reflections have added a valuable tool to auroral studies. Since they are unaffected by daylight and cloudy weather, they are important for statistical studies. Unfortunately, since some types of aurorae apparently do not produce radar reflections and since the geometry of the situation enters the picture, the tool is not so sharp as could be desired. Experiments by Forsyth, Petrie, and Currie (1949, 1950) indicated that at 3000 megacycles there was radio emission from aurorae; but these observations have not been verified since (see Sec. 3.3).

2.3. HIGH-ALTITUDE TECHNIQUES

The study of the airglow and the aurora by rocket and balloon flights has recently come under consideration. The airglow has been studied on several flights, both by balloon and by rocket, with partial success. The only such experiment relating to aurorae dealt with the detection of incoming, low-energy protons (Van Allen, 1954). In this regard the distinction between cosmic-ray research and auroral research is very slight.

If balloon flights were made during an aurora to the 30-km level, it might be possible to observe for the first time the λ 2972 "transauroral" line of $^3_1$[O I]. It should be present also in the airglow, but with much lower intensity than λ 5577, which would render its recording rather difficult. Certainly one could envisage very useful experiments on the vertical magnetic-perturbation gradient from long-duration flights during auroral activity.

3. AURORAE

3.1. IDENTIFICATIONS IN AURORAL SPECTRA

The complexity of the auroral spectrum makes the assignment of correct identifications a difficult task. Atomic and molecular features are well mixed throughout the spectrum, and key lines are often obscured by strong molecular bands. Since this important fact is not apparent from wave-length tables, we have, instead, reproduced *microphotometer tracings* of spectra, with identifications of the most prominent features indicated. Figures 1–7 were obtained from plates taken by Messrs. Petrie and Small, kindly made available for incorporation in this chapter. They were taken with a grating spectrograph used in the second and third orders, giving dispersions of 42 and 28 A/mm (Petrie and Small, 1952b). Figure 8 has been published before (Meinel, 1951a), but the vibrational numbering of the N_2^+ bands has been corrected. The publication of the tracings will assist the reader to make his own critical evaluation of the conclusions presented in this section.

The history of auroral identifications is confusing and should be avoided. Numerous features have been attributed to various transitions simply because of a wave-length coincidence, and often the wave lengths themselves were greatly in error. The critical analyses by Nicolet (1938, 1939) and Bates, Massey, and Pearse (1948) first began to sift the welter

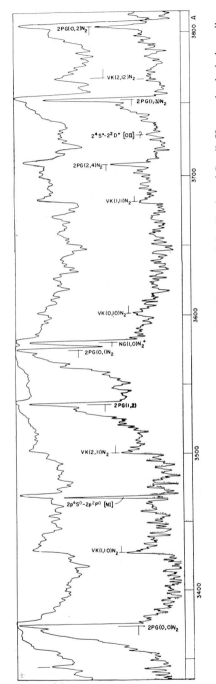

FIG. 1.—Two microphotometer tracings of a broad auroral spectrum made with a step-slit by Petrie and Small. Upper edge is dark reading (large intensity), lower edge is arbitrary. VK = Vegard-Kaplan bands; $1\ PG$ = First Positive Group, etc. Additional identifications are found in Chamberlain and Oliver (1953c). Halftone reproductions of these spectra are found in Petrie and Small (1952b). Region 3340–3800 A.

521

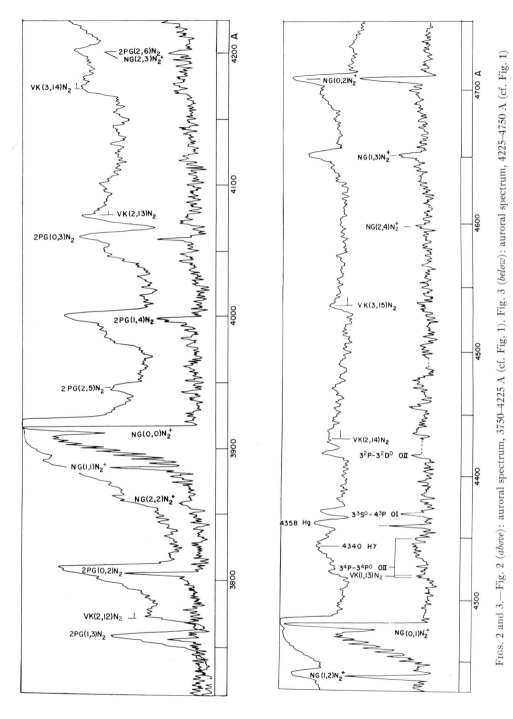

FIGS. 2 and 3.—Fig. 2 (*above*): auroral spectrum, 3750–4225 A (cf. Fig. 1). Fig. 3 (*below*): auroral spectrum, 4225–4750 A (cf. Fig. 1)

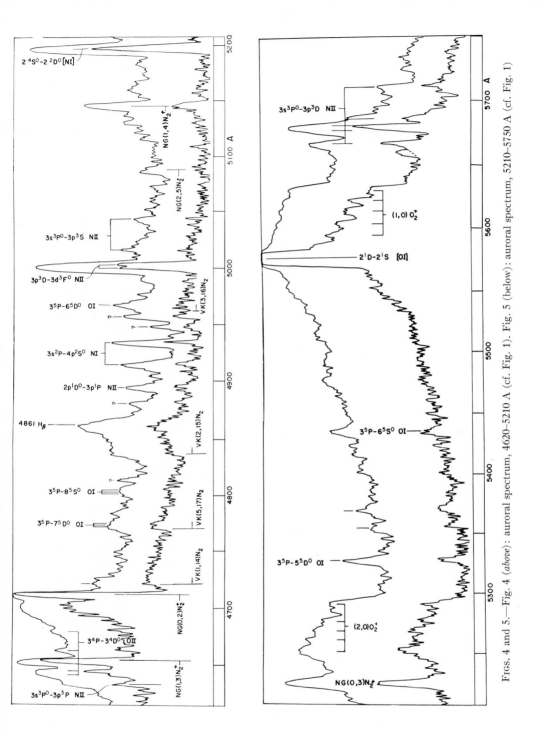

FIGS. 4 and 5.—Fig. 4 (*above*): auroral spectrum, 4620–5210 A (cf. Fig. 1). Fig. 5 (below): auroral spectrum, 5210–5750 A (cf. Fig. 1)

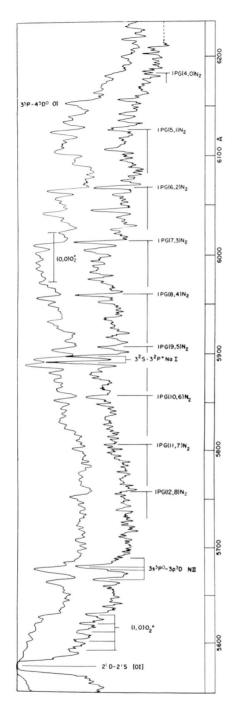

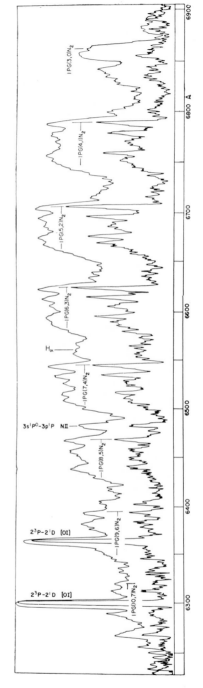

Figs. 6 and 7.—Fig. 6 (*above*): auroral spectrum, 5550–6240 A (cf. Fig. 1). Fig. 7 (*below*): auroral spectrum, 6240–6900 A (cf. Fig. 1)

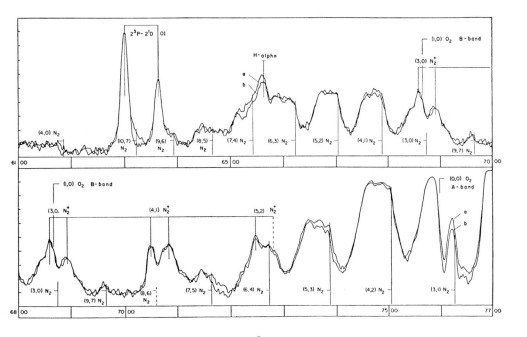

a

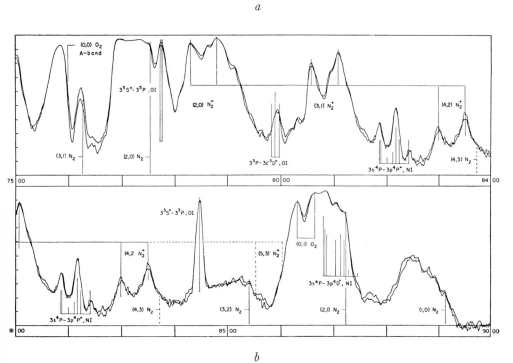

b

FIG. 8(*a, b*).—Auroral spectrum, 6100–9000 A, from a plate by Meinel. Dispersion 250 A/mm

525

of auroral "identifications" in the light of physical processes. At first, numerous faint atomic lines were rejected which have since been re-identified beyond doubt. The first generally accepted identification of permitted atomic lines was by Meinel (1948), who observed strong O I and N I lines in the relatively unexplored infrared.

Chamberlain and Oliver (1953c) reviewed the identifications made in recent years by several observers and have attempted to sort out the transitions that seemed consistent with experimental and theoretical relative intensities. The identifications shown on the microphotometer tracings are substantially from this paper.

3.11. *Forbidden atomic lines.*—In general, the transition probability of a $^2_1[\ \ ]$ line[1] is much smaller (10^{-2} or less) than for the corresponding $^3_2[\ \ ]$ line, whereas the latter is some 10^{-7} of that of a strong permitted transition. Because of the long lifetimes of the middle terms (26 hours for $^2D^0$ of N I), collisional de-excitation may be an important factor in suppressing $^2_1[\ \ ]$ transitions in the high atmosphere. Transition probabilities for many forbidden lines of atoms and ions of astrophysical and geophysical interest are available from papers by Bowen (1936), Pasternack (1940), Aller, Ufford, and Van Vleck (1949), Ufford and Gilmour (1950), and Garstang (1951, 1952) (see Fig. 9).

The λ 5577 $^3_2$[O I] line and the λ 6300 and λ 6364 $^2_1$[O I] lines are among the strongest features of the aurora, whereas λ 2972 $^3_1$[O I] is unobservable because of ozone absorption. The latter should be detectable in the airglow and the aurora above the ozonosphere, even though its transition probability is about 16 times smaller than that of λ 5577, $^3_2$[O I].

The λ 3727 $^2_1$[O II] doublet is listed in tables by Vegard and Kvifte (1945). Barbier and Williams (1951), Petrie and Small (1952b), and Oliver, Wolnik, Scanlon, and Chamberlain (1953) have found on some exposures a weak but sharp feature at λ 3727, situated between two strong N₂ bands, that may be this line. The question can be settled only if the line can be resolved into its two components (2.8 A separation). Of interest in this connection, but not conclusive, is the possible presence of the $^3_2$[O II] lines at 7319 and 7330 A. Petrie (1952b) made a special search for these lines but did not find them on his spectra. However, Chamberlain and Roesler (1955) have pointed out that these lines would be blended with two OH lines from the airglow and therefore would have to be rather strong to be detected.

The $\lambda\lambda$ 5007, 4959, and 4363 lines of [O III] have been listed in the past by Vegard and his associates. However, these attributions were not gen-

---

1. See Sec. 1.2 for definitions of the forbidden-line notation used in this chapter.

erally accepted, and they have been withdrawn by those authors in their more recent wave-length lists.

The λ 3466 $^3_1$[N I] and λ 5200 $^2_1$[N I] transitions are present in moderate intensity, but the $^3_2$[N I] line is in the photoelectric infrared at 10,400 A and has not yet been observed. Bernard (1939b, 1948a) firmly established the identification of λ 3466. The λ 5200 $^2_1$[N I] line is of particular interest

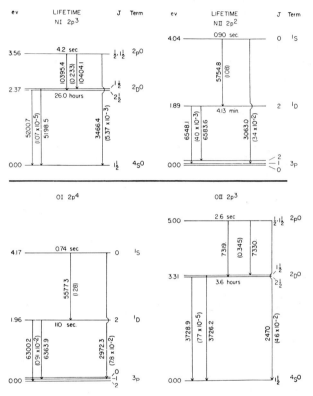

Fig. 9.—Levels and transitions within the ground configurations of neutral and ionized atomic nitrogen and oxygen. Included are the mean lifetimes for each excited term, the wave lengths in air for the lines, and (in parentheses) transition probabilities of the multiplets in units of sec^{-1} (Garstang, 1951, 1952; Pasternack, 1940). These transitions are strictly forbidden by electric dipole selection rules, although each level has a small but finite probability of radiating by means of electric quadrupole and/or magnetic dipole transitions.

because of the long lifetime of the middle term. As a consequence, this line must originate from very high in the atmosphere, which is evidenced by the spectra of Dufay and Tcheng (1942) and Götz (1947). The λ 5200 line is enhanced in low-latitude aurorae, probably because south of the auroral region one can observe weak emission from high in the aurora without the superposition of strong emissions from lower layers. It is often supposed that at low latitudes the aurorae occur predominantly at high altitudes. This is not borne out by height measurements. Probably it is only observational selection that makes high aurorae more easily observed at some distance from the auroral zone.

The only [N II] line reported is λ 5755 $\frac{3}{2}$[N II] (Petrie, 1952b). It occurs in a region filled with N_2 First Positive bands, and considerable resolution is required to make a conclusive identification. Confirmation would be desirable.

In summary, we may say that the lines of [O I] and [N I] are commonly observed, whereas [O II] and [N II] are very weak, if, indeed, they are present at all. There is no good evidence for [O III].

3.12. *Permitted atomic lines.*—In discussing permitted atomic lines it is of greater physical interest to consider the electron transitions than the lines themselves. In the cases of neutral and ionized oxygen, all the transitions between excited configurations and the ground configuration produce emission in the inaccessible ultraviolet. Transitions between two excited configurations are often in the photographic region, and proper identifications of these transition arrays offer an excellent means of studying the mechanisms exciting the atmospheric constituents.

For O I the 3s—3p transition array is prominent in the infrared. The 3s—4p and 3s—5p transition arrays are much weaker but undoubtedly present, whereas several transitions of the type 3p—ns and 3p—nd may be present. Only one O II transition array, 3s—3p, seems to be present, although a few weak lines ascribed to other arrays have been reported.

For N I, 3s—3p and 3s—4p are prominent, but the N II lines from the 3s—3p and 3p—3d transitions are considerably stronger. In fact, λ 5003 N II (a blend of $3p^3D-3d^3F^0$ and $3s^3P^0-3p^3S$), λ 5686 N II ($3s^3P^0-3p^3D$), and other lines in the same multiplets are the strongest permitted atomic lines in the visible and ultraviolet.

The resonance or "D" lines of Na I (λ 5893), which are quite strong in the airglow, appear faintly in auroral spectra, especially at high latitudes. Vegard (1949) has reported considerable fluctuations in their intensity.

3.13. *Hydrogen lines.*—The Balmer lines of hydrogen have been listed by Vegard and his associates since 1939, but the identifications were considered doubtful by most investigators. The study of the relative intensity ratios of these lines by Gartlein (1950) from a large number of aurorae removed all doubt about their identification. Gartlein (1950) and Vegard (1950) pointed out that the hydrogen lines were quite broad, and they attributed this to Doppler effects. Most of their spectra were apparently obtained with the instruments looking approximately toward the magnetic horizon, for they did not measure any appreciable Doppler shift in the line centers.

Doppler-shifted $H\alpha$ was first observed by Meinel (1951a), when his spectrograph was pointed toward the magnetic zenith during a brilliant aurora. The $H\alpha$ profile was, moreover, decidedly asymmetrical, and the violet wing indicated incoming proton velocities of at least 3300 km/sec. Meinel's spectra obtained from the magnetic horizon show broadened, but undisplaced, $H\alpha$. These data lend definite support to the theory that aurorae are produced by an influx of particles ejected from the sun. The observations of Meinel (1954) and Dahlstrom and Hunten (1951) indicate that hydrogen appears strongest in homogeneous arcs and is weak in the rayed structure of an aurora. Large intensity variations in hydrogen have also been noted by Vegard (1952) and Meinel (1952) on plates taken in rapid succession.

A number of faint features in the auroral spectrum have been ascribed by Bernard (1948b) to He I, but the absence of a strong line at 3188 A on the ultraviolet spectra, obtained by Barbier and Williams (1951), renders these identifications very doubtful. Also Fan and Meinel (1953) have not detected any helium lines in their laboratory (or synthetic) aurorae by bombardment of air with α-particles, so that the absence of He I from the aurora does not seem inconsistent with the entry into the atmosphere of solar particles with mixed composition.

3.14. *Molecular-band systems.*—The most prominent band systems in the aurora belong to the neutral and ionized nitrogen molecules. Molecular oxygen systems are quite weak except in aurorae that reach significantly below the 100-km region, apparently because molecular oxygen is very scarce above that level. No NO bands are observed, although these bands are strong in laboratory discharges.

The N_2 First Positive bands. These bands are the strongest auroral emission in the photographic spectrum; as a result, the system reaches even into the green, although the 0–0 band is at 10,440 A. The infrared bands drop off rapidly in intensity with increasing v', but the bands in the visible decrease only slowly with v'. Some bands in the infrared once identified with large v' values have since been identified with the Meinel N_2^+ bands. All First Positive bands are characterized by multiple maxima for each band. They are not useful for determinations of rotational temperature, since each band is composed of 27 branches. About 40 bands with v' up to 12 have been observed.

The N_2 Second Positive bands. These bands fall in the ultraviolet, and consequently some of them are blended with the N_2^+ First Negative and N_2 Vegard-Kaplan systems. With allowance for this, the system seems to have been satisfactorily observed for $v' \leq 3$. A few identifications of the $v' \geq 4$ progressions are doubtful.

The N_2 Vegard-Kaplan bands. These bands are degraded toward the red, unlike the other systems in the blue and ultraviolet, a circumstance that assists in identifications. The presence of these bands in aurorae is well established, at least for the $v' = 1, 2$, and 3 progressions. Estimated relative intensities within these progressions by Barbier and Williams (1951) have a good correlation with the vibrational transition probabilities (Jarmain, Fraser, and Nicholls, 1953). Only three bands show anomalous intensities, and these are explained by blends. The 0–10 band is the only one commonly observed in the $v' = 0$ progression, but this is probably due in part to blends.

The N_2^+ First Negative bands. Although λ 3914 0–0 is the strongest feature in the blue and ultraviolet, the intensities in this system fall off rapidly with increasing v'. Excitation up to $v' = 3$ certainly exists, and several bands of higher excitation have been reported.

The N_2^+ Meinel bands. Several intense multiple-headed bands in the infrared have been shown by Meinel (1951b) to arise from the $A\ ^2\Pi \rightarrow X\ ^2\Sigma$ transition. The $A\ ^2\Pi$ level had been predicted but not observed in the laboratory. Since its discovery in auroral spectra, this system has been produced in the laboratory by Dalby and Douglas (1951), Herman (1951), and Sayers (1952), and the rotational and vibrational constants have been determined (Douglas, 1953). The bands are extremely weak in the synthetic aurorae produced by protons and α-particles but are strong under electron bombardment (Fan, 1954).

The O_2 Atmospheric bands. The Kaplan-Meinel 0–1 band at 8645 A, which is prominent in the infrared airglow, is greatly enhanced in aurorae. A brightening of this band was also found in the nightglow when there was no noticeable aurora in other radiations (Meinel, 1950c). Chamberlain, Fan, and Meinel (1954) have also resolved the 1–1 band at 7688 A from a neighboring First Positive band.

The O_2^+ First Negative bands. Vegard (1950) tentatively attributed the multiple-headed bands at λ 5603 and λ 5234 to O_2^+. Later, Gartlein and Sherman (1952) confirmed these identifications by comparing observed spectra with theoretical band profiles corrected for the blending produced by a wide slit.[2] As many as five low-level bands in this system were identified by Dahlstrom and Hunten (1951), who recorded the spectrum from 5577 to 6500 A in 2 minutes with a photoelectric spectrometer. Hunten

2. See also Nicolet and Dogniaux (*J. Geophys. Res.*, **55**, 21, 1950).

has since found evidence for several more transitions. The bands are greatly enhanced in a type-B aurora and probably are responsible, along with the N_2 First Positive bands, for the dark-red lower border of these aurorae (see Fig. 10). The O_2^+ bands are always weak when observed photographically, but the exposures required are much longer than the lifetime of a type-B aurora.

3.2. VARIATIONS IN AURORAL SPECTRA

It is now recognized that differences exist between the spectra of different aurorae. They are usually small but may be significant in the study of auroral physics. Since auroral emission can be found from extreme

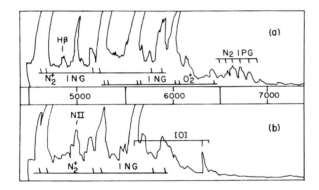

Fig. 10.—Auroral spectra obtained by Hunten and Dahlstrom with a rapid-scanning photoelectric spectrometer. Spectrum a is of a bright, active feature containing a large amount of type-B aurora (red lower border). Spectrum b was made 4 minutes later on an ordinary drapery. Note in a the great enhancement of O_2^+ First Negative and N_2 First Positive bands, and the almost total absence of λ 6300 [O I]. Hunten (private communication) emphasizes that, although $H\beta$ appears in this particular type-B aurora, it is often absent; he has even observed $H\beta$ to appear or disappear within 10 seconds.

heights, of about 1100 down to 70 km, a wide range of physical situations is encountered. For example, the transition zone between atomic and molecular oxygen is found near the lower limit of this range. The transition between atomic and molecular nitrogen is expected to occur higher up; however, it cannot be so sharp a zone as for oxygen, since N_2^+ is observed in even the highest sunlit aurorae. The fluorescence of this N_2^+ accounts for the bluish color of sunlit aurorae.

The density range has pronounced effects on the forbidden emissions, both atomic and molecular. As would be expected, the ratio of λ 6300 $_1^2[O\ I]$ to λ 5577 $_2^3[O\ I]$ increases with height, and in sunlit aurorae the red line is much stronger than the green (Størmer, 1938). Meinel (1952), however, noticed that the red $^2_1$[O I] emission appears to be spread over the entire auroral region and has little correlation with the visible auroral features. More studies, in which the aurora is imaged on a long slit, are needed to separate the height effects.

Latitude effects are more difficult to assess. The only well-established effect is that hydrogen emissions are stronger in lower-latitude aurorae.

Time changes in aurorae are prominent. In particular, hydrogen lines tend to appear primarily in the early phase of the display and in homogeneous arcs rather than in rayed structures. Meinel (1952) published spectra showing parallel changes in the intensities of Hα and N_2^+ compared with the N_2 First Positive bands, as the aurora transformed from an arc to a ray structure. Similar rapid changes have been reported by Vegard, Tønsberg, and Kvifte (1950). If the emissions from arcs and rays result from different modes of excitation, there should be additional changes in the spectra; however, careful photometric studies will be required to establish such changes quantitatively.

The laboratory proton- and electron-impact studies by Fan (1954) have demonstrated that certain features, notably the N II λ 5004 and λ 5680 lines and the Meinel N_2^+ bands, are dependent upon the species of particle causing the excitation. It will be a major advance if the presence or absence of similar changes is established for aurorae.

3.3. THE EMITTING LAYERS

3.31. *Heights.*—Auroral heights can be determined rather accurately by triangulation from simultaneous photographs made at two or more stations. For most of this information we are indebted to Størmer (1916, 1946, 1948, 1949), who has obtained parallactic measurements of many thousands of aurorae (see Fig. 11). In southern Norway he observed some aurorae as low as 70 km and a few sunlit rays extending to 1100 km, but more than one-third of his measurements gave heights between 90 and 120 km. The aurorae in northern Norway also showed a large clustering about 110 km, but hardly any extremely high aurorae were observed. This may be due to observational selection, since high-altitude aurorae are rare and are more easily observed from outside the auroral zone. Similar heights for aurorae, of 110 km, were found by Currie (1934) in Canada and by Fuller and Bramhall (1937) in Alaska.

Arcs seldom extend vertically for more than 100 km and usually about 50 km. Rays, on the other hand, are often several hundred kilometers long. The formation of arcs may be explained, qualitatively at least, by the penetration of fast particles into the upper atmosphere (Bates and Griffing, 1953a; Chamberlain, 1954c, d). But why the region above an arc suddenly becomes excited and produces the ray structure is a mystery that remains to be solved. If vertical electric-field gradients exist, then ions could perhaps be transported to these heights in the required time. The problem merits close study and may provide an important clue to auroral phenomena.

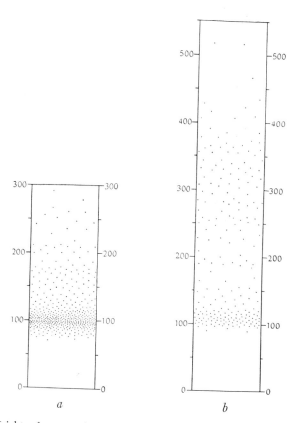

FIG. 11.—Heights of aurorae observed from southern Norway during the polar year, 1932–1933 (Størmer, 1952). a, distribution of heights of the *lower* borders of all auroral forms; b, distribution of heights for the *highest* visible points of all auroral forms.

From statistical analyses of the heights of different auroral forms, Størmer found that extremely high aurorae were usually sunlit and that this type usually occurs between 200 and 400 km. Rays often extend upward for several hundred kilometers and normally occur at higher altitudes than other forms. According to Størmer (1952), both sunlit rays and rays entirely within the earth's shadow are likely to extend higher during a sunspot maximum than at minimum. There is observational evidence, however, that the radius of the auroral zone decreases toward sunspot minimum, in accordance with most auroral theories, which predict that the zonal radius increases with the number and speed of the incoming particles. Hence some of the auroral variations correlated with the solar cycle may be, in part, latitude effects.

A discussion of the variation of spectra with height is found in Section 3.2, but we emphasize here that there is a great need for parallactic photographs made simultaneously with auroral spectra. Only then can we hope to understand the variations in auroral spectra in terms of the excitation mechanisms.

3.32. *Motions.*—It is now generally accepted that protons (and probably other particles) penetrating the upper atmosphere with high velocities are related to the production of auroral emissions. The precise mechanism is not yet known.

From an examination of photographic sequence records, Meinel and Schulte (1952) have reported that auroral features drift westward in the evening and eastward in the morning hours. Previously it was generally believed that the motions were predominately westward throughout the night, and the interpretation was that the earth rotated under an excitation pattern more or less fixed in space. Meinel and Schulte have interpreted the motion of auroral features toward the sunlit hemisphere as indicating mass motions in a circulating ionosphere. This explanation finds some support in the similar motions found in airglow excitation patterns (Roach, Williams, and Pettit, 1953b) and in Vestine's (1954) ionospheric current systems, which reverse their direction at midnight. Also, Meinel and Schulte suggest that rayed aurorae result when the influx of extraterrestrial ions triggers an atmospheric discharge.

The chief objection to this interpretation is that the apparent motions sometimes attain speeds of the order of 1 km/sec, which is considerably faster than ionospheric winds are usually believed to travel, although radio-fading rates also suggest these velocities. Martyn's (1951) theory predicts an ion drift, reversing at local midnight; but the observed directions are opposite to those expected from the Martyn theory.

The well-known spring and fall maxima in auroral occurrences may also be related to the ionospheric motions. It is interesting in this respect that Jensen and Currie (1953) have found that the orientations of auroral arcs relative to their geomagnetic meridians vary with the season.

3.33. *Ionization.*—Since the end of World War II considerable attention has been devoted to determining auroral electron densities by radar techniques. A close correlation between sporadic ionization in the E-region and visible aurorae was first found by Appleton, Naismith, and Builder (1933); and later investigators have continued to study the relationships between aurorae, sporadic-E ionization, and high-frequency radio transmission (Heppner, Byrne, and Belon, 1952). For a detailed study of auroral ionization it has been necessary to use frequencies higher than those used normally in ionospheric probing. Amateur radio operators have often communicated over extremely large distances on 50–60 Mc/sec by pointing the transmitting and receiving antennas toward aurorae (Moore, 1951; Bowles, 1952). Extensive observations of auroral reflections at 106 and 56 Mc/sec have recently been made at Saskatoon. From a statistical study of the relative amplitudes of the echoes at these frequencies, Forsyth (1953) concluded that the echoes arose primarily from critical reflections by (possibly small) volumes, containing over 10^8 electrons/cm^3. The alternatives, that the echoes originate from *partial* reflections by large ionized regions or from scattering by inhomogeneities in the auroral ionization, failed to give satisfactory interpretations of the data.

Currie, Forsyth, and Vawter (1953) found that echoes were observed when aurorae exhibited ray structure and that the echoes apparently originated from an approximately constant height of 110 km, that is, close to the lower edge of the aurorae. The diurnal variations in echo intensity were also correlated with changes in the visible aurorae. This correlation seems to vary with the time of year and probably with the solar cycle, so that much more data are needed for the analyses. One peculiar feature is a secondary maximum in the 56-Mc/sec echoes at about 07 hours local time, regardless of the time of sunrise. Auroral echoes have not been observed during other daylight hours except late afternoon.

Harang and Landmark (1954) have published results of an extensive series of echo studies made near Oslo and at Tromsoe (in northern Norway) at 35 and 74 Mc/sec. They found that although the presence of echoes was closely correlated with geomagnetic and auroral activity, there was little or no correlation with the position of the aurorae in space. Echoes were received primarily from low elevations toward the north, and even when the antennas were directed to strong auroral forms, no radio echoes were received. They thus concluded that the observed echoes are *not* reflections direct from the auroral forms, but are back-scatter from land or sea, the signal being reflected back via a strong sporadic-E layer formed in the auroral zone during aurorae.

Partly because of Harang and Landmark's results, McNamara and Currie (1954) reassessed all the Saskatoon data on 56- and 106-Mc/sec echoes. They found a possibility that some of the echoes on 56 Mc/sec could have been backward scatter from the land, via the lower part of the ionosphere. Hence they set up antennae having sufficient resolution to distinguish between direct reflection (of the primary-lobe radar signal) and ground back-scatter (of the secondary-lobe signal). They conclude that virtually all their echoes were due to direct reflection from aurorae.

It should be pointed out, however, that although there is a high correlation between aurorae and radar echoes, it is not certain that the reflections occur in the regions producing visible aurorae. But if the Saskatoon data and interpretations are correct, the auroral ionization is at least 10^3 times the normal nighttime electron density in the ionized layers. Seaton (1954a), from a discussion of the intensities of the nitrogen bands, has also deduced electron densities of about $10^8/cm^3$.

Only a few electrons per cubic centimeter with energies high enough to excite or ionize the gas molecules are required to explain the brightness of average aurorae, and Bates (1949a), with an order-of-magnitude calculation, has shown that the density of low-energy electrons must be *far* greater than the number of "active" electrons. The amount of ionization in aurorae may fluctuate rapidly with time and position; but if very high electron densities are actually produced in aurorae, the mean electron energy (that is, the electron temperature) may be fairly low, with the tail of the velocity distribution-curve supplying the few necessary fast electrons.

The Saskatoon group has also reported detecting radio "noise" from aurorae at 10 cm (3000 Mc/sec), although no echoes were ever obtained in this region (Forsyth, Petrie, and Currie, 1949, 1950). Their conclusion was that the emission originated in plasma oscillations, which implies that electron densities of about $10^{11}/cm^3$ existed for at least brief intervals of time. Later observations, closer to the time of sunspot minimum, have failed to show any auroral noise (Chapman and Currie, 1953), but this may well be an effect of decreased auroral activity. A confirmation of the earlier observations would be of major importance.

3.4. Auroral Temperatures

Determinations of auroral temperatures by spectrographic methods not only are valuable as a means of finding effective kinetic temperatures during aurorae but are also intimately related to the problem of auroral excitation mechanisms. Indeed, observed relative intensities of lines and bands arising from different upper levels offer an excellent means for testing the various excitation processes proposed. With the low densities prevailing in the upper atmosphere, the relative populations of atomic and molecular levels may depart greatly from those found in thermodynamic equilibrium at the same kinetic temperatures. Unfortunately, this distinction has not always been made, with the result that a number of spurious temperatures have been reported.

3.41. *Doppler temperatures.*—In principle, kinetic temperatures might be determined directly from measurements of Doppler broadening of atomic lines. This is seen as follows. Forbidden lines such as λ 5577 of $\frac{3}{2}$[O I] have very little "natural width," and, since collisional broadening is negligible in the upper atmosphere, the line broadening is due entirely to the Doppler effect. Temperatures determined by this method would require precision measurements of line widths or profiles, however, which have not yet been obtained. Moreover, some ambiguities may arise in the interpretations if the atmospheric turbulence motions are of the same order as the thermal velocities.

3.42. *Rotational temperatures.*—Rotational temperatures may be safely interpreted as kinetic temperatures in those instances where the molecule remains in the excited state long enough for a few collisions to take place (Massey, 1948). In this event the relative populations of the J-levels come into equilibrium with the free particles according to the Boltzmann excitation equation (see Aller, 1953, p. 74). Thus rotational temperatures determined from forbidden systems should be reliable. There is considerable difficulty, however, in obtaining accurate relative intensities from auroral spectra. Not only does one encounter the usual problems associated with spectrophotometry of photographic plates, but when rotational lines are not clearly resolved (which is usually the case in auroral spectra), the observed band profile is distorted because of the finite resolving power of the spectrograph. Hence it is necessary to correct the profile for this instrumental broadening. There is also the possibility of distortion of a profile by other emissions superimposed on the band; therefore, several bands arising from a common vibrational level may give different apparent temperatures.

It is doubtful whether rotational temperatures of a permitted system, like N_2^+ First Negative, should be regarded as kinetic temperatures. If the First Negative bands are excited from either the ground state of N_2 or that of N_2^+ by electron collisions, then upon excitation there will be little change in the relative populations of the J-levels (Branscomb, 1950). If the molecule radiates before redistribution can take place, the kinetic temperature should be computed with the rotational constant, $B_{v''}$, of the lower state. In most cases the difference $B_{v''} - B_{v'}$ and the resulting correction are small. On the other hand, if excitation of the molecules occurs by some other means, such as photochemical association or proton collision, then there is likely to be a considerable change in the molecular angular momentum, with the result that the rotational temperature would not be reliable (Duffendack, Revans, and Roy, 1934; Oldenberg, 1934).

Jones, Hunten, and Shepherd (1953) have obtained spectra with 7 A/mm of the N_2^+ First Negative band at 3914 A, in which the R branch is completely resolved (Fig. 12). Subsequent spectra (Jones, private communication) yielded temperatures between 250° and 370° K. By means of a photoelectric spectrometer to resolve the rotational lines, Hunten and

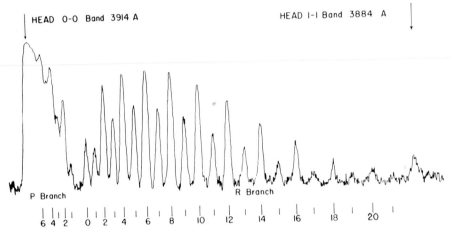

HEAD 0-0 Band 3914 A   HEAD 1-1 Band 3884 A

P Branch   R Branch

6 4 2   0   2   4   6   8   10   12   14   16   18   20

FIG. 12.—The auroral N_2^+ First Negative band at 3914 A. The complete resolution of the rotational fine structure allows the derivation of accurate rotational temperatures. Dispersion 7 A/mm. Courtesy A. V. Jones.

Shepherd (private communication) have measured rotational temperatures from 190° to 325° K and have simultaneous height measurements for some of these spectra. From the data so far obtained at Saskatoon it seems probable that there is an increase of T_{rot} with height, but the precise relationship is not yet known. These temperatures vary considerably from those obtained by Vegard and his collaborators, using lower-dispersion spectra. Recently Vegard, Tønsberg, and Kvifte (1950) gave rotational temperatures of the order of 250° K for both low- and high-altitude aurorae. Earlier, the N_2^+ temperatures obtained over several years by Vegard and Tønsberg (1944) averaged about 225° K. However, the resolution on these spectra was only partial, so the corrections for the instrumental profile were uncertain. The constant intensity distribution with height found by these authors does not seem consistent with the large variations in temperature, density, ionization, etc., believed to exist in the upper atmosphere (Bates, chap. 12).

The 0–1 Atmospheric band of O_2 during an aurora gave a rotational temperature of about 200° K (Chamberlain, Fan, and Meinel, 1954). This band is forbidden and probably is a good measure of the kinetic temperature. Oxygen becomes dissociated between 80 and 120 km, although convection may carry an appreciable amount of O_2 considerably higher (see Nicolet, chap. 13). However, the temperature of 200° K seems consistent with an emitting height in the lower auroral regions (cf. chap. 10).

Partial resolution of some of the Vegard-Kaplan bands has enabled Petrie (1952, 1953) to derive a rotational temperature of roughly 850° K for an undetermined height. This value seems high, but, as the bands form a forbidden system, they may arise from the higher auroral regions, where the ionospheric temperature is of this order of magnitude.

Gartlein and Sprague (1952) reported that the peaks of the N_2 First Positive bands appear to be shifted toward higher rotational temperatures during times of intense $H\alpha$. This observation must be questioned, since a change in temperature causes large changes in the relative intensities of the several maxima for each band before any noticeable wave-length shift occurs.

3.43. *Vibrational temperatures.*—The relative intensities of bands within a band system lead to a "vibrational temperature" of the upper electronic state. To interpret these intensities as directly indicating the kinetic temperature in the emitting region is completely false, since the particle densities in the upper atmosphere do not allow the relative populations to be redistributed in the upper state before spontaneous emission occurs. In general, vibrational equilibrium is much more difficult to establish than is rotational equilibrium. The vibrational temperatures up to 7700° K found by Rosseland and Steenshold (1933) were severely criticized by Oldenberg (1934) because thermodynamic equilibrium rather than the Franck-Condon principle was used in discussing the excitation.

Bates (1949a) has analyzed the observations of Vegard and Kvifte (1945) and Barbier (1947c) on the First Negative N_2^+ system in order to determine the vibrational temperature of the unexcited molecule (which is more likely to be close to the kinetic temperature than are the excited states), with various assumptions about the mechanism of excitation. He shows that the excitation of the First Negative bands, by electron impact with either the ground state of N_2 or that of N_2^+, can explain the observations only if the vibrational temperature of the ground state is exceedingly high. Petrie and Small's (1953) intensities, however, give a somewhat lower value (1000° K). Similarly, Bates (1949a) found that Vegard and Kvifte's (1945) measurements of the Second Positive bands of N_2 required vibrational temperatures over 10,000° K in the ground electronic state if the system were excited by inelastic electron collisions. However, Petrie and Small (1952a) have obtained a quite different intensity distribution at Saskatoon and, with the same excitation mechanism, have derived a vibrational temperature of less than 500° K.

The appreciable differences found between the Norwegian and lower-latitude spectra may in part be real; there is the possibility, however, that systematic errors exist in some of the data, and it is desirable that more measurements of intensities be obtained by other observers.

3.44. *Excitation temperatures.*—"Excitation temperatures" of several thousand degrees have been obtained by Petrie (1947, 1948, 1950) from the relative intensities of permitted atomic lines. Here, again, the temperatures should not be taken literally as indicating the kinetic temperature. The departures of the relative populations from those in thermodynamic equilibrium have been worked out for the case of atomic hydrogen under various excitation conditions (Baker and Menzel, 1938; Chamberlain, 1953, 1954c). Similar treatments for oxygen or nitrogen, however, would be much more difficult. Selective excitation of a level (such as the resonance excitation of the 3d $^3D^0$ term of O I by Lyman-β emission, which may occur during proton influx) would further complicate the analysis of relative multiplet intensities. More recently, Petrie and Small (1953) have presented an approximate analysis of measured relative multiplet intensities, in an attempt to gain information on the excitation mechanisms. Their results are discussed in Section 3.5.

3.45. *Other methods.*—Auroral temperatures of a nonspectrographic nature have been estimated from measurements of the variation in luminosity along auroral streamers (Harang, 1945); but Bates and Griffing (1953a) have shown that this approach involves a number of erroneous assumptions that invalidate the results.

3.5. Auroral Excitation Mechanisms

Various atomic and molecular reactions that may occur in the high atmosphere during an aurora are discussed by Bates in chapter 12. Here we review the difficulties involved in the interpretation of auroral spectra and some of the conclusions that have been drawn from these data.

3.51. *Associated theoretical and laboratory work.*—A complete understanding of the observations requires many quantum-mechanical calculations, which, in turn, depend upon the availability of accurate wave functions for the atomic and molecular species present in the ionosphere. Most of these data are extremely difficult to compute, and consequently our present information is largely based on experimental determinations.

Transition probabilities for forbidden oxygen and nitrogen lines have been computed with reasonable accuracy (see Sec. 3.11), and accurate calculations have been made for hydrogen (Menzel and Pekeris, 1935) and helium (Goldberg, 1939). Bates and Damgaard (1949) have given tables useful for approximate calculations of absolute line strengths in certain cases. Bibliographies of experimental and theoretical determinations of f-values (which may be converted to Einstein coefficients) are given by Unsöld (1948), Claas (1951), and Aller (1953, p. 156). In many cases only relative line or multiplet strengths are required, and for the cases where the atom approximates LS (Russell-Saunders) coupling we may make use of tables given by Russell (1936) and Goldberg (1935, 1936).

Relative vibrational-transition probabilities have been computed for a number of molecules by various authors. Bates (1952) has presented a set of tables facilitating the computations for cases where the change in the internuclear separation is small. R. W. Nicholls and his associates have developed improved methods for the vibrational calculations and have recently presented results for several band systems of geophysical interest (Jarmain, Fraser, and Nicholls, 1953).

Data on continuous absorption coefficients (absorption cross-sections) are of importance to auroral physics in so far as they are necessary for an understanding of the ionized layers and reactions in the "undisturbed" ionosphere. The status of this subject has been reviewed by Bates (1946) and Weissler (1951).

Auroral excitation mechanisms depend vitally on the cross-sections for recombinations, for various exciting and ionizing inelastic collisions, and for de-exciting collisions. Slow atomic and molecular collisions have been discussed by Massey (1949), and an application of these data to the aurora is given by Bates (chap. 12). The most accurate cross-sections for excitation of the atomic forbidden lines by electron collisions have been computed by Seaton (1953a, b).

Additional information on auroral excitation mechanisms may be obtained from laboratory studies of discharges and afterglows, flame spectra, and synthetic aurorae produced by high-energy bombarding particles. It is quite likely that some of the mechanisms operating in these laboratory sources are identical to auroral processes, and research in all these fields will be mutually advantageous.

The production of synthetic aurorae is of particular interest, as it may indicate directly the particles responsible for the production of the different emissions. Laboratory studies of the auroral spectrum have been made by Fan and Meinel (1953) by bombarding air with various accelerated particles of different masses and energies. The puzzling presence of strong N $_\text{II}$ lines and the almost complete absence of N $_\text{I}$ lines in the aurora was also observed in the laboratory. The ratio of λ 5003 N $_\text{II}$ to N_2^+ was found to be sensitive to the type of positive particle but insensitive to the energies over a range of a factor of 10, the N $_\text{II}$ being relatively stronger for He^+ and heavier ions. Assuming that positive particles from above are responsible for the aurora, Fan found the He/H ratio for the incoming particles to be of the order of $1/10$. The most outstanding discrepancy between the auroral and positive-particle spectra is the complete absence of the infrared N_2^+ bands and the weakness of the First Positive N_2 bands in the laboratory spectra.

When electrons were used as the bombarding particles, Fan (1954) found a different situation. The resultant spectrum was quite sensitive to the energy of the electrons. At higher energies the A $^2\Pi \to$ X $^2\Sigma$ infrared N_2^+ bands became the most intense feature in the spectra, and the First Positive bands were even stronger than the First Negative N_2^+ bands. This condition was obviously more extreme than in the aurora. It is impossible to explain the auroral spectrum if the only particles that penetrate to auroral heights are electrons. The best relative intensities of the infrared bands are found for 200–400 eV electrons, much too low an energy to penetrate to auroral heights. If subsequent laboratory studies confirm this result, then we must look for a vertical potential gradient that can take secondary electrons at around 30 eV and accelerate them to energies of the order of 200 eV. Such a potential might be sufficient to cause aurorae to show a transition from impact excitation produced by incoming positive particles to discharge excitation by moderate-energy electrons.

3.52. *Discussion.*—One of the chief problems in auroral physics is to determine the collisions or reactions responsible for the various emissions. One important case is that of hydrogen, whose emission arises primarily from incoming protons that capture bound electrons from atmospheric atoms and molecules. Chamberlain (1954c) has presented a quantitative discussion of this problem, utilizing theoretical cross-sections (Bates and Griffing, 1953b; Bates and Dalgarno, 1953a) and also experimental data. The solution indicates that each proton captures and loses an electron about 700 times in passing through the atmosphere. Each capture does not result in a quantum of Hα, however, so that only about 50 Hα transitions occur for each incident proton. Rough estimates of the brightness of $H\alpha$ in low-latitude auroral arcs indicate fluxes of the order of 10^7–10^8 protons/cm^2 sec entering the atmosphere during the first stage of a moderately strong auroral storm. The theoretical treatment predicts a Balmer decrement of $I_\alpha : I_\beta : I_\gamma = 3.34 : 1.00 : 0.33$; but no accurate measurements of these ratios are available.

The $H\alpha$ profile computed by Chamberlain is displaced somewhat farther to the violet than Meinel's (1951a) observed profile for an arc in the magnetic zenith. The discrepancy is probably due to the fact that the incident protons do not follow rectilinear paths down the magnetic lines of force, as was assumed in the calculations, but possess considerable dispersion in directions (Chamberlain, 1954d). The trajectories of charged particles through the atmosphere are also complicated by the presence of the magnetic field. The fact that $H\alpha$ is quite broad (but undisplaced), even when observed on the magnetic horizon, suggests that there is considerable deviation from undeflected, rectilinear paths.

Computations of the luminosity distribution with height for hydrogen light give a considerably narrower arc than would be expected from air ionized by the same monoenergetic protons (Bates and Griffing, 1953a). This is in accord with Meinel's (1952) observation (which has since been confirmed on numerous spectra) that auroral arcs are much sharper in $H\alpha$ than in other emissions, although the bottom edge of the arc nearly coincides in all wave lengths. The observed luminosity-curves are much broader than the computed, however; and Griffing and Stewart (1954) have shown that the discrepancy is probably not due to a foreshortening effect in the observations. Again, the differences between the simple theory and the observations may be due to a neglect of the scattering of the incident protons. This would have the effect of producing a dispersion of velocities at each height, which would tend to broaden the observed arc. An alternative, but rather unattractive, explanation is that the incident protons initially possessed a dispersion in velocities. At any rate, the alternative would not reconcile the computed and observed $H\alpha$ profiles, which are independent of the initial velocity of the protons.

For the excitation of air particles, processes other than direct proton excitation are undoubtedly important. This is emphasized by the appearance of aurorae, especially rayed features, which show no (or extremely weak) $H\alpha$. The laboratory experiments suggest that the N_2^+ Meinel bands are excited by *electron* collisions, which raises the problem of whether these electrons are primary or secondary and of explaining how they obtain sufficient energy to produce excitation. Also, much of the auroral radiation may be produced indirectly by recombinations following dissociation or ionization, rather than by direct impact. Auroral excitation problems are closely related to the structure of the normal ionosphere. Considerable theoretical work has been done on the production of the N_2^+ First Negative system, but it is still not definitely known whether these bands are excited from the ground state of N_2 or from that of N_2^+, and whether the excitation is accomplished by electrons or protons.

Excitation of any of the visible auroral emissions by thermal electrons would require extremely high temperatures. It seems likely, however, that during an aurora some of the secondary electrons depart significantly from a Maxwellian curve. Bates (1949a) suggested that, in practice, nearly all the electrons follow a Maxwellian curve for a fairly low temperature but that a few electrons have quite high energies. An electron ionized in a proton collision with N_2, for example, will possess an energy of several electron volts which it may use to produce further excitation. Seaton (1954b) has discussed the excitation of the auroral forbidden lines by these fast or "active" electrons. He concludes that the [O I] red and green lines are probably produced by electron collisions. For other ions the data on identifications and intensities are too tenuous for definite conclusions to be drawn. The main uncertainty in discussing forbidden-line excitation is in evaluating the importance of collisional de-excitations.

Petrie and Small (1953) have measured relative intensities of permitted oxygen and nitrogen atomic lines in spectra obtained at Saskatoon and have attempted to interpret these data in terms of excitation mechanisms. The difficulty is that one does not know what the relative populations of the excited levels *should* be for various types of excitation. If the excitation process does not give preference to a few excited levels (as might be the case in resonance processes), the populations of the levels, as well as the *rates* of populating and depopulating, should decrease with increasing quantum number. But since all the upper levels producing the observed permitted lines of any one element have comparable excitation potentials, their populations may decrease quite slowly. Moreover, there may be very small differences in the relative populations for two different excitation processes (e.g., inelastic electron collisions and recombinations plus cascading). The excitation of levels with different multiplicity might occur by inelastic electron collisions with exchange, but recombinations and intercombination transitions (when the levels depart appreciably from LS coupling) could also be effective. Hence the analysis of atomic multiplets is an extremely complex problem, and although Petrie and Small's conclusions on the excitation mechanisms seem reasonable from general considerations, it is questionable whether their conclusions follow from their relative multiplet intensities.

3.6. AURORAL THEORIES

Before passing on to a discussion on the airglow, we will summarize here the auroral data that must eventually be explained. Aurorae seem definitely to be related to magnetic storms and the influx of charged particles from the sun. Hence, auroral physics encompasses three distinct problems:

1) *The ejection of particles from the sun.*—There may be several mechanisms by which this is accomplished. A solar flare occurring near the center of the disk has a good probability of being followed after a day or so by an aurora and a magnetic storm (I, 444). Observations of several flares near the limb of the sun have shown that solar hydrogen and ionized calcium particles are often ejected from the sun with high velocity at the beginning of the flare (Dodson, Hedeman, and Chamberlain, 1953; I, 701). These ejections also seem to be associated with major bursts of solar radio noise (Dodson, Hedeman, and Owren, 1953; I, 508 ff.). Another possible mechanism is that particles evaporate into space from coronal streamers (I, 450), which may be associated with the solar M regions that were hypothesized on the basis of 27-day recurrences of minor magnetic storms. It may well be that both the chromosphere and the corona furnish aurora-producing particles.

2) *The trajectories of particles between the sun and earth.*—Birkeland (1896) and Størmer (1904) investigated the paths that charged particles of one sign would follow in penetrating the earth's magnetic field. They neglected electrostatic repulsion of the individual particles, and this led Chapman and Ferraro (1931, 1932, 1933, 1940) to develop their theory of an electrostatically neutral but ionized stream of particles. Additional theories and extensions have been put forth in recent years by Alfvén (1948), Martyn (1951), Bennett and Hulburt (1954), and others. Excellent summaries of auroral theories have been given by Chapman (1948) and Hulburt (1954). Empirically, the existence of particles traveling between the sun and earth is indicated by the observations of Richardson (1944) and Brück and Rutllant (1946), who found very weak abnormal absorptions shortward of the solar H and K lines of Ca II prior to magnetic storms.

3) *The production of visible aurorae.*—When a theory for the aurora is constructed, one usually discovers that several important observational data are not satisfied. Let us examine the information.

I. Geographic relationships

  a) Aurorae occur in two zones, one approximately concentric about the north geomagnetic axis point, the other about the south geomagnetic axis point; the radii of the zones are of the order of 20°–25°.

  b) Whenever aurorae show vertical structure, the elements are nearly parallel to the geomagnetic lines of force.

  c) Auroral arcs are aligned approximately along parallels of magnetic latitude.

  d) Aurorae appear to occur simultaneously in both zones. The data on this point are extremely meager, and more southern observations are needed.

  e) The rayed auroral features tend to drift westward in the evening and eastward in the morning, similar to the known current systems in the ionosphere. It is not known whether the drift pattern is the same or opposite in the Southern Hemisphere; this information would be of great interest in testing auroral theories. The observed drift in the Northern Hemisphere is opposite to that predicted from Martyn's theory.

II. Time relationships

  a) Aurorae show strong seasonal variations, the maxima occurring near the equinoxes. Since the equinox and the earth's crossing of the solar equatorial plane are nearly coincident, it is not obvious which is responsible.

  b) Aurorae observed from south of the zone of maximum occurrence show an 11.1-year cycle of activity. Minimum activity coincides with the sunspot minimum, but the maximum activity occurs about 2 years after sunspot maximum (Meinel, Negaard, and Chamberlain, 1954).

  c) Aurorae shift systematically southward during years of high solar activity and recede northward during years of minimum activity. This could explain the apparent 11.1-year cycle observed south of the auroral zone. Because of this latitude shift, it is not clear how much the total number changes. Observations during the 1932–1933 Polar Year indicated that in high latitudes aurorae are most frequent during *minimum* solar activity, just out of phase with the low-latitude results.

  d) Unusual auroral activity appears to follow unusual solar activity; however, somewhere in the auroral zone an aurora occurs almost *every* clear night. Accordingly, we must not rely on a rare situation to produce aurorae.

  e) Aurorae appear to be essentially nighttime phenomena. Ever since radar reflection studies have been made, auroral echoes have been received no earlier in the day than late afternoon. The reflections always disappear at dawn.

  f) Auroral activity is always accompanied by localized geomagnetic activity. On the other hand, world-wide geomagnetic activity is not always accompanied by significant auroral activity, although there are examples of major auroral activity preceding by some hours world-wide geomagnetic activity. A closer examination of these relationships is needed.

III. Spectra

  The application of physical principles has removed a welter of misidentifications of auroral wave lengths. The present list harmonizes observation and theory, although some puzzling features have only recently been explained through the laboratory work by Fan. The spectrum often changes significantly with time in a single aurora. The salient points concerning auroral spectra are:

a) The spectrum is largely produced by impact excitation.

b) The Balmer hydrogen lines show that protons precipitate into the atmosphere during the *quiet-arc* phase of a simple aurora, whereas the Balmer lines are undetectable in simple *rayed* aurorae.

c) The infrared N_2^+ bands indicate that fast electrons (about 400 eV) are also important; these bands apparently cannot be excited by positive ions or by the secondary electrons ejected in particle encounters.

d) Details of the spectrum of aurorae change with altitude, reflecting density and composition changes, as well as variations in excitation conditions.

4. THE AIRGLOW

4.1. IDENTIFICATIONS IN AIRGLOW SPECTRA

4.11. *Atomic lines.*—The only atomic emissions conclusively identified in the airglow are λ 5577 $^3_2$[O I] and $\lambda\lambda$ 6300–6364 $^2_1$[O I] and the resonance Na–D lines at 5893 A. The identifications of the green and red [O I] lines have been confirmed by accurate measurements with interferometers. This work has been aptly summarized by Cabannes, J. Dufay, and Gauzit (1942), and we will not elaborate on it. Studies of intensity variations and emission heights of the forbidden lines suggest that the red and green lines do not arise entirely from the same mechanism; but so far there is no completely satisfactory explanation of either emission, although several proposals have been put forth.

Bernard (1938a) and Cabannes, J. Dufay, and Gauzit (1938) showed conclusively by interferometric and spectrographic observations that the strong yellow line arises from Na I. The origin of this sodium is unknown. If it enters the atmosphere from outer space, a comparison of the cosmic abundances and transition probabilities would lead one also to expect the resonance line λ 4227 of Ca I in emission. This feature, if present, however, would be blended with the absorption line near λ 4227 (see Sec. 4.13), which probably arises in part from stellar Ca I.

There have been a few instances where the nebular transition λ 5200 $^2_1$[N I] has been reported (Courtes, 1950). M. Dufay (1951) consequently made a special search for this line and concluded that it does appear occasionally as a weak line during twilight and early night (see Sec. 4.15). The λ 3466 $^3_1$[N I] line has not been detected in the airglow. The $^3_2$[N I] transition at 10,400 A has likewise not been detected, but the extremely intense OH bands would make this difficult, even though it should be fifteen times stronger than the λ 3466 $^3_1$[N I] line (where we neglect differential atmospheric absorption). Better data are needed before [N I] can be definitely added to the list of airglow wave lengths. No *permitted* O I or N I emissions are found in the airglow.

4.12. *Bands in the infrared and red.*—With the exception of the atomic lines cited above, all the emissions so far identified for $\lambda > 5500$ A may be attributed to O_2 and OH. The *P*- and *R*-form branches of the 0–1 band in the forbidden Atmospheric ($b\,^1\Sigma_g^+ \rightarrow X\,^3\Sigma_g^-$) system of O_2 (Herzberg, 1950) were identified by Meinel (1950*d*). Subsequently, J. Dufay (1951) suggested that Krassovsky's (1950) infrared observations with a photoelectric image-converter indicated the presence of the 0–2 band of O_2 at 9976 A. According to theoretical intensities (Fraser, Jarmain, and Nicholls, 1954), the 0–2 band should be about thirty times weaker than the 0–1 band of O_2 and consequently undectable by image-tube techniques. The intrinsically strong 0–0 emission is completely absorbed by molecular oxygen in the lower atmosphere, and no radiation has been detected from any levels with $v' > 0$. The laboratory afterglow spectrum of O_2 also consists only of the $v' = 0$ progression (Kaplan, 1947*a, b;* Branscomb, 1952), and the same selective excitation mechanism may well operate in both the laboratory afterglow and the airglow.

The vibration-rotation bands of OH (Fig. 13) were first identified by Meinel (1950*a*), and for $\lambda < 9000$ A a total of 12 bands have so far been definitely identified (see, e.g., Chamberlain and Oliver, 1953*a*). In addition, five strong OH bands have probably been observed by Krassovsky between 9000 and 11,000 A (J. Dufay, 1951) and by Kron (1950). Jones and Gush (1953) have recently measured the OH bands out to $2\,\mu$ with a PbS photoconductive cell (see Fig. 14), a remarkable achievement. Since their discovery in the airglow, three low-excitation Meinel OH bands have been observed in oxyacetylene flames and studied under high dispersion. Complete analyses of such data by Herman and Hornbeck (1953) and by Déjardin, Janin, and Peyron (1953) have led to determinations of vibrational constants that predict accurate wave lengths up to $v' = 6$ but do not adequately represent the higher-excitation bands ($v' = 8$ and 9). Chamberlain and Roesler (1955) have combined accurate airglow wave lengths with the laboratory data and have shown that four vibrational constants are required to represent the levels up to $v = 9$. (In most molecular states two or three constants suffice.)

Before the identification of the Meinel bands, some of the emissions in the visible (Elvey, 1950; Elvey, Swings, and Linke, 1941) and photoelectric-infrared (Stebbins, Whitford, and Swings, 1944, 1945) were tentatively attributed to the First Positive system of N_2. The OH bands have given such a satisfactory explanation to all these observations that no observational evidence remains for the presence of the N_2 bands. The resolution in the photoelectric infrared is still quite low, however, so that the

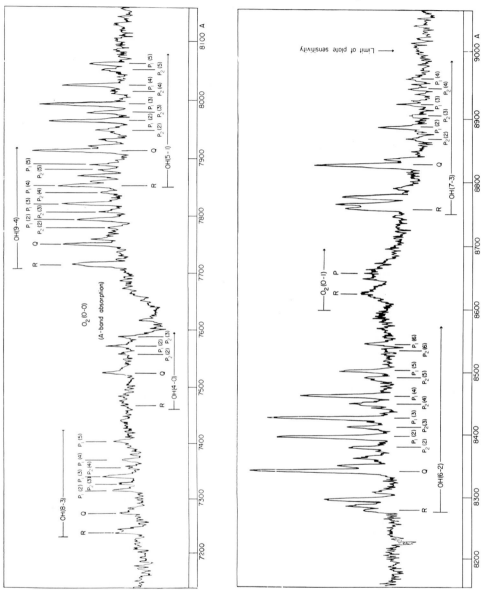

FIG. 13.—Microphotometer tracing of the airglow spectrum in the photographic infrared, from a plate by Chamberlain. Dispersion 70 A/mm. *a*, 7100–8150 A; *b*, 8150–9000 A. Note that in the Meinel OH bands the P_2 lines (which arise from levels in the upper or $^2\Pi_{1/2}$ state) are considerably weaker than P_1 (from levels in the lower or $^2\Pi_{3/2}$ state). This alternation is not observed in the high-temperature laboratory sources of OH.

presence of the 0–0 N₂ band cannot be definitely disproved—although there is no apparent reason why it should be expected.

4.13. *The continuum.*—Our understanding of the blue and violet regions of the airglow spectrum has long been in a very unsatisfactory state, in spite of the fact that this region has received more attention than any other, owing in part to the high speed of undyed photographic plates. Many of the difficulties encountered can be traced to an improper interpretation of the continuum, although a review of researches over the last 30 years suggests that a few workers, including Lord Rayleigh, did ascribe the continuum to starlight and sunlight.

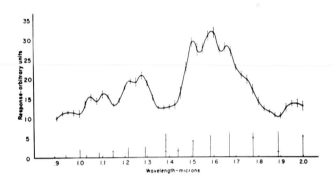

Fig. 14.—Airglow spectrum, 9000–20,000 A, from a record obtained by Jones and Gush with a PbS photoconductive cell. The predicted positions of OH bands are indicated by vertical lines at the bottom of the figure. The lengths indicate the predicted intensities; the bars, the intensities reduced by atmospheric water vapor.

The early spectra of Rayleigh (1920) showed the H and K Fraunhofer lines of Ca II. Later, in his thesis on the night sky, J. Dufay (1928) listed a number of wave-length coincidences for solar absorption lines ranging from 3047 A to the G band at 4300 A. Cabannes and Dufay (1944) summarized their collection of a large number of plates and concluded that several strong Fraunhofer lines were in the night-sky spectra, but they seem to have overlooked the implications of this result in their later identifications of "emission" features.

Barbier (1945), from a study of his own spectra, rejected these absorption lines primarily because a number of strong solar lines in the ultraviolet did not appear in the night sky. He thus felt that the previously listed absorptions were accidental gaps between emissions. In an extensive study of the region shortward of 5000 A, Elvey, Swings, and Linke (1941) did not list any absorption features, and although they realized that there were some similarities with the solar spectrum, they believed that these co-incidences were fortuitous (P. Swings, private communication, 1953).

The concept of a true airglow continuum began to appear shortly after World War II. Barbier (1947b) noticed that the spectrum dropped off rather rapidly shortward of 3900 A, and he ascribed about 80 per cent of the light in the blue-violet region to a continuum. In his estimate only 12 per cent of this light was due to starlight, another 15 per cent was due to the zodiacal light, and the remaining 53 per cent was attributed to un-resolved bands. Other workers have felt that this interpretation was unsat-isfactory, and a considerable effort was made to discover an atmospheric reaction that would produce a continuum beginning at 3900 A and extend-ing toward the red (e.g., Kastler, 1946).

The question of the continuum has recently been clarified by Meinel (1953), working with a plate obtained by Barbier, and independently by Chamberlain and Oliver (1953b). From spectra having rather high resolu-tion they found that the strong absorption lines were extremely deep, indi-cating that very little airglow radiation can exist at these wave lengths. Moreover, the general intensity distribution with wave length was found to be similar to that of galactic starlight, and the relative strength of absorption lines indicated a stellar spectral type similar to that of the Milky Way. Detailed comparisons of the night-sky spectra with spectra of the sun and of faint gaseous nebulae (which show the continuous spec-trum of the stellar background, as well as the stronger emissions from the nebulae and airglow) leave little doubt that the continuum arises primar-ily from the zodiacal light and starlight.

In the ultraviolet the true emission bands are strong enough to make the continuum less prominent. Similarly, the strong atomic lines and the Meinel OH bands dominate the red region, so that the continuum is not so conspicuous on well-resolved plates, although it is definitely present.

The return to the starlight interpretation of the continuum reopens the problem of identifications of the true emissions in the green and blue. Chamberlain and Oliver (1953b) and Meinel (1953) agreed that the air-glow feature at 3914 A (see Fig. 15) is real and that the most likely identi-fication is the 0–0 First Negative band of N_2. It shows strong twilight enhancement, but the mechanisms are probably different in twilight and at night. In twilight, resonance scattering appears to be operating, where-as at night the cosmic-ray flux may be responsible. This is suggested by the laboratory result that λ 3914 is the strongest emission produced by proton bombardment in air. Since in the nightglow it is so comparatively weak, no other emissions due to heavy-particle impacts are expected.

In addition to the starlight continuum, there may actually be a true atmospheric continuum becoming important at longer wave lengths. This is suggested by the fact that the stellar absorption lines are less conspicuous in the green than in the blue, even though the continuum is still quite strong. Broida and Gaydon (1954) have suggested that the air afterglow continuum, which was present on their laboratory emission spectra of the O_2 Herzberg system, contributes to the night-sky continuum. The photoelectric measures by Roach, Pettit, and Meinel (1955a) indicate that approximately 20 per cent of the control-filter emission at λ 5300 is of upper-atmospheric origin.

4.14. *Band systems in the blue and ultraviolet.*—In an attempt to evaluate the observations of the ultraviolet airglow spectrum, J. Dufay and Déjardin (1946) collected the wave lengths that had been published by a number of observers and subjected them to a critical analysis. They used a statistical method developed by Russell and Bowen (1929), wherein the number of airglow features coinciding (within the limits of observational accuracy) with computed wave lengths was compared with the number of coincidences expected from random fluctuations. If the ratio of the first to the second figure was of the order of unity, there could be little doubt that the identification was fortuitous. In this way, they succeeded in ruling out a large number of band systems from the airglow. Some additional evidence was obtained from the relative intensities of the bands and their degradation toward the red or ultraviolet. Thus they concluded that there was good evidence for the existence of the bands of Vegard-Kaplan of N_2; Herzberg of O_2; Schumann-Runge of O_2 (progressions with $v' = 0, 1$); and Lyman of N_2 ($v' = 0, 1$). It should be pointed out that, as only a few

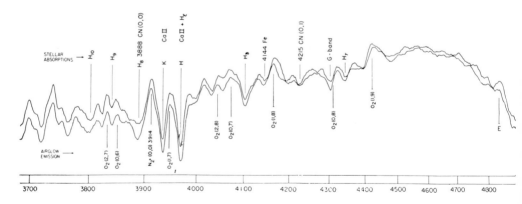

Fig. 15.—Two traces from a night-sky spectrum, 3700–4900 A, taken by Barbier. E is an unidentified emission. Absorption lines arising from the background stellar radiation and zodiacal light are indicated.

Vegard-Kaplan bands seem to appear in the airglow for $\lambda < 4000$ A, their conclusion on this system was based in part on observations and identifications in the green and blue (Cabannes and J. Dufay, 1946). A study of spectra covering the region from 5000 to 3000 A was made by Barbier (1947a), who favored the presence of the forbidden Vegard-Kaplan and Herzberg systems.

Recently, the study of the Vegard-Kaplan bands was reopened. The system is clearly defined in aurorae, where the relative band intensities are well correlated with the best available transition probabilities (Chamberlain and Oliver, 1953c); however, in the airglow the correlation is extremely poor. It is now *considered doubtful whether any Vegard-Kaplan bands appear in the airglow* (Barbier, 1953b; Chamberlain and Oliver, 1953b; Meinel, 1951c).

By a new statistical method, Barbier had concluded that there was another system of bands present, which he tentatively ascribed to CO. This identification was criticized by Herzberg (1953) and later withdrawn by Barbier (1953b).

The identification, originally proposed by J. Dufay (1941), of the Herzberg bands of O_2 is attractive, inasmuch as it is a forbidden system of low excitation (4.4 eV). In fact, the upper state has about the same energy as the ^1S level of O I (4.2 eV), which gives rise to the green line at 5577 A. Still, the identifications in general have been in an unsatisfactory state. Whereas most authors have agreed on the presence of the Herzberg system, there has been considerable doubt as to whether progressions with $v' \geq 2$ are present. Also, since there seemed to be fair coincidences in the cases of the Schumann-Runge and Lyman systems for only a couple of the low-energy progressions, the data have been insufficient to be certain of the identifications. Thus Auberger (1953) objected to the identification of the Herzberg bands and suggested that many of these features may arise from various forbidden systems of N_2. Götz and Nicolet (1951) have discussed the possible contribution of OH electronic bands for $\lambda < 3200$ A.

Only recently, when a high-resolution spectrum was obtained by Chamberlain (1954b), has an unambiguous evaluation of the ultraviolet bands become possible. The rotational structure on this plate shows (see Fig. 16) that these bands arise from *transitions with $v' \leq 7$ in the Herzberg system of O_2* and confirms most of the assignments made by Swings (1943). Also this spectrum shows that the Lyman bands of N_2, Schumann-Runge of O_2, and Vegard-Kaplan of N_2 are absent or extremely weak.

At $\lambda > 3600$ A the underlying starlight continuum becomes noticeable and tends to obscure the structure in the O_2 bands. Also, there are a few

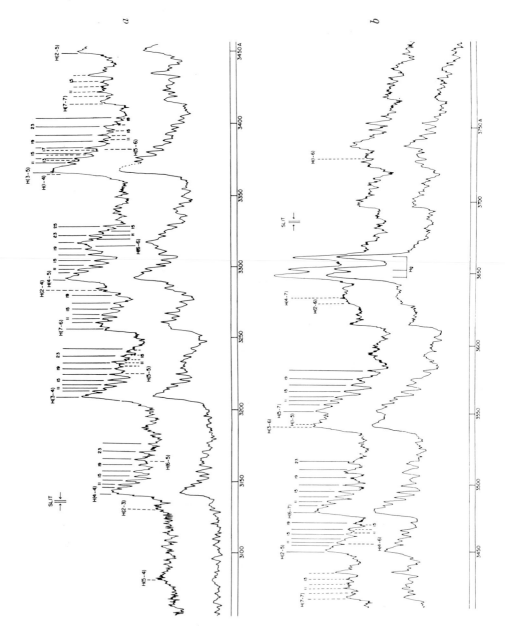

Fig. 16.—Microphotometer tracing of the ultraviolet airglow spectrum, from a 75-hour exposure by Chamberlain. Dispersion 23 A/mm. *a*, 3060–3450 A; *b*, 3400–3800 A. Rotational lines of the Herzberg O_2 bands are indicated; dashed lines represent uncertain identifications. Broida and Gaydon's (1954) vibrational numbering is used. The Hg lines are from street lights scattered by the sky.

bands in the ultraviolet still unidentified and a few more are suspected, because of the peculiar structure in some of the Herzberg bands (Chamberlain, 1955). In the blue region (Fig. 15) a number of O_2 bands may be identified superimposed on the continuum. The relative intensities of the bands indicate a steady increase in the populations of the levels in the upper state with increasing v'.

4.15. *Twilightglow spectra.*—The most outstanding difference between the twilightglow and the nightglow spectra are the enhancement in twilight of $\lambda\lambda$ 6300–6364 ${}^2_1[O\ I]$ and the Na–D lines and the appearance of the N_2^+ First Negative bands.

The Na flash was first observed by Bernard (1938a, 1939a), who interpreted the observations as indicating resonance excitation by solar radiation. Later Vegard and Kvifte (1945) suggested that the excitation was due to molecular dissociation by ultraviolet solar radiation. Their results were criticized by Bricard and Kastler (1950, 1952), who have derived a method for interpreting observations made on the zenith and horizon successively. They concluded from a study of intensities and polarization that resonance scattering was responsible. The most recent work is that of Hunten and Shepherd (1954), who have observed the Na flash with a photoelectric spectrometer that records one spectrum per minute. Their results favor the resonance process and indicate an exponential decrease of Na atoms above 80 km, with a fairly sharp cutoff below 80 km. This distribution agrees very well with that expected from an equilibrium between sodium and oxygen, as proposed by Chapman (1939). Some of the observed seasonal effects have been explained by Hunten (1954) in terms of a variation of the Na–Na$^+$ equilibrium (Bates, 1947).

During evening astronomical twilight, the ${}^2_1[O\ I]$ lines at 6300 and 6364 A decrease rapidly (Elvey, 1948); a slower decrease follows after astronomical twilight has ended. The reverse effect appears at morning twilight, except that the relative change is not quite so great as in the evening. The ${}^3_2[O\ I]$ line (λ 5577) does not seem to undergo any appreciable twilight enhancement.

M. Dufay (1953) has made a careful study of the twilight enhancement of a line at 5200 A, which probably arises from ${}^2_1[N\ I]$. Like its [O I] analogue, this line shows greater enhancement in evening than in morning twilight. Dufay noted considerable fluctuation in the intensity of λ 5200 from night to night and a seasonal variation with maximum intensity in the summer. There was no significant correlation of λ 5200 with magnetic activity, although the N_2^+ twilight bands were usually more enhanced when magnetic activity was high. Thus, if the twilight λ 5200 is indeed due to $^2_1$[N I] and cannot be ascribed to low-latitude aurorae, it presents an interesting problem in airglow excitation. Owing to the extremely long lifetime of the upper term (26 hours), the altitude of the emitting layer cannot be determined directly from the intensity variation during twilight, even if the levels are populated by absorption of solar radiation at 3466 A (see Fig. 9). Collisional de-excitation must be very important in order to quench the radiation within an hour or so after sunset. The λ 5200 twilight line will require more investigation before any real significance can be ascribed to its presence. At present, even the identification itself is somewhat doubtful.

The appearance of the N_2^+ at twilight has been investigated by Slipher (1933), Dufay and Dufay (1947), Vegard, Tønsberg, and Kvifte (1950), and others. M. Dufay (1948, 1953) determined that the emission originated from a fairly thick layer around 100 km high. The mechanism producing the bands is probably resonance excitation from the ground state of either N_2 or N_2^+. Whereas most investigators prefer the excitation from the ground state of N_2^+, the possibility of excitation directly from N_2 must be considered (Bates, 1949b). The decision as to which is more likely depends upon the equilibrium abundance of N_2^+. It is possible that sufficient N_2^+ exists, from the cosmic-ray flux, far-ultraviolet sunlight, or coronal X-rays, to scatter the λ 3914 solar radiation. If it is a resonance phenomenon, the rotational line intensities should show an intensity distribution influenced by absorption lines in the exciting solar spectrum, since the J-levels are probably not redistributed by collisions before emission. No observations with resolution sufficient to show this effect have yet been made.

4.2. Variations in Nightglow Spectra

During recent years it has become apparent that some of the nightglow emissions are "patchy," so that the spectrum varies slightly from one area in the sky to the next. In addition, there are slow variations of the *average* nightglow intensity over the sky. These variations occur through the night, with the seasons, with solar activity, and with latitude.

a) Dufay and Tcheng (1946) have made a thorough study of the *diurnal* variations of the strong atomic lines by means of numerous low-dispersion spectra. The λ 5577 $^3_2$[O I] line reaches a maximum around midnight and then decreases toward morning twilight. The midnight maximum was questioned by Elvey (1948) but has been verified by refined photoelectric techniques by Roach and Pettit (1951). On the other hand, λλ 6300–6364 $^2_1$[O I] and Na–D decrease in brightness after evening twilight and increase before morning, but are fairly stable during the main portion of the night. There are often considerable fluctuations from night to night, but the general trends seem quite definite. The 0–1 band of O_2 at λ 8645 A should show enhancement during early twilight by fluorescent scattering. Observation of this enhancement is still uncertain, although it has been reported by Meinel (1951c) and Berthier (1953a). Berthier also reports a smaller but significant enhancement for the OH bands. The latter cannot be a consequence of resonance scattering or fluorescence but can be explained only by an increase in the reaction rate of the photochemical process responsible for the OH emissions in the nightglow.

b) J. Dufay (1948) has discussed the *seasonal* variations from observations extending over 3 years. Again λ 6300 and the Na–D lines were similar in their average behavior, reaching a minimum in June and a maximum around December. The λ 5577 line was much more erratic but seemed to indicate a strong maximum in October and secondary maxima in February and May. Following a technique of Spencer Jones, Dufay represented the annual intensity variations by a harmonic series and noted that the fluctuations in λ 5577 could be represented fairly well by including a semiannual term with an amplitude of about half that of the annual term. The OH bands show considerable seasonal variation (Cabannes, Dufay, and Dufay, 1950) and probably do not differ greatly, on the average, from λ 6300 and the Na–D lines. The intensity ratio in the infrared of O_2/OH shows some seasonal effect (Dufay and Dufay, 1951); however, the 0–1 band of O_2 shows erratic behavior, sometimes becoming very intense (Meinel, 1950c). Berthier (1954) has found a close correlation between OH and Na over a period of a few nights.

Barbier (1954) has obtained some interesting preliminary results with a new 8-color photometer at Haute Provence. He has divided the radiations into two groups, according to their type of variation. Group A has λ 5577 $^3_2$[O I], the "continuum" (wave length unspecified by Barbier), the O_2 Herzberg bands, and the unidentified bands in the blue. Group B includes OH, Na, and λλ 6300–6364 of $^2_1$[O I]. The red oxygen lines were somewhat peculiar in their behavior, but otherwise emissions within the same group show a close correlation throughout the night.

c) Correlations with *solar activity* are less certain: there is some evidence that λ 5577 may exhibit a 27-day periodicity and may be stronger during sunspot maximum, but similar variations have not been reported for λλ 6300–6364 and Na–D. The λ 5577 line is very sensitive to auroral activity, which may affect the airglow intensity measurements even at middle latitudes (Vassy and Vassy, 1953). However, one would expect a weak aurora to affect the red lines as well.

d) Some of the airglow emissions may vary in intensity with *latitude*. Currie (1950) has reported that the over-all sky brightness at Saskatoon is appreciably greater than at lower latitudes, even when no visible aurora is present. The seasonal variations suggested, however, that the increased brightness was due to very faint auroral activity. Barbier and H. Pettit (1953) reported that the airglow λ 5577 line at College, Alaska, was about the same intensity as at middle latitudes, but that the Na–D line and the continuum, measured at 5210 A, were much weaker. Abadie, Vassy, and Vassy (1950) have made measurements on the latitude effect of λ 5577 and λλ 6300–6364 that suggest that the airglow is brighter at lower latitudes, but this conclusion is uncertain.

Very little is known of the latitude variations of the weaker features. Long auroral exposures at high latitudes often show airglow features, especially in the infrared, but it is difficult to make a comparison with low-latitude intensities. The OH bands have been photographed with approximately the same exposure times and the same spectrograph in northern Greenland, northern United States, and Puerto Rico (Oliver, private communication), but this merely indicates that the intensities are of the same order of magnitude.

4.3. HEIGHTS AND MOTIONS OF EMISSION REGIONS

Virtually all the information available on heights of the nightglow emission layers has been obtained by application of the van Rhijn (1921) method. Owing to the curvature of the earth, the intensity of emission at a given zenith angle depends on the emission height; hence measurements of the relative intensity at various zenith angles may be used to deduce this height. In practice there are several difficulties involved, with the net result that there is always a considerable uncertainty in any deduced height: (1) the corrections to the observed intensities for extinction and multiple scattering are difficult to determine; (2) the corrections for the background radiation (stars and zodiacal light) are likewise uncertain; (3) the van Rhijn method of reduction applies only to a fairly thin emission layer; (4) it has become obvious during the past decade that the emissions are not uniformly spread over the sky but occur primarily in moving clouds of variable brightness.

The effect of patchiness can be eliminated by averaging over a large number of observations made in various directions. On the other hand, 1, 2, and 3 above may be considered as problems in radiative-transfer theory that might be solved by the methods developed largely by Chandrasekhar (1950). Even a reasonably approximate solution of the complete transfer equation for the light of the night sky would be extremely difficult; but it should nevertheless be feasible, and the importance of determining emission heights would certainly justify the effort. The transfer equation should consider an emitting layer having a finite thickness; thus the intensity incident on the scattering atmosphere from any particular direction will depend on the height and the thickness of the layer. Because of diffuse reflection from the ground, there will also be some radiation incident upon the scattering atmosphere from below. The contribution from a layer at infinite distance (starlight and zodiacal light) should be represented. An exact treatment of Rayleigh scattering would include the effects of polarization on the scattering phase function (Chandrasekhar, 1950).

Barbier (1944, 1952, 1953a) took the first steps toward a realistic solution of the problem of atmospheric scattering and absorption. He made an approximate solution to the transfer equation and recently applied the results to an analysis of photometric measurements in the ultraviolet.

A further attempt to make the van Rhijn method suitable for height determinations has been made by Roach, Pettit, and Meinel (1955a). They have introduced corrections to the observations for Rayleigh scattering and ozone absorption (which must be treated separately) and have also corrected for the fairly large field of view of the photometer.

As Figure 17 shows, the effective absorption coefficient and the amount of extra-terrestrial (background) light have marked effects on $I(75°)/I(0°)$, and therefore on the deduced heights. Roach, Pettit, and Meinel have eliminated the starlight and zodiacal-light component by the following procedure: They assume the observations include just two components, one at infinity and one in the region 50–300 km. Throughout the latter region the ratio $I(40°)/I(0°)$ is almost independent of the height of the layer. Thus, after the data have been corrected for scattering, etc., an equal intensity is subtracted from all zenith distances until the ratio $I(40°)/I(0°)$ equals the "theoretical" value. The amount of intensity subtracted is taken to be the background component. The height of the emission component is then determined from the angular variation of this residual intensity at *large* zenith distances. In practice a second approximation with this technique is quite sufficient.

Strictly speaking, the observations can usually be represented fairly accurately by numerous combinations of a high layer and a fairly low layer. For example, Abadie, Vassy, and Vassy (1945) interpreted their measures on the red and green [O I] lines as arising from two layers each, one near 70 km and one at about 1000 km, the intensity of the first being about 35–40 per cent of the total. Roach, Pettit, and Meinel (1955b) have shown that an alternative interpretation of these data is an emission component (65 per cent of the total) at 130–150 km plus an infinity component. This interpretation gives a somewhat better representation of the observations than do the two finite layers of Abadie, Vassy, and Vassy.

To attribute the higher component to astronomical sources is more satisfactory than ascribing all emissions to two discrete atmospheric layers. Moreover, it is convincing that the *absolute* intensity of the background component, as derived by this method at four different wave lengths, agrees well with the combined intensity to be expected from starlight, galactic light, and zodiacal light.

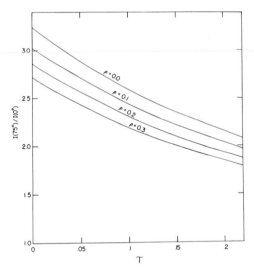

Fig. 17.—Curves showing the ratio of intensity at $z = 75°$ to that at the zenith, when the airglow emission is at 100 km, computed for different values of ρ and τ; ρ is the ratio of the surface brightness of light placed at infinity (that is, well outside the atmosphere) to that of the airglow; τ is the absorption coefficient of the (lower) atmosphere. Adapted from computations by Bates and Dalgarno (1953b).

In Table 1 are listed a number of recent determinations of emission heights. Inspection of the different heights obtained for the same emission illustrates the unsatisfactory state of affairs. The importance of τ, the effective absorption and scattering coefficient, for the deduced height cannot be overemphasized. For a given emission most observers agree quite well on the observed intensity distribution with zenith angle. Where they differ is in the determination of τ.

Probably the best method of resolving the difficulties associated with determining heights by the van Rhijn method would be direct measurements made by a night-fired rocket. Such an undertaking would be well worth the difficulties and expense involved, as it would give detailed and unambiguous data that would be highly useful in discussing ionospheric structure and reactions. Another method, which makes use of the patchi-

TABLE 1

RECENT DETERMINATIONS OF AIRGLOW EMISSION HEIGHTS
BY THE VAN RHIJN METHOD

Emission	Height (km)	Observer(s)	Reference
λ 5577 ${}_{2}^{3}$[O I].........	62–104*	Roach, Pettit, and Meinel	1955a
	215	J. Dufay and Tcheng	1954
	250	J. Dufay, Berthier, and Morignat	1953
	200	Roach, Williams, and Pettit	1953a
	200	Roach and Pettit	1952
	250	Roach and Pettit	1951
	215	Barbier, J. Dufay, and Williams	1951
	1000–400 (variable)	Abadie, Vassy, and Vassy	1950
	260	Karimov	1947
	103	J. Dufay and Tcheng	1947
	900 and 75 (two layers)†	Abadie, Vassy, and Vassy	1945
λ 6300 ${}_{1}^{2}$[O I].........	116–143*	Roach, Pettit, and Meinel	1955a
	275	Roach and Pettit	1952
	1000–400 (variable)	Abadie, Vassy, and Vassy	1950
	180	J. Dufay and Tcheng	1947
	1000 and 65 (two layers)‡	Abadie, Vassy, and Vassy	1945
λ 5893 Na I.........	108–129*	Roach, Pettit, and Meinel	1955a
	275	Roach and Pettit	1952
	310	Barbier and Roach	1950
	80	J. Dufay and Tcheng	1947
	150§	Barbier	1944
Herzberg O_2......... (U.V. region)	200	Barbier	1953a
	350	Barbier	1947b
"Vegard-Kaplan N_2".. (blue-green region)	900	Barbier	1947b
Meinel OH..........	150	Berthier	1953
	70	Roach, Pettit, and Williams	1950
	300	Huruhata	1950
Atmospheric O_2...... (Kaplan-Meinel band)	130	Berthier	1953
	Same as OH	Meinel	1950c
Continuum $\begin{cases} \lambda\ 5300... \\ \lambda\ 5180... \end{cases}$	43–78*	Roach, Pettit, and Meinel	1955a
	460	Barbier, J. Dufay, and Williams	1951

* Depends on assumptions regarding the extinction coefficient.
† Roach, Pettit, and Meinel (1955b) obtain 130 km in a re-evaluation of the data.
‡ Roach, Pettit, and Meinel (1955b) obtain 150 km in a re-evaluation of the data.
§ Based on the observational data of Garrique (1936).

ness of the emission layer, is simple triangulation. Roach, Williams, and Pettit (1953) have used this technique on λ 5577 and estimated the emission height at 180 km. Triangulation studies between Cactus Peak and Sacramento Peak have shown that the $\frac{3}{2}$[O I] emission is not from a thin, but rather from a *thick*, layer.

Most of the van Rhijn type deductions on λ 5577 seem to indicate a height between 200 and 250 km. Dufay and Tcheng (1947) and Roach and Pettit (1954) place λ 6300–6364 somewhat higher than the λ 5577 line, which agrees with the expectation of finding the nebular transition favoring lower densities. The height of 310 km for Na–D determined by Barbier and Roach (1950) is much higher than the twilight resonance emission layer. It is noted that the Na–D emission must originate below 100 km (Bates and Nicolet, 1950a) if the emission is derived from a photochemical reaction, which is the most likely process of excitation.

The low height of 70 km for OH (Roach, Pettit, and Williams, 1950) is probably more accurate than the 300 km determined by Huruhata (1950) or the 150 km found by Berthier (1953b), who have not adequately discussed the effects of atmospheric absorption and scattering, because the three sets of measured intensity ratios agree quite well. It is thus apparent that the discrepancies arise from disagreement on the effective absorption coefficient. Photochemical processes adequately explain the OH emissions, but again the height must be low, near 70–80 km, in order for such processes to occur at a sufficient rate.

The emission height of the 0–1 Atmospheric O_2 band is not significantly different from OH (Meinel, 1950c; Berthier, 1953b). This emission presents a unique problem which is discussed separately in Section 4.4.

The determinations of heights for the Herzberg and "Vegard-Kaplan" systems are uncertain because of the increased effect of scattering in the violet and because of the uncertainty in the contribution from other atmospheric emissions and from stellar light; similar difficulties arise with the height of the continuous emission. Although Barbier (1953a) estimates the Herzberg bands at 200 km, he points out that the data do not definitely exclude any height between 100 and 400 km.

During recent years Roach and his associates have made detailed studies of the diurnal variation of λ 5577. They find that although on the average there is a maximum of intensity near the middle of the night, there are significant variations from one night to the next and that the emitting layer is quite patchy rather than uniformly bright. A comparison of observations at Cactus Peak, California, and at Haute Provence, France, suggested that the excitation patterns were roughly similar at the two stations for the same local time (Roach, Williams, and Pettit, 1953*a*). Their suggestion was that the earth rotates under a more or less fixed excitation pattern, causing an apparent westward motion of the pattern. Recent observations (Roach, Williams, and Pettit, 1953*b;* Roach, Pettit, Williams, St. Amand, and Davis, 1953) indicate that an additional motion was superimposed upon the diurnal variation. The westward motion of this excitation pattern, although predominant during the first half of the night, stops about midnight and then reverses, although the motion is less systematic in the morning hours while tending toward the south and east. These observations might be related to those of Meinel and Schulte (1953) on the motions of auroral features, although the airglow velocities are much lower (about 100 m/sec compared with 500–1000 m/sec for aurorae). As is true for aurorae, the departures from a constant westward drift of the pattern raise some doubts as to whether the motions are due entirely to the rotation of the earth under a near-stationary source of excitation; ionospheric winds may be important also. It must be stated, however, that simultaneous observations at two stations 1160 km apart (Roach, Williams, St. Amand, Pettit, and Weldon, 1954; Manring, St. Amand, Pettit, Roach, Williams, and Weldon, 1954) have confirmed that the λ 5577 variations are primarily a function of local time.

4.4. Airglow Temperatures

Rotational and vibrational temperatures of the airglow entail the same problems of interpretation and many of the same observational difficulties as do auroral temperatures (see Sec. 3.4). Measurements of the Doppler width of [O I] lines again offer the best hope of obtaining high-altitude temperatures. J. Gauzit (1945) has raised some doubt as to whether a kinetic temperature (i.e., a Maxwellian distribution of velocities) for O I exists during the day, since the motions of the atoms are governed primarily by conservation-of-energy requirements related to the photodissociation of O_2. At night there is no such difficulty, but twilight measurements of the width of λ 5577 may not indicate true temperatures.

Spectrographic temperatures have been obtained from the rotational structure of the 0–1 band at λ 8645 A of the forbidden Atmospheric system of O_2. Meinel (1950*c*) found that usually the rotational temperature was 150° K with a variation of $\pm 20°$ K; but on one occasion, when the band was abnormally strong, the temperature was 200° $\pm$ 10° K. Similarly, Dufay and Dufay (1951) obtained $T_{rot} = 130°$ K. Branscomb (1952) has investigated the band system in the laboratory and concluded that collisions are frequent enough in the upper atmosphere to establish thermal equilibrium between the free particles and the rotational levels of the excited molecule before radiation is emitted.

Bates (chap. 12, p. 620) mentions that since the atmosphere reabsorbs radiation from the intense 0–0 band, the $v' = 0$ level will be continually re-populated, thereby enhancing the 0–1 transition. Chamberlain (1945a) investigated this effect by means of Chandrasekhar's (1950) radiative-transfer theory and found that in the absence of collisional de-excitation the fluorescence mechanism could account for as much as 75 per cent of the 0–1 emission and that this portion would arise from a thick layer at about 50 km. One possible interpretation of the low rotational temperature is that the weaker lines are scattered at lower heights than the stronger ones and are thereby reduced more by collisional de-excitation. The result would be *a distorted band profile which resembles the normal profile for a lower temperature.* An implication of the fluorescence mechanism seems to be that O_2 could be emitted from any level above the observed height of 70 km. Hence it is doubtful whether it is possible to determine the height where the original emission occurs, except from rocket flights into the primary emitting layer.

The most accurate rotational temperatures obtained from airglow spectra are from the Meinel (vibration-rotation) bands of OH. These bands arise from levels with fairly long lifetimes, and it is reasonable that they should indicate directly the kinetic temperature. Also, since the bands are probably emitted at fairly low heights (70 km at middle latitudes), where collisions would be rather frequent, the rotational temperatures will probably not depart greatly from the kinetic temperature. Meinel (1950b) found that the temperatures derived from several OH bands agreed best when the B_v value for the excited state is used, which indicates that redistribution does occur. In view of the steep temperature gradient around 70 km found from rocket observations, the temperature and height determinations of OH appear compatible.

The OH bands in the P-branch are easily resolved into the component lines, and from the relative intensities of these lines Meinel (1950b) obtained $T_{rot} = 260° \pm 5°$ K from several bands in the infrared. An alternative method of determining the rotational temperature is to compare the relative intensities of the P-, Q-, and R-branches. Although this method is less accurate, it leads to about the same value (Meinel, 1950b).

Several OH bands in the yellow and red were studied by Cabannes, Dufay, and Dufay (1950), who found considerable variation in the temperature, which ranged from 150° to 250° K. In the infrared, the French workers, using fairly low dispersion, estimated temperatures of 255°–

270° K from the maxima of the *P*-branches (Dufay and Dufay, 1951).

Spectra of the infrared and the visible OH bands were obtained by Chamberlain and Oliver (1953*a*) in northern Greenland, and these plates yielded temperatures between 300° and 350° K, considerably higher than the middle-latitude determinations. The altitude of the emitting layer in the Arctic has not been determined, but it is probably not greatly different from that height at lower latitudes. Thus the increased rotational temperature seems to be an indication of a higher kinetic temperature over the polar regions. This result is consistent with the idea that convection is of major importance in the transfer of energy in the high atmosphere below 80 km. Kuiper (1952, p. 418) has suggested that the large fluctuations in the O_2 temperatures might also be due to varying convection currents, and he relates this convection to the temperature minimum and formation of noctilucent clouds at about 80 km.

Rotational temperatures of 230° K were found for several features believed to be the N_2 Vegard-Kaplan bands by Cabannes and Dufay (1946) from the widths of the bands and from the distances between the maxima of the strong *R*- and very weak *P*-branch. The few bands upon which they based their determination lie in the 4050–4550 A region, where the stellar continuum is quite strong and greatly affected by absorption (see Sec. 4.13). Hence there are likely to be large errors in their differential wave lengths. Moreover, these measurements are extremely difficult to make with the low dispersion and resolution employed, and there is considerable doubt as to the identification of these bands (Sec. 4.14).

Swings (1943) and Barbier (1947*b, d*) have estimated temperatures from the O_2 Herzberg bands in the ultraviolet, and again the values are quite low (150°–220° K). From a plate with considerably better resolution, Chamberlain (1955) obtained $T_{rot} \leq 200°$ K, but was not able to assign a definite value. The difficulty is that the rotational maximum is very close to the band head, and consequently its position cannot be accurately determined. It is true that the rotational lines with large quantum numbers are resolved on the best spectra (cf. Fig. 16). But the uncertainties—in photographic photometry on extremely long exposures and in the theoretical line strengths for this system—render of dubious value temperatures based on the relative intensities of these lines. At any rate, the temperature derived from the Herzberg O_2 bands, like that from the Atmospheric O_2, is quite low. This spectroscopic result suggests that the emitting layer resides in the 80–100-km region (see chap. 10, Fig. 1) rather than the higher layers indicated by Barbier's (1953) photometric investigation.

4.5. AIRGLOW EXCITATION MECHANISMS

Reference is again made to chapter 12 by Bates for a detailed examination of various reactions that may take place in the upper atmosphere. We shall limit ourselves here to a few general remarks suggested by the observational data.

The view has been widely held that the entire nightglow may be explained on the basis of photochemical reactions; that is, solar radiant energy is absorbed during the day, stored in the form of ionization or dissociation, and then gradually released at night. This hypothesis has recently been questioned, however, and it is well to examine the observations in terms of other mechanisms.

The data on emission heights are too uncertain for arranging all the radiations according to their layer of formation, but it seems fairly definite that OH is formed at low levels by a photochemical reaction and that the green line of $^3_2[\text{O I}]$ and probably several other emissions originate appreciably higher. The motions of the luminous clouds emitting the green line raise the question of whether the excitation energy is linked with the energy of ionospheric winds or electric currents. Some airglow excitation may be produced by incoming solar or cosmic-ray particles; for example, Meinel (1953) has attributed λ 3914 N_2^+ to cosmic-ray excitation. S. K. Mitra (1945) reported a correlation between the airglow intensity and the F-layer ionization, but the physical relation between the two phenomena, if any, is not understood.[3]

The observed emissions of [O I], Na I, OH, and the forbidden bands of O_2 (see Fig. 18) have excitation potentials of less than 5 eV. The upper states of the Schumann-Runge O_2 and Vegard-Kaplan N_2 systems have potentials in the neighborhood of 6 eV. The N_2^+ level giving rise to λ 3914 lies 3.14 eV above the ground of N_2^+, which is quite consistent with the other observed energies. To excite λ 3914 from the ground state of N_2 would require an additional 15.6 eV, and it would seem strange that additional high-energy radiations are not observed in the airglow. According to Bates (1949b), the twilight N_2^+ emissions may be explained by assuming only small amounts of N_2^+ in the ionosphere, but further observational work is necessary to decide on the precise mechanisms.

In the airglow OH spectrum, the $v' = 9$ progression is the strongest, and no emission has been detected from $v' \geq 10$. Hence, the excitation mechanism must be one giving preference to $v' = 9$ and excluding higher excitation. Bates and Nicolet (1950b) and Herzberg (1951) suggested the presence of a resonance reaction, whereby atomic hydrogen and ozone combine to form O_2 and OH ($v' \leq 9$). But Oldenberg (1952) has raised

3. Recently Nicolet (*Phys. Rev.*, **93**, 633, 1954) has suggested that 5577 is excited in the F by dissociative recombination of O_2^+.

objections to this mechanism on the grounds that $v' = 9$ is not necessarily the preferred, but only the highest, level excited by their mechanism and that the observations are thus not adequately explained. Recently, however, McKinley, Garvin, and Boudart (J. Chem. Phys., *in press*) have produced the bands with $v' \leq 9$ by mixing ozone with atomic hydrogen. The intensities in their infrared spectrum closely resemble those in the airglow spectra, with $v' = 9$ giving the strongest bands. This work seems

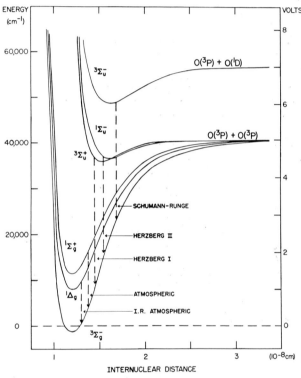

FIG. 18.—Potential-energy diagram for the known lower electronic states of O_2. Identified band systems, some of which have so far been observed in absorption only, are indicated.

to substantiate completely the $H + O_3$ reaction as the source of the airglow OH bands.

Thus far, OH is the only nightglow source whose excitation is understood reasonably well. However, the study of the laboratory afterglows promises much relevant information (Oldenberg, 1953). In particular, the intensities of bands in oxygen afterglows (Kaplan, 1947*a, b;* Broida and Gaydon, 1954) show many similarities to O_2 bands in the infrared and ultraviolet airglow. It seems likely that the excitation in both afterglow and airglow occurs as a result of reassociation of two oxygen atoms (see Fig. 18), although this is by no means certain.

REFERENCES

ABADIE, P.; VASSY, A.;
and Vassy, E.   1945   *Ann. de géophys.*, **1**, 189.
                       1950   *Ibid.*, **5**, 157.
ALFVÉN, H.   1948   *Emission Spectra of the Night Sky and Aurora* ("Reports of the Gassiot Committee" [London: The Physical Society]), p. 132.
ALLER, L. H.   1953   *Astrophysics* (New York: Ronald Press Co.).
ALLER, L. H.; UFFORD,
C. W.; and VAN
VLECK, J. H.   1949   *Ap. J.*, **109**, 42.
APPLETON, E. V.; NAI-
SMITH, R.; and
BUILDER, G.   1933   *Nature*, **132**, 340.
AUBERGER, L.   1953   *J. Geophys. Res.*, **58**, 231.
BABCOCK, H. D.   1923   *Ap. J.*, **57**, 209.
BAKER, J. G., and
MENZEL, D. H.   1938   *Ap. J.*, **88**, 52.
BARBIER, D.   1944   *Ann. de géophys.*, **1**, 144.
                       1945   *Ibid.*, p. 224.
                       1947a   *Ann. d'ap.*, **10**, 47.
                       1947b   *Ibid.*, **10**, 141.
                       1947c   *Ann. de géophys.*, **3**, 227.
                       1947d   *C.R. Acad. Sci., Paris*, **224**, 635.
                       1952   *Ann. d'ap.*, **15**, 247.
                       1953a   *Ibid.*, **16**, 96.
                       1953b   *C.R. Acad. Sci., Paris*, **237**, 599.
                       1954   *Ibid.*, **238**, 770.
BARBIER, D.; DUFAY, J.;
and WILLIAMS, D.   1951   *Ann. d'ap.*, **14**, 399.
BARBIER, D., and
PETTIT, H.   1953   *Ann. de géophys.*, **8**, 232.
BARBIER, D., and
ROACH, F. E.   1950   *Trans. Amer. Geophys. Union*, **31**, 7.
BARBIER, D., and
WILLIAMS, D. R.   1951   *J. Geophys. Res.*, **14**, 121.
BATES, D. R.   1946   *M.N.*, **106**, 423.
                       1947   *Terr. Mag.*, **52**, 71.
                       1949a   *Proc. R. Soc. London, A*, **196**, 217.
                       1949b   *Ibid.*, p. 562.
                       1952   *M.N.*, **112**, 614.
BATES, D. R., and
DALGARNO, A.   1953a   *Proc. Phys. Soc. London, A*, **66**, 972.
                       1953b   *J. Atm. Terr. Phys.*, **4**, 112.
BATES, D. R., and
DAMGAARD, A.   1949   *Phil. Trans. R. Soc. London, A*, **242**, 101.

BATES, D. R., and
  GRIFFING, G.   1953a   *J. Atm. Terr. Phys.*, **3**, 212.
                       1953b   *Proc. Phys. Soc. London*, *A*, **66**, 961.

BATES, D. R.; MASSEY,
  H. S. W.; and PEARSE,
  R. W. B.   1948   *Emission Spectra of the Night Sky and Aurora* ("Reports of the Gassiot Committee" [London: The Physical Society]), p. 97.

BATES, D. R., and
  NICOLET, M.   1950a   *J. Geophys. Res.*, **55**, 235.
                       1950b   *Ibid.*, p. 301.

BENNETT, W. H., and
  HULBERT, E. O.   1954   *Phys. Rev.*, **95**, 315.

BERNARD, R.   1938a   *C.R. Acad. Sci., Paris*, **206**, 928.
                       1938b   *Nature*, **142**, 164.
                       1939a   *Ap. J.*, **89**, 133.
                       1939b   *Phys. Rev.*, **55**, 511.
                       1941   *Ann. d'ap.*, **4**, 13.
                       1948a   *Emission Spectra of the Night Sky and Aurora* ("Reports of the Gassiot Committee" [London: The Physical Society]), p. 91.
                       1948b   *Ibid.*, p. 93.

BERTHIER, P.   1953a   *C.R. Acad. Sci., Paris*, **236**, 1808.
                       1953b   *Ibid.*, **237**, 928.
                       1954   *Ibid.*, **238**, 263.

BIRKELAND, K.   1896   *Arch. Sci. Phys.* (Geneva), **1**, 497.

BLAMONT, J.-E.   1953   *C.R. Acad. Sci., Paris*, **237**, 1320.

BOWEN, I. S.   1936   *Rev. Mod. Phys.*, **8**, 55.

BOWLES, K.   1952   *J. Geophys. Res.*, **57**, 191.

BRANSCOMB, L. M.   1950   *Phys. Rev.*, **79**, 619.
                       1952   *Ibid.*, **86**, 258.

BRICARD, J., and
  KASTLER, A.   1950   *Ann de géophys.*, **6**, 286.
                       1952   *Mém. Soc. R. Sci. Liége*, **12**, 87 (proceedings of the Liége conference, September, 1951).

BROIDA, H. P., and
  GAYDON, A. G.   1954   *Proc. R. Soc. London*, *A*, **222**, 181.

BRÜCK, H. A., and
  RUTLLANT, F.   1946   *M.N.*, **106**, 130.

CABANNES, J., and
  DUFAY, J.   1944   *Ann. de géophys.*, **1**, 1.
                       1946   *Ibid.*, **2**, 290.

CABANNES, J.; DUFAY,
  J.; and DUFAY, M.   1950   *C.R. Acad. Sci., Paris*, **230**, 1233.

CABANNES, J.; DUFAY,
  J.; and GAUZIT, J.   1938   *Ap. J.*, **88**, 164.
                       1942   *L'Astronomie*, **56**, 149.

CHAMBERLAIN, J. W.   1953   *Ap. J.*, **117**, 387.
                         1954*a* *Ibid.*, **119**, 328.
                         1954*b* *C.R. Acad. Sci., Paris*, **238**, 1329.
                         1954*c* *Ap. J.*, **120**, 360.
                         1954*d* *Ibid.*, Vol. **120**, No. 3.
                         1955   *Ibid.*, Vol. **121**, No. 1.
CHAMBERLAIN, J. W.;
    FAN, C. Y.; and
    MEINEL, A. B.   1954   *Ap. J.*, Vol. **120**, No. 3.
CHAMBERLAIN, J. W.,
    and OLIVER, N. J.   1953*a* *Phys. Rev.*, **90**, 1118.
                         1953*b* *Ap. J.*, **118**, 197.
                         1953*c* *J. Geophys. Res.*, **58**, 457.
CHAMBERLAIN, J. W.,
    and ROESLER, F. L.   1955   *Ap. J.*, Vol. **121**, No. 2.
CHANDRASEKHAR, S.   1950   *Radiative Transfer* (Oxford: Clarendon Press).
CHAPMAN, R. P., and
    CURRIE, B. W.   1953   *J. Geophys. Res.*, **58**, 363.
CHAPMAN, S.   1939   *Ap. J.*, **90**, 309.
                         1948   *Emission Spectra of the Night Sky and Aurora* ("Reports of the Gassiot Committee" [London: The Physical Society]), p. 120.
CHAPMAN, S., and FER-
    RARO, V. C. A.   1931   *Terr. Mag.*, **36**, 77, 171, and 186.
                         1932   *Ibid.*, **37**, 147 and 421.
                         1933   *Ibid.*, **38**, 79.
                         1940   *Ibid.*, **45**, 245.
CLAAS, W. J.   1951   *Recherches Astr. Utrecht*, Vol. **12**, No. 1.
COURTES, G.   1950   *C.R. Acad. Sci., Paris*, **231**, 62.
CURRIE, B. W.; FOR-
    SYTH, P. A.; and
    VAWTER, F. E.   1953   *J. Geophys. Res.*, **58**, 179.
DAHLSTROM, C. E., and
    HUNTEN, D. M.   1951   *Phys. Rev.*, **84**, 378.
DALBY, F. W., and
    DOUGLAS, A. E.   1951   *Phys. Rev.*, **84**, 843.
DÉJARDIN, G.; JANIN, J.;
    and PEYRON, M.   1953   *Cahiers de physique*, No. 46.
DODSON, H. W.; HEDE-
    MAN, E. R.; and
    CHAMBERLAIN, J. W.   1953   *Ap. J.*, **117**, 66.
DODSON, H. W.; HEDE-
    MAN, E. R.; and
    OWREN, L.   1953   *Ap. J.*, **118**, 169.
DOUGLAS, A. E.   1953   *Ap. J.*, **117**, 380.

DUFAY, J.   1928   *Bull. Obs. Lyon*, **10**, No. 9, 81.
                                    1941   *C.R. Acad. Sci., Paris*, **213**, 284.
                                    1948   *Emission Spectra of the Night Sky and Aurora* ("Reports of the Gassiot Committee" [London: The Physical Society]), p. 51.
                                    1951   *Ann. de géophys.*, **7**, 1.

DUFAY, J.; BERTHIER,
  P.; and MORIGNAT, B.   1953   *C.R. Acad. Sci., Paris*, **237**, 828.
DUFAY, J., and
  DÉJARDIN, G.   1946   *Ann. de géophys.*, **2**, 249.
DUFAY, J., and DUFAY,
  M.   1947   *C.R. Acad. Sci., Paris*, **224**, 1834.
                            1951   *Ibid.*, **232**, 426.

DUFAY, J., and TCHENG
  MAO-LIN   1942   *Cahiers de phys.*, **2**, 51.
                            1946   *Ann. de géophys.*, **2**, 189.
                            1947   *Ibid.*, **3**, 282.
                            1954   *Ibid.*, **10**, 1.
DUFAY, M.   1948   *C.R. Acad. Sci., Paris*, **227**, 777.
                            1951   *Ibid.*, **233**, 419.
                            1953   *Ann. de phys.*, **8**, 813.

DUFFENDACK, O. S.;
  REVONS, R. W.;
  and ROY, A. S.   1934   *Phys. Rev.*, **45**, 807.
ELVEY, C. T.   1948   *Emission Spectra of the Night Sky and Aurora* ("Reports of the Gassiot Committee" [London: The Physical Society]), p. 16.
                            1950   *Ap. J.*, **111**, 432.

ELVEY, C. T.; SWINGS,
  P.; and LINKE, W.   1941   *Ap. J.*, **93**, 337.
FAN, C. Y.   1954   *Ap. J.*, **119**, 294.
FAN, C. Y., and MEINEL,
  A. B.   1953   *Ap. J.*, **118**, 205.
FORSYTH, P. A.   1953   *J. Geophys. Res.*, **58**, 53.
FORSYTH, P. A.; PETRIE,
  W.; and CURRIE,
  B. W.   1949   *Nature*, **164**, 453.
                            1950   *Canadian J. Res.*, A, **28**, 324.

FRASER, P. A.; JARMAIN,
  W. R.; and NICHOLLS,
  R. W.   1954   *Ap. J.*, **119**, 286.
FULLER, V. R., and
  BRAMHALL, E. H.   1937   *Misc. Pub. U. Alaska*, Vol. **3**.
GARRIQUE, H.   1936   *C.R. Acad. Sci., Paris*, **202**, 1807.
GARSTANG, R. H.   1951   *M.N.*, **111**, 115.
                            1952   *Ap. J.*, **115**, 506.

GARTLEIN, G. W.   1950   *Trans. Amer. Geophys. Union*, **31**, 18.
GARTLEIN, G. W., and
    SHERMAN, D.   1952   *Mém. Soc. R. Sci. Liége*, **12**, 187 (proceedings of the
                                        Liége conference, September, 1951).

GARTLEIN, G. W., and
    SPRAGUE, G.   1952   *Mém. Soc. R. Sci. Liége*, **12**, 191 (proceedings of the
                                        Liége conference, September, 1951).

GAUZIT, J.   1945   *Ann. de géophys.*, **1**, 233.
GÖTZ, F. W. P.   1947   *Experimentia*, **3**, 185.
GÖTZ, F. W. P., and
    NICOLET, M.   1951   *J. Geophys. Res.*, **56**, 577.
GOLDBERG, L.   1935   *Ap. J.*, **82**, 1.
                                 1936   *Ibid.*, **84**, 11.
                                 1939   *Ibid.*, **90**, 414.

GRIFFING, G. W., and
    STEWART, A. L.   1954   *J. Atm. Terr. Phys.*, **4**, 339.
HARANG, L.   1945   *Geofys. Pub.*, Vol. **16**, No. 6.
                                 1951   *The Aurorae* (New York: John Wiley & Sons).

HARANG, L., and LAND-
    MARK, B.   1954   *J. Atm. Terr. Phys.*, **4**, 322.
HARRISON, G. R.   1949   *J. Opt. Soc. Amer.*, **39**, 522.
HEPPNER, J. P.; BYRNE,
    E. C.; and BELON,
    A. E.   1952   *J. Geophys. Res.*, **57**, 121.
HERMAN, R.   1951   *C.R. Acad. Sci., Paris*, **233**, 926.
HERMAN, R. C., and
    HORNBECK, G. A.   1953   *Ap. J.*, **118**, 214.
HERZBERG, G.   1950   *Spectra of Diatomic Molecules* (2d ed.; New York:
                                        D. Van Nostrand Co.), p. 278.
                                 1951   *J.R.A.S. Canada*, **45**, 100.
                                 1953   *Canadian J. Phys.*, **31**, 657.
HULBURT, E. O.   1954   *Scientific Month.*, **78**, 100.
HUNTEN, D. M.   1953   *Canadian J. Phys.*, **31**, 681.
                                 1954   *J. Atm. Terr. Phys.*, **5**, 44.

HUNTEN, D. M., and
    SHEPHERD, G. G.   1954   *J. Atm. Terr. Phys.*, **5**, 57.
HURUHATA, MASAAKI   1950   *Rept. Ionospheric Res. Japan*, **4**, 137.
JARMAIN, W.; FRAṢER,
    P.; and NICHOLLS,
    R. W.   1953   *Ap. J.*, **118**, 228.
JENSEN, R. E., and
    CURRIE, B. W.   1953   *J. Geophys. Res.*, **58**, 201.
JONES, A. V., and GUSH,
    H.   1953   *Nature*, **172**, 496.
JONES, A. V.; HUNTEN,
    D. M.; and SHEPHERD,
    G. G.   1953   *Ap. J.*, **118**, 350.

KAPLAN, J.   1947a   *Nature*, **159**, 673.
                                1947b   *Phys. Rev.*, **71**, 274.
KARIMOV, M. G.   1947   *A.J. Soviet Union*, **24**, 118.
KASTLER, A.   1946   *Ann. de géophys.*, **2**, 315.
KRASSOVSKY, V. J.   1949   *Doklady Akad. Nauk. SSSR*, Vol. **66**, No. 1.
                                1950   *Ibid.*, **70**, 999.
KRON, G. E.   1950   *Pub. A.S.P.*, **62**, 264.
KUIPER, G. P.   1952   *The Atmospheres of the Earth and Planets* (rev. ed.;
                                        Chicago: University of Chicago Press).

McLENNAN, J. C., and
  SHRUM, G. M.   1925   *Proc. R. Soc. London, A*, **108**, 501.
McNAMARA, A. G., and
  CURRIE, B. W.   1954   *J. Geophys. Res.*, **59**, 279.
MANRING, E.; ST.
  AMAND, P.; PETTIT,
  H. B.; ROACH, F. E.;
  WILLIAMS, D. R.;
  and WELDON, R. G.   1954   *Ann. d'ap.*, **17**, 186.
MARTYN, D. F.   1951   *Nature*, **167**, 92.
MASSEY, H. S. W.   1949   *Rept. Prog. Phys.*, **12**, 248.
MEINEL, A. B.   1948   *Pub. A.S.P.*, **60**, 373.
                                1950a   *Ap. J.*, **111**, 555.
                                1950b   *Ibid.*, **112**, 120.
                                1950c   *Ibid.*, p. 464.
                                1950d   *Trans. Amer. Geophys. Union*, **31**, 21.
                                1951a   *Ap. J.*, **113**, 50 and 583.
                                1951b   *Ibid.*, **114**, 431.
                                1951c   *Rept. Prog. Phys.*, **14**, 121.
                                1952   *Mém. Soc. R. Sci. Liége*, **12**, 203 (proceedings of the
                                        Liége conference, September, 1951).
                                1953   *Ap. J.*, **118**, 200.
                                1954   *Proceedings of the Conference on Auroral Physics,
                                        London, Ontario, July, 1951*, ed. N. C. GERSON
                                        (Air Force Cambridge Research Center, "Geo-
                                        physical Research Papers," No. 30).
MEINEL, A. B., and Fan,
  C. Y.   1952   *Ap. J.*, **115**, 330.
MEINEL, A. B.; NE-
  GAARD, B. J.; and
  CHAMBERLAIN, J. W.   1954   *J. Geophys. Res.*, **59**, 407.
MEINEL, A. B., and
  SCHULTE, D. H.,   1953   *Ap. J.*, **117**, 454.
MENZEL, D. H., and
  PEKERIS, C. L.   1935   *M.N.*, **96**, 77.
MITRA, S. K.   1945   *Nature*, **155**, 786.
MOORE, R. K.   1951   *J. Geophys. Res.*, **56**, 97.
NICOLET, M.   1938   *Ann. d'ap.*, **1**, 381.
                                1939   *Bull. Cl. d. Sci., Acad. R. Belgique*, **25**, 81.

OLDENBERG, O.   1934   *Phys. Rev.*, **46**, 210.
                                 1952   *Ibid.*, **87**, 786.
                                 1953   *Ibid.*, **90**, 727.

OLIVER, N. J.; WOLNIK,
S. J.; SCANLON, J. C.;
and CHAMBERLAIN,
J. W.   1953   *J. Opt. Soc. Amer.*, **43**, 710.

OSTERBROCK, D., and
SHARPLESS, S.   1951   *Ap. J.*, **113**, 222.

PASTERNACK, S.   1940   *Ap. J.*, **92**, 129.

PETRIE, W.   1947   *Canadian J. Res.*, *A*, **25**, 293.
                                 1948   *Ibid.*, **26**, 359.
                                 1950   *J. Geophys. Res.*, **55**, 143.
                                 1952a   *Phys. Rev.*, **86**, 790.
                                 1952b   *Ibid.*, **87**, 1002.
                                 1953   *J. Atm. Terr. Phys.*, **4**, 5.

PETRIE, W., and SMALL,
R.   1952a   *J. Geophys. Res.*, **57**, 51.
                                 1952b   *Ap. J.*, **116**, 433.
                                 1953   *Canadian J. Phys.*, **31**, 911.

RAYLEIGH, LORD   1920   *Nature*, **106**, 8.

RICHARDSON, R. S.   1944   *Trans. Amer. Geophys. Union*, **25**, 558.

ROACH, F. E., and
PETTIT, H. B.   1951   *J. Geophys. Res.*, **56**, 325.
                                 1952   *Mém. Soc. R. Sci. Liége*, **12**, 13 (proceedings of the
                                         Liége conference, September, 1951).

ROACH, F. E.; PETTIT,
H. B.; and MEINEL,
A. B.   1955a   *Ap. J.*, Vol. **121** (in press).
                                 1955b   *Ap. J.*, Vol. **121** (in press).

ROACH, F. E.; PETTIT,
H. B.; and WILLIAMS,
D. R.   1950   *J. Geophys. Res.*, **55**, 183.

ROACH, F. E.; PETTIT,
H. B.; WILLIAMS,
D. R.; ST. AMAND, P.;
and DAVIS, D. N.   1953   *Ann. d'ap.*, **16**, 185.

ROACH, F. E.; WILLIAMS,
D. R.; and PETTIT,
H. B.   1953a   *J. Geophys. Res.*, **58**, 73.
                                 1953b   *Ap. J.*, **117**, 456.

ROACH, F. E.; WILLIAMS,
D. R.; ST. AMAND, P.;
PETTIT, H. B.; and
WELDON, R. G.   1954   *Ann. d'ap.*, **17**, 172.

RODIONOV, S. F., and
FISHKOVA, L. M.   1950   *Doklady Akad. Nauk SSSR*, **70**, 1001.

ROSSELAND, S., and
    STEENSHOLD, G.   1933   *Det. Norsk Vidensk. Akad. Avk.*, Vol. **1**, No. 5.
RUSSELL, H. N.   1936   *Ap. J.*, **83**, 129.
RUSSELL, H. N., and
    BOWEN, I. S.   1929   *Ap. J.*, **69**, 196.
SAYERS, N. D.   1952   *Proc. Phys. Soc. London, A*, **65**, 152.
SEATON, M. J.   1953a   *Phil. Trans. R. Soc. London*, **245**, 469.
                            1953b   *Proc. R. Soc. London*, **218**, 400.
                            1954a   *J. Atm. Terr. Phys.*, **4**, 285.
                            1954b   *Ibid.*, p. 295.
SLIPHER, V. M.   1933   *M.N.*, **93**, 666.
STEBBINS, J.; WHITFORD,
    A. E.; and SWINGS, P.   1944   *Phys. Rev.*, **66**, 225.
                            1945   *Ap. J.*, **101**, 39.
STØRMER, C.   1904   *Kristiania, Skr. Vidensk. Selsk.*, **1**, 3.
                            1916   *Terr. Mag.*, **21**, 153.
                            1938   *Nature*, **142**, 1034.
                            1946   *Terr. Mag.*, **51**, 501.
                            1948   *Ibid.*, **53**, 251.
                            1949   *C.R. Acad. Sci., Paris*, **228**, 1904.
                            1952   *Geofys. Pub. Oslo*, Vol. **18**, No. 7.
SWINGS, P.   1943   *Ap. J.*, **97**, 72.
UFFORD, C. W., and
    GILMOUR, R. M.   1950   *Ap. J.*, **111**, 580.
UNSÖLD, A.   1948   *Zs. f. Ap.*, **24**, 306.
VAN ALLEN, J.   1954   Private communication.
VAN RHIJN, P. J.   1921   *Pub. Astr. Lab. Groningen*, No. 21.
VASSY, A., and VASSY, E.   1953   *J. Geophys. Res.*, **58**, 283.
VEGARD, L.   1949   *Proc. of First Meeting, Mixed Commission on
                                     Ionosphere, Conseil International des Unions
                                     Scientifiques* (Brussels: Secrétariat Général,
                                     U.R.S.I.), p. 111.
                            1950   *C. R. Acad. Sci., Paris*, **230**, 1884.
                            1952   *Nature*, **170**, 536.
VEGARD, L., and
    HARANG, L.   1934   *Geofys. Pub.*, Vol. **11**, No. 1.
VEGARD, L., and
    KVIFTE, G.   1945   *Geofys. Pub.*, Vol. **16**, No. 7.
                            1950   *Ibid.*, Vol. **18**, No. 3.
VEGARD, L., and
    TØNSBERG, E.   1937   *Geofys. Pub.*, Vol. **11**, No. 16.
                            1944   *Ibid.*, Vol. **16**, No. 2.
VEGARD, L.; TØNSBERG,
    E.; and KVIFTE, G.   1950   *Geofys. Pub.*, Vol. **18**, No. 4.
VESTINE, E. H.   1954   *J. Geophys. Res.*, **59**, 93.
WEISSLER, G. L.   1952   *Mém. Soc. R. Sci. Liége*, **12**, 281 (proceedings of
                                     the Liége conference, September, 1951).

CHAPTER 12

The Physics of the Upper Atmosphere

By D. R. BATES
Queen's University, Belfast, Northern Ireland

1. INTRODUCTION

ONLY certain selected aspects of the physics of the upper atmosphere will be considered in this chapter. The main discussion will relate to the photochemistry of the constituent gases, the formation and equilibrium of the ionized layers, the airglow, the aurorae, the temperature, and the thermobalance. Several other topics will be treated briefly. As will be seen, few of the problems can be regarded as satisfactorily solved.

2. THE PHOTOCHEMISTRY OF THE CONSTITUENTS

2.1. OXYGEN

Photodissociation of molecular oxygen can take place either through the intense Schumann-Runge continuum, commencing at λ 1760,

$$O_2 + h\nu \rightarrow O\,(^3P) + O\,(^1D)\,, \tag{1}$$

or through the feeble Herzberg continuum, commencing at λ 2420,

$$O_2 + h\nu \rightarrow 2O\,(^3P)\,. \tag{2}$$

The absorption cross-section at the peak of the former is almost 2×10^{-17} cm^2; that near the threshold of the latter is only some 10^{-24}–10^{-23} cm^2 (cf. Fabry, 1950; Ditchburn, 1954). Because of the rapid attenuation of the incoming radiation, the photodissociation due to the Schumann-Runge continuum is confined to great altitudes; in contrast, that due to the Herzberg continuum is significant throughout the atmosphere. There are two maxima to the total photodissociation rate, one near the 100-km level, and another near the 30-km level. The approximate yield of oxygen atoms is 1×10^7/cm^3 sec in the upper, and 5×10^7/cm^3 sec in the lower

(Bates and Witherspoon, 1952). These oxygen atoms may recombine either in the presence of a third body,

$$O + O + M \rightarrow O_2 + M , \tag{3}$$

or with the emission of a stabilizing photon,

$$O + O \rightarrow O_2 + h\nu . \tag{4}$$

Alternatively, they may unite with oxygen molecules,

$$O + O_2 + M \rightarrow O_3 + M . \tag{5}$$

The ozone thus formed may be destroyed by the collision process,

$$O_3 + O \rightarrow 2O_2 , \tag{6}$$

and by photodissociation in the strong Hartley continuum,

$$O_3 + h\nu \rightarrow O_2 + O(^1D) , \tag{7}$$

or in the weak Chappuis continuum,

$$O_3 + h\nu \rightarrow O_2 + O(^3P) , \tag{8}$$

the maxima of which lie near $\lambda\ 2550$ and $\lambda\ 6100$, respectively (cf. Fabry, 1950).

Chapman (1930a, b; 1931a), Mecke (1931), Wulf and Deming (1936, 1937, 1938), Nicolet (1945a), Rakshit (1947), Penndorf (1949), and others have investigated the equilibrium resulting from these mechanisms and have succeeded in determining the general features of the distribution of the oxygen allotropes. Unfortunately, a precise calculation is not yet possible, owing mainly to the lack of laboratory data. To indicate the extent of the uncertainties, the kind of assumption that must be made will be briefly described.

As there is no evidence on the effectiveness of reaction (3), little can be done but to suppose that its rate coefficient k_{11} is of the normal order of magnitude for reactions of this type, that is, that at the temperature T,

$$k_{11} = 5 \times 10^{-34} T^{1/2} \text{ cm}^6/\text{sec} . \tag{9}$$

The $T^{1/2}$ power law is conventional but is without justification (Bates and Nicolet, 1950a). Sometimes an attempt is made to take account of the fact that the different species of atmospheric particle may not be equally effective as third bodies. This refinement is, however, rather unrealistic in view of the status of the basic approximation. If k_{11} is not seriously over-estimated by (9), then (4) is probably unimportant compared with (3) up to at least the 110-km level; and it is usually neglected.

Eucken and Patat (1936) have measured k_{12}/k_{13}, the ratio of the rate coefficient of (5) to that of (6), over a considerable temperature range. If it is assumed that no activation energy is associated with the former and no steric hindrance with the latter, it is possible to deduce the values of the separate coefficients (cf. Bates and Nicolet, 1950a). As need scarcely be emphasized, the reliability of the figures obtained in this way is poor.

Since the absorption cross-sections are known (Fabry, 1950; Ditchburn, 1954) and since fair estimates are available for the intensity of the incident solar flux,[1] J_2 and J_3, the reciprocals of the lifetimes of O_2 and O_3 toward photodissociation through (1) and (2) and through (7) and (8), respectively, can be computed. The errors are unlikely to be serious except at very low altitudes, where uncertainties in the degree of attenuation of the far-ultraviolet radiation enter.

Various complications also arise. The processes cited are not the only ones operative; thus a significant loss of O and O_3 may be caused by collisions with such atoms and radicals as H, OH, and HO_2 (Bates and Nicolet, 1950a) and by various surface reactions at or near ground level. Again, true local equilibrium does not necessarily exist at all altitudes; in the troposphere, for example, the equilibrium between O and O_3 is rapidly established, but the production of the equilibrium number of *odd* oxygen atoms (in the form of O and O_3) requires many days, so that mixing effects may be important.

From the remarks in the preceding paragraphs it is clear that a proper quantitative treatment of the photochemistry of the atmospheric oxygen cannot be developed at present. Nevertheless, some useful conclusions have been reached. The general equations governing the equilibrium may be readily written down; but as they are rather cumbersome, it is convenient to consider the simplified versions of them which are valid in certain specific regions.

Above about the 70-km level,

$$\frac{n(O)}{n(O_2)} \simeq \left\{ \frac{J_2}{k_{11} n(M) \, n(O_2)} \right\}^{1/2}, \tag{10}$$

where each n denotes the concentration of the constituent indicated. As Chapman (1930b) has pointed out, it follows at once that oxygen must be almost completely dissociated at sufficiently great altitudes; for with increasing altitude $n(M) n(O_2)$ becomes smaller and J_2 becomes larger (tending asymptotically to the value at zero optical depth). The detailed cal-

---

1. This flux has now been measured directly for $\lambda > 910$ A; cf. Vol. I, chap. 9. Sec. 9.

culations of the various later workers show that, at least if mixing effects[2] are neglected, the transition from the molecular to the atomic form takes place in a narrow altitude range located near the 100-km level. Figure 1 (taken from Bates and Witherspoon, 1952) shows the type of distribution obtained. The only direct observational evidence on the state of oxygen at great altitudes is that O I lines are prominent in the spectra of aurorae

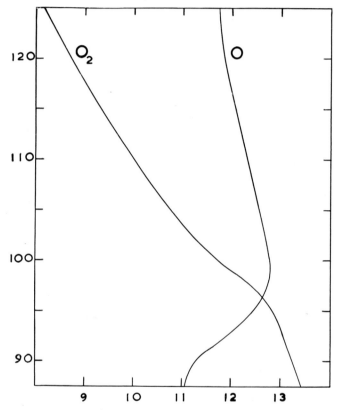

Fig. 1.—Distribution of $n(O)$ and $n(O_2)$; daytime equilibrium. *Abscissae*, log (particle concentration); *ordinates*, altitude in kilometers.

and of the night and (more significantly) of the twilight airglow (cf. the preceding chapter).

At altitudes lower than about 60 km,

$$\frac{n(O_3)}{n(O_2)} \simeq \left\{ \frac{J_2 k_{12} n(M)}{J_3 k_{13}} \right\}^{1/2}.$$ (11)

2. The influence of mixing has been discussed by Nicolet and Mange (1952, 1954) who find that $n(O_2)$ must be considerably larger at great altitudes than it would be if there were local chemical equilibrium. Cf. chap. 13.

By an argument similar to that used in connection with (10), it may easily be deduced that there is a maximum in the ozone distribution. The existence of an ozone layer has, of course, long been recognized, and its properties have been studied by spectroscopic methods (cf. Fabry, 1950; Tousey, 1953). Though there is a tendency for the predicted altitude of the maximum to be too low and for the predicted abundance to be too great, the quantitative deductions from (11) are in fair general accord with observation, suggesting that the main processes operative are as assumed. The atmospheric region under consideration also contains free oxygen atoms. Their concentration is no longer given by (10) but is, instead, given by

$$n\,(O) \simeq \left\{ \frac{J_2 J_3}{k_{12} k_{13} n\,(M)} \right\}^{1/2}. \tag{12}$$

The main trend is clearly for $n(O)$ to decrease with increasing depth below the transition region. However, over a considerable range the decrease is slight, and it may even not be monotonic; for J_2 and J_3 decrease only slowly, owing to the smallness of the absorption cross-sections in the Herzberg and Chappuis continua and, moreover, k_{13} also decreases in certain regions, owing to its temperature dependence.

Bates and Witherspoon (1952) have recently prepared a set of curves showing the altitude distribution of the oxygen allotropes. *Below* the 40-km level the observational data on $n(O_3)$ were used, and $n(O)$ was deduced from it by means of the relation

$$n\,(O) = n\,(O_3) \frac{J_3}{k_{12} n\,(O_2)\, n\,(M)}. \tag{13}$$

In the region *above*, theory alone was used. Figure 2 gives the curves obtained. Though their accuracy is low, the general features exhibited are probably real. Special note should be taken of the great atomic oxygen *ledge*, the existence of which is not always fully appreciated. Attention may also be drawn to the fact that the ozone concentration decreases rather slowly below the maximum; even at ground level its value (which, since it is very variable, is not given in the figure) is frequently as much as $1 \times 10^{12}/cm^3$ (Paneth and Glückauf, 1941). In an atmosphere such as the Martian, containing little oxygen, the altitude of the layer peak would be lower than for the earth, and consequently the rate of loss of the element due to the oxidation of the surface by ozone would be faster (Wildt, 1937). However, it is clear from what has just been said that the increase in the ground-level value of $n(O_3)$ would be but moderate, and so the effect mentioned would not be very marked. On the other hand, the depletion of the atmosphere due to the corresponding action of atomic oxygen (which is chemically one of the most reactive of substances) would be much more rapid; for, as can be seen from Figure 2 or equation (12), the increase in the ground-level value of $n(O)$ would be extremely great.

The concentrations so far given refer to the noon equilibrium. In principle it is, of course, possible to determine their diurnal variations by the numerical solution of the appropriate differential equations; but such a procedure would not be profitable at present, owing to the serious uncertainties in the rate coefficients. The type of variation that must occur can

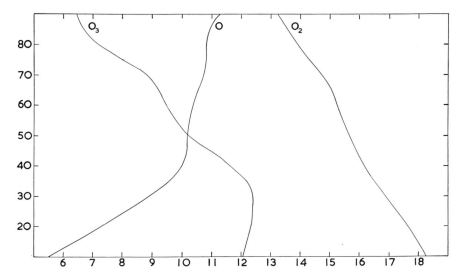

FIG. 2.—Distribution of $n(O)$, $n(O_2)$, and $n(O_3)$; daytime equilibrium. *Abscissae*, log (particle concentration); *ordinates*, altitude in kilometers.

easily be deduced from general considerations. There are two effects. Owing to the vanishing of J_2 and J_3 at sunset, $n(O_3)$ begins to grow at the expense of $n(O)$ (because of [5]); and $n(O_2)$ begins to grow at the expense of both (because of [3], [6], and the reactions involving minor atoms and radicals to which reference has already been made).

Throughout the main ozone layer, $n(O_2)$ is large, so that (5) can proceed rapidly. As a result, $n(O)$ decreases almost immediately to a minute value; but it is so low initially that the associated augmentation of $n(O_3)$ is negligible.

In the region of the upper part of the atomic oxygen ledge, (5) is much less effective. The number of such collisions occurring in the course of a night, though no longer sufficient to produce a significant fall in $n(O)$, causes the smaller $n(O_3)$ to increase markedly[3] (cf. Bates and Nicolet, 1950a). There must be some destruction of both atomic oxygen and ozone by the various processes mentioned (especially those involving H, OH, and HO_2). The extent of this effect is of interest in connection with the long-continued excitation of some of the airglow emissions, but unfortunately it is difficult to estimate.

Above the transition layer $n(O)$ remains essentially constant, because (3), which is the main loss process, is very slow at the gas densities prevailing there (cf. Fenndorf, 1949). By using (10) to eliminate the uncertainty in k_{11}, it may be shown that even $n(O_2)$ increases by a factor of only about 1.5 during the dark hours.

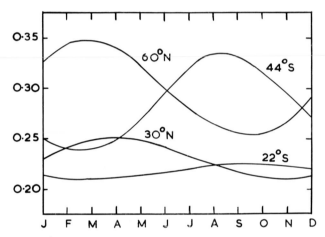

Fɪɢ. 3.—Ozone content of atmosphere. *Abscissae*, month of the year; *ordinates*, abundance of ozone, in cm-atm. Latitude of station is indicated on individual curves.

The changes taking place at sunrise are in the opposite sense to those just described but are otherwise similar.

Interesting seasonal effects undoubtedly occur, but the only one which has been extensively studied is the variation in $\mathfrak{N}(O_3)$, the total amount of ozone in a vertical column. Figure 3, which is based on data given by Dobson (1930), shows the observational results for a number of stations. It will be noted that $\mathfrak{N}(O_3)$ has maxima in spring and minima in autumn and that both the absolute value and the fractional change are less at low latitudes than at high latitudes. A theoretical investigation has been carried out by Chapman (1930a), who examined in particular how the

3. The amount of ozone in a vertical column is, of course, controlled by the concentration near the layer peak and hence would not be expected to change significantly from day to night.

time required to reach equilibrium affects the slow growth and decay of $n(O_3)$ throughout the year. Later Nicolet (1945a) drew attention to the necessity of taking account of the great sensitivity of k_{13} in (11) to the temperature and to the possible influence of the global circulation of the atmosphere. The detailed observational results have not yet been fully explained; but in view of the complexity of the problem, this is to be expected—there is no reason to suppose that the theory lacks any essential feature.

Brief mention may be made of the variation of $n(O_2)$ in the region just above the transition layer. Obviously, the value at any given level is greater in winter than in summer, since the sun is above the horizon for a shorter time and since its mean angle of elevation is less. Crude calculations indicate that the ratio of the winter to the summer value is about 8 at a latitude of 50° (Bates, 1949a). The effect is of importance in connection with one of the theories of formation of the E layer.

Notation.—The system used in Section 2.1 is applicable only to discussions on the O–O_2–O_3 equilibrium (for which it is well established). In the following sections the respective rate coefficients of two-body, three-body, and radiative processes will be denoted by the symbols α, β, and γ, with the appropriate equation number as an identifying subscript.

2.2. NITROGEN AND ITS OXIDES[4]

Molecular nitrogen possesses no observable continuum in the spectral region where the solar emission is sufficiently intense to give appreciable dissociation (cf. Chapman and Price, 1936; Price, 1943). It has been suggested that atomic nitrogen might be produced by some less direct process, such as

$$N_2^+ + h\nu \rightarrow N + N^+ , \tag{14}$$

but, as may easily be verified, the yield from this is utterly negligible. Other proposals were advanced, but no real progress was made until a few years ago, when Herzberg and Herzberg (1948) drew attention to the fact that predissociation occurs through

$$\left. \begin{array}{l} N_2\,(X\ ^1\Sigma_g^+) + h\nu \rightarrow N_2\,(a\ ^1\Pi_g) \\ N_2\,(a\ ^1\Pi_g) \rightarrow 2\,N \end{array} \right\} \tag{15}$$

and pointed out that the radiation involved ($\sim\lambda\lambda\ 1200$–1250) must penetrate deeply into the atmosphere. The importance of their paper was not generally appreciated at the time, as it was widely, but mistakenly, be-

4. As nitrous oxide is not a member of the main photochemical family (nitric oxide, nitrogen peroxide, etc.), it will be discussed in a separate section, 2.34.

lieved that the intense airglow band at λ 10440, now attributed to OH, was a member of the First Positive system of N_2 and was excited through the association of N atoms; many of the theorists in the field were therefore seeking a more powerful source.

Assuming that dissociation always occurs, it may be seen that the rate coefficient associated with the Herzberg-Herzberg mechanism may be expressed as

$$\gamma_{15} = \frac{\Omega p\, r}{\tau}\, e^{-\epsilon/k\,T}, \tag{16}$$

where Ω is the dilution and p the attenuation of the incoming radiation, r is the ratio of the statistical weight of the upper state to that of the lower, ϵ is the photon energy, T is the absolute temperature of the equivalent solar black body, τ is the relevant radiative lifetime (taking into account only transitions to the zeroth vibrational level of N_2, $X\,^1\Sigma_g^+$), and k is Boltzmann's constant. Most of the quantities appearing in this formula are known. Thus Ω is 5.4×10^{-6}; p depends on the altitude, but above about 90 km it is probably almost unity, and at 75 km it is perhaps 0.05 (cf. Bates and Seaton, 1950); r is 2; ϵ is 9.8 eV; and T may be taken[5] as approximately 5000° K (Nicolet, 1945b; Greenstein, 1949). Though τ is uncertain, some figures given by Herzberg (1946) suggest that it may be of the order of $1 \times 10^{-3}/\mathrm{sec}$, which is not unreasonable for a magnetic dipole transition. Accepting this, substitution in (16) gives γ_{15} to be $1 \times 10^{-12}/\mathrm{sec}$ at 90 km and above, and perhaps $5 \times 10^{-14}/\mathrm{sec}$ at 75 km. The possible error in these tentative estimates is considerable.

In a pure nitrogen atmosphere, free atoms would associate only through

$$N + N + M \rightarrow N_2 + M, \tag{17}$$

since the corresponding radiative process is disallowed. There is some experimental evidence that the rate coefficient, β_{17} is about 1.5×10^{-32} $\mathrm{cm^6/sec}$, or even rather higher (Rabinowitch, 1937; Schumacher, 1938).

The presence of oxygen makes possible a large number of other reactions (cf. Bamford, 1943). Nitric oxide is formed directly by

$$N + O + M \rightarrow NO + M, \tag{18}$$

$$N + O_2 \rightarrow NO + O, \tag{19}$$

$$N + O_3 \rightarrow NO + O_2, \tag{20}$$

5. From rocket measurements Friedman, Lichtman, and Byram (1951) deduce that the effective temperature in a band centered at λ 1200 (and including Lyman-α) is some 6000° K (see Vol. I, chap. 9, Sec. 9, for more definitive results).

and indirectly (through nitrogen peroxide) by

$$N + O_2 + M \rightarrow NO_2 + M , \qquad (21)$$

$$N + O_3 \rightarrow NO_2 + O , \qquad (22)$$

followed by

$$NO_2 + h\nu \rightarrow NO + O , \qquad (23)$$

$$NO_2 + O \rightarrow NO + O_2 , \qquad (24)$$

$$NO_2 + N \rightarrow 2 NO . \qquad (25)$$

It may be oxidized by

$$NO + O \rightarrow NO_2 + h\nu , \qquad (26)$$

$$NO + O + M \rightarrow NO_2 + M , \qquad (27)$$

$$2 NO + O_2 \rightarrow 2 NO_2 , \qquad (28)$$

$$NO + O_3 \rightarrow NO_2 + O_2 , \qquad (29)$$

and disrupted by

$$\left. \begin{array}{l} NO + h\nu \rightarrow NO \, (A \, {}^2\Sigma^+, \, C \, {}^2\Sigma^+) \\ NO \, (A \, {}^2\Sigma^+, \, C \, {}^2\Sigma^+) \rightarrow N + O \end{array} \right\} \qquad (30)$$

$$NO + N \rightarrow N_2 + O . \qquad (31)$$

This last process is of special interest, as it leads to the union of *odd* nitrogen atoms. Other such processes are

$$N + NO + M \rightarrow N_2O + M , \qquad (32)$$

$$N + NO_2 \rightarrow N_2 + O_2 , \qquad (33)$$

$$2 NO \rightarrow N_2 + O_2 . \qquad (34)$$

Unfortunately, only the most general statements can be made about most of the rate coefficients. It is convenient to present the scanty information available in the following tabulation:

Process   Remarks

a) Two-body type:

(19), (20), (22)..........At the low and moderate temperatures concerned, the rate coefficients are extremely sensitive to the activation energies. As these are unknown, a_{19}, a_{20}, and a_{22}, cannot be estimated even crudely. It should be noted that if the steric hindrance factors were the same, a process with an activation energy of 5 kcal would be 2×10^4 times faster at 250° K than one with an activation energy of 10 kcal.

(29) ....According to Johnston and Crosby (1954), the activation energy of reaction (29) is 2.5 kcal and at 250° K, a_{29} is about $8 \times 10^{-15} \mathrm{cm}^3/\mathrm{sec}$.

Process   Remarks

(24), (25), (31), (33)......The experiments of Spealman and Rodebush (1935) indicate that (24), (25), and (31) are quite rapid and
that (33) is probably considerably slower. Accepting
these, it seems not unlikely that α_{24}, α_{25}, and α_{31} are
within about an order of magnitude of 10^{-17} cm³/sec
at 200° K; of 10^{-16} cm³/sec at 250° K; and of 10^{-15}
cm³/sec at 300° K. No statement can be made about
α_{33} except that it is smaller.

(26).................Since the absorption cross-section of what appears to be
the inverse process has been measured (Holmes and
Daniels, 1934), the Einstein coefficient associated with
the stabilizing transition concerned in (26) can be determined. From the value obtained, it may be shown
that α_{26} is, at most, only some 10^{-17} cm³/sec. The
larger figure sometimes assumed (Gaydon, 1944) is
based on an overestimate of the relevant Einstein
coefficient.

(34).................There is no doubt that the activation energy of (34) is
prohibitively high (cf. Hirshfelder, 1941).

b) *Three-body type:*

(18), (21), (27)..........It is reasonable to assume that β_{18} is of the same order
of magnitude as β_{17} and that, because of steric hin-
drance, β_{21} and β_{27} are smaller—values of 10^{-35} cm⁶/
sec, or even less, are possible.

(28).................In the temperature range of interest, β_{28} is known to be
about 3×10^{-38} cm⁶/sec (Glasstone, Laidler, and
Eyring, 1941).

(32).................The work of Flory and Johnston (1935) indicates that
(32) is slow.

c) *Radiative type:*

(23).................Calculations based on the absorption measurements of
Holmes and Daniels (1934) give γ_{23} to be about $5 \times
10^{-3}$/sec. Attenuation is unimportant, as the thresh-
old lies near λ 3700.

(30).................The radiative lifetimes of NO, A $^2\Sigma^+$, and C $^2\Sigma^+$ have not
been determined, but, since perpendicular transitions
are involved, they are likely to be approximately
10^{-6} sec; and τ (of formula [16]) is perhaps 10 times
greater. The use of these crude estimates gives γ_{30} to
be of order 10^{-7}/sec at zero optical depth. The active
radiation ($\sim\lambda$ 1900) penetrates to about the 50-km
level (cf. Tousey, Watanabe, and Purcell, 1951).

In spite of the grievous lack of reliable basic data, it is perhaps worth
considering the equilibrium equations. Above the O–O₂ transition layer,

only (15), (17), (18), (30), and (31) are important, and it may readily be
seen that

$$n(N) = \left\{ \frac{\gamma_{15}\, n\,(N_2)}{n\,(M)} \left[\beta_{17} + \beta_{18} \left(\frac{a_{31}n\,(O)}{\gamma_{30} + a_{31}n\,(N)} \right) \right]^{-1} \right\}^{1/2} \qquad (35)$$

and

$$n(NO) = n(N) \left\{ \frac{\beta_{18}n\,(O)\, n\,(M)}{\gamma_{30} + a_{31}n\,(N)} \right\}, \qquad (36)$$

from which it is apparent that $n(N)$ initially tends to increase with altitude, whereas $n(NO)$ decreases rapidly. The atomic oxygen clearly reduces
the degree of dissociation of the molecular nitrogen. Thus, for reasons of
abundance, (18) can occur readily; and though some of the nitric oxide
formed is destroyed by (30), some will react with atomic nitrogen through
(31), which, being a two-body process, is quite effective in spite of the low

TABLE 1*

CALCULATED CONCENTRATIONS OF ATOMIC NITROGEN
AND NITRIC OXIDE

Total Particle Concentration n(M) (/cm³)	Actual Atmosphere		Pure Nitrogen Atmosphere Concentration of Atomic Nitrogen n(N) (/cm³)
	Concentration of Atomic Nitrogen n(N) (/cm³)	Concentration of Nitric Oxide n(NO) (/cm³)	
1×10^{13}............	4×10^{7}	1×10^{8}	8×10^{9}
1×10^{12}............	2×10^{8}	3×10^{6}	8×10^{9}

* The sole purpose of this table is to illustrate certain features of the equilibrium. It must be stressed that the concentrations given may differ greatly from
the true concentrations.

gas density. To illustrate the position, solutions to (35) and (36) were obtained for the levels where $n(M)$ is 1×10^{13}/cm³ and 1×10^{12}/cm³. The
temperature (which influences a_{31}) was taken to be 300° K at both levels,
though it is, in fact, an increasing function of altitude. Table 1 gives the
deduced values of $n(N)$ and $n(NO)$ in the case of the actual atmosphere
and, for comparison, the corresponding values of $n(N)$ in the case of a
hypothetical pure-nitrogen atmosphere—in which, of course, $n(NO)$ is
zero. No reliance can be placed on the detailed results, since only dubious
order-of-magnitude estimates are available for the rate coefficients on
which they depend. Nevertheless, the figures demonstrate the effect that
atomic oxygen may have in catalyzing the re-formation of molecular
nitrogen. They suggest, too, that nitric oxide must be very rare at altitudes of 150 km and above; the possibility that absorption of solar radia-

tion by the gas contributes appreciably to the heating of the atmosphere in the region of the F layers (cf. Bates, 1951) thus seems rather remote; and so seems the possibility that NO^+ is the unidentified molecular ion which is supposed to take part in dissociative recombination in the F layers (cf. Sec. 4.3). It should, however, be mentioned that the formation of nitric oxide from oxygen and nitrogen atoms by radiative association has been neglected throughout the discussion, as it is thought that the process is slow. Should this not prove to be the case, an extra term would have to be included in the denominator of (35) and in the numerator of (36), which would, of course, make $n(N)$ smaller and $n(NO)$ larger, the effect being most pronounced at the greater altitudes.

It should be noted that it is improper to argue from the form of (35) that, like oxygen, nitrogen must be almost entirely in the atomic form at high enough levels. Spitzer (1949) has pointed out that photochemical equilibrium does not persist to all altitudes; it is eventually replaced by diffusive equilibrium. The reason for this is, of course, that in a region of sufficiently low gas density the rate of production and destruction of atoms by photochemical processes is less than the rates of gain and loss by diffusion. Now the lifetime of a nitrogen molecule toward dissociation by (35) is some thousands of years; and the calculations of Spitzer show that a nitrogen atom takes at most a few months to fall from the fringe of the atmosphere to the altitude where the total particle concentration is $1 \times 10^{12}/cm^3$ and where, therefore, collisions resulting in association can occur quite readily. Hence the Herzberg-Herzberg mechanism cannot result in $n(N)/n(N_2)$ increasing indefinitely with altitude. Indeed, the initial increase caused by it probably does not extend as high as the 150-km level. Other processes may, however, be operative. In particular, ionization followed by dissociative recombination,

$$\left.\begin{array}{l} N_2 + h\nu \rightarrow N_2^+ + e \\ N_2^+ + e \rightarrow N' + N'' \end{array}\right\}, \qquad\qquad (37)$$

may be an important source of nitrogen atoms (Bates and Massey, 1947). (Atoms in *exited* states are denoted by primes and double primes.) The number liberated in this way is certainly negligible at low altitudes but may well be considerable in the region of the F layers. An admittedly indirect and inconclusive argument may be given (Bates, 1951) which suggests that it may rise to $10^3/cm^3$ sec or even more. The degree of dissociation that would ensue is difficult to estimate. As a tentative exploration of the possibilities, suppose that the figure just quoted is correct and that the nitrogen atoms disappear mainly by falling to, and associating at, the level X, which can just be reached within their life. Using the results of Spitzer's calculations and taking account of the collision processes already described, it may be shown that X is to be identified as the level where the total particle is about $3 \times 10^{12}/\mathrm{cm}^3$, and that $n(N)/n(N_2)$ there is of order 0.01 (which is greater than would result from predissociation). Such deductions must, of course, be treated with reserve, since the yield from (37) is very uncertain. In the circumstances it is scarcely worth attempting to estimate the factor by which $n(N)/n(N_2)$ increases between X and the F layers.

As may readily be verified from (36), the earlier statement, concerning the rarity of nitric oxide near and above the 150-km level, is in no way invalidated by the introduction of the new atomic nitrogen source.

The equations describing the equilibrium in the region below the O–O_2 transition layer are rather cumbersome. Fortunately, however, the neglect of (25), (28), (32), (33), and (34) simplifies them greatly without being likely to lead to serious error. Introducing

$$A = \beta_{18} n\,(O)\, n\,(M) + a_{19} n\,(O_2) + a_{20} n\,(O_3)\,,$$

$$B = \beta_{21} n\,(O_2)\, n\,(M) + a_{22} n\,(O_3)\,,$$

$$C = \gamma_{23} + a_{24} n\,(O)\,, \tag{38}$$

$$D = a_{26} n\,(O) + \beta_{27} n\,(O)\, n\,(M) + a_{29} n\,(O_3)\,,$$

we obtain

$$n\,(N) = \frac{\gamma_{15} n\,(N_2) + \gamma_{30} n\,(NO)}{A + B + \beta_{17} n\,(N)\, n\,(M)}\,, \tag{39}$$

$$n\,(NO) = \frac{A + B}{a_{31} + \gamma_{30}/\,n\,(N)}\,, \tag{40}$$

$$n\,(NO_2) = \frac{B n\,(N) + D n\,(NO)}{C}\,. \tag{41}$$

While it would be unprofitable at present to attempt any detailed quantitative calculations, it may be noted that, since $(A + B)$ is almost certainly larger than $\beta_{17} n(N) n(M)$, the combination of (39) and (40) gives

$$n\,(N)\, n\,(NO) = \frac{\gamma_{15} n\,(N_2)}{a_{31}}\,, \tag{42}$$

which is quite tractable. Consider the 75-km and 90-km levels. Taking the respective values of $n(N_2)$ to be $8 \times 10^{14}/\mathrm{cm}^3$ and $7 \times 10^{13}/\mathrm{cm}^3$, and taking those of γ_{15}/a_{31} to be $5 \times 10^3/\mathrm{cm}^3$ and $1 \times 10^4/\mathrm{cm}^3$ (corresponding to temperatures of $200°$ and $250°$ K), it can be seen that (42) gives

$[n(N)n(NO)]^{1/2}$ to be of order $2 \times 10^9/\text{cm}^3$ near the former level and of order $1 \times 10^9/\text{cm}^3$ near the latter. Now, though there may be complications due to the sensitivity of the rate coefficients of the two-body processes to the temperature, it appears likely from (39) and (40) that $n(N)/n(NO)$ is a decreasing function of the depth below the O–O$_2$ transition layer and falls well below unity before the 75-km level is reached. The crude estimates of $\{n(N)n(NO)\}^{1/2}$ just given thus suggest that the absolute value of $n(NO)$ may be considerable. Much depends on the efficiency of mixing effects; for example, several years would be required to build up a concentration of $10^{10}/\text{cm}^3$ if γ_{15} is as estimated.[6] Durand, Oberly, and Tousey (1949) report that solar spectra obtained from rockets have an absorption band between λ 2200 and λ 2300, which might be interpreted as due to nitric oxide. Later flights (Tousey, 1953) have confirmed the presence of this absorption band and have added several others (cf. Vol. 1, pp. 671–672); but none of these are due to telluric NO. From their infrared measurements, Migeotte and Neven (1952) infer that the telluric abundance of NO is almost certainly less than 0.02 cm NTP. Photodissociation (23) is so rapid that during the day $n(NO_2)/n(NO)$ must be kept small down to quite low levels. At night the ratio must increase, though to what extent is not easy to predict. It should be noted in this connection that radiation near λ 4000 (but not beyond the photodissociation limit at λ 3700) is strongly scattered by nitrogen peroxide, owing to absorption followed by re-emission[7] (cf. Noyes and Leighton, 1941). For sunlight the photon intensity of the scattered radiation should be of the order of $10^{-2}/$ illuminated NO$_2$ molecule/sec. If even a moderate concentration of the gas accumulated during the dark hours, the scattering would be considerable at sunrise—though the fact that a broad spectral region is involved might make the observation of it difficult. Measurements giving an upper limit to the intensity would be useful.

Apart from nitrogen peroxide, other higher oxides, such as nitrogen pentoxide, are slowly formed. They are also subject to destruction by photodissociation and by a number of collision processes (some of which have been listed by Bamford, 1934). A detailed investigation of the equilibrium is not possible, but it can be said that upper-atmospheric condi-

6. The uncertainty in the value of this coefficient is again stressed; and the possibility that there is an atomic nitrogen source other than (15) cannot be excluded—for example, Weissler (1952) suggests that, contrary to the earlier belief, nitrogen *does* possess photodissociation continua.

7. Baxter (1930) finds that the re-emission occurs near λ 6000, but collisions are probably too infrequent in the upper atmosphere to cause such degradation.

tions are, in general, not conducive to an abundance of such complex reactive molecules.

Evidence relating to several of the deductions that have been made will be referred to later when discussing the theory of the formation of the ionized layers and the interpretation of the spectra of the airglow and of aurorae.

2.3. Minor Constituents

Some attention has recently been given to the photochemistry of such minor constituents as water vapor (Bates and Nicolet, 1950a), carbon dioxide, methane, and nitrous oxide (Bates and Witherspoon, 1952). A very large number of reactions arise, and only the more important of them will be mentioned here. The whole problem is dominated by the fact that the earth has an abundant supply of oxygen; for, because of their great continua, O_2 and O_3 serve as a shield for the other constituents, protecting them from the full dissociating action of the solar radiation in a wide and important spectral range. It will be seen later that the continuum of O may exert a rather similar control on the ionization of the atmosphere.

2.31. *Water vapor.*—The threshold for the photodissociation of water vapor

$$H_2O + h\nu \rightarrow OH \; (X \, ^2\Pi) + H \; (^2S) , \qquad (43)$$

lies near λ 2400, but the cross-section associated with the process remains extremely small until almost λ 1800, where it is rising rapidly (Wilkinson and Johnston, 1950). The most effective radiation is thus in the Schumann-Runge region, and consequently its depth of penetration into the atmosphere is limited by molecular oxygen. Among the rapid secondary processes following (43) are oxidation through

$$H + O_3 \rightarrow OH + O_2 , \qquad (44)$$
$$H + O_2 + M \rightarrow HO_2 + M , \qquad (45)$$

and reduction through

$$OH + O \rightarrow H + O_2 , \qquad (46)$$

$$HO_2 + O \rightarrow OH + O_2 . \qquad (47)$$

It is clear that, as the altitude is increased, conditions become more and more unfavorable to oxidation as compared with reduction, so that the abundance of hydroxyl and perhydroxyl relative to atomic hydrogen diminishes. This greatly hinders the re-formation of water vapor by such processes as

$$H + OH + M \rightarrow H_2O + M , \qquad (48)$$

$$H + HO_2 \rightarrow H_2O + O \qquad (49)$$

Molecular hydrogen is formed and destroyed mainly by

$$H + OH \rightleftharpoons H_2 + O .\qquad(50)$$

Since the reactants on the right are a few kcal more stable than those on the left, its concentration should be a maximum at a temperature minimum. Bates and Nicolet (1950a) have attempted to estimate the various day equilibrium distributions. Their results are given in Figure 4, which is intended to be illustrative rather than quantitative.

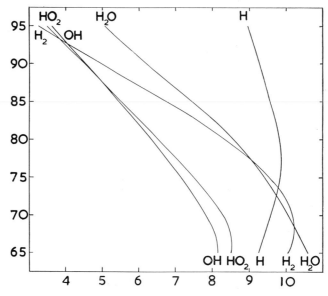

Fig. 4.—Distribution of $n(H)$, $n(OH)$, $n(HO_2)$, $n(H_2O)$, and $n(H_2)$; daytime equilibrium. *Abscissae*, log (particle concentration); *ordinates*, altitude in kilometers.

2.32. *Carbon dioxide.*—Carbon dioxide can be dissociated by $\lambda < 1690$ A:

$$CO_2 + h\nu \rightarrow CO + O\,(^1D) .\qquad(51)$$

This radiation is strongly absorbed by the Schumann-Runge continuum of molecular oxygen. Above the 100-km level photodissociation limits $\tau(CO_2)$, the lifetime of a carbon dioxide molecule, to about 5×10^6 sec. Oxidation of carbon monoxide proceeds through

$$CO + O + M \rightarrow CO_2 + M ,\qquad(52)$$

$$CO + OH \rightarrow CO_2 + H ,\qquad(53)$$

$$CO + HO_2 \rightarrow CO_2 + OH .\qquad(54)$$

It may easily be shown that if there were local chemical equilibrium between (51), (52), (53), and (54), the carbon would be almost entirely in the dioxide form below 100 km, and in the monoxide form above. However, such equilibrium is unlikely to prevail. It is known that (52) is extremely slow (Jackson, 1934; Groth, 1937); and even if it should prove that (53) and (54) have activation energies as small as 5 kcal, $\tau(CO)$ would be of the order of years at altitudes down to at least 80 km. In these circumstances the carbon monoxide would not be confined to the photodissociation region. Instead, considerable quantities of it would exist in the region below, since any conveyed there by the mixing action of winds would persist for a very long time, and its altitude distribution would not show a sharp break at the 100-km level. While the total abundance of the carbon monoxide resulting from photodissociation must be greatly increased by the lack of local equilibrium, it is unlikely to be sufficient to produce the infrared absorption lines observed in the solar spectrum by Migeotte (1949) and others. Combustion on the earth's surface is a much more important source of the gas (cf. Bates and Witherspoon, 1952; and Hutchinson's chap. 8, p. 394).

2.33. *Methane.*—Collision processes involving atomic oxygen and perhydroxyl are more effective than photoaction in producing dissociation of methane in the upper atmosphere. Atomic oxygen reacts through

$$CH_4 + O \rightarrow CH_2 + H_2O \tag{55}$$

or

$$CH_4 + O \rightarrow HCHO + H_2 . \tag{56}$$

According to Steacie and Parlee (1938), the activation energy of the more rapid of these is about 8 kcal. Perhydroxyl attacks methane even at temperatures below 100° K (Geib and Harteck, 1934). The detailed mechanism has not been determined, but the activation energy associated with it must be very small indeed. From crude estimates of the rate coefficients, it appears that the processes mentioned restrict $\tau(CH_4)$ to perhaps about 10^3 sec at 100 km, 10^5 sec at 85 km, 10^4 sec at 70 km, and 10^5–10^6 sec at 55 km (Bates and Witherspoon, 1952). As the re-formation of a polyatomic molecule like CH_4 is difficult, there can be little doubt that the concentration at any particular level is determined by the relative rates of the destructive processes and of the atmospheric mixing effects. Little is known about these latter, but they can scarcely be very efficient in the region of a thermo-incline. Judging from the values of $\tau(CH_4)$ just quoted, it would hence seem certain that methane must be almost completely absent from the region above the 100-km level; and it would seem probable that its fractional abundance begins to fall off well below this. The ultimate products of reaction are, of course, the oxides of carbon and of hydrogen. Since both OH and HO_2 are highly active radicals, their formation at quite moderate altitudes is of considerable interest.

2.34. *Nitrous oxide.*—Nitrous oxide possesses several continua. Weak absorption, corresponding to

$$N_2O + h\nu \rightarrow N_2 + O \, (^3P, \, ^1D) \,, \tag{57}$$

commences at λ 3070, and the main absorption, corresponding probably to

$$N_2O + h\nu \rightarrow NO + N \, (^4S) \,, \tag{58}$$

at about λ 2400 or slightly above (cf. Bamford, 1943; Gaydon, 1947). By using the laboratory data of Dutta (1932), Sponer and Boner (1940), and Romand and Mayence (1949), the photodissociation rate can be calculated approximately. As an initial approach, it is useful to consider the ground level and the 70-km level and to suppose that all the nitrous oxide, 2×10^{19} molecules/cm^2 column (Adel, 1949), is concentrated in a 10-km-thick layer at either level. If it were concentrated at the lower level, then the number of N_2O molecules being destroyed there during daylight would be about 5×10^4/cm^3 sec; and if it were at the upper (where the incident radiation is but little attenuated by the oxygen allotropes), the number would be about 3×10^7/cm^3 sec. Both are large. The fact that such rapid destruction must be occurring was not taken properly into account in the early investigations on the source of the atmospheric nitrous oxide. Until recently it has usually been assumed that the gas is formed at considerable altitudes, and a variety of collision processes have been suggested, of which the following are representative,

$$O^- + N_2 \rightarrow N_2O + e \,, \tag{59}$$

$$N_2 \, (A \, ^3\Sigma_u^+) + O + M \rightarrow N_2O + M \,. \tag{60}$$

The yield from these is, however, utterly inadequate. By examining the alternatives systematically (Bates and Witherspoon, 1952), it may be shown that the only parent-particles which are likely to be involved are either oxygen atoms or ozone molecules. The supply of both is ample. It seems at least conceivable that the process sought is

$$O + N_2 + M \rightarrow N_2O + M \tag{61}$$

or

$$O_3 + N_2 \rightarrow N_2O + O_2 \,. \tag{62}$$

Thus a sufficient replenishment of nitrous oxide would take place in the lower atmosphere even if the rate coefficient of (61) were only about

1×10^{-38} cm^6/sec, or even if that of (62) were only about 5×10^{-27} cm^3/ sec. These values do not appear to be in conflict with any published experimental data. In the case of (61) the required rate coefficient is larger than would be expected theoretically and is near a limit suggested by some investigations described by Leighton (1938) (who does not, however, report the results in sufficient detail to enable a proper test to be applied); but in the case of (62) the required rate coefficient is so minute that detection of the process would be difficult with present techniques. Possible modifications of (61) and of (62) (which will be referred to as [61'] and [62']) are that the O(^{1}D) atoms provided by (7) and the activated O$_3^*$ molecules provided by (5) are involved. Like soil microörganisms (which Adel, 1946, 1951, advocates as the source), both these and the original two processes would lead to the prevalence of nitrous oxide in the troposphere. All four must, of course, be regarded as speculative, in view of the lack of positive evidence favoring them. Among the later work we mention that of Goody and Walshaw (1953), which lends some support to the soil-microörganism hypothesis of Adel; and that of Harteck and Dondes (1954), which lends some support to the gas-phase reaction hypothesis of Bates and Witherspoon. Cf. also chapter 8.

As an argument in support of a low-lying bank, it may be pointed out that if the nitrous oxide were at moderate altitudes, photodissociation through (58) would proceed rapidly, providing a rich supply of nitric oxide and atomic nitrogen, which would react with, for example, ozone to yield NO$_2$ and other higher oxides; and there might be an unacceptable accumulation of the various oxides, since the equilibrium likely to be established would be unfavorable to the limited number of processes by which molecular nitrogen could be re-formed (cf. Sec. 2.2). There is no difficulty in this connection with soil microörganisms or with (61); but it is rather doubtful whether (61'), (62), or (62') would give a sufficiently confined bank (Bates, 1952).

3. MODELS OF THE UPPER ATMOSPHERE

Much of the remainder of this chapter will be concerned with the region above the 100-km level. As the structure of this region is still very uncertain, it will be convenient to have available, for reference, data on a wide variety of models. In one particularly simple set which has recently been investigated, the 110-km level was chosen as standard; the temperature there was taken to be 300° K and the particle concentration to be 7.4×10^{12}/cm^3; and it was specified that, above, the temperature rises linearly to a value of T_B at an altitude h_B, and thereafter remains constant. The

D. R. BATES

vertical distribution of the particle concentration for any member of the set, $M(T_B; h_B)$, can readily be determined. Computations were carried out for all combinations of the following

$$T_B = 500, 1000, 1500, 2000° \text{K} ;$$

$$h_B = 200, 300, 400, 500 \text{ km (above ground level)} .$$

Table 2 shows the results. They are based on the assumption that the mean molecular mass at all levels is 23.8, which is the value appropriate

TABLE 2

UPPER-ATMOSPHERIC MODELS: INITIAL TEMPERATURE RISE LINEAR

MODEL $M(T_B; h_B)$	TEMPERA- TURE GRA- DIENT IN LINEAR- RISE REGION (° K/km)	ALTITUDE (km) LOG₁₀ (NUMBER OF PARTICLES /cm³)							
		150	200	250	300	400	500	750	1000
M(500° K; 200 km).....	2.22	11.40	10.00	8.85	7.75	5.55	3.40	−1.65	−6.35
M(500° K; 300 km).....	1.05	11.35	9.70	8.30	7.10	4.90	2.75	−2.25	−6.95
M(500° K; 400 km).....	0.69	11.35	9.60	8.10	6.70	4.25	2.15	−2.90	−7.60
M(500° K; 500 km).....	0.51	11.35	9.55	7.95	6.45	3.85	1.55	−3.50	−8.20
M(1000° K; 200 km)....	7.78	11.50	10.55	10.00	9.40	8.30	7.25	4.75	2.40
M(1000° K; 300 km)....	3.68	11.45	10.20	9.30	8.60	7.50	6.45	3.90	1.55
M(1000° K; 400 km)....	2.41	11.40	10.00	8.95	8.05	6.65	5.60	3.10	0.75
M(1000° K; 500 km)....	1.80	11.40	9.90	8.70	7.70	6.05	4.80	2.30	−0.05
M(1500° K; 200 km)....	13.33	11.55	10.75	10.40	10.00	9.30	8.55	6.90	5.30
M(1500° K; 300 km)....	6.32	11.45	10.45	9.75	9.25	8.50	7.80	6.10	4.55
M(1500° K; 400 km)....	4.14	11.45	10.25	9.40	8.75	7.75	7.00	5.35	3.80
M(1500° K; 500 km)....	3.08	11.40	10.10	9.15	8.35	7.15	6.25	4.60	3.00
M(2000° K; 200 km)....	18.89	11.55	10.85	10.60	10.30	9.75	9.25	7.95	6.80
M(2000° K; 300 km)....	8.95	11.50	10.60	10.00	9.60	9.05	8.50	7.25	6.10
M(2000° K; 400 km)....	5.87	11.45	10.40	9.70	9.15	8.35	7.80	6.55	5.40
M(2000° K; 500 km)....	4.36	11.45	10.30	9.45	8.80	7.85	7.15	5.85	4.70

to an atmosphere of nitrogen and oxygen in the same proportions as at ground level, with the former in the molecular, and the latter in the atomic, form. Approximate distributions allowing for diffusive separation can readily be obtained from the figures given (cf. Bates, 1951). Nicolet and Mange (1952) have investigated such separation. They concluded that complete diffusive equilibrium may occur at altitudes as low as 160 km.

The introduction of the discontinuity at h_B is rather unsatisfactory. A

TABLE 3
UPPER-ATMOSPHERIC MODELS: INITIAL TEMPERATURE RISE NONLINEAR

MODEL $\mathfrak{M}(T_B; h_B, \Delta)$	QUANTITY	ALTITUDE (km)							
		150	200	250	300	400	500	750	1000
$\mathfrak{M}(1000°$ K; 200 km, 100 km)......	Temperature (° K)*	560	780	915	1000	1000	1000	1000	1000
	$\log_{10}[n(\mathrm{M}|z)]$	11.50	10.50	9.75	9.15	8.05	7.00	4.45	2.10
$\mathfrak{M}(1000°$ K; 300 km, 100 km)......	Temperature (° K)	440	590	720	830	1000	1000	1000	1000
	$\log_{10}[n(\mathrm{M}|z)]$	11.40	10.15	9.20	8.45	7.15	6.10	3.60	1.25
$\mathfrak{M}(1500°$ K; 200 km, 100 km)......	Temperature (° K)	750	1120	1355	1500	1500	1500	1500	1500
	$\log_{10}[n(\mathrm{M}|z)]$	11.55	10.75	10.20	9.75	9.05	8.35	6.65	5.10
$\mathfrak{M}(1500°$ K; 300 km, 100 km)......	Temperature (° K)	535	795	1015	1205	1500	1500	1500	1500
	$\log_{10}[n(\mathrm{M}|z)]$	11.45	10.45	9.70	9.10	8.20	7.50	5.80	4.25

* $n(\mathrm{M}|z)$ is total number of particles per cubic centimeter at elevation z. Decimals in *italics* are uncertain.

useful alternative set of models is one in which the temperature at a distance z above the standard level is

$$T(z) = \frac{\overline{m} \, g(z)}{k} \cdot \frac{C}{b} (b - e^{-\beta z}), \tag{63}$$

where $\overline{m}$ is the mean molecular mass, k is Boltzmann's constant, $g(z)$ is the acceleration of gravity, and C, b, and β are parameters, only two of which are adjustable (since $T[0]$ is already fixed). As the corresponding scale height is

$$H(z) = \frac{C}{b}(b - e^{-\beta z}), \tag{64}$$

the integration of the differential equation for the total particle concentration, $n(M|z)$, can readily be carried out, yielding

$$\frac{n(M|z)}{n(M|0)} = \frac{T(0)}{T(z)} \left\{ \frac{b-1}{b \, e^{\beta z} - 1} \right\}^{1/\beta C}. \tag{65}$$

It is instructive to choose the parameters so that at the standard level the temperature gradient is the same as in model $M(T_B; h_B)$ and so that at a level whose altitude is $h_B + \Delta$ the temperature T_B is reached and to assume that above this level the atmosphere is isothermal.[8] Some results for such models, which will be designated $\mathfrak{M}(T_B; h_B, \Delta)$, are displayed in Table 3. The rate at which the particle concentration falls off is naturally greater than in the corresponding model with a linear temperature rise; but the difference is not very marked.

4. IONOSPHERE

4.1. Properties

The ionized layers have been studied very extensively by radio scientists, and much detailed information is now available concerning them. We will, however, content ourselves with giving briefly the basic data essential in connection with the theory of their formation and equilibrium and will make no attempt to describe the morphology or the irregularities (such as sudden ionospheric disturbances, sporadic E ionization, and magnetic storms). A number of excellent reviews have been published (Appleton, 1937, 1947; Berkner, 1939; Hulburt, 1939; Mitra, 1947).

There are four main layers known as D, E, F_1, and F_2. The last two are distinct only when the elevation of the sun is high. A subsidiary layer, E_2, lying above E, is sometimes observed.

The properties of E and F_1 are relatively simple. Their altitudes are

---

8. Because of this assumption, the discontinuity in the temperature gradient is not completely eliminated.

rather greater in winter than in summer; but, for the purpose of compiling a simplified model of the layers, they may be taken to be about 110 and 200 km, respectively, during the day. The maximum electron concentration in E may be expressed approximately as

$$n_m^E (e \mid \chi) = 1.35 \times 10^5 (1 + 0.0097R)^{1/2} (\cos \chi)^{1/2} / \mathrm{cm}^3 \qquad (66)$$

and that in F_1 approximately as

$$n_m^{F_1} (e \mid \chi) = 2.40 \times 10^5 (1 + 0.0124R)^{1/2} (\cos \chi)^{1/2} / \mathrm{cm}^3 , \qquad (67)$$

where χ is the solar zenith angle and R is the sunspot number (Allen, 1948). In theoretical studies, values of $1.5 \times 10^5 / \mathrm{cm}^3$ and $2.5 \times 10^5 / \mathrm{cm}^3$ are frequently adopted. By analyzing measurements made during eclipses

TABLE 4

DATA ON THE F_2 LAYER

(Over Slough, Southern England, at Noon)

	SUNSPOT MINIMUM		SUNSPOT MAXIMUM	
	Summer	Winter	Summer	Winter
Altitude (km).................	290	220	400	290
Max. electron concentration (/cm³)..	2.9×10^5	4.3×10^5	6.8×10^5	1.7×10^6

and by other methods, radio scientists have determined the apparent rate at which electrons disappear and have hence deduced that the associated recombination coefficient, a, is about 1×10^{-8} cm³/sec in the E layer and 7×10^{-9} cm³/sec in the F_1 layer.[9] References to the numerous original papers on the topic will be found in various summaries (cf. Bates and Massey, 1946; Bates, 1951).

Some of the more important features of the complicated behavior of F_2 can be seen from Table 4, which was compiled from graphs given by Appleton (1947). Attention is directed to the wide range of values of the altitude and of the maximum electron concentration. The coefficient measuring the rate at which electrons disappear is also far from constant— some of the values of a obtained are as low as 4×10^{-11} cm³/sec and others as high as 1×10^{-9} cm³/sec (cf. Bates, 1951). Mohler (1940) has collected evidence which indicates that it is a decreasing function both of the alti-

9. Piddington (1951) believes that the radio scientists have usually underestimated the coefficient. This view is in harmony with the evidence obtained from the consideration of the thermobalance (cf. Sec. 7.2).

tude[10] and of the maximum electron concentration. As Appleton (1947) has pointed out, this effect provides at least a partial explanation for the peculiar seasonal variation (cf. Table 4).

Comparatively few data have been published on the D layer, which consists of a bank of ionization lying below the E layer. It is convenient to consider two levels, one at 90 km and another at 75 km. Piggott (1950) finds that the noon values of $n(e)$ and a at 90 km are about $1.5 \times 10^4/cm^3$ and 3×10^{-8} cm^3/sec, respectively. According to Weekes (1950), the corresponding value of $n(e)$ at 75 km is about $2.5 \times 10^2/cm^3$; that of a has not been properly determined, but there is some evidence for supposing that it is at least as great as 1×10^{-6} cm^3/sec (Bates and Seaton, 1950). One of the most striking characteristics of the D layer is that the ionization may be much augmented during solar flares, causing radio fade-outs (Dellinger, 1937).

4.2. FORMATION

4.21. *General theory.*—Chapman (1931*b*) has developed the mathematical equations governing the formation of an ionized layer. In the case of a plane isothermal atmosphere, the ionization rate of a constituent, X, at an altitude, h, and at a solar zenith angle, χ, can be shown to be

$$I(X \mid h, \chi) = S A (X) n (X \mid h) \exp\{ - A (X) H (X) n (X \mid h) \sec \chi\}, \quad (68)$$

where S is the incident photon flux in the spectral region concerned, $A(X)$ is the relevant ionization cross-section, $n(X \mid h)$ is the particle concentration, and $H(X)$ is the scale height. This rate attains its maximum,

$$I_m (X \mid \chi) = \frac{S \cos \chi}{e H (X)} \quad (69)$$

(e being the Naperian base) at the level where the particle concentration is

$$n_m (X \mid \chi) = \frac{\cos \chi}{A (X) H (X)}, \quad (70)$$

which is at an altitude

$$h_m (X \mid \chi) = H (X) \log (\sec \chi) + \text{const} . \quad (71)$$

Below its maximum it falls off extremely rapidly (cf. Table 5).

Allowance can be made for the finiteness of $\Re$, the radius of the earth, by introducing in place of $\sec \chi$, an auxiliary function, $f(\chi, \Re + h)$, which has been tabulated by Chapman. It is found that correction is unimportant except when the sun is near or below the horizon. The modifications caused by a temperature gradient in the atmosphere will be given later.

---

10. A more significant statement is that it is a decreasing function of the gas density.

Formulae 68–71 describe only the direct action of solar radiation and take no account of the fact that if the primary ions were formed by the ejection of inner-shell electrons, they would emit radiation capable of producing secondary ions. Hoyle and Bates (1948) have discussed this possibility. Their conclusions may be expressed in the same notation as that used before, if superscripts P and S are added to distinguish between quantities relating to the primary and secondary radiation, respectively. It appears that the extent to which I^S differs from I^P is controlled by the ratio

$$\rho = \frac{n\ (X^S\,|\,h)\ A\ (X^S)}{n\ (X^P\,|\,h)\ A\ (X^P)\ \sec\chi}. \tag{72}$$

Briefly, I^S has essentially the same form and location as I^P if $\rho \gtrsim 0.7$; but it is markedly more diffuse and lower if $\rho \lesssim 0.3$. Further, in the former

TABLE 5

ALTITUDE DISTRIBUTION OF IONIZATION RATE IN
A CHAPMAN LAYER

$[h-h_m(X\,|\,\chi)]/H(X)$	$I(X\,|\,h,\,\chi)/I_m(X,\,\chi)$	$[h-h_m(X\,|\,\chi)]/H(X)$	$I(X\,|\,h,\,\chi)/I_m(X,\,\chi)$
+3.0	0.129	−0.5	0.862
+2.5	0.206	−1.0	0.488
+2.0	0.321	−1.5	0.138
+1.5	0.485	−2.0	1.24×10^{-2}
+1.0	0.692	−2.5	1.70×10^{-4}
+0.5	0.899	−3.0	1.03×10^{-7}
0.0	1.000		

case, I_m^S is nearly proportional to the first power of $\cos\chi$ (as is I_m^P); but in the latter case a rather higher power is involved.

Radio scientists do not study $I(X\,|\,h,\,\chi)$, but rather $n(e\,|\,h,\,\chi)$, the electron distribution. Most of the measurements, indeed, refer to the peak of the layer. They can, however, be related to the ionization rate if the free charges disappear by a recombination-type process, so that

$$\frac{dn\ (e\,|\,h,\,\chi)}{dt} = I\ (X\,|\,h,\,\chi) - a\,n^2\ (e\,|\,h,\,\chi)\ , \tag{73}$$

where a is the rate coefficient of the loss mechanism. In general, this equation can be treated only by numerical methods (Millington, 1932, 1935); but clearly

$$n\ (e\,|\,h,\,\chi) = \left\{\frac{I\ (X\,|\,h,\,\chi)}{a}\right\}^{1/2} \tag{74}$$

is an approximate solution near noon, as the electron concentration is then changing very slowly. Provided that a is constant, it follows that the level of maximum electron concentration coincides with the level of maximum electron production, so that formulae (70) and (71) are immediately applicable. Since (69) and (74) yield

$$n_m (e \mid \chi) = \left\{ \frac{S}{e H (X) a} \right\}^{1/2} (\cos \chi)^{1/2}, \qquad (75)$$

the basic assumptions made can be readily tested from the observational data on the variation of $n_m(e \mid \chi)$ with χ (that is with time of day, season, or latitude). Comparison with (66) and (67) shows that a must be almost constant in the E and F_1 layers. Rearrangement of (75) gives

$$S = e a n_m^2 (e \mid \chi) H (X) \sec \chi , \qquad (76)$$

which in principle allows the photon flux required to produce a given layer to be determined from ionospheric parameters. Another useful formula can be obtained by substituting (68) in (74) and expanding the exponentials in a power series (cf. Appleton and Beynon, 1940). It may be shown in this way that

$$n (e \mid h, \chi) \simeq n_m (e \mid \chi) \left(1 - \frac{z^2}{4 H^2 (X)} \right), \qquad (77)$$

where

$$z = h - h_m (X \mid \chi) . \qquad (78)$$

Hence

$$H (X) = \frac{\tau}{2}, \qquad (79)$$

with τ defined as the half-thickness of an equivalent parabolic layer.

Chapman's treatment can be readily extended so that it applies to an atmosphere in which neither the temperature nor the recombination coefficient is constant. It is instructive to consider the case in which the temperature (and thus the scale height) varies linearly and in which the recombination coefficient varies at some power of the particle concentration. Such a model atmosphere may be represented by the equations

$$H (X \mid h) = H_m (X \mid \chi) + c z , \qquad (80)$$

$$a (X \mid h) = a_m (X \mid \chi) \left(\frac{n (X \mid h)}{n_m (X \mid \chi)} \right)^p, \qquad (81)$$

where c and p are constants and where, as before, the subscript m indicates that the parameter to which it is affixed has the value appropriate to the level of the maximum of the layer. The following modifications of the more important original formulae may be derived by elementary analysis:

$$n_m (X | \chi) = \frac{(1 - p) (1 + c) \cos \chi}{A (X) H_m (X | \chi)},\qquad(82)$$

$$S = \frac{\exp [(1 - p) (1 + c)]\, a_m (X | \chi)\, n_m^2 (e | \chi)\, H_m (X | \chi) \sec \chi}{(1 - p) (1 + c)},\qquad(83)$$

$$H_m (X | \chi) = \tfrac{1}{2} \tau (1 - p) (1 + c).\qquad(84)$$

4.22. *Detailed theory.*—The processes responsible for the production of the ionized layers cannot be identified with certainty until much more precise and reliable information is available on the distribution and composition of the atmosphere, on the cross-sections of the constituents toward the absorption of radiation, and on the intensity of the solar ultraviolet emission. Nevertheless, considerable progress has been made in the understanding of the factors which have to be taken into account.

An obvious approach is to attempt to determine the ions actually present in the layers by spectroscopic methods. In favorable circumstances these can be very sensitive. Thus even in the region where its concentration is greatest, free atomic sodium is some 10^{12} times less abundant than the other atmospheric gases; but in spite of this, it reveals itself by resonance scattering in the D lines during twilight (cf. chap. 11).

The four ions of most interest are O^+, O_2^+, N^+, and N_2^+. Unfortunately, the first three do not scatter appreciably in the observable spectral range, as any low-lying levels they possess can be reached only by an optically forbidden transition. The last, however, scatters strongly in the bands of the First Negative system,

$$\left. \begin{aligned} N_2^+ (X\ ^2\Sigma_g^+) + h\nu &\rightarrow N_2^+ (B\ ^2\Sigma_u^+) \\ N_2^+ (B\ ^2\Sigma_u^+) &\rightarrow N_2^+ (X\ ^2\Sigma_g^+) + h\nu \end{aligned} \right\}.\qquad(85)$$

Calculations on the expected intensity of the (0–0) band, λ 3914 (which is the most prominent member of the system), were carried out a few years ago (Bates, 1949a). Since then Shull (1950) has published the results of a refined theoretical investigation on the oscillator strength of the transition involved. On making the necessary minor revision to the original work, it may be shown that an illuminated layer of thickness t km, and of mean ion concentration $\bar{n}(N_2^+)/cm^3$, would be judged by an observer, whose line of sight is at an elevation of some $10°$ or $20°$ above the horizon, to give an effective photon emission of approximately

$$10^4 t \bar{n}\ (N_2^+)\ /\ cm^2\ \text{oblique column/sec}\qquad(86)$$

Dufay and Dufay (1947) have investigated the spectrum of the twilight atmosphere. They found that the intensity of the so-called N_2^+ flash varies greatly and that there is some correlation between it and magnetic activity. From their results Bates (1949a) was able to make some admittedly crude estimates of $Q(h_L)$, the effective photon emission in λ 3914 when the altitude of the lowest observed level outside the shadow zone is h_L. These are given in Table 6, together with the deduced values of $t\bar{n}(N_2^+)$.

Since the F layers are exposed to sunlight when h_L is 200 km, and since their t value is perhaps 100 km, it follows that for them $\bar{n}(N_2^+)$ is only of order 10/cm³, which is far smaller than the mean total ion concentration. Several alternative explanations of the extreme rarity of N_2^+ can be offered.

TABLE 6

DATA RELATING TO ABUNDANCE OF N_2^+ IONS
IN TWILIGHT ATMOSPHERE

h_L (km)	$Q(h_L)$ (Photons /cm² Oblique Column/sec)	$t\bar{n}(N_2^+)$ (km/cm³)
200.........	Always $< 10^7$	Always $< 10^3$
100.........	Normally $< 10^8$	Normally $< 10^4$
60.........	Sometimes $> 10^9$	Sometimes $> 10^5$

a) It may simply be that the incident radiation does not give rise to much photoionization of molecular nitrogen. This would require either that the solar flux falls off sharply near the 15.5 eV potential (which seems unlikely) or that the atmospheric nitrogen is mainly in the atomic form in the region concerned.

b) Dissociation recombination, (37), may be very rapid. The rate coefficient, $a(N_2^+)$, may well exceed 10^{-8} cm³/sec, in which case any N_2^+ ions produced in the main part of the F layers would have a life of only about 100 seconds, or less, so that they would not survive sufficiently long to affect the critical twilight observations. However, the atmospheric region whose altitude, h_u, exceeds about 600 km remains bathed in ultraviolet radiation until after visual sunset on the 200-km level. For it, what is of relevance is the equilibrium concentration,

$$n(N_2^+ \mid h_u) = \frac{I(N_2 \mid h_u)}{n(e \mid h_u)\, a(N_2^+)} . \qquad (87)$$

Assuming provisionally that $n(e \mid h_u)$ is 10^5/cm³ and that $a(N_2^+)$ has the value mentioned above, it can be seen that for $n(N_2^+ | h_u)$ to be $10/cm^3$, or smaller, it is necessary that

$$I(N_2 | h_u) < 10^{-2}/cm^3 \text{ sec} . \tag{88}$$

This condition is consistent with a very considerable rate of ionization of molecular nitrogen in the main part of the layer. Even if the rate at the 250-km level were $10^3/cm^3$ sec (cf. Sec. 7.2), it would be satisfied, provided that $n(N_2)$ falls by a factor of order 10^5 in an altitude range of approximately 400 km. Such a fall coresponds to a mean scale height of 35 km, which is not impossible (particularly as the degree of dissociation may increase); the assumption (in an earlier discussion) that the mean scale height is 100 km is not necessarily correct. Moreover, $a(N_2^+)$ may actually be some 10^{-7} or 10^{-6} cm^3/sec,[11] so that a smaller fall in $n(N_2)$ may suffice. It must, of course, be borne in mind that the values adopted for the other parameters appearing in (87) are tentative.

c) On hypothesis a or b some gas other than molecular nitrogen must be supposed to be responsible for the formation of the F layers, since an unidentified species of ion is certainly abundant. There is, however, the possibility that the need for the supposition is removed by processes such as

$$N_2^+ + O \rightarrow N_2 + O^+ , \tag{89}$$

$$N_2^+ + O \rightarrow N + NO^+ , \tag{90}$$

$$N_2^+ + N \rightarrow N_2 + N^+ . \tag{91}$$

It is inadmissible to invoke a mechanism which would be effective in the region where a comparatively large N_2^+ concentration is occasionally established (cf. Table 6). Quantitative elaboration of this shows that (89) and (90) are open to objection (even with the flexibility given by an assumed strong temperature dependence). Though (91) is rather more promising, certain severe requirements would have to be satisfied to enable it to proceed sufficiently rapidly: the rate coefficient would have to be of the order of that associated with gas kinetic collisions, and, in addition, the nitrogen would have to be dissociated to a considerable extent.

d) Some combination of hypotheses a, b, and c may, of course, occur. In particular, dissociative recombination may keep the concentration of N_2^+ low; and charge transfer, though insufficiently rapid to do this, may nevertheless be effective enough to yield the other species of ion present. It may be readily verified that in these circumstances the electron concen-

---

11. The most recently reported measurements (Faire, Fundingsland, and Aden, 1954) give $a(N_2^+)$ to be as high as 10^{-6} cm^3/sec.

tration would follow a $(\cos \chi)^{2/3}$ law if complications due to temperature variations, etc., do not arise. The difference between this and the standard $(\cos \chi)^{1/2}$ law (followed by F_1) cannot be regarded as significant, in view of the simplifying assumptions.

Clearly, the simplest interpretation of the spectroscopic evidence is that nitrogen molecules are subject to photoionization but are not the parent neutral particles from which the F layers are formed. Oxygen molecules are so rare at the altitudes concerned that they may be ignored. The possibility that free atoms of either of these two substances are responsible must therefore be given close attention. Fortunately, the photoionization cross-sections can be obtained by quantal methods. Bates and Seaton (1949) have carried out the necessary detailed calculations, using exchange wave functions and both the dipole length and dipole velocity formulae. They find that, at the spectral heads,

$$A \ (\mathrm{N}) = 9 \times 10^{-18} \ \mathrm{cm}^2 , \tag{92}$$

$$A \ (\mathrm{O}) = 2.6 \times 10^{-18} \ \mathrm{cm}^2 . \tag{93}$$

The accuracy of these values is difficult to assess, as the Hartree-Fock formulation employed has been properly tested only in the case of systems with but a single outer electron[12] (for which it is an excellent approximation). But it is thought likely to be fair. For since there is little cancellation in the transition matrix elements, minor defects in the wave functions cannot have an important effect. The theory would have to be unexpectedly poor to cause either cross-section to be in error by a factor of 2 or more.

With the aid of Chapman's formula (70) we can now evaluate $H(\mathrm{N}) \cdot n_m(\mathrm{N}|\chi)$ and $H(\mathrm{O})n_m(\mathrm{O}|\chi)$ for any chosen zenith angle; that is, we can evaluate the product of the scale heights and the particle concentrations of atomic nitrogen and of atomic oxygen at the levels where the ionization due to each is at its maximum. Taking $\cos \chi$ to be 0.8 (a representative figure) and using (92) and (93), we have

$$H \ (\mathrm{N}) \ n_m \ (\mathrm{N} | \mathrm{arc} \cos 0.8) = 9 \times 10^{16} \ \mathrm{cm}^{-2} \tag{94}$$

and

$$H \ (\mathrm{O}) \ n_m \ (\mathrm{O} | \mathrm{arc} \cos 0.8) = 3 \times 10^{17} \ \mathrm{cm}^{-2} . \tag{95}$$

For the model atmospheres described earlier, we know the mean scale height $H_m^{F_1}(\mathrm{M})$ and total particle concentration $n_m^{F_1}(\mathrm{M})$ at 200 km, the alti-

12. Since this was written, the formulation has been used by Seaton (1951) in calculations on the photoionization cross-section of neon. The results obtained are in close agreement with the corresponding experimental results of Lee and Weissler (1953) and of Ditchburn (1954).

tude of the peak of the F_1 layer. Table 7 gives a selection of the values of the products of these two quantities.

In setting up the models it was assumed, for simplicity, that the nitrogen is completely molecular and that the oxygen is completely atomic. The tabulated values of $H_m^{F_1}(M)n_m^{F_1}(M)$ remain useful even if the former assumption is incorrect—though, of course, the temperatures of the associated models are rather lower. In deducing $H_m^{F_1}(N)n_m^{F_1}(N)$ and $H_m^{F_1}(O) \cdot n_m^{F_1}(O)$, we can ignore the differences in the scale heights, and, since the

TABLE 7

DATA RELATING TO THE F_1 LAYER

Model Atmosphere	$H_m^{F_1}(M)n_m^{F_1}(M)$	Model Atmosphere	$H_m^{F_1}(M)n_m^{F_1}(M)$
M($500°$ K; 200 km)......	2×10^{16} cm^{-2}	M($1500°$ K; 200 km)......	3×10^{17} cm^{-2}
M($1000°$ K; 200 km)....	1×10^{17} cm^{-2}	M($2000°$ K; 200 km)......	5×10^{17} cm^{-2}

relative abundance of nitrogen and oxygen nuclei must be closely the same as at ground level, we have

$$n\,(N) \simeq \left\{\frac{4x}{3+2x}\right\} n\,(M)\,, \tag{96}$$

$$n\,(O) \simeq \left\{\frac{1}{3+2x}\right\} n\,(M)\,, \tag{97}$$

where x is the fraction of the original nitrogen which is dissociated. From these relations, the data in Table 7 and equations (94) and (95) it would appear that the temperature of the upper atmosphere must be very high if the F_1 layer arises from the ionization of either atomic nitrogen or atomic oxygen by photons just above the threshold. However, so far we have made the customary assumption that molecular nitrogen has not an appreciable absorption continuum below the first ionization potential at 15.6 eV. Weissler (1952) has recently suggested that there may, in fact, be a continuum in which $A(N_2)$ is of order 4×10^{-18} cm^2. Should this be the case, the location requirement would be satisfied by a more tenuous atmosphere; for if the active radiation, besides being absorbed in the photoionization of a constituent, X, is, in addition, being absorbed in some way by another constituent, Y, formula (70) must be modified to

$$\{n\,(X\,|\,\chi) + n\,(Y\,|\,\chi)\,\} = \frac{\cos\chi}{\bar{A}\,H\,(X)}\,, \tag{98}$$

where $\bar{A}$ is the mean absorption cross-section defined by

$$\bar{A} = \frac{A\,(X)\,n\,(X\,|\,\chi) + A\,(Y)\,n\,(Y\,|\,\chi)}{n\,(X\,|\,\chi) + n\,(Y\,|\,\chi)}. \tag{99}$$

The intensity of the solar emission may, of course, fall off quite slowly above the Lyman limit, so that the photoionization of atomic oxygen at the second and third thresholds (16.9 and 18.6 eV) may be important. It would naturally be accompanied by the photoionization of molecular nitrogen (and, as pointed out earlier, the twilight investigations do *not* imply that this process is feeble). According to the measurements of Weissler (1952), $A(N_2)$ is about 2×10^{-17} cm² for the main part of the photoionization continuum; and according to the calculations of Bates and Seaton (1949), $A(O)$ is about 8×10^{-18} cm² for photon energies between 16.9 and 18.6 eV and is about 1.2×10^{-17} cm² for higher photon energies (up to perhaps 25 eV). Clearly, therefore, the greatest change in $\bar{A}$ occurs at 15.6 eV, the molecular nitrogen threshold. From (99) we find that for an (N_2, O) atmosphere, unaffected by diffusive separation, $\bar{A}$ averages some 1.5×10^{-17} cm² above this energy. Hence the maximum ionization occurs where

$$H\{n(N_2|\chi) + n(O|\chi)\} \simeq 5 \times 10^{16} \text{ cm}^{-2}. \tag{100}$$

On referring to Table 7 it may be seen that the altitude would correspond to that of F_1 if one of the cooler models were adopted. Similar considerations apply if the nitrogen is partially dissociated; but this case is not worth examining in detail, since there are too many unknown parameters.

From the foregoing discussion we conclude that lack of information on upper-atmospheric conditions and on the solar emission makes the application of Chapman's formula indecisive as far as the origin of the F_1 layer is concerned.

The theory of the formation of the F_2 layer is dependent on that of the formation of the F_1 layer, since the constituent X, which is responsible for the latter, probably produces considerable ionization at the altitude of the former. In the case of an atmosphere where the scale-height gradient is constant and equal to c it may easily be seen that

$$I_m^{F_2}(X) = I_m^{F_1}(X) \frac{n_{mF_2}(X)}{n_{mF_1}(X)} \exp\left\{(1+c)\left[1 - \left(\frac{H_{F_2}n_{mF_2}(X)}{H_{F_1}n_{mF_1}(X)}\right)\right]\right\}. \tag{101}$$

For illustrative purposes it is sufficient to neglect the gradient and adopt a mean scale height. Some representative means were chosen and the necessary computations performed, assuming h_{mF_1} to be 200 km; h_{mF_2} to be 300 or 400 km; and $I_m^{F_1}(X)$ to be 250/cm³ sec. Table 8 gives the values of $I_m^{F_2}(X)$ obtained. In considering them, one should remember that a single model can scarcely describe the atmospheric distribution both when h_{mF_2} is 300 km and when it is 400 km.

Because of the uncertainty in the effective recombination coefficient, the actual ionization rate in the F_2 layer is not known reliably; but, according to the radio scientists, it is of the order of a third that in the F_1 layer. Inspection of Table 8 shows that the process which produces F_1 may itself provide all or most of this. Indeed, such a conclusion is difficult to avoid if the temperature of the upper atmosphere is high. It thus seems likely that the splitting of F is not due to the action of two distinct photo-ionization mechanisms, but instead is due mainly to the diminution with altitude of the effective recombination coefficient. On this view, F_2 is formed far above the region where the intensity of the incident solar radiation is reduced by a factor equal to the Naperian base (Bradbury, 1938). In contrast to F_1, which is essentially of the Chapman type, it is what may be termed *a low-attenuation layer*.

TABLE 8

IONIZATION RATE IN F_2 LAYER FROM CONSTITUENT GIVING
RISE TO F_1 LAYER

Mean Scale Height, $H(\mathrm{X})$ (km)	$I_m^{F_2}(\mathrm{X})$ (When h_{mF_2} Is 300 km) (/cm³ sec)	$I_m^{F_2}(\mathrm{X})$ (When h_{mF_2} Is 400 km) (/cm³ sec)	Mean Scale Height, $H(\mathrm{X})$ (km)	$I_m^{F_2}(\mathrm{X})$ (When h_{mF_2} Is 300 km) (/cm³ sec)	$I_m^{F_2}(\mathrm{X})$ (When h_{mF_2} Is 400 km) (/cm³ sec)
20............	5	....	80............	146	51
40............	51	5	100...........	173	81
60............	106	23			

Some processes may, of course, be more effective in the F_2 layer than in the F_1 layer. Quantal calculations (Bates and Seaton, 1949) show that at the second ionization $A(\mathrm{O})$ is about three times greater than at the first ionization potential. The trend of $A(\mathrm{N_2})$ is similar. Thus in the spectral range concerned (cf. Table 9) the atmospheric opacity is an irregularly increasing function of the photon energy. There is therefore a tendency for the upper part of the actual electron production distribution to be enhanced relative to the idealized distribution (68) characteristic of monochromatic radiation. The magnitude of the effect cannot, however, be assessed until more is known concerning the solar emission.

Because of certain selection rules (cf. Bates, 1946), atomic nitrogen has only a single ionization potential of importance (that at 14.54 eV). But it may contribute more to F_2 than to F_1 since its fractional abundance may increase with altitude.

In spite of such possibilities, the probability remains that F_2 is at least partially a low-attenuation layer. This may be demonstrated by examining the conditions that would have to be satisfied in order that the attenuation factor should be the Naperian base. Table 10 gives the necessary values of the weighted mean absorption cross-section of the atmospheric constituents,

$$\bar{A} = \frac{\displaystyle\sum_{X} n(X) A(X)}{\displaystyle\sum_{X} n(X)}. \tag{102}$$

TABLE 9

DATA ON IONIZATION ENERGIES OF SOME ATMOSPHERIC CONSTITUENTS

Constituent	Energy for Single Ionization (eV)	Energy for Double Ionization (eV)	Reference
Na	5.14	52.43	Moore (1949)
H	13.59	. . . .	Moore (1949)
O	13.61, 16.94, 18.63	48.76	Moore (1949)
N	14.54, 16.44, 18.60	44.14	Moore (1949)
NO	9.2	. . . .	Inn (1953)
O_2	12.0, (16.0)	. . . .	Herzberg (1950), Inn (1953)
O_3	(12.5)	. . . .	Mulliken (1948)
H_2O	12.6	. . . .	Price (1942)
N_2O	12.7	. . . .	Price (1942)
CH_4	13.1	. . . .	Lossing, Tickner, and Bryce (1951)
CO_2	13.7	. . . .	Price (1942)
CO	14.0	. . . .	Herzberg (1950)
H_2	15.4	. . . .	Herzberg (1950)
N_2	15.6, 16.7, 18.7	. . . .	Herzberg (1950), Douglas (1953)

Bearing in mind the Thomas-Kuhn sum rule and noting that f_c, the oscillator strength associated with the continuum, is approximately

$$9 \times 10^{15} \int_\epsilon \bar{A}(\epsilon) \, d\epsilon, \tag{103}$$

where ϵ is the photon energy in eV, it can be seen that the requirements for $M(500° K; 200 km)$ and $M(1000° K; 200 km)$ are scarcely acceptable. Those for $M(1500° K; 200 km)$ and $M(2000° K; 200 km)$ may be met; but with these models the radiation producing the F_1 layer *must* give rise to considerable ionization at the level of the F_2 layer (cf. Table 8).

As will be recalled, the identification of the photoionization peak due to

$$O + h\nu \, (\geqslant 13.61 \text{ eV} \leqslant 16.94 \text{ eV}) \rightarrow O^+ + e \tag{104}$$

with F is not altogether satisfactory. It is natural, therefore, to inquire whether this peak might not, in fact, be the E layer. To favor the hypothesis, we assume that, in the region concerned, the temperature gradient as high as $30°$ K/km and the effective recombination coefficient are constant, so that in (82) (which must be used instead of [70]) c is about unity and p is zero. From (93) we then obtain,

$$H_m(O)\, n_m(O \mid \text{arc} \cos 0.8) \simeq 6 \times 10^{17} \text{ cm}^{-2} . \tag{105}$$

Taking h_m^E to be 110 km (cf. Sec. 4.1), we have

$$H_m^E(O)\, n_m^E(O) \simeq 3 \times 10^{18} \text{ cm}^{-2} . \tag{106}$$

The supposition that (104) is the cause of the main E layer is thus unattractive—a somewhat more likely supposition is that it is the cause of E_2, as this lies at a rather greater altitude. Furthermore, the ionization of

TABLE 10

WEIGHTED MEAN ABSORPTION CROSS-SECTIONS REQUIRED TO ATTENUATE INCOMING RADIATION BY FACTOR EQUAL TO NAPERIAN BASE AT ALTITUDE OF F_2 LAYER

Model	$\bar{A}$ (Altitude of 300 km)	$\bar{A}$ (Altitude of 400 km)	Model	$\bar{A}$ (Altitude of 300 km)	$\bar{A}$ (Altitude of 400 km)
M(500° K; 200 km).....	7×10^{-15}	1×10^{-12}	M(1500° K; 200 km)...	1×10^{-17}	7×10^{-17}
M(1000° K; 200 km)...	8×10^{-17}	1×10^{-15}	M(2000° K; 200 km)...	5×10^{-18}	2×10^{-17}

O is less than that of N_2 or of N, and its absorption cross-section does not fall below the value it has at the spectral head until photon energies of at least some 25 eV are reached. Consequently, the other processes discussed need not be considered in the present connection; for radiation of the necessary frequency clearly cannot penetrate sufficiently deeply.

The opacity arising from (104) does not affect

$$O_2 + h\nu \, (\geqslant 12.0 \text{ eV} \leqslant 13.6 \text{ eV}) \rightarrow O_2^+ + e . \tag{107}$$

Some years ago it was thought that this might be the process yielding E (which is in the region where molecular oxygen is first encountered). Evidence is now available that its cross-section is small. Moreover, at the altitudes concerned, the oxygen is probably still principally in the atomic form. As a result the location requirement (82) is not even approximately satisfied. Though the original proposal apparently must be abandoned, an important modification to it has been introduced by Nicolet (1945c), who has pointed out that a number of intense discrete bands lie within the continuum and has suggested that absorption in them might be followed by spontaneous ionization,

$$O_2 + h\nu \ (\geqslant 12.0 \ \text{eV} \leqslant 13.6 \ \text{eV}) \rightarrow O_2' \left.\begin{array}{c} \\ \\ \end{array}\right\} \cdot \qquad (108)$$
$$O_2' \rightarrow O_2^+ + e$$

On this basis a plausible theory of the formation of the layer can be constructed. The rarity of molecular oxygen is balanced by the great strength of the band absorption. Other effects of photodissociation have to be taken into account. The discussion of them is rather lengthy (Bates, 1949) and may be omitted, since it is sufficient to mention that they appear to cause no insuperable difficulty. Wainfan, Walker, and Weissler (1953) have confirmed experimentally that pre-ionization (reactions 108) does, in fact, occur; moreover, with the aid of rockets, Tousey, Watanabe, and Purcell (1953) have shown that the incident photons carry ample energy for the production of the E layer and are absorbed mainly between 88 and 127 km elevation.

Attention must not be confined to radiation below the threshold of (104), since radiation far enough above can also penetrate the atomic oxygen barrier (Hulburt, 1938; Vegard, 1938). Moreover, the recent theoretical work of Hoyle (1949) indicates that the solar corona is a powerful source of high-energy photons; and this is confirmed by the rocket measurements of Burnight (1949), Tousey, Watanabe, and Purcell (1951), and Friedman, Lichtman, and Byram (1951). From X-ray absorption data it may be shown that the location requirements would be satisfied by a photon distribution having a maximum near 300 eV or near 1200 eV. The former distribution is favored, since undesirable complications arise in the case of the latter, owing to the secondary emission that follows the ejection of K-shell electrons (Hoyle and Bates, 1948). Though not unreasonable, it is, of course, speculative to suppose that the actual coronal emission approximates to either distribution and is, in addition, sufficiently intense.[13]

High-energy photons ionize all atmospheric constituents. It is necessary, therefore, to inquire whether (if they are sufficiently intense to produce the E layer) they would cause the N_2^+ concentration to exceed the limit set by the spectroscopic evidence (Bates, 1949). Detailed examination of the matter shows that there is not necessarily any discrepancy. Dissociative recombination or charge-transfer collisions may remove the

13. The most recently published rocket measurements (Byram, Chubb, and Friedman, 1954a) indicate that the intensity in the spectral region concerned is of the required order of magnitude.

N_2^+ sufficiently rapidly and yet allow a considerable concentration of them to be established on certain occasions (cf. Table 6) by a comparatively weak additional source of ionization. Doubts as to this were expressed a few years ago, but it was not then realized that a dissociative recombination coefficient as great as 10^{-7}–10^{-6} cm^3/sec cannot be excluded, and account was not taken of the probable temperature dependence of the coefficient associated with charge transfer. The necessary modifications to the quantitative discussion originally presented are trivial and need not be given here.

The number of possible processes by which the D layer might be formed is severely limited by the atmospheric opacity in the far ultraviolet. Thus 12 eV or more are needed to ionize normal O, O_2, O_3, N, N_2, N_2O, CO, CO_2, H, H_2, H_2O, or CH_4 (Table 9); and radiation of this photon energy cannot reach sufficiently low levels. Jouaust, Vassy, and Vassy (1941, 1942) have indeed asserted that the penetration requirement is satisfied only by radiation of photon energy below 7 eV and have hence argued that

$$\text{Na} + h\nu \rightarrow \text{Na}^+ + e \qquad (109)$$

(the threshold of which is 5.1 eV) must be the process operative. This process is unacceptable, since atomic sodium is such a rare constituent that the ionization due to it is inappreciable except perhaps near the extreme base of the layer (Bates and Seaton, 1950). Further, the claim that the atmosphere above the D layer is completely opaque to radiation of photon energy 7–12 eV is unjustified—there are actually several windows of quite high transmissibility in the region between 10 and 11 eV (Preston, 1940; Hopfield, 1946; Friedman, Lichtman, and Byram, 1951). One of these windows is of particular interest because it includes the Lyman-α line of atomic hydrogen. Some years ago Chapman and Price (1936) drew attention to the close coincidence between λ 1215.6, the wave length of this line, and λ 1217.6, the wave length of the radiation required to raise atomic oxygen from the metastable p^4 ^{1}S level to the highly excited p^{3}s ^{1}P level. They also pointed out that ionization might occur through

$$\text{O}(^1\text{S}) + \text{Ly}(\alpha) \rightarrow \text{O}(^1\text{P}),$$
$$\text{O}(^1\text{P}) + \text{X} \rightarrow \text{O}^+(^4\text{S}) + \text{X} + e + 0.75\,\text{eV}. \qquad (110)$$

Martyn, Munro, Higgs, and Williams (1937) have suggested that the mechanism is important in the D layer; but Bates and Seaton (1950) have shown that, in fact, the contribution from it is almost certainly negligible.

Solar X-rays do not appear to reach below the 87-km level (Friedman,

Lichtman, and Byram, 1951). The view that they are the source of the ionization (Piddington, 1951) is, therefore, very difficult to accept.

Because of the failure of the alternative proposals that have been advanced, serious consideration must be given to

$$NO + h\nu \rightarrow NO^+ + e \;, \tag{111}$$

which is the one remaining obvious possibility (Nicolet, 1949). As the threshold lies at 9.2 eV, there is no difficulty about the penetration of radiation of sufficient photon energy. We have seen, too (Sec. 2.2), that nitric oxide is expected to be quite abundant in the atmospheric region concerned. An exploratory survey which has been made (Bates and Seaton, 1950) shows that the process is quite promising both for the ordinary D layer and for the fade-out enhancement (provided that Lyman-α is intensified during the solar flare). Unfortunately, a proper quantitative appraisal of the situation is impossible at present, the NO concentration being unknown. Since the publication of the original estimates of Bates and Seaton, measurements have been made on the relevant photoionization cross-section (Watanabe, Marmo, and Inn, 1953) and on the attenuation of the active radiation by the atmosphere (Byram, Chubb, and Friedman, 1954b). The results are not unfavorable to the hypothesis.

4.3. Equilibrium

Bates and Massey (1946, 1947) have discussed the reactions controlling the rate at which the free charges produced by photoionization disappear. Their description of the equilibrium depends on several unproved assumptions which were regarded by them as plausible but not fully satisfactory.

The simple radiative process,

$$X^+ + e \rightarrow X' + h\nu \quad (X = O, O_2, \text{etc.}) \;, \tag{112}$$

was believed by early workers to be important, but this is not the case, since calculations (Bates, Buckingham, Massey, and Unwin, 1939) show that its rate coefficient is only of the order of 10^{-12}–10^{-11} cm^3/sec (cf. Sec. 4.1).

After the dismissal of (112), consideration was given to the possible influence of negative ions. In the E and F layers the main sequence is

$$O + e \rightarrow O^- + h\nu \;, \tag{113}$$

$$O^- + h\nu \rightarrow O + e \;, \tag{114}$$

$$O^- + O \rightarrow O_2 + e \;, \tag{115}$$

$$O^- + X^+ \rightarrow O' + X' \tag{116}$$

Denoting the rate coefficients of these by η, ρ, κ, and a_i, respectively, it may be seen that

$$\frac{dn\,(e)}{dt} = q - an^2\,(e)\ , \tag{117}$$

where

$$q = \frac{I\,(X\,|\,h,\,\chi)}{1+\lambda}\ , \tag{118}$$

$$a = \lambda a_i\ , \tag{119}$$

$$\lambda = \frac{n\,(O^-)}{n\,(e)} = \frac{\eta n\,(O)}{\rho + \kappa n\,(O) + (1+\lambda)\,a_i n\,(e)}\ . \tag{120}$$

On comparing (117) with (73) it is apparent that q is the *effective* ionization rate, and a is the *effective* recombination coefficient.

Quantal methods have been used to determine η and ρ (which are, of course, related). Their values depend on whether or not the field of an oxygen atom is strong enough to bind an excess electron in an *excited* state (Bates and Massey, 1943). If it is (case A), then

$$\left.
\begin{aligned}
\eta &= 6 \times 10^{-14}\ \text{cm}^3/\text{sec}\ (250^\circ\,\text{K})\ , \\
\eta &= 3 \times 10^{-14}\ \text{cm}^3/\text{sec}\ (500^\circ\,\text{K})\ , \\
\eta &= 1.5 \times 10^{-14}\ \text{cm}^3/\text{sec}\ (1000^\circ\,\text{K})\ , \\
\eta &= 8 \times 10^{-15}\ \text{cm}^3/\text{sec}\ (2000^\circ\,\text{K})\ , \\
\rho &= 0.85/\text{sec}\ ;
\end{aligned}
\right\} \tag{121}$$

if it is not (case B), then

$$\left.
\begin{aligned}
\eta &= 1.1 \times 10^{-15}\ \text{cm}^3/\text{sec}\ (\text{almost independent of temperature}) \\
\rho &= 0.35/\text{sec}\ .
\end{aligned}
\right\} \tag{122}$$

Moreover, $\kappa n(O)$ must be the major term in the denominator of (119) at the levels of the E and F_1 layers; for otherwise $n_m(e)$ would not follow the $(\cos \chi)^{1/2}$ law even approximately. Supposing it to be at least four times greater than ρ, and taking $n^E(O)$ to be $2 \times 10^{12}/\text{cm}^3$, we have, for case A,

$$\kappa = 2 \times 10^{-12}\ \text{cm}^3/\text{sec}\ . \tag{123}$$

Substituting in (120), we find

$$\lambda^E < 3 \times 10^{-2}\ ; \tag{124}$$

and hence from (119) we see that if a^E is to be about $1 \times 10^{-8}\ \text{cm}^3/\text{sec}$ or greater (as observed), it is necessary that

$$a_i > 3 \times 10^{-7}\ \text{cm}^3/\text{sec}\ , \tag{125}$$

which is barely acceptable. Further, Bates and Massey considered case B
as the more likely, and with it we obtain an even smaller λ^E and an a_i
so large that the term $a_i n_m^E(e)$ dominates (120), with the result that the
$(\cos \chi)^{1/2}$ law is not obeyed. For the F_1 layer the difficulties are clearly
still more acute.

The behavior of the F_2 layer is not such as to require the supposition
that collisional detachment is very rapid. Ignoring it (to favor the theory)
and observing that λ is certainly small, we have from (119) and (120),

$$a^{F_2} = \frac{a_i \eta n^{F_2}(O)}{\rho + a_i n_m^{F_2}(e)}. \tag{126}$$

Table 11 gives the result obtained from this equation if a_i is taken to be
5×10^{-7} cm^3/sec; if $n_m^{F_2}(e)$ is taken to be 1×10^6/cm^3 during the day and

TABLE 11*

CONTRIBUTION FROM NEGATIVE IONS TO EFFECTIVE RECOMBI-
NATION COEFFICIENT IN F_2 LAYER

ASSUMED $n^{F_2}(O)$ AND T^{F_2}	ASSUMED η AND ρ	DEDUCED CONTRIBUTION TO a^{F_2} (cm^3/sec)	
		Day	Night
$n^{F_2}(O)=3\times10^9$ cm^3/sec	Case A	1.5×10^{-11}	1.5×10^{-10}
$T^{F_2}=1500°$ K	Case B	2×10^{-12}	1.5×10^{-11}
$n^{F_2}(O)=1\times10^{10}$ cm^3/sec	Case A	3×10^{-11}	3×10^{-10}
$T^{F_2}=2000°$ K	Case B	6×10^{-12}	4×10^{-11}

* Cf. Table 2. The $n^{F_2}(O)$ and T^{F_2} adopted correspond to the 300-km level of models M
(1500° K; 200 km) and M (2000° K; 200 km). At the 400-km level the deduced values of a^{F_2} are
about four times smaller than those given.

to be 2.5×10^5/cm^3 during the night; and if the other assumptions indicated are made. As will be seen, the daytime value of a^{F_2} is low in spite of
the large a_i adopted; and though the nighttime value (which does not depend on a_i) is considerable in case A, it is barely appreciable in the more
readily accepted case B. The conclusion would thus appear to be that the
influence of negative ion formation on the effective recombination coefficient in the F_2 layer is insignificant during the day and is probably not of
major importance even at night.

Dissociative recombination seems to be the only remaining reaction
meriting consideration. Bates and Massey suggested that, in the E layer,

$$O_2^+ + e \rightarrow O' + O'', \tag{127}$$

the O_2^+ ions being formed either directly or through charge-transfer collisions, such as

$$O_2 + O^+ \rightarrow O_2^+ + O \, . \tag{128}$$

At the time little was known about dissociative recombination, but there is now some experimental and theoretical evidence which suggests that it may indeed be as rapid as is required (Biondi and Brown, 1949; Biondi, 1951a; Bates, 1951). The hypothesis is therefore at least plausible.

A similar mechanism was suggested for the F layers. Their behavior could be explained by supposing that the rate-limiting process in F_1 is dissociative recombination and that that in F_2 is charge transfer. A detailed discussion will not be given here, but it must be mentioned that a difficulty arises from the fact that the unidentified molecules, presumed to be involved in the charge transfer, are destroyed by the subsequent dissociative recombination; and it is not readily apparent how they can be replenished sufficiently rapidly at the low gas densities prevailing in the F layers. One of the proposals originally made by Bates and Massey (1943) was that O_2 might be the unidentified molecular species. At the time, the rate of replenishment could not be estimated; but as a result of some recent work Nicolet (1954) considers that it may well be adequate. A final conclusion cannot be reached until the rate coefficient associated with (128) is determined.

If the difficulty should prove insurmountable, it would be necessary to examine carefully the loss of ions and electrons due to downward diffusion.

The situation in the D layer is different from that in the upper layers, in that the negative ion to electron ratio is relatively large. In particular, there is some experimental evidence that attachment to molecular oxygen occurs quite rapidly (Bradbury, 1933; Block and Bradbury, 1935). As the nature of the mechanism is not yet understood, it is not easy to extrapolate the rate coefficients measured in the laboratory to D-layer conditions. In addition, photodetachment from O_2^- has not been studied. A quantitative theory cannot therefore be given at present. Bates and Massey (1951) have, however, attempted a preliminary survey of the position. Using a formula closely corresponding to (119) and adopting the best available estimates of the parameters appearing in it, they deduced that during the day λ^D (which now represents $n[O_2^-]/n[e]$) is likely to be of order 6 at 75 km, and of order 0.4 at 90 km. To account for the effective recombination coefficients (cf. Sec. 4.1), it would thus be necessary for a_i to be of order

10^{-7} cm^3/sec.[14] The fact that this value is rather high need not cause undue concern, in view of the crudeness of the basic data. While it thus appears that ionic recombination may well be adequate, it should be noted that dissociative recombination cannot be dismissed with certainty, since recent laboratory measurements (Biondi and Brown, 1949) give rate coefficients of the required order of magnitude. The relative effectiveness of the two processes is very different during the night. Because of attachment, the electrons probably disappear almost completely shortly after sunset. Consequently, dissociative recombination virtually ceases, and only ionic recombination is operative. It would therefore be instructive to have information on the decay in the ion concentration throughout the dark hours. This might be obtained by observations at sunrise on the increase in the electron concentration due to photodetachment.

4.4. MAGNETIC VARIATIONS

It is widely believed that the small periodic variations in the earth's magnetic field are caused by the electric currents set up by the dynamo action resulting from the solar, S, and lunar, L, tidal motions of the ionized layers (Chapman and Bartels, 1940). Martyn (1948) has advanced reasons for supposing that D and E are the layers involved.[15] The dynamo theory requires that the products of $K_S^\perp$ and $K_L^\perp$, the transverse conductivities of the atmospheric regions concerned, with l_S and l_L, the factors by which the speeds of the S and L tidal motions in them exceed the corresponding speeds at ground level, are both approximately 2.5×10^{-5} electromagnetic units. Cowling (1945) has given an expression for the transverse conductivity in terms of the permanent magnetic field, the electron and ion concentrations, and collision frequencies. Numerical substitution shows that the contribution from the electrons is inadequate. The contribution from the ions is difficult to calculate, since their concentration cannot be obtained directly from radio measurements. There has been a tendency in the past to take advantage of this lack of knowledge and to suppose arbitrarily that it is very many times that of the electrons.

14. It may be remarked, however, that just after Bates and Massey carried out the analysis summarized above, Biondi (1951b) applied the new microwave technique to the study of attachment in molecular oxygen and obtained a much smaller rate coefficient than did the earlier workers to whom reference has been made. No explanation of the discrepancy has yet been given. If Biondi's result should prove to be correct, the estimates of λ^D given would have to be revised downward, by a factor of about 10, and the estimate of the requisite value of α_i would have to be revised upward by the same amount (Bates and Massey, 1952).

15. Measurements made with magnetometers mounted on high-altitude rockets (Singer, Maple, and Bowen, 1951, 1952) have since shown that the location of the current system is actually the lower part of the E layer.

By also invoking a high tidal amplification factor, it was then possible to explain the magnetic variations. The position has recently been critically examined (Bates and Massey, 1951). Improbably favorable assumptions about the relevant reaction rates were made, but, in spite of this, the deduced ionic concentration was, according to Cowling's formula, far too small to yield a transverse conductivity which would be sufficient, even if used in conjunction with the maximum acceptable tidal amplification factor. It was concluded that either the dynamo theory or the method of calculating the transverse conductivity requires modification.[16]

5. AIRGLOW

5.1 NIGHT AIRGLOW

The atomic oxygen in the upper atmosphere forms what is probably the main energy reservoir supplying the night airglow—though the atomic nitrogen may conceivably also be involved. It is convenient to divide the reactions by which the energy is released into three groups.

a) Oxygen molecules in the X $^3\Sigma_g^-$, a $^1\Delta_g$, b $^1\Sigma_g^+$, and A $^3\Sigma_u^+$ states may be formed by simple three-body association, since normal oxygen atoms may approach each other along the appropriate attractive potentials. Now in the region near the 100-km level three-body association is the main process opposing photodissociation (Sec. 2.1). By equating the two rates, we find that the mean number of oxygen molecules formed in this region is about $2 \times 10^{12}/\text{cm}^2$ column·sec. There is no obvious reason why the ground X $^3\Sigma_g^-$ state should be favored to any very marked extent. Hence, the entry into the excited a $^1\Delta_g$, b $^1\Sigma_g^+$, and A $^3\Sigma_u^+$ states would be expected to be considerable, and the infrared atmospheric, the Kaplan-Meinel atmospheric, and the Herzberg band systems (which originate from them) would be expected to be very intense. The first of these systems lies in an unobserved spectral region, so that nothing can be said about it at present. The other two are certainly prominent in the airglow (see preceding chapter). Their combined photon intensity is, however, only a small fraction of $2 \times 10^{12}/\text{cm}^2$ column·sec. Collisional deactivation could not account for the discrepancy, so that it would seem that either the total three-body association rate is slower than supposed or that some factor, such as a maximum to the potential curves (which may, of course, be affected by the presence of the third body), inhibits the population of

16. Several investigators (Hirono, 1950, 1952; Baker and Martyn, 1952; Cowling, 1953; Lucas, 1953) who have recently re-examined the theory have come independently to the conclusion that the discrepancy can be removed by taking proper account of the Hall current. Much detailed work, however, is still required.

the two states concerned. The recent work of Meckler (1953) suggests that some of the potential curves may indeed possess a maximum.

It may be remarked here that the theoretical study of the electronic structure of the oxygen molecule, made by Moffitt (1951), shows that at least two stable states can be formed from normal oxygen atoms in addition to the four well-known states already mentioned. One of these states is of the $^1\Sigma_u^-$ type and the other of the $^3\Delta_u$ type. Both are predicted to lie below, but close to, the A $^3\Sigma_u^+$ state. They should be populated by three-body association, and emissions from them should appear in the spectrum of the airglow.

The rotational and vibrational temperatures of the oxygen molecules are probably high immediately after the association takes place. As is well known (Massey, 1948), a few collisions are sufficient to transfer any excess rotational energy to translational energy. But the corresponding transfer of excess vibrational energy is extremely difficult. It might therefore appear anomalous that Meinel (1950a) fails to observe bands originating from any but the zeroth vibration level of $O_2(b\ ^1\Sigma_g^+)$. However, there is not necessarily any difficulty, for the lowering of the vibrational temperature can be brought about indirectly through collisions in which interchange of electronic energy occurs,

$$O_2\,(b\ ^1\Sigma_g^+, v' > 0) + O_2\,(X\ ^3\Sigma_g^-, v'' = 0) \rightarrow O_2\,(X\ ^3\Sigma_g^-, v'' > 0)$$
$$+ O_2\,(b\ ^1\Sigma_g^+, v' = 0)\,. \tag{129}$$

The approximate equality of the r_e and ω_e values of the b $^1\Sigma_g^+$ and X $^3\Sigma_g^-$ states is likely to facilitate the process.

Though the (0, 1) band of O_2 (b $^1\Sigma_g^+ \rightarrow$ X $^3\Sigma_g^-$), λ 8600, is strong, the (0, 0) band, λ 7600, is absent because of atmospheric absorption (Meinel, 1950a). It should be noted that much of the λ 7600 radiation is not lost but is, instead, degraded to λ 8600, since

$$\lambda 7600 + O_2\,(X\,^3\Sigma_g^-, v'' = 0) \rightarrow O_2\,(b\ ^1\Sigma_g^+, v' = 0) \tag{130}$$

is generally followed by

$$O_2\,(b\ ^1\Sigma_g^+, v' = 0) \left\{ \begin{array}{l} \rightarrow O_2\,(X\ ^3\Sigma_g^-, v'' = 1) + \lambda 8600 \quad (a) \\ \rightarrow O_2\,(X\ ^3\Sigma_g^-, v'' = 0) + \lambda 7600 \quad (b) \end{array} \right\}, \tag{131}$$

rather than by deactivating collisions; and, while there is only about a 1 in 30 chance of (131a) occurring, (131b) again leads to (130), so that the sequence repeats. Because of this degradation, it is incorrect to assume that the total population rate of $O_2(b\ ^1\Sigma_g^+)$ is some 30 times the observed photon intensity of λ 8600; the ratio of the two may be much less. More-over, the rotational structure of the band does not give the temperature of the level at which the primary excited molecules are formed; it gives the temperature of the much lower level where the principal absorption occurs. It would be useful to solve the radiation-transfer problem pre-sented;[17] the twilight period should be included in the investigation, for it seems likely that an enhancement will be caused by the absorption (130) and re-emission (131) of solar radiation.

If Gaydon's views (1947) on the structure of molecular nitrogen are correct, the A $^3\Sigma_u^+$ state could be populated through simple three-body association. The rate coefficient should not be unduly low and, if atomic nitrogen is at all abundant, the process might give rise to appreciable emission of the Vegard-Kaplan band system. It is now doubtful, however, whether this system occurs in the airglow spectrum (cf. chap. 11, Sec. 4.14).

b) A modification of the simple type of process just discussed is that part of the available energy is used up in exciting the third body. Chap-man (1931) has suggested that the ^{1}S and ^{1}D levels of atomic oxygen are populated in this way. The mechanism may be written

$$(O+O) (A \, ^3\Sigma_u^+) +O \, (^3P) \rightarrow O_2 \, (X \, ^3\Sigma_g^-) +O \, (^1D \text{ or } ^1S) , \qquad (132)$$

to take a representative case,[18] and may thus be regarded as similar to the ordinary transfer of electronic excitation,

$$X Y' + Z \rightarrow X Y + Z', \qquad (133)$$

which has recently been discussed by Massey (1948). Though the transi-tions involved in (132) are forbidden, there is no reason to suppose that the cross-section is smaller than is required. However, the utterly different diurnal, seasonal, and sunspot-cycle variations of the red and green lines (chap. 11, Sec. 4.2) make it difficult to believe that the excitation processes operative are closely related. Indeed, an acceptable explanation of the behavior of neither line has yet been given.

Unlike Gaydon, Herzberg (1950) does not consider that two nitrogen atoms can approach along the A $^3\Sigma_u^+$ potential. However, by a collision similar to (132), they could excite a nitrogen molecule.

c) Oxygen atoms may unite through

$$(O+O) (A \, ^3\Sigma_u^+) \rightarrow O_2 \, (X \, ^3\Sigma_g^-) + h\nu . \qquad (134)$$

17. This has now been done by Chamberlain (1954a). Cf. also chap. 11, Sec. 4.4.

18. Other molecular transitions may, of course, occur.

Denoting the rate coefficient in the usual way, and taking the atomic oxygen distribution to be as given in Figure 1, we find that the photon intensity of the emitted continuum is some $3 \times 10^{31} \, a_{134}/cm^2$ column·sec. Unless a_{134} is extremely low, this should be observable. The radiative association of atomic oxygen and nitric oxide, (26), is of interest, since it is known to give rise to a continuum at $\lambda > 4000 \, A$ (cf. Stoddard, 1934; Gaydon, 1944), which is just the spectral region where, according to Swings (1948), the continuum of the airglow is strongest. Lack of reliable information on $n(NO)$ and a_{26} prevents a proper calculation of the intensity; but the possible values of these quantities (cf. Sec. 2.2) are such that it might be considerable.

 d) In the processes already discussed, the potential energy stored by the free atoms is used directly. Sequences of reactions may also be important. Thus Herzberg (1950b) and Bates and Nicolet (1950a) have independently proposed that the Meinel hydroxyl bands are excited by

$$OH + O \rightarrow H + O_2 , \qquad (135)$$

$$H + O_3 \rightarrow OH \; (X \, {}^2\Pi, v \leqslant 9) + O_2 . \qquad (136)$$

The comparative rarity of some of the reactants is probably compensated for by the fact that the collisions are of the two-body type.

Again, Chapman (1939) has pointed out that any sodium in the upper atmosphere must be continually oxidized and reduced, and has suggested that the latter may proceed through

$$NaO + O \rightarrow Na \; ({}^2P) + O_2 \qquad (137)$$

and so lead to the emission of the D lines. Alternatively (Bates and Nicolet, 1950b), the excited atoms may be produced by

$$NaO + H \rightarrow Na \; ({}^2P) + OH , \qquad (138)$$

or, with NaH as the intermediary compound, by

$$NaH + H \rightarrow Na \; ({}^2P) + H_2 . \qquad (139)$$

It is known that (138) and (139) are exothermic, but the energy balance in (137) is uncertain. A laboratory study of the chemiluminescence of sodium-oxygen mixtures should be made, taking care to avoid conditions suitable for

$$NaO + Na_2 \rightarrow Na_2O + Na \; ({}^2P) . \qquad (140)$$

Attention may be drawn to the fact that

$$Na + O_2 + M \rightarrow NaO_2 + M \qquad (141)$$

is extremely rapid. The rate coefficient (which is a decreasing function of the temperature) is some 5×10^{-30} cm^6/sec at 250° K. (Haber and Schasse, 1931; Bawn and Evans, 1937), so that the life of a free sodium atom at 70 km is limited to about 1 second or slightly less. Account must be taken of this process in discussions on the formation of the intermediary compound responsible for the appearance of the D lines in the airglow.

Other sequences may yield the red forbidden line of atomic oxygen. Considering only the final reactions, we have, for example, the possibility of

$$N + O_3 \rightarrow NO_2 + O\,(^1D) \tag{142}$$

or (less attractive, since it requires spin reversal)

$$N + NO \rightarrow N_2 + O\,(^1D). \tag{143}$$

Unfortunately, the rate coefficient of neither is known. Yet another possibility is that the fast electrons liberated in the E layer by

$$O + O^- \rightarrow O_2 + e + 2.9 \text{ eV} \tag{144}$$

produce the excitation through inelastic collisions with oxygen atoms. An upper limit to the yield can be obtained by estimating the rate of formation of negative ions at night. Its value is within an order of magnitude of that required, but, as usual, the basic data employed are too crude for any firm conclusion to be reached.

In view of objections to accepting (132) as the origin of λ 5577, the bimolecular processes occurring in the upper atmosphere were listed as systematically as possible and examined. None was found which could provide oxygen atoms in the ^1S state. It may be that we are incorrect in assuming a chemical source of energy. Certainly such a source is not easy to reconcile with the recent altitude determinations of Roach and Pettit (1951) and of Barbier, Dufay, and Williams (1951). A satisfactory alternative is not, however, obvious. Mitra's view (1947) that the excited atoms result from ionic recombination in the F layers encounters a number of apparently serious difficulties (Bates, 1948); and though the hypothesis that incoming particles, or accelerated atmospheric electrons, are responsible is mentioned by many authors, it is always left very vague. Thus the origin of the best-known of all the airglow emissions is still uncertain.

5.2. TWILIGHT AIRGLOW

Resonant or fluorescent scattering of solar radiation intensifies some of the lines and bands of the airglow during the twilight period (see the preceding chapter). We have already discussed the interpretation of the enhancement of the First Negative system of N_2^+ (Sec. 4.22). The theoretical treatment of the twilight behavior of λ 5892 and λ 5577 is essentially similar and will not be described, since no features of particular interest are involved. As regards λ 6300, it will only be mentioned that simple scattering seems inadequate to account for the observed intensity variation Other processes, such as

$$O^- + h\nu \rightarrow O\,(^1D) + e \;, \tag{145}$$

have been considered; but as yet no satisfactory theory has been developed (cf. Bates, 1948). The recent report (Courtès, 1950; Dufay, 1951) that λ 5200 sometimes appears in the airglow just after sunset has aroused great interest. Calculations on the abundance of atomic nitrogen have been carried out on the assumption that

$$N\,(^4S) + h\nu \rightarrow N\,(^2D) \tag{146}$$

and

$$\left.\begin{array}{l} N\,(^4S) + h\nu \rightarrow N\,(^2P) \\[4pt] N\,(^2P) \rightarrow N\,(^2D) + h\nu \end{array}\right\} \tag{147}$$

are responsible. Undue significance should not be attached to the results obtained, since it is very uncertain whether this assumption is justified (Bates, 1952). Owing to the long lifetime of $N(^2D)$, it is not essential to invoke a process which occurs through the direct action of solar radiation. Other processes which proceed more rapidly during the day than during the night could account for the observed behavior of the line. Dissociative recombination,

$$N_2^+ + e \rightarrow N + N\,(^2D \text{ or } ^2P) \;, \tag{148}$$

is one such possibility. Further study of the enhancement at sunrise, which has been reported by Dufay (1952), would help to elucidate the position. See also the discussion in chapter 11, Section 4.15.

6. AURORAE

Theorists have not reached unanimity concerning the origin of the primary auroral particles (cf. Hoyle, 1949; Alfvén, 1951; Martyn, 1951; Chapman, 1952); but thanks to the efforts of the observers (Vegard, 1940, 1948; Gartlein, 1950; and particularly Meinel, 1950b), we now at least know something of their nature. Protons are certainly included; and they must be accompanied by electrons. It is therefore of interest to consider through what thickness of atmosphere these two species can penetrate. Table 12 (which was compiled from laboratory data collected by Das Gupta and Ghosh, 1946) gives some information of relevance. We note that, for equal speeds, by far the greater range is possessed by the protons and that, for equal energies, it is possessed by the electrons. It may be observed that above the 80-, 100-, and 120-km levels, respectively, there is the equivalent of about 10, 1.0, and 0.1 cm of air at S.T.P. A graph showing energy versus altitude reached for protons has been published by Bates and Griffing (1953a). Because of scattering effects, an accurate corresponding graph for electrons is not easily prepared.

An incoming proton may capture an electron from one of the atmospheric atoms or molecules,

$$H^+ + M \rightarrow H' + M^+, \tag{149}$$

TABLE 12

RANGE OF PROTONS AND ELECTRONS OF DIFFERENT SPEEDS

PROTONS			ELECTRONS		
Speed (10^4 km/sec)	Energy (10^6 eV)	Range (cm in Air at S.T.P.)	Speed (10^4 km/sec)	Energy (10^6 eV)	Range (cm in Air at S.T.P.)
0.10	0.005	0.01	1	0.0003	0.01
0.25	0.033	0.05	3	0.0026	0.04
0.5	0.13	0.2	6	0.011	0.2
1	0.52	0.8	12	0.047	3.4
2	2.1	7.5	18	0.13	18
3	4.7	30	24	0.34	83
5	13	190	27	0.66	220
10	53	3000	29.7(=0.99c)	3.1	1300

and, if an excited state is entered, downward cascading then occurs with the emission of radiation. The cross-section for this capture process is normally[19] greatest when the incident speed of the proton is approximately equal to that of the electron in its Bohr orbit. Above the maximum it falls off as some high power of the speed. Consequently, as was first pointed out by Meinel, the observed Doppler displacement of the hydrogen lines in aurorae gives only a lower limit to the speed of the primary protons.

A quantal investigation of (149) is being made (Bates and Dalgarno, 1952, 1953; Dalgarno and Yadav, 1953), but the computations are not yet complete except for capture from a hydrogen atom (which is relatively

19. This generalization does not apply to the case of close energy resonance for which the maximum occurs at very low speeds. It should be noted that the energy balance of

$$H^+ + O(2p^4, {}^3P) \rightarrow H(1s, {}^2S) + O^+(2p^3, {}^4S)$$

is almost exact.

simple to treat). Though this case is not of importance in the present connection, the results may serve as a guide. As would be expected, the cross-section for capture into the lower levels is larger than the cross-section for capture into the higher levels (Jackson and Schiff, 1953). Now visible radiation does not arise from the two lower levels; and it comprises but a part of the radiation emitted by the third and higher levels. Consequently, the observed photon intensity of the Balmer lines represents only a small fraction of the number of captures which take place. Furthermore, for the protons to be able to reach the 100-km level, their initial energy must be of the order of 5×10^5 eV, so that each is likely to produce some 2×10^4 excitations and ionizations. Consequently, the fact that the emission from atomic hydrogen is feeble is in no way inconsistent with the view that incident protons are the dominant cause of aurorae. To obtain a full appreciation of the position, account will eventually have to be taken of the collisional excitation and ionization of the hydrogen atoms and of further captures. A few of the necessary quantal calculations have been done (Bates and Griffing, 1953b, 1954), and interesting applications of the results have been made by Chamberlain (cf. chap. 11, Sec. 3.52).

The ordinary constituents of the atmosphere are, of course, affected by the collisions taking place. It seems likely that the primary protons and the secondary electrons ejected by them exert a more important influence than do the primary electrons and the hydrogen atoms formed by capture. The main collision processes and the observable spectral features that would be expected to be emitted as a result of them may be listed briefly. Insufficient is known about the cross-sections for a proper analysis.

a) *Simple excitation.*—Kaplan-Meinel atmospheric band of O_2; Vegard-Kaplan, First and Second Positive bands of N_2; allowed and forbidden lines of O I. (Possibly: β bands of NO; allowed and forbidden lines of N I.)

b) *Ionization.*—First Negative bands of O_2^+; Meinel and First Negative bands of N_2^+; allowed and forbidden lines of O II. (Possibly: allowed and forbidden lines of N II.)

c) *Dissociation.*—Allowed and forbidden lines of O I and N I.

d) *Simultaneous ionization and dissociation.*—Allowed and forbidden lines of O II and N II.

It is important to note that the protons are unable to excite the O_2 and N_2 bands and the forbidden lines of O I and N I directly, since the transitions concerned are of the exchange type, and that, though electrons (and systems containing an electron) can excite them, the cross-section is extremely small at high speeds (cf. Massey and Burhop, 1952). Attention may also be drawn to the fact that the N I and N II lines can be obtained from molecular nitrogen through processes c and d though in general exchange is required; it is incorrect to assume that processes a and b are necessarily the main source and to make deductions about the concentration of atomic nitrogen from the observed intensities. Most lines arising from c and d would be expected to be broad, whereas lines arising from a and b would be narrow. Interferometric measurements on the widths would therefore be invaluable.

The processes so far mentioned involve the conversion of kinetic energy into potential energy. Another group of processes occurs owing to changes in the upper atmosphere brought about by the entry into it of the auroral particles. The most important of these changes is the increased degree of ionization. Because of this increase, recombination must be taken into account; and since in equilibrium it proceeds at a rate equal to the ionization rate, the photon yield from it is likely to be comparable with that from the intense Negative-band systems. Radiative recombination, as usual, is unimportant; but dissociative recombination may give a significant contribution to the forbidden lines of O I and N I, and ionic recombination to these and to some of the bands of O_2 and N_2 (cf. Mitra, 1947; Bates, Massey, and Pearse, 1948). Contrary to the claims some workers have made, it is not possible at present to make any specific predictions as to which emissions are likely to be augmented.

An entirely different type of process is important in the case of sunlit aurorae. It appears probable that their remarkable brilliance is due to the incoming corpuscles *sensitizing* the atmosphere by producing along their track N_2^+ ions, which subject the solar radiation to resonance scattering, (85), and thus are a powerful source of the First Negative band system (cf. Bates, 1949a). The divided aurorae of Störmer (1947) provide an interesting illustration of the effect. Above the earth's shadow line there is a section of these which is rendered luminous by resonance scattering in the sensitized part of the atmosphere through which the corpuscular stream passes. Immediately below this line is a dark section arising because excitation by collisions is not sufficiently efficient to produce a detectable amount of photon emission from an atmospheric region of such tenuity. Finally, if the auroral corpuscles penetrate to levels where the gas density is high enough, a third section, luminous like the first, naturally appears.

In addition to the uncertainty caused by the lack of reliable knowledge of the rates of most of the processes described, there are complications due to collisions which deactivate some of the metastable particles (cf. Seaton, 1954) or transfer their energy of excitation to other particles. It is clear, therefore, that we are not yet in a position to attempt to interpret the spectra of aurorae in full. Nevertheless, certain aspects of the problem can be attacked.

The First Negative system of N_2^+ is generally regarded as arising from

$$N_2 \, (X \,^1\Sigma_g^+) + e \rightarrow N_2^+ \, (B \,^2\Sigma_u^+) + 2 \, e \,. \qquad (150)$$

Using quantal methods, the relative rates, r_v, at which the different vibrational levels, v, would be populated by this process have been calculated (Bates, 1949b). They depend, of course, on T(vib.), the assumed vibrational temperature of the nitrogen molecules. Table 13 gives these theoretical values, together with some observed values deduced from the measurements of Vegard and Kvifte (1945) on high-latitude aurorae, and

TABLE 13

DATA ON THE FIRST NEGATIVE SYSTEM OF N_2^+

ASSUMED VIBRATIONAL TEMPERATURE OF NITROGEN MOLECULES (° K)		RELATIVE RATES OF POPULATION OF VIBRATIONAL LEVELS OF $N_2^+(B \,^2\Sigma_u^+)$			
		r_0	r_1	r_2	r_3
a) Theory (process [150])	500....	1.00	0.11	0.00	....
	1000....	1.00	.13	.01	....
	2000....	1.00	.26	.07	....
	4000....	1.00	.47	.22	....
	8000....	1.00	.68	.47	....
b) High-latitude aurorae......... (Vegard and Kvifte, 1945)		1.00	.25	.12	(0.05)
c) Low-latitude aurorae......... (Barbier, 1947)		1.00	0.65	0.46	0.34

from the measurements of Barbier (1947) on low-latitude aurorae. The following points will be noted: (a) there is a marked difference between the two sets of observed distributions, the diminution of r_v as v is increased being more marked for high- than for low-latitude aurorae; (b) the vibrational temperatures in high- and in low-latitude aurorae must apparently be as great as 2000° and 8000° K, respectively, if the excitation process is as postulated.

It might be suggested that the peculiarities revealed could be explained by supposing that T (vib.) is not equal to T (trans.), the translational temperature, but is instead much greater. Detailed investigations show that this is not easy to accept. Since a temperature of 2000° K at an altitude of 120 km (as indicated by high-latitude aurorae), and one of 8000° K at an altitude of 250–300 km (as indicated by low-latitude aurorae), are quite impossible, it would thus seem that (150) is not the main process operative. Arguments for rejecting

$$N_2^+ (X\ ^2\Sigma_g^+) + e \rightarrow N_2^+ (B\ ^2\Sigma_u^+) + e\ , \qquad (151)$$

which is the most obvious alternative, have been given (Bates, 1949b). There is, however, the possibility that collisions between fast heavy particles (presumably protons) and nitrogen molecules are responsible. It is known that such collisions tend to populate the higher vibrational levels (Smyth and Arnott, 1930; Vegard and Raastad, 1950; Fan and Meinel, 1953; Branscomb, Shalek, and Bonner, 1954). Should the hypothesis prove to be correct, the difference between the two types of aurorae would repay close study. Special efforts should be made to determine whether it is a latitude or an altitude effect.

The Second Positive system of N_2 has also been investigated (Bates, 1949b). If it is excited through

$$N_2 (X\ ^1\Sigma_g^+) + e \rightarrow N_2 (C\ ^3\Pi_u) + e\ , \qquad (152)$$

a T(vib.) of well over 10,000° K would be required to explain the high-latitude measurements[20] of Vegard and Kvifte (1945). The heavy-particle hypothesis is not readily acceptable in this case, for, as has already been pointed out, protons are unable to cause multiplicity charge transitions; and hydrogen atoms cannot be invoked with much conviction. It is very doubtful, however, whether the measurements of Vegard and Kvifte are reliable. Petrie and Small (1952) have recently repeated them with great care and thoroughness. They obtain entirely different results. On being analyzed, these yield a T(vib.) of less than 500° K, which is, of course, completely acceptable. A process other than (152) need not therefore be postulated. It is natural to inquire whether it is worth attaching any significance to the inferences drawn from the study of the First Negative system. The measurements made at high latitudes by Vegard and Kvifte are certainly suspect and should be checked independently; process (150) may well prove to be adequate. However, the low-latitude peculiarity is real, as is also shown by the early work of Rayleigh (1922). We again emphasize that it may actually be an altitude effect.

7. THE TEMPERATURE OF THE REGION ABOVE THE 100-KM LEVEL

There are numerous reasons for believing that the temperature increases above the 100-km level and reaches a high value (perhaps some 1500° K) at great altitudes. We will summarize the main evidence briefly,

---

20. No low-latitude measurements are available.

indicating the unsatisfactory nature of much of it, and then discuss the problem of the thermobalance.

7.1. EVIDENCE

7.11. *Ionosphere.*—As has already been seen (Sec. 4.3), the formation of the upper ionized layers is not easy to understand unless the temperature rises rapidly to at least about 1000° K. The difficulties encountered if low temperatures are assumed are very serious indeed, and considerable weight must therefore be attached to the argument.

Radio observers have made determinations of the half-thickness of the F_2 layer (cf. Gerson, 1951). They obtain very large values, from which, by (78), temperatures of up to 2000° K or even higher have been inferred. The estimates are not reliable, since they depend on the simplifying assumption that F_2 is a Chapman layer. In fact, the effective recombination coefficient in it appears to be a decreasing function of the altitude; the ionization may be produced by several processes; and diffusion may not be negligible. These factors could be responsible for a considerable part of the thickness. Other complications have been pointed out by Gerson (1951). It is also impossible at present to make quantitative deductions from the observed collision frequencies (cf. Cowling, 1945; Nicolet, 1953).

7.12. *Aurorae.*—Harang (1945, 1951) has carried out a careful series of measurements on the intensity distribution along auroral streamers and from them has attempted to deduce the scale heights and hence the temperatures in the region between the 100-km and the 270-km levels. The results he obtained are in fair accord with the ionospheric estimates; but, unfortunately, this must be regarded as fortuitous, as the method employed in analyzing the observational data is unsound in several respects. Thus in spite of the fact that the aurorae lying at the greater altitudes were illuminated by solar radiation, Harang took no account of resonance scattering by N_2^+ ions, though this must have given rise to much of the emission (cf. Sec. 6). Again, he took the ultimate source of the energy to be an incoming homogeneous beam of fast *electrons* and based his calculations on the assumptions that the flux in such a beam falls off exponentially with the air mass penetrated and that the intensity of the luminosity at any level is proportional to the local rate of diminution of the flux (which he supposed to be a measure of the rate of dissipation of energy). There is, however, no justification for the adoption of an absorption law; the whole phenomenon is much more involved (cf. Bates and Griffing, 1953a), and, in the mathematical description of it, allowance must be made for the scattering of the electrons and for the fact that their efficiency in causing inelastic collisions increases as their speed decreases. The inadequacy of the original treatment can perhaps be seen most readily by considering the entry of a beam of fast electrons into a gas of uniform density. If an absorption law were followed, the luminosity would fall off exponentially; actually, it rises to a maximum before the end of the range.

Quite apart from the factors which have just been discussed, it must be remembered that the fundamental assumption that the primary auroral corpuscles are electrons is far from certain. Instead, they may well be protons. More properly, it is doubtful whether either electrons alone or protons alone are involved, even as primary particles, as is indicated by the experimental work of Meinel and Fan (cf. chap. 11, Secs. 3.5–3.6). Representative luminosity-altitude curves associated with protons can be readily calculated, since scattering is unimportant; but at least at present it does not seem feasible to make deductions concerning the structure of the atmosphere from them. Thus, if the protons are assumed homogeneous in energy, the calculated curves for the lower aurorae are far sharper than are the observed curves, irrespective of the atmospheric model chosen. The possibility that the protons actually have a wide energy spread therefore presents itself; and this introduction of an additional unknown severely complicates the task of making quantitative deductions from the measured intensity distributions. It may be mentioned here that the Hα emission provides at least some support for the hypothesis that all the incoming protons do not have the same energy (Bates and Griffing, 1953a). According to chapter 11, the maximum Doppler displacement of the line corresponds to a kinetic energy of about 50 keV, which is therefore the greatest energy at which electron capture through (149) is appreciable. Now at the 100-km level the range of a 50-keV proton is only some 1.3 km; and, consequently, if the incident protons were homogeneous, the Hα emission would be mainly confined to this narrow altitude interval. No indication of such a limitation is indicated by the observational work of Meinel (1952 and chap. 11). The suggestion that the true vertical extent of an aurora may be obscured by its width in latitude has been examined by Griffing and Stewart (1954), who concluded that the effect could not explain the discrepancy. However, the basic assumption that the incident protons travel in straight paths may be false. Chamberlain (1954b) has shown that if it is abandoned, it is possible to account for both the observed luminosity distribution and the observed Hα profile (which also had presented a difficulty). Cf. also chapter 11, Section 3.52.

Sunlit rays stretching to an altitude of about 1000 km have been reported by Störmer (1947). The total particle concentration required for the emission is uncertain, but it could scarcely be less than $10^4/\text{cm}^3$; and, on referring to Table 2, we see that even this extremely low value could not be provided unless the temperature reached at least about $1000°$ K. Quantitative interpretation of the observations is made very difficult by the fact that the emitting particles are N_2^+ ions: for example, complications may arise from their being charged, and, moreover, the extent to which the parent-substance is dissociated is not known.

Vegard and Tönsberg (1944) claim that measurements on the rotational structure of the First Negative bands of N_2^+ show that even toward the summit of auroral streamers, at perhaps 200 km, the temperature is not greater than $340°$ K. This result is incompatible with the current views on the structure of the upper atmosphere (cf. Bates, 1949c) and has long been regarded with suspicion; but in view of its nature it could not readily be completely discarded. However, the position has been much clarified by an important series of observations which have been carried out by Petrie (1952), who made a study of the rotational structure of the Vegard-Kaplan bands and found that the temperature is actually $850°$ K or even higher. The difference between this figure and that given by Vegard and Tönsberg cannot be attributed to one of the band systems being allowed and the other forbidden.

Upper-atmospheric temperatures may, in principle, be obtained from interferometric determinations of line widths (Babcock, 1933). From some measurements on $\lambda\,5577$, Vegard (1937) concluded that the temperature in the auroral region does not increase with altitude; but, as Spitzer (1949) has shown, this conclusion is unjustified, because the order of interference used was such that even a very considerable change in the temperature would not have affected the apparent sharpness of the fringes. Armstrong (1953) has recently pointed out that the sensitivity of the method could be greatly improved by measuring the intensity distribution across the fringe pattern, and he plans to repeat the earlier work with this refinement.

7.13. *Escape of atmospheric constituents.*—Because of the thermal motion, the lighter constituents tend to escape into interplanetary space. The most recent treatment of the problem is that of Spitzer (1949). He showed that the total abundance of a constituent would fall by a factor equal to e (the Naperian base) in a time

$$t_c = \frac{\sqrt{6\pi} HCB\mathfrak{R}}{3MG}\, e^{MG/g\mathfrak{R}H}; \qquad (153)$$

where H is the scale height of the constituent, and C is the root-mean-square velocity of the individual atoms or molecules, both taken at a critical level (the base of the isothermal region termed the *exosphere*); the latter is situated so that a fraction $1/e$ of a group of particles moving upward from it at high speed would suffer no collisions as they go to infinitely great altitudes; B is the ratio of the actual abundance to the value the abundance would have if the density above the critical level were left unaltered but that below were altered so as to make the distribution isothermal throughout; M and $\mathfrak{R}$ are the mass and radius of the earth; and g is the acceleration and G is the constant of gravity. Using this formula, Spitzer computed t_c for various constituents and for various assumed values of T_x the temperature at, and above, the critical level (which he estimated to be at an altitude between 500 and 1000 km). His results are given in Table 14.

The case of helium is of special interest. According to Lindemann (1939), the number of He atoms discharged into the atmosphere in geo-

TABLE 14

ESCAPE FROM TERRESTRIAL ATMOSPHERE, GIVEN BY t_c (YEARS)

TEMPERATURE T_x (° K)	ATOM			
	H	He	N	O
500.	2.4×10^7	4.2×10^{25}	10^{92}	10^{105}
1000.	3.6×10^4	4.0×10^{13}	10^{45}	10^{51}
2000.	1.8×10^3	2.4×10^7	3.9×10^{22}	1.0×10^{26}

logical time (2×10^9 years) is about $6 \times 10^{21}/\text{cm}^2$ column, whereas the number actually present is found by Paneth (1947) to be $5 \times 10^{20}/\text{cm}^2$ column. The natural inference is that the gas is escaping at an appreciable rate. Hence it might seem likely that T_x is about 1500° K.

It must be remembered, however, that if there is a pronounced variation throughout the sunspot cycle (Sec. 7.2) the escape might be confined to the years when T_x is near its peak. Apart from this, there may be fluctuations caused by solar outbursts and, as Spitzer (1949) has pointed out, the helium equilibrium is consistent with a T_x which is very high for occasional brief periods but which is usually low.

Useful information on the temperature cannot be obtained from the consideration of the other constituents. The figures are, however, of interest in connection with the photodissociation of water vapor (Sec. 2.3). Clearly, the hydrogen atoms liberated escape rapidly, but their original oxygen partners accumulate. It is possible that the number of these latter

added to the atmosphere in geological time is comparable with the number
now present (cf. Dole, 1949; Bates and Nicolet, 1950).

7.14. *Direct measurement.*—Finally, the results obtained in high-altitude flights must be mentioned. As reported by the Rocket Panel (1952),
density measurements have been made at the 156- and 219-km levels.
These are insufficient to define the structure uniquely: the temperature
gradient is in no sense determined by them, and, of course, the mean
molecular mass remains unknown. Table 15, which is based on an analysis
carried out by the Rocket Panel, gives the temperatures and particle concentrations at the 150- and 200-km levels for two of the possible structures.

As is apparent, a comparatively cool and tenuous atmosphere is indicated. Should the measurements be confirmed, a complete revision of

TABLE 15

ROCKET DATA

ALTITUDE (km)	MEAN MOLECULAR MASS CORRESPONDING TO NITROGEN IN MOLECULAR FORM AND OXYGEN IN ATOMIC FORM		MEAN MOLECULAR MASS CORRESPONDING TO BOTH NITROGEN AND OXYGEN IN ATOMIC FORM	
	Temperature (° K)	Particle Concentration (/cm³)	Temperature (° K)	Particle Concentration (/cm³)
150.....	415	8.5×10^{10}	250	1.4×10^{11}
200.....	655	4.3×10^{9}	395	7.1×10^{9}

much of the work that has been done would be required. The new results
were not received in time for this to be attempted here; and in any case it
would be rather premature at present. Such a revision would encounter
certain difficulties; but, as far as can be judged (cf. Bates, 1954), none of
these is necessarily so acute as to justify the rejection of the rocket measurements (which does not, of course, mean that further measurements are
not essential). The gravest difficulty is concerned with the formation of
the F_1 layer at the 200-km level, since, if the particle concentration there
is as low as the values in Table 15, an unacceptably high value of the mean
absorption cross-section, $\bar{A}$, would clearly be required (cf. Sec. 4.22).
This difficulty may not, however, be real, for Nicolet and Mange (1952)
have suggested that the radio scientists may have seriously overestimated
the altitude of the layer and Piggott (1954), who has recently examined
the various sources of error, has concluded that the uncertainties are far
greater than had been supposed.

7.2. THERMOBALANCE

Some consequences of the high-temperature hypothesis must now be examined. In a discussion on the thermobalance, Spitzer (1949) drew attention to the importance of conduction as a heat-loss process, showing incidentally that it insures that the atmosphere is almost isothermal both in, and far below, the exosphere. Later Bates (1951) pointed out that account must also be taken of the energy radiated through the magnetic dipole connecting the two lower levels of the ground term of atomic oxygen. This is very effective, as the transition probability associated with it is as high as $8.9 \times 10^{-5}/\sec$ (Pasternack, 1940) and as the separation of the two levels is only 0.020 eV (Moore, 1949) so that the upper can readily be populated by ordinary thermal collisions with other atoms or molecules or with electrons.

The radiation responsible for the F_1 and F_2 layers is generally regarded as the major heat source. This view has some subsidiary attractions. According to it, the temperature of the upper atmosphere should increase through the sunspot cycle. Such an increase is suggested by the observations on the altitude of the ionized layers (Appleton, 1947) and of aurorae (Störmer, 1942).

Estimations of the contribution from the ionizing radiation may be made by using the radio measurements on the electron concentration, $n(e)$, and the effective recombination coefficient, a, which together give the ionization rate. The values obtained are much smaller than the heat loss due to the combined effect of conduction and emission by atomic oxygen if the temperature is high. In the case of model $M(1500°\,K; 200$ km), for example, the calculated heat gain is too low by a factor of at least 20 at sunspot maximum and by a factor of at least 60 at sunspot minimum (Bates, 1951). If the high-temperature hypothesis is to be retained, some additional source must be found. A number of possibilities were investigated. The most likely seems to be that unobserved ionization occurs. It may readily be seen that the occurrence of such radiation is in no way implausible. Suppose that ions X_1^+ and X_2^+ are produced at rates q_1 and q_2 and that a_1 and a_2 are the recombination coefficients associated with them. In equilibrium their concentrations, n_1 and n_2, are related by the equation

$$\frac{a_1 n_1}{q_1} = \frac{a_2 n_2}{q_2}. \tag{154}$$

Hence, if

$$a_1 \gg \frac{a_2 q_1}{q_2}, \tag{155}$$

then

$$n_1 \ll n_2 , \qquad (156)$$

even though

$$q_1 \gg q_2 . \qquad (157)$$

In these circumstances the X_2^+ ions would control the main properties of the layer, and it would not be apparent to radio scientists that X_1^+ ions were being formed and destroyed rapidly. Their measurements, therefore, give only a lower limit to the incident flux of photons of energy 13.6 eV and above. A similar conclusion has recently been reached by Piddington (1951) by different reasoning. The apparent discrepancy in the thermo-balance can thus be removed. It is natural to suppose that molecular nitrogen is the constituent subject to the strong ionization and that dissociative recombination is the loss process involved. If correct, this is of importance in connection with the degree of dissociation of the nitrogen in the upper atmosphere (Sec. 2.2) and with the formation of the ionized layers (Sec. 4.2). The upward revision of the intensity of the ionizing radiation allowed by the radio measurements should be noted by solar physicists. Such a revision is also suggested by the direct observations carried out by Tousey, Watanabe, and Purcell (1951) with the aid of rockets.

REFERENCES

ADEL, A.	1946	*Science,* **103,** 280.
	1949	*The Atmospheres of the Earth and Planets,* ed. G. P. KUIPER (Chicago: University of Chicago Press), p. 13.
	1951	*Science,* **113,** 624.
ALFVÉN, H.	1951	*Nature,* **157,** 984.
ALLEN, C. W.	1948	*Terr. Mag. Atm. Elect.,* **53,** 433.
APPLETON, E. V.	1937	*Proc. R. Soc. London, A,* **162,** 451.
	1947	*J. Inst. Elect. Eng.,* Part 3A, **94,** 186.
APPLETON, E. V., and BEYNON, W. J. G.	1940	*Proc. Phys. Soc.,* **52,** 518.
ARMSTRONG, E. B.	1953	*J. Atm. Terr. Physics,* **3,** 274.
BABCOCK, H. D.	1923	*Ap. J.,* **57,** 209.
BAKER, W. G., and MARTYN, D. F.	1952	*Nature,* **170,** 1090.
BAMFORD, C. H.	1943	*Rep. Prog. Phys.,* **9,** 75 (Phys. Soc. London).
BARBIER, D.	1947	*Ann. géophys.* **3,** 227.
BARBIER, D.; DUFAY, J.; and WILLIAMS, D.	1951	*Ann. d'ap.,* **14,** 399.

BATES, D. R.
1946   *M.N.*, **106**, 432.
1948   *Emission Spectra of the Night Sky and Aurorae: Report of the Gassiot Committee* (London: Phys. Soc.), p. 21.
1949a   *Proc. R. Soc. London, A*, **196**, 562.
1949b   *Ibid.*, p. 217.
1949c   *M.N.*, **109**, 215.
1950   *Phys. Rev.*, **78**, 492.
1951   *Proc. Phys. Soc., B*, **64**, 805.
1952   *Ann. géophys.*, **8**, 194.
1954   *Rocket Exploration of the Upper Atmosphere*, ed. R. L. F. BOYD and M. J. SEATON (London: Pergamon Press), p. 347.

BATES, D. R.;
BUCKINGHAM, R. A.;
MASSEY, H. S. W.;
and UNWIN, J. J.   1939   *Proc. R. Soc. London, A*, **170**, 322.

BATES, D. R., and
DALGARNO, A.   1952   *Proc. Phys. Soc., A*, **65**, 919.
1953   *Ibid.*, **66**, 972.

BATES, D. R., and
GRIFFING, G.   1953a   *J. Atm. Terr. Physics*, **3**, 212.
1953b   *Proc. Phys. Soc., A*, **66**, 961.
1954   *Ibid.*, **67**, 663.

BATES, D. R., and
MASSEY, H. S. W.   1943   *Phil. Trans. R. Soc., A*, **239**, 269.
1946   *Proc. R. Soc. London, A*, **187**, 261.
1947   *Ibid.*, **192**, 1.
1951   *J. Atm. Terr. Physics*, **2**, 1.
1952   *Ibid.*, **2**, 253.

BATES, D. R.;
MASSEY, H. S. W.;
and PEARSE, R. W. B. 1948   *Emission Spectra of the Night Sky and Aurorae: Report of the Gassiot Committee* (London: Phys. Soc.), p. 97.

BATES, D. R., and
NICOLET, M.   1950a   *J. Geophys. Res.*, **55**, 301.
1950b   *Ibid.*, p. 235.

BATES, D. R., and
SEATON, M. J.   1949   *M.N.*, **109**, 698.
1950   *Proc. Phys. Soc., B*, **63**, 129.

BATES, D. R., and
WITHERSPOON,
AGNES E.   1952   *M.N.*, **112**, 101.

BAWN, C. E. H., and
EVANS, A. G.   1937   *Trans. Faraday. Soc.*, **33**, 1571, 1580.

BAXTER, W. P.   1930   *J. Am. Chem. Soc.*, **52**, 3920.

BERKNER, L. V.   1939   *Terrestrial Magnetism and Electricity*, ed. J. A. FLEMING (New York and London: McGraw-Hill Book Co.), p. 434.

BIONDI, M. A.   1951a   *Phys. Rev.*, **83**, 1078.
                     1951b   *Ibid.*, **84**, 1072.

BIONDI, M. A., and
    BROWN, S. C.   1949   *Phys. Rev.*, **76**, 1697.

BLOCH, F., and
    BRADBURY, N. E. 1935   *Phys. Rev.*, **48**, 689.

BRADBURY, N. E.   1933   *Phys. Rev.*, **44**, 883.
                     1938   *Terr. Mag. Atm. Elect.*, **43**, 55.

BRANSCOMB, L. M.;
    SHALEK, R. J.; and
    BONNER, T. W.   1954   *Trans. Amer. Geophys. Union*, **35**, 107.

BURNIGHT, T. R.   1949   *Phys. Rev.*, **76**, 165.

BYRAM, E. T.; CHUBB,
    T.; and FRIEDMAN, H.   1954a   *Rocket Exploration of the Upper Atmosphere*, ed. R. L. F. BOYD and M. J. SEATON (London: Pergamon Press), p. 274.
                     1954b   *Ibid.*, p. 276.

CHAMBERLAIN, J. W.   1954a   *Ap. J.*, **119**, 328.
                     1954b   *Ibid.*, Vol. **120**, No. 3.

CHAPMAN, S.   1930a   *Mem. R. Meteorol. Soc.*, **3**, 103.
                     1930b   *Phil. Mag.*, **10**, 345, 369.
                     1931a   *Proc. R. Soc. London*, A, **132**, 353.
                     1931b   *Proc. Phys. Soc.*, **43**, 26 and 483.
                     1939   *Ap. J.*, **90**, 309.
                     1952   *Ann. géophys.*, **8**, 205.

CHAPMAN, S., and
    BARTELS, J.   1940   *Geomagnetism* (Oxford: Clarendon Press).

CHAPMAN, S., and
    PRICE, W. C.   1936   *Rept. Prog. Phys.*, **3**, 55 (Phys. Soc., London).

COURTÈS, G.   1950   *C.R. Acad. Sci., Paris*, **231**, 62.

COWLING, T. G.   1945   *Proc. R. Soc. London*, A, **183**, 453.
                     1953   *Observatory*, **73**, 59.

DALGARNO, A., and
    YADAV, H. N.   1953   *Proc. Phys. Soc. A*, **66**, 173.

DAS GUPTA, N. N., and
    GHOSH, S. K.   1946   *Rev. Mod. Phys.* **18**, 225.

DELLINGER, J. H.   1937   *Terr. Mag. Atm. Elect.*, **42**, 49.

DITCHBURN, R. W.   1954   *Rocket Exploration of the Upper Atmosphere*, ed. R. L. F. BOYD and M. J. SEATON (London: Pergamon Press), p. 313.

DOBSON, G. M. B.   1930   *Proc. R. Soc. London*, A, **129**, 411.

DOLE, M.   1949   *Science*, **109**, 77.

DOUGLAS, A. E.   1953   *Ap. J.*, **117**, 380.

DUFAY, M. 1951 *C.R. Acad. Sci., Paris*, **233**, 419.

1952 *Mém. Soc. R. Sci., Liége*, 4th ser., **12**, 141.

DUFAY, M. and
DUFAY, J. 1947 *C. R. Acad. Sci.*, Paris, **224**, 1834.

DURAND, E.; OBERLY,
J. J.; and TOUSEY, R. 1949 *Ap. J.*, **109**, 1.

DUTTA, A. K. 1932 *Proc. R. Soc. London*, A, **138**, 84.

EUCKEN, A., and
PATAT, F. 1936 *Zs. f. phys. Chem.*, **33**, 459.

FABRY, C. 1950 *L'Ozone atmosphérique* (Paris: Centre National de la Recherche Scientifique).

FAN, C. Y., and
MEINEL, A. B. 1953 *Ap. J.*, **118**, 205.

FERRARO, V. C. A. 1945 *Terr. Mag. Atm. Elect.*, **50**, 215.

FLORY, P. J., and
JOHNSTON, H. L. 1935 *J. Amer. Chem. Soc.*, **57**, 2641.

FRIEDMAN, H.;
LICHTMAN, S. W.; and
BYRAM, E. T. 1951 *Phys. Rev.*, **83**, 1025.

GARTLEIN, C. W. 1950 *Trans. Amer. Geophys. Union*, **31**, 7.

GAYDON, A. G. 1944 *Proc. R. Soc. London*, A, **183**, 111.

1947 *Dissociation Energies* (London: Chapman & Hall).

GEIB, K. H., and
HARTECK, P. 1934 *Zs. f. phys. Chem.*, A, **170**, 1.

GERSON, N. C. 1951 *Rept. Prog. Phys.*, **14**, 316 (Phys. Soc., London).

GLASSTONE, S.;
LAIDLER, K. J.; and
EYRING, H. 1941 *The Theory of Rate Processes* (New York and London: McGraw-Hill Book Co.).

GOODY, R. M., and
WALSHAW, C. D. 1953 *Quart. J. R. Meteorol. Soc.*, **79**, 496.

GREENSTEIN, J. L. 1949 *The Atmospheres of the Earth and Planets*, ed. G. P. KUIPER (Chicago: University of Chicago Press), p. 112.

GRIFFING, G. W., and
STEWART, A. L. 1954 *J. Atm. Terr. Phys.*, **4**, 339.

GROTH, W. 1937 *Zs. f. phys. Chem.*, B, **37**, 307.

HABER, F., and
SCHASSE, H. 1931 *Zs. f. phys. Chem.* (Bodenstein-Band), p. 831.

HARANG, L. 1945 *Geofys.* Pub. Oslo, Vol. **16**, No. 6.

1951 *The Aurorae* (London: Chapman & Hall).

HARTECK, P., and
DONDES, S. 1954 *Phys. Rev.*, **95**, 320.

HERZBERG, G. 1946 *Phys. Rev.*, **69**, 362.

1950a *Molecular Spectra and Molecular Structure—Diatomic Molecules* (New York: Van Nostrand Co.).

HERZBERG, G.   1950b   *Pasadena Symposium on Upper Atmospheric Research.*

HERZBERG, G., and
   HERZBERG, L.   1948   *Nature*, **161**, 283.

HIRONO, M.   1950   *Jap. J. Geomag. Geoelect.*, **2**, 1 and 113.
     1952   *Ibid.*, **4**, 7.

HIRSCHFELDER, J. O.   1941   *J. Chem. Phys.*, **9**, 645.

HOLMES, H. H., and
   DANIELS, F.   1934   *J. Amer. Chem. Soc.*, **56**, 630.

HOPFIELD, J. J.   1946   *Ap. J.*, **104**, 208.

HOYLE, F.   1949   *Some Recent Researches in Solar Physics* (Cambridge: At the University Press).

HOYLE, F., and
   BATES, D. R.   1948   *Terr. Mag. Atm. Elect.*, **53**, 51.

HULBURT, E. O.   1938   *Phys. Rev.*, **53**, 344.
     1939   *Terrestrial Magnetism and Electricity*, ed. J. FLEMING (New York and London: McGraw-Hill Book Co.), p. 492.

INN, E. C. Y.   1953   *Phys. Rev.*, **91**, 1194.

JACKSON, J. D., and
   SCHIFF, H.   1953   *Phys. Rev.* **89**, 359.

JACKSON, W. F.   1934   *J. Amer. Chem. Soc.*, **56**, 2631.

JOHNSTON, H. S., and
   CROSBY, H. J.   1954   *J. Chem. Phys.*, **22**, 689.

JOUAUST, R., and
   VASSY, E.   1941   *C.R. Acad. Sci., Paris*, **213**, 139.

LEE, Po, and WEISSLER,
   G. L.   1953   *Proc. R. Soc. London, A*, **219**, 71.

LEIGHTON, P. A.   1938   *The Determination of the Mechanism of Photochemical Reactions* (Paris: Herman).

LINDEMANN, F. A.   1939   *Quart. J. R. Meteorol. Soc.*, **65**, 330.

LOSSING, F. P.;
   TICKNER, A. W.; and
   BRYCE, W. A.   1951   *J. Chem. Phys.*, **19**, 1254.

LUCAS, I.   1953   *Naturwissenschaften*, **40**, 239.

MARTYN, D. F.   1948   *Proc. R. Soc. London, A*, **194**, 445.
     1951   *Nature*, **167**, 92.

MARTYN, D. F.; MUNRO,
   G. H.; HIGGS, A. J.;
   and WILLIAMS, S. E.   1937   *Nature*, **140**, 603.

MASSEY, H. S. W.   1948   *Rept. Prog. Phys.*, **12**, 248 (Phys. Soc., London).

MASSEY, H. S. W., and
   BURHOP, E. H. S.   1952   *Electronic and Ionic Impact Phenomena* (Oxford: Clarendon Press).

MECKE, R.   1931   *Trans. Faraday. Soc.*, **27**, 375.

MECKLER, A.   1953   *J. Chem. Phys.*, **21**, 1750.

MEINEL, A. B. 1950*a* *Trans. Amer. Geophys. Union*, **31**, 9.

1950*b* *Science*, **112**, 590.

1952 *Mém. Soc. R. Sci., Liége*, 4th ser., **12**, 203.

MIGEOTTE, M. V. 1949 *Phys. Rev.*, **75**, 1108.

MIGEOTTE, M. V., and

NEVEN, L. 1952 *Mém. Soc. R. Sci. Liége*, 4th ser., **12**, 165.

MILLINGTON, G. 1932 *Proc. Phys. Soc.*, **44**, 580.

1935 *Ibid.*, **47**, 263.

MITRA, S. K. 1947 *The Upper Atmosphere* (Calcutta: Royal Asiatic Society of Bengal).

MOFFITT, W. 1951 *Proc. R. Soc. London*, A, **210**, 224.

MOHLER, F. L. 1940 *Bur. Stand. J. Res. Washington*, **25**, 507.

MOORE, CHARLOTTE E. 1949 *Atomic Energy Levels* (Washington: National Bureau of Standards).

MULLIKEN, R. S. 1942 *Rev. Mod. Phys.*, **14**, 204.

NICOLET, M. 1945*a* *Inst. R. Météorol. Belgique, Misc.*, No. 19.

1945*b* *Ibid.*, No. 18.

1945*c* *Inst. R. Météorol. Belgique Mém.*, No. 19.

1949 *J. Geophys. Res.*, **54**, 373.

1953 *J. Atm. Terr. Phys.*, **3**, 200.

1954 *Rocket Exploration of the Upper Atmosphere*, ed. R. L. F. BOYD and M. J. SEATON (London: Pergamon Press), p. 361.

NICOLET, M., and

MANGE, P. 1952 *Scientific Report of the Ionospheric Research Laboratory of Pennsylvania State College*, No. 13.

1954 *J. Geophys. Res.*, **59**, 15.

NOYES, W. A., and

LEIGHTON, P. A. 1941 *The Photochemistry of Gases* (New York: Reinhold Publishing Corp.).

PANETH, F. A. 1937 *Quart. J. R. Meteorol. Soc.*, **63**, 433.

PANETH, F. A., and

GLÜCKAUF, E. 1941 *Nature*, **147**, 614.

PASTERNACK, S. 1940 *Ap. J.*, **92**, 129.

PENNDORF, R. 1949 *J. Geophys. Res.*, **54**, 7.

PETRIE, W. 1952 *Phys. Rev.*, **86**, 790.

PETRIE, W., and

SMALL, R. 1952 *J. Geophys. Res.*, **57**, 51.

PIDDINGTON, J. H. 1951 *J. Geophys. Res.*, **56**, 409.

PIGGOTT, W. R. 1950 Private communication.

1954 In press.

PRESTON, W. M. 1940 *Phys. Rev.*, **57**, 887.

PRICE, W. C. 1943 *Rept. Prog. Phys.*, **9**, 10 (Phys. Soc., London).

RABINOWITCH, E. 1937 *Trans. Faraday Soc.*, **33**, 283.

RAKSHIT, H. 1947 *Indian J. Phys.*, **21**, 57.

RAYLEIGH, LORD 1922 *Proc. R. Soc. London*, A, **101**, 114 and 312.

ROACH, F. E., and
    PETTIT, H. B.   1951   *J. Geophys. Res.* **56**, 325.
ROCKET PANEL   1952   *Phys. Rev.,* **88**, 1027.
ROMAND, J., and
    MAYENCE, J.   1949   *C.R. Acad. Sci., Paris,* **228**, 998.
SCHUMACHER, H. J.   1938   *Chemische Gasreaktionen* (Dresden: Steinkopff).
SEATON, M. J.   1951   *Proc. R. Soc., London, A,* **208**, 408.
                             1954   *J. Atm. Terr. Phys.,* **4**, 295.
SHULL, H.   1950   *Ap. J.,* **112**, 352.
SINGER, S. F.; MAPLE, E.;
    and BOWEN, W. A.   1951*a*   *J. Geophys. Res.,* **56**, 365.
                             1951*b*   *Phys. Rev.,* **82**, 957.
                             1952   *Nature,* **170**, 1093.
SMYTH, H. D., and
    ARNOTT, E. G. F.   1930   *Phys. Rev.,* **36**, 1021.
SPEALMAN, M. L., and
    RODENBUSH, W. H.   1935   *J. Amer. Chem. Soc.,* **57**, 1474.
SPITZER, L.   1949   *The Atmospheres of the Earth and Planets,* ed. G. P.
                                     KUIPER (Chicago: University of Chicago Press),
                                     p. 213.
SPONER, H., and
    BONNER, L. G.   1940   *J. Chem. Phys.,* **8**, 33.
STEACIE, E. W. R., and
    PALLEE, N. A. D.   1938   *Canadian J. Res., B,* **16**, 203.
STODDARD, E. M.   1934   *Proc. R. Soc. London, A,* **147**, 464.
STÖRMER, C.   1942   *Geofys. Pub. Oslo,* Vol. **13**, No. 7.
                             1947   *Observatory,* **67**, 161.
SWINGS, P.   1949   *The Atmospheres of the Earth and Planets,* ed. G. P.,
                                     KUIPER (Chicago: University of Chicago Press),
                                     p. 159.
TOUSEY, R.   1953   *J. Opt. Soc. Amer.,* **43**, 245.
TOUSEY, R.;
    WATANABE, K.; and
    PURCELL, J. D.   1951   *Phys. Rev.,* **83**, 792.
VASSY, A., and VASSY, E.   1942   *Cahiers de phys.,* **9**, 28.
VEGARD, L.   1937   *Phil. Mag.,* **24**, 588.
                             1938   *Geofys. Pub. Oslo,* Vol. **12**, No. 5.
                             1940   *Ibid.,* No. 14.
                             1948   *Emission Spectra of the Night Sky and Aurorae:
                                     Report of the Gassiot Committee* (London: Phys.
                                     Soc.), p. 82.
VEGARD, L., and
    KVIFTE, G.   1945   *Geofys. Pub. Oslo,* Vol. **16**, No. 7.
VEGARD, L., and
    RAASTAD, H.   1950   *Geofys. Pub. Oslo,* Vol. **17**, No. 7.
VEGARD, L., and
    TÖNSBERG, E.   1944   *Geofys. Pub. Oslo,* Vol. **16**, No. 2.

WAINFAN, N.; WALKER,
  W. C.; and WEISSLER,
  G. L.   1953   *J. Appl. Phys.*, **24**, 1318.
WATANABE, K.; MARMO,
  E. F.; and INN,
  E. C. Y.   1953   *Phys. Rev.*, **91**, 1155.
WEEKES, K.   1950   Private communication.
WEISSLER, G. L.   1952   *Mém. Soc. R. Sci. Liége*, 4th ser., **12**, 281.
WILDT, R.   1937   *Ap. J.*, **86**, 321.
WILKINSON, P. G., and
  JOHNSTON, H. L.   1950   *J. Chem. Phys.*, **18**, 190.
WULF, O. R., and
  DEMING, L. S.   1936   *Terr. Mag. Atm. Elect.*, **41**, 299, 375.
                      1937   *Ibid.*, **42**, 195.
                      1938   *Ibid.*, **43**, 283.

CHAPTER 13

Dynamic Effects in the High Atmosphere

By M. NICOLET

Royal Meteorological Institute, Brussels

1. INTRODUCTION

Before discussing dynamic effects in the high atmosphere and present-
ing a review of results obtained on the motions found in that region, it
must be admitted that the dynamics of the atmosphere as a whole is an
unresolved problem. Even the problem of the general circulation of the
lower atmosphere, of paramount importance to meteorology, has not been
solved completely, in spite of recent advances (see Byers, chap. 7). The
knowledge of meridional and zonal transports and of modes of energy
transfer is still schematic. Another matter is atmospheric turbulence, the
physical approach to which is perhaps somewhat neglected, so that great
advances are still to be expected. In some respects an investigation of atmospheric dynamics might be included under the physics of the high atmosphere rather than under meteorology, which specializes in the complex problems of the lower atmosphere. At any rate, the general dynamical problem still requires much progress before quantitative explanations
of the observations are possible.

2. CHEMICAL COMPOSITION AND PHYSICAL CONSTITUTION OF THE HIGH ATMOSPHERE

2.1. Atmospheric Nomenclature

It is convenient to treat the high atmosphere by using the nomenclature
proposed by Chapman (1950a, b; see also Nicolet, 1950b; Kaplan, 1953)
and recommended by the International Union of Geodesy and Geophysics
at its Brussels meeting in August, 1951. As used by the meteorologist, the
terms *troposphere, tropopause,* and *stratosphere* (cf. Byers, chap. 7) lead to
the following classification with height, in terms of temperature (Fig. 1).

The *troposphere* is the region between ground level and the *tropopause* (upper boundary). The tropopause varies in height, depending on the latitude, from about 7 km at high latitudes to about 18 km at the equator. At mean latitudes the tropopause level may range from about 7 to 14 km, depending on atmospheric conditions (high or low pressure and local perturbations). Thus there is a wide variation in the behavior of the lowest of the upper layers.

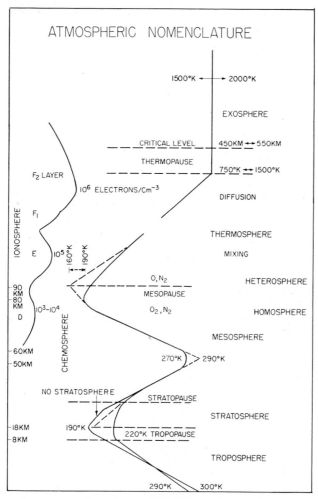

Fig. 1.—Atmospheric nomenclature. The characterization of the atmospheric regions is based primarily on a thermal classification: troposphere, stratosphere, mesosphere, thermosphere, and exosphere. Classified according to composition, the terms are the *homosphere* and *heterosphere*. When the classification is descriptive of various processes, the designations are the *ionosphere*, *chemosphere*, and *ozonosphere*, each of which belongs to several atmospheric regions. The suffix "pause" signifies the upper boundary.

The name *stratosphere* was originally given to the nearly isothermal region above the tropopause but has been used also to include a much higher region. It seems desirable to retain the original meaning and de-limit the stratosphere at the *stratopause*, the level (35–40 km) at which the temperature begins to increase at a distinctly larger rate. The strato-pause varies in height with place and time. In low latitudes there is often no nearly isothermal region just above the tropopause and therefore no stratosphere; the tropopause and the stratopause then coincide.

The *mesosphere* is the region between the stratopause and the *meso-pause*, the latter term designating the level between 85 and 95 km, at which the principal temperature minimum occurs. As is true for the tropo-pause and the stratopause, the mesopause must have a tendency for a wide variation in height due to the atomic and molecular processes related to atmospheric motions. The mesosphere is particularly important for the physics of the high atmosphere, because it is possible to study chemical reactions as well as day-to-day variations in terms of hydrodynamics.

The *thermosphere* is the region above the mesopause and can be consid-ered as a layer in which the temperature increases with height. The upper limit of the thermosphere, the *thermopause*, is situated at a high level, of the order of 400–500 km.

The *exosphere* is the outermost region (cf. Spitzer, 1949), in which tem-perature is practically constant on the basis of the vertical distribution of neutral particles. The thermopause level may not be too different from the *critical level*, which is the base of the exosphere. At the critical level the horizontal mean free path of a neutral particle is approximately equal to the scale height.

If the basis for the characterization of atmospheric regions is the pres-ence of ionization, the general term for that region beginning at a height of about 60 km and extending to the highest limits of the atmosphere will be the *ionosphere*. In the same sense, the regions where chemical reactions are dominant are designated as the *chemosphere*.

Finally, it is of fundamental importance to classify atmospheric levels on the basis of composition. The *homosphere* is that region where the com-position does not change. Here the application of the hydrostatic equa-tion is very simple, and the variation of temperature with height may be deduced directly from pressure measurements. The *homopause*, that level at which the composition first begins to change materially, may be placed at the height of the mesopause. The *heterosphere* is the overlapping region where the composition is affected by molecular dissociation and also by other processes, such as diffusion. In the heterosphere the vertical distribution of the constituents depends on the prominent process of a group, including mixing, diffusion, photodissociation, photoionization, and re-combination processes.

2.2. INTERRELATION BETWEEN PRESSURE AND TEMPERATURE IN A MIXED ATMOSPHERE

The principal empirical data on the high atmosphere have already been given in chapters 9–12. In order to determine the physical conditions associated with dynamical processes, a self-consistent atmospheric model is necessary. Pressure measurements up to 220 km obtained by Havens, Koll, and LaGow (1952) from rocket flights are taken as the basic data.

The interrelation between pressure, composition, and temperatures can be determined if various hypotheses are made concerning the chemical and physical transformations affecting the mean molecular weight or mass (Nicolet, 1952).

Neglecting the vertical acceleration, the atmospheric pressure p is governed by the hydrostatic equation,

$$dp = - g\rho dz ,\qquad(1)$$

and, neglecting small corrections which may be incorporated in such formulas, by the ideal gas law,

$$p = nkT ,\qquad(2)$$

in which ρ, n, and T denote, respectively, the density, the molecular concentration, and the absolute temperature; g is the acceleration of gravity; and k is Boltzmann's constant. If the atmospheric constituents at height z have different molecular masses, m_j, and if the concentration of the jth constituent is n_j, we write

$$\rho = n_1 m_1 + n_2 m_2 + \ldots = \Sigma n_j m_j \equiv nm .\qquad(3)$$

Taking into account (2) and (3) for (1), we write the general equation in the following form:

$$\frac{dp}{p} = \frac{dn}{n} + \frac{dT}{T} = - \frac{dz}{H} ,\qquad(4)$$

in which H denotes the local scale height,

$$H = \frac{kT}{m g}.\qquad(5)$$

If complete mixing exists in the atmosphere, the various gases remain in the same proportions, and the mean molecular mass is a constant. Assuming a mean value of g for a layer of definite thickness, we may write

$$\frac{dT}{T} = \frac{dH}{H}\qquad(6)$$

and from (4)

$$\frac{dn}{n} = -\frac{dH + dz}{H}.$$ (7)

Pressure measurements obtained by rocket can be used to find the temperature and vertical molecular distribution by means of (4) and (7).

2.3. Effects of Dissociation and Diffusion

If the use of (6) is not valid, the exact temperature distribution cannot be found from pressure measurements alone. In the high atmosphere there are two important cases.

a) If the dissociation of one essential compound occurs at some height, the mean molecular mass is altered, and it is necessary to obtain the exact ratio of the concentrations for the undissociated molecule and the atomic components. In particular, the exact distribution will be difficult to determine in the molecule-to-atom transition of oxygen. For example, Bates (chap. 12) gives in his Figure 1 a distribution of atomic and molecular oxygen based on a photochemical equilibrium, and the Rocket Panel (Whipple, chap. 10) gives an arbitrary distribution based on the assumption of a linear dissociation of O_2 in the altitude range from 80 to 120 km. Furthermore, the Rocket Panel has introduced a linear dissociation of N_2 from 120 to 220 km. Thus, in such cases, the interrelation between pressure and temperature is subject to the mean molecular mass chosen.

b) If there is no complete mixing of the principal constituents in an atmospheric region, the mean molecular mass is also affected, and the temperatures or concentrations deduced from measured pressures may be incorrect.

Since, whenever diffusive separation becomes effective, the mean molecular mass gradually changes, it is not yet possible to describe such a diffusion effect quantitatively. We are still unable to determine the factors promoting mixing and counteracting the diffusive separation. The auroral spectrum showing the presence of ionized nitrogen molecules up to very great heights and also the atomic nitrogen radiations indicate the difficulty in determining the part played by diffusive separation of gases.

In a region with a diffusion equilibrium, it is easy to write the general equations for the pressure-height distribution. If

$$p = p_1 + p_2 + \ldots$$ (8)

and

$$\frac{dp_j}{p_j} = -\frac{dz}{H_j},$$ (9)

we obtain the following relation:

$$\frac{1}{H} = \sum \frac{n_j/n}{H_j},$$ (10)

where H denotes the atmospheric scale height.

Thus, in an atmosphere in which diffusion exists, the vertical distribution of the temperature cannot be determined without a knowledge of the level at which diffusive separation effectively begins. However, a detection of the ratio of the principal constituents at a certain height (absorption spectrum) is a means of determining the interrelations between pressure, temperature, and composition in a diffusion equilibrium.

2.4. MEAN MOLECULAR MASSES

The predominance of nitrogen, oxygen, and argon effectively determines the mean molecular mass at ground level. One may use

$$m = 0.781 \times 46.5 \times 10^{-24} + 0.2095 \times 53.1 \times 10^{-24} + 0.0096$$
$$\times 66.3 \times 10^{-24} = 48.08 \times 10^{-24} \text{ gm}.$$ (11)

At mesospheric levels, we adopt the approximation

$$m(N_2, O_2) = 0.8 \times 46.5 \times 10^{-24} + 0.2 \times 53.1 \times 10^{-24}$$
$$= 47.8 \times 10^{-24} \text{ gm},$$ (12)

which gives, as a round figure for the ratio of nitrogen and oxygen concentrations,

$$\frac{n(N_2)}{n(O_2)} = 4.$$ (13)

The mean molecular mass will change at the level of complete oxygen dissociation as follows:

$$m(N_2, O) = \frac{m(N_2, O_2)}{1.2} = 39.8 \times 10^{-24} \text{ gm},$$ (14)

which still gives a round figure,

$$\frac{n(N_2)}{n(O)} = 2.$$ (15)

These practical figures, (13) and (15), assume that there is uniform mixing after any small diffusive effect which may occur at lower heights.

The assumption of constancy in composition cannot be used up to extreme heights. The effect of mixing action at very high levels must become less important relative to diffusive separation (cf. Hulburt, 1952). The use of a constant mean molecular mass in the upper regions of the ionosphere is certainly a very rough approximation.

2.5. Linear Variation of the Scale Height

For the uppermost atmosphere, no direct temperature measurements exist, and only indirect information can be used. Perhaps the most valuable information is obtained from the escape of helium from the atmosphere. The fact that the total number of helium atoms present in the atmosphere is less than that produced by radioactive rocks during geologic time indicates a high temperature (Spitzer, 1949) at the critical level. If this conclusion is correct, the best procedure is to choose a linear variation between the last known value of the scale height and the temperature at the critical level, which cannot be less than $1500°$ K. Consequently,

$$dH = \beta dz ,\qquad (16)$$

where β denotes a constant for various layers, is an excellent approximation. Under these circumstances, (4) and (7) can be written in equivalent form

$$\frac{dp}{p} = -\frac{1}{\beta}\frac{dH}{H}\qquad (17)$$

and

$$\frac{dn}{n} = -\frac{1+\beta}{\beta}\frac{dH}{H}.\qquad (18)$$

Equations (16) and (17) then have the simple solutions,

$$\frac{p}{p_0} = \left(\frac{H}{H_0}\right)^{-1/\beta}\qquad (19)$$

and

$$\frac{n}{n_0} = \left(\frac{H}{H_0}\right)^{-(1+\beta)/\beta},\qquad (20)$$

where p_0, n_0, and H_0 denote pressure, concentration, and scale height at a starting level $z = 0$.

The total number of particles above a level z per vertical column of unit cross-section is (eq. [20])

$$\int_z^\infty n\,dz = nH .\qquad (21)$$

2.6. The Thermosphere without Diffusion

Above 100 km, rocket data may give the pressures within an order of magnitude. From measurements up to 160 and 220 km (Havens, Koll, and LaGow, 1952) it is clear that the following values can be used between 120 and 220 km: for the pressure at 120 km, $p = 3.5 \times 10^{-5}$ mm Hg; for the scale height at 120 km, $H = 10$ km; and for the gradient of the scale height, $\beta = 0.2$.

Now it is possible to compute the pressure at high levels if we assume a constant scale-height gradient with an atmosphere consisting of molecular nitrogen and atomic oxygen. But we have to keep in mind that diffusive separation may exist at these great altitudes. In order to construct an initial atmospheric model, we make the following assumptions:

1. The variation of pressure in the thermosphere between 110 and 220 km as given by rocket measurements yields a varying scale height, the gradient of which is constant.

2. An extrapolation above 220 km may be made, using the same scale-height gradient.

3. The highest temperature (at the thermopause level) cannot be less than the temperature necessary for the escape of helium, namely, 1500° K.

TABLE 1

PRESSURE AS A FUNCTION OF ALTITUDE (MIXING)

Altitude (km)	Scale Height (km)	Pressure (mm of Hg)	Temperature (° K)	Altitude (km)	Scale Height (km)	Pressure (mm of Hg)	Temperature (° K)
100	7	4.06×10^{-4}	191	230	32	1.01×10^{-7}	839
110	8	1.05×10^{-4}	218	240	34	7.70×10^{-8}	889
120	10	3.50×10^{-5}	271	250	36	5.79×10^{-8}	938
130	12	1.41×10^{-5}	324	260	38	4.42×10^{-8}	987
140	14	6.51×10^{-6}	377	270	40	3.42×10^{-8}	1036
150	16	3.34×10^{-6}	430	280	42	2.68×10^{-8}	1085
160	18	1.85×10^{-6}	482	290	44	2.12×10^{-8}	1133
170	20	1.09×10^{-6}	534	300	46	1.70×10^{-8}	1181
180	22	6.79×10^{-7}	586	325	51	1.01×10^{-8}	1299
190	24	4.40×10^{-7}	637	350	56	6.35×10^{-8}	1416
200	26	2.95×10^{-7}	688	375	61	4.14×10^{-9}	1531
210	28	2.03×10^{-7}	738	400	66	2.86×10^{-9}	1645
220	30	1.44×10^{-7}	789	500	86	7.44×10^{-10}	2080

4. The maximum of the temperature will be reached at the critical level, if this level is different from the level of the thermopause.

5. The composition is still uniform and corresponds to a constant ratio of molecular nitrogen and atomic oxygen concentrations.

6. Atomic nitrogen and other constituent concentrations are negligible compared with the molecular nitrogen and atomic oxygen concentrations.

Results of a computation made with (16) through (21) are given in Table 1, The temperature is deduced from the following expression, assuming a constant molecular mass:

$$\frac{p}{m\,g} = nH \, . \tag{22}$$

2.7. The Thermosphere with Diffusion

It is practically impossible to discuss the molecular diffusion in an atmospheric model where only the variation of pressure is known. Nevertheless, it is interesting to study the possible effect of a diffusive separation of gases in an atmospheric model which follows the observed pressure approximately and assumes the vertical distribution of temperature deduced from a model based on the condition of complete mixing (Table 1).

Another difficulty arises in choosing the level where the diffusive separation of gases is effective. No indication can be obtained from observational results,[1] and we have to discuss the diffusion, using the model computed above (Table 1). With these conditions, we may say that the time of diffusion is of the order of 3 days at 120 km, 5 hours at 160 km, and 1 hour at 200 km.

Computing for a complete diffusive separation beginning, respectively, at these three levels, one obtains various distributions of pressure. In Figure 2, one may compare these three diffusion-curves with the curve representing the data of Table 1. The circles represent the rocket data and follow a pressure-curve, with diffusive separation beginning at 160 km. Of course, the diffusion effect must take place gradually and may not be permanent at lower heights, because atmospheric disturbances occur at such levels, leading to a vertical mixing which destroys the diffusion equilibrium. Consequently, the altitude at which diffusion begins is not always the same, depending upon various factors, such as season of the year, latitude, or the general atmospheric situation. Likewise, the composition may be variable below 200 km. Computing a gradual diffusive separation is certainly a correct way to apply molecular diffusion in the atmosphere but does not necessarily lead to an exact vertical distribution of the constituents because of our lack of knowledge of the mixing effects. In order to simplify the computations, we adopt 160 km as an average level where a diffusion equilibrium exists, keeping in mind that the exact level is probably between 160 and 200 km. Crude comparison with Mitra and Rakshit's data (1938) and Spitzer's results (1949) indicates a different conclusion; for the pressure found by rocket is less than the pressures computed previously. Adopting Mitra and Rakshit's data at the measured pressures, more than 50 per cent of diffusion occurs at 160 km and about 80 per cent at 200 km. Spitzer's results are obtained for a constant scale height of 88 km, differing from our varying scale height, which ranges from 10 to 60 km.

---

1. From rocket results on the argon distribution above 100 km, it seems that vertical mixing is still effective between 100 and 140 km. (Townsend, Meadows and Pressly, 1954).

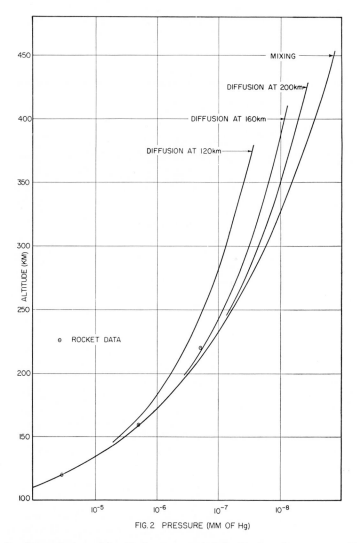

FIG. 2.—Atmospheric models with the same vertical distribution of temperature. Diffusive equilibria, beginning at 200 km, 160 km, and 120 km, show how the pressure increases compared with complete mixing.

If the diffusion equilibrium suddenly begins at 160 km where the total pressure is 1.85×10^{-6} mm of Hg and if the vertical distribution of temperature presented in Table 1 is adopted, we can use the Dalton law (9), so that

$$\frac{dp\,(O)}{p\,(O)} = -\frac{1}{\beta\,(O)}\frac{dH\,(O)}{H\,(O)} \qquad (23)$$

and

$$\frac{dp\,(N_2)}{p\,(N_2)} = -\frac{1}{\beta\,(N_2)}\frac{dH\,(N_2)}{H\,(N_2)}. \qquad (24)$$

In (23) and (24), at 160 km, $H(O) = 27$ km and $H(N_2) = 15.42$ km; $\beta(O)$ and $\beta(N_2)$ are obtained according to the ratio of their own masses to the mean molecular mass at 160 km:

$$\beta\,(O) = \beta\,(M)\,\frac{M}{m\,(O)} \qquad \text{and} \qquad \beta\,(N_2) = \beta\,(M)\,\frac{M}{m\,(N_2)}.$$

TABLE 2

ATMOSPHERIC MODEL WITH DIFFUSION BEGINNING AT 160 km

Altitude (km)	Scale Height (km)	Pressure (mm of Hg)	$n(O)$ (cm^{-3})	Scale Height (Oxygen)	$n(N_2)$ (cm^{-3})	Scale Height (Nitrogen)	Temperature (° K)
160	18.0	1.85×10^{-6}	1.24×10^{10}	27	2.47×10^{10}	15.4	482
180	23.4	6.92×10^{-7}	5.21×10^{9}	33	6.17×10^{9}	18.9	586
200	29.3	3.26×10^{-7}	2.54×10^{9}	39	2.03×10^{9}	22.3	688
220	35.5	1.75×10^{-7}	1.38×10^{9}	45	7.68×10^{8}	25.7	789
240	41.9	1.04×10^{-7}	8.05×10^{8}	51	3.28×10^{8}	29.1	888
260	48.4	6.70×10^{-7}	5.00×10^{8}	57	1.54×10^{8}	32.6	987
280	55.0	4.55×10^{-8}	3.26×10^{8}	63	7.85×10^{7}	36.0	1085
300	61.6	3.22×10^{-8}	2.21×10^{8}	69	4.24×10^{7}	39.4	1181
350	77.9	1.57×10^{-8}	9.48×10^{7}	84	1.12×10^{7}	48.0	1416
400	93.9	8.71×10^{-9}	4.77×10^{7}	99	3.70×10^{6}	56.6	1645
450	109.7	5.18×10^{-9}	2.52×10^{7}	114	1.43×10^{6}	65.1	1866
500	125.3	3.48×10^{-9}	1.54×10^{7}	129	6.14×10^{5}	73.6	2080

The numerical results are presented in Table 2, in which the scale heights for atomic oxygen and molecular nitrogen are shown in the fifth and seventh columns. The total pressure $P = p(N_2) + p(O)$ in mm of Hg and an *equivalent* atmospheric scale height are presented in the third and second columns. The fourth and sixth columns give the concentrations of atomic oxygen and molecular nitrogen. The last column indicates the temperatures which correspond to the chosen values for the model without diffusion.

Comparison between results obtained with or without diffusion, indicated in Tables 1 and 2, shows a difference of total pressures at heights as great as 500 km; for the atomic oxygen concentration does not decrease so rapidly with a diffusion equilibrium as with complete mixing, owing to the vertical distribution of the scale heights. These scale heights are to be associated with the ionospheric scale heights according to the constituent responsible for the formation of a layer, such as the F layer.

2.8. THE EXOSPHERE

In the exosphere, where collisions are negligible, the distribution of neutral atoms is that of an isothermal gas (cf. Spitzer, 1949). If we consider the critical level to be the level where the horizontal mean free path equals the local atmospheric scale height, we may obtain its altitude. With 3×10^{-8} cm as a collision diameter, the total number $n_c H_c$ of neutral particles in a vertical column of 1 cm² section above the critical level, z_c, is by Table 2,

$$n_c H_c = 2.5 \times 10^{14} \text{ cm}^{-2} \text{ at } 450 \text{ km} ,$$

when the diffusion equilibrium is effective at 160 km. Nevertheless, with consideration of diffusion beginning at higher levels ($\sim$200 km) or a greater scale-height gradient ($\sim$0.25 instead of 0.2), the critical level would be 50 km lower or higher, respectively. In the first case, the thermopause would be identified with the critical level, above which the temperature of 1600° K remains constant up to the greatest altitude; and, in the second case, the temperature at the critical level would be not less than 2300° K.

Because of the current impossibility of finding the exact temperature at the critical level, it is not yet possible to present a definitive answer as to the concentration of atomic oxygen and molecular nitrogen above 500 km. However, provisional conclusions can be made. With the usual reservations, we may say that the concentration of atomic oxygen is, in round figures, 10^7 cm^{-3} at 550 km and between 10^5 cm^{-3} and 10^6 cm^{-3} at 1000 km. Molecular nitrogen is more sensitive to the assumed temperature. An average value of the order of 5×10^5 cm^{-3} may represent the usual conditions at 550 km, while a round figure of 1000 cm^{-3} at 1000 km may be in error by a factor of 10 (10^2 cm^{-3} or 10^4 cm^{-3} as actual values), according to which of the two extreme possibilities is considered.

3. VELOCITY AND TIME OF DIFFUSION

3.1. VELOCITY OF DIFFUSION

Since we have no clear factual basis to estimate the efficiency of the atmospheric transport phenomena, it is not yet possible to enter into details about their action. But for purposes of illustration it is useful to calculate data with the hypothesis of a diffusion effect.

Considering the diffusion of a minor constituent whose concentration is n_1 and whose vertical velocity is w_1, we may write a general equation,

$$n_1 w_1 = -D\left[\frac{\partial n_1}{\partial z} + n_1\left(\frac{1}{T}\frac{\partial T}{\partial z} + \frac{m_1 g}{kT}\right)\right],$$ (25)

in which D denotes the diffusion coefficient (Chapman and Cowling, 1939). If the atmospheric scale height H corresponds to complete mixing, equation (25) is written, using (6) and (16), as follows:

$$w_1 = -D\left[\frac{1}{n_1}\frac{\partial n_1}{\partial z} + \left(\beta + \frac{m_1}{m}\right)\frac{1}{H}\right],$$ (26)

where m_1/m is the mass ratio of constituents of mass m_1 and mean mass m.

Starting with perfect mixing, we can write (eq. [18]),

$$\frac{1}{n_1}\frac{\partial n_1}{\partial z} \equiv \frac{1}{n}\frac{\partial n}{\partial z} = -\frac{1+\beta}{H};$$ (27)

and, in these circumstances, (26) may be rewritten in the simple form

$$w_1 = \left(1 - \frac{m_1}{m}\right)\frac{D}{H}.$$ (28)

It is convenient to write D, given by Chapman and Cowling (1939), as follows:

$$D = \frac{3}{4}\frac{1}{(8\pi)^{1/2}\sigma^2}\left(1 + \frac{m}{m_1}\right)^{1/2}\frac{g^{1/2}H^{1/2}}{n},$$ (29)

where $\sigma = 3 \times 10^{-8}$ cm is the collision distance. Then the diffusion velocity has the final form (eqs. [28], [29], and [2]),

$$w_1 = 1.66 \times 10^{14}\left(1 + \frac{m}{m_1}\right)^{1/2}\left(1 - \frac{m_1}{m}\right)m\, g^{3/2}p^{-1}H^{1/2}.$$ (30)

Thus in an atmosphere which is uniform in composition, the diffusion leads to a downward velocity if $m_1 > m$, and to an upward velocity if $m_1 < m$. For example, for molecular oxygen in an atmosphere where there is mixing and where $m = 39.8 \times 10^{-24}$ gm (Table 1), the downward velocity of diffusion would be, in round figures, as follows:

Altitude (km)......	100	120	140	160	180	200
Velocity (cm sec⁻¹)..	0.1	2	8	45	130	330

In order to maintain permanent mixing above 100 km, we may conclude that it is necessary to have an upward mixing velocity $w_{mixing} > -w_{diffusion}$, namely, of the order of 1 cm sec⁻¹ at 100 km and of 1 m sec⁻¹ at 160 km.

At 120 km, for example, where the diffusion coefficient is about 5×10^6 cm^2 sec^{-1}, the mass exchange coefficient should be of the order of 10^{-4} gm cm^{-1} sec^{-1} to maintain the mixing, that is to say, an atmospheric motion much more efficient than at 20 km.

3.2. TIME OF DIFFUSION

Because it will be useful to compare diffusion with other physical processes like dissociation or recombination, it is interesting to employ the time of diffusion τ_{diff} between two levels a and b. From (30), we obtain

$$\tau_{\text{diff}} = \frac{p_a H_a^{1/2} - p_b H_b^{1/2}}{1.66 \times 10^{14} g^{3/2} (1 + m/m_1)^{1/2} (m - m_1) (\beta/2 - 1)}. \qquad (31)$$

With $m = 39.8 \times 10^{-24}$ gm and mixing (Table 1), the time of diffusion of molecular oxygen (downward velocity) is about 1 day at 145 km, 10 days at 115 km, 1 month at 105 km, and 100 days at 97.5 km. At 200 km the time of diffusion is less than 1000 sec; it appears then that it is not possible to maintain a vertical distribution of neutral particles which are not in a diffusion equilibrium.

The preceding results, which describe in a very simple form possibilities of mixing or diffusion, may be used only where there are no sources or sinks. The processes of chemical reactions or photochemical transformations have to be taken into consideration. But, before introducing their effect, the absorption of solar radiation must be studied.

4. ABSORPTION OF SOLAR RADIATION AND LAYER BEHAVIOR

4.1. ABSORPTION IN AN ATMOSPHERE WITH VARYING SCALE HEIGHT

Chapman's treatment of the absorption of solar radiation in an isothermal atmosphere can be extended (cf. Nicolet, 1947, 1950a) to an atmosphere with varying scale height.

Without any preliminary hypothesis on the spectral distribution of the solar radiation, let us consider the absorption of radiation of frequency ν with flux density $S(\nu)$ (cm^{-2} sec^{-1}). The number of photons absorbed per second and per cubic centimeter in an elementary layer, dz, is

$$dq(\nu) = q(\nu) \, nK(\nu) \, dz \sec \chi \qquad (32)$$

if $q(\nu) = S(\nu)/h\nu$, χ is the solar zenith distance, and $K(\nu)$ is the atomic absorption coefficient.

The variation of $q(\nu)$ with height is obtained by integration of (32), with the help of (21),

$$q(\nu) = q_\infty(\nu) \, e^{-\sec \chi \, nK(\nu) H} \qquad (33)$$

in which $q_\infty(\nu)$ denotes the number of photons where the optical depth $\tau(\nu)$ is

$$\tau(\nu) = \sec \chi \, n K(\nu) H = 0 . \tag{34}$$

If we adopt a mean value K of the absorption coefficient in a certain spectral range, we obtain the number $\mathfrak{N}$ of absorption processes per second and per cubic centimeter,

$$\mathfrak{N} = n K Q , \tag{35}$$

in which Q is the total number of photons for the spectral range considered at a height z. Thus, by (33),

$$\mathfrak{N} = n K Q_\infty \, e^{-nKH \sec \chi} . \tag{36}$$

The maximum of the rate $\mathfrak{N}$ of the absorption processes is obtained from (36) by the following condition:

$$n_M K H_M \sec \chi = 1 + \beta , \tag{37}$$

where n_M and H_M denote, respectively, the atomic concentration and scale height with gradient β at the altitude z_M of the maximum absorption.

If z_M^* is the altitude of the absorption peak when $\chi = 0$ (sun in zenith), the condition for a maximum becomes

$$n_M^* K H_M^* = 1 + \beta , \tag{38}$$

and the maximum rate is

$$\mathfrak{N}_M^* = \frac{(1+\beta) \, Q_\infty}{H_M^* \, e^{1+\beta}} . \tag{39}$$

Writing

$$\frac{H}{H_M^*} = e^{\beta \zeta} , \tag{40}$$

we find the vertical distribution of the absorption rate, by (36) and (39), to be

$$\mathfrak{N} = \mathfrak{N}_M^* \exp \left[\, (1+\beta) \, (1 - \zeta - \sec \chi \, e^{-\zeta}) \, \right] . \tag{41}$$

In the case of a parabolic approximation, (41) becomes

$$\mathfrak{N} = \mathfrak{N}_M^* \left[1 + \frac{(1+\beta) \, \zeta^2}{4} \right] . \tag{42}$$

The variation of the maximum rate $\mathfrak{N}_M$ with χ may be obtained from (41) as follows:

$$\mathfrak{N} = \mathfrak{N}_M^* \, (\cos \chi)^{1+\beta} . \tag{43}$$

We note that Chapman's formulae and $\zeta = (z - z_M^*)/H$ are recovered for the special case of $\beta = 0$, corresponding to a constant scale height.

4.2. Equilibrium with Varying Recombination Coefficient

In considering the formation of an ionized layer or of a dissociation region, the effects of the recombination may yield different vertical distributions according to the variation of the recombination coefficient with height.

In a steady state (photoequilibrium), the recombination coefficient a can, by eq. (40), be written as follows:

$$a = a_M^* \left(\frac{n}{n_M^*} \right)^{\eta} = a_M^* e^{-\eta(1+\beta)\zeta} . \tag{44}$$

Instead of (41), we must write an expression of the form[2]

$$n(a) = n(a_M^*) \exp \left\{ \tfrac{1}{2}(1+\beta)[1 - \zeta(1-\eta) - \sec \chi \, e^{-\zeta}] \right\} . \tag{45}$$

A peak is obtained if ζ is

$$\zeta_M = -\ln(1-\eta)\cos\chi , \tag{46}$$

where ζ_M is given by

$$H_M = H_M^* e^{\beta \zeta_M} . \tag{47}$$

A peak cannot be obtained if $\eta \geq 1$. In an isothermal atmosphere, no peak is possible if the recombination coefficient is proportional to the pressure. But, with a varying scale height, and if a is proportional to pressure, $\eta = 1/(1+\beta)$, and equation (45) becomes

$$n(a) = n(a_M^*) \exp\left\{ \tfrac{1}{2}(1+\beta)\left[1 - \frac{\beta}{1+\beta}\zeta - \sec\chi \, e^{-\zeta} \right] \right\} . \tag{48}$$

Above 110 km, if $\beta = 0.2$, the layer peak obtained from (48) is 2.15 H_M^* above the absorption peak and corresponds to a value of $\zeta = 2.3 \log_{10} [(1+\beta)/\beta]$. The variation of the layer peak with solar zenith distance is

$$n(a_M) = n(a_M^*)(\cos\chi)^{\beta/2} , \tag{49}$$

that is to say, a very small variation.

In order to follow the differences between absorption distribution and layer formation with recombination proportional to the pressure, a set of curves is presented in Figure 3.

4.3. The Total Density Distribution

It is useful to know the total electron density below and above the layer peak. In a steady state with complete mixing, we may use (45), which yields, after integration,

$$\int_{-\infty}^{\infty} n_e \, dz = (n_e)_M^* \int_{-\infty}^{\infty} \exp\left\{ \tfrac{1}{2}(1+\beta)[1 - \zeta(1-\eta) - \sec\chi \, e^{-\zeta}] \right\} d\zeta . \tag{50}$$

2. $n(a) = (\mathfrak{R}/a)^{1/2}$. If $n(a) = \mathfrak{R}/a$, the exponential term is $1 + \beta$ instead of $\tfrac{1}{2}(1+\beta)$.

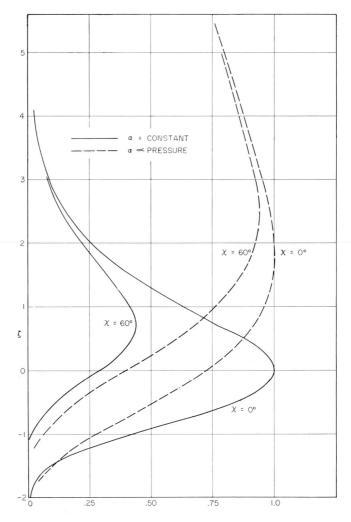

FIG. 3.—Vertical distribution of the absorption of solar radiation and the resulting distributions for two extreme cases of equilibrium conditions. *Abscissae*, relative values of the vertical distribution, normalized to unity for an overhead sun ($\chi = 0$). *Ordinates*, the parameter ζ of the vertical distribution, given by the pressure variation $p/p_{max} = \exp (\zeta)$, in which p_{max} denotes the pressure at $\zeta = 0$ corresponding to $\chi = 0$. The solid curve corresponds to a production of atoms or ions when the recombination coefficient is constant with height; the dashed curves show the displacement of the peak and vertical distribution when the recombination coefficient is proportional to the pressure.

If $\frac{1}{2}(1+\beta)e^{-\zeta}\sec\chi \equiv y$, we have $y_M \equiv \frac{1}{2}(1+\beta)(1-\eta)$ instead of ζ_M; and (50) may be rewritten in the following form:

$$\int_{-\infty}^{\infty} n_e dz = \int_{-\infty}^{z_M} n_e dz + \int_{z_M}^{\infty} n_e dz \equiv N_1 + N_2 \equiv N$$

$$= (n_e)_M^* \frac{e^{(1+\beta)/2}}{[\frac{1}{2}(1+\beta)]^{y_M}} \left[\int_{y_M}^{\infty} y^{y_M-1} e^{-y} dy + \int_0^{y_M} y^{y_M-1} e^{-y} dy \right] (\cos\chi)^{y_M}.$$ (51)

Calculations made with this formula, using $\beta = 0.2$, representative of an atmospheric value above 110 km, provide the variation of the ratio N/N_1; that is to say, the ratio of the total electron content of the column to the content below the peak is as follows:

y_M	0.1	0.2	0.3	0.4	0.5	0.6
N/N_1	5.8	4.2	3.7	3.3	3.2	3.0

If $y_M = 0.6$, the recombination coefficient is constant, and the electron content below the peak is one-third the total content of the column. If $y_M = 0.1$, the recombination coefficient is proportional to the pressure, and the content below the peak is only one-sixth the total content of the column. The former result seems to correspond to a normal ionospheric layer, such as the E layer, but the latter is to be associated with a layer such as that in the F_2 region. Results obtained by Smith (1952) on the refraction of radio waves from radio sources show a variation of N/N_1, from 3 in winter to 6 in summer. This result indicates that the electron concentration at the peak cannot be proportional to the electron content below the peak, as the latter is not necessarily a constant ratio of the total content. A full understanding of the F region is, therefore, related to the deformation of this comparatively thick region compared with a conventional layer in which the ratio of the electron contents above and below the ionization peak is constant.

4.4. DIFFUSION VELOCITY ACCORDING TO VARIOUS VERTICAL DISTRIBUTIONS

Instead of considering an initial mixing, it is interesting to study what happens when dissociation of a molecule occurs at high altitudes, i.e., when there is dissociation of N_2 above 100 km. The vertical distribution of the dissociation rate will be found by a formula like (41), and before recombination plays an important role or equilibrium is approached, it is possible (cf. Sec. 7.2) that diffusion transport becomes important.

Since the instantaneous velocity of diffusion of a minor constituent is given by (26), the first term of the second member will be, by (41),

$$\frac{1}{n_1}\frac{\partial n_1}{\partial z} = -\frac{1+\beta}{H}(1 - \sec\chi\, e^{-\zeta}).$$ (52)

Furthermore, the diffusion coefficient can be written, using (40), as

$$D = D_M^* \left(\frac{n_M^*}{n}\right)\left(\frac{H}{H_M^*}\right)^{1/2} = D_M^* e^{(1+3\beta/2)\varsigma}.$$
(53)

Thus (26) is rewritten, according to (52) and (53), as

$$w_1 = \frac{D_M^*}{H_M^*}\left[\left(1 - \frac{m_1}{m}\right)e^{(1+\beta/2)\varsigma} - (1+\beta)\sec \chi\, e^{3\varsigma/2}\right].$$
(54)

At the absorption peak for an overhead sun, $\sec \chi = 1$ and $\varsigma = 0$, and, by (54),

$$w_M^* = -\left(\beta + \frac{m_1}{m}\right)\frac{D_M^*}{H_M^*};$$
(55)

since $\beta > 0$ the atoms produced by photodissociation have a downward diffusion velocity.

Using numerical values (atomic nitrogen and $\beta = 0.2$), one obtains the following downward velocities below the absorption peak:

ς	0	-1	-2	-3	-4
v/w_M	1	0.95	0.95	0.91	0.75

Thus a continuous downward diffusion of atomic nitrogen below the production peak is possible if the time of recombination is not too short.

When a vertical distribution follows a law like (45), indicating an effect proportional to the pressure, there results

$$w_M^* = -\frac{D_M^*}{H_M^*}\left(1 + \beta + \frac{m_1}{m}\right);$$
(56)

that is to say, there is a downward velocity larger than the velocity given by (55). In any case, a departure from photoequilibrium can occur if the rapidity of recombination is small compared with the diffusion velocity. Such properties will be considered above 100 km.

5. ATMOSPHERIC OZONE AND ITS VARIATIONS

5.1. THE PHOTOCHEMICAL EQUILIBRIUM

When the behavior of molecules like N_2O, CH_4, and O_3 is considered, their actual vertical distribution must be discussed in comparison with the distribution resulting from a photoequilibrium. Nitrous oxide and methane follow the atmospheric distribution in the troposphere and cannot attain photoequilibrium, while ozone, having a peak above 20 km, is related to a photochemical action. The presence of an ozone layer requires that there be a photochemical equilibrium dependent upon atomic processes involved in the formation or destruction of O_3.

The photochemical theory developed by Chapman (1930a) and considered in detail by Wulf and Deming (1936a, b, 1937) and others has been worked out again (in the mesosphere) by Bates and Nicolet (1950) in order to study theoretically the OH emission in the airglow (cf. also Bates, chap. 12).

Depending on the importance of various recombination processes for atomic oxygen, different regions of the ozonosphere may be considered according to the following equations:

$$O + O + M \rightarrow O_2 + M , \tag{57}$$

$$O + O_2 + M \rightarrow O_3 + M , \tag{58}$$

$$O + O_3 \quad \rightarrow 2 O_2 , \tag{59}$$

having the respective rate coefficients k_1, k_2, and k_3.

In a steady state the ozone concentration is given by

$$n (O_3) = \frac{n (O) k_2 n (O_2) n (M)}{J_3 + k_3 n (O)}, \tag{60}$$

in which J_3 denotes the dissociation coefficient of O_3. Its numerical value will depend on the atomic oxygen concentration.

At about the 100-km level, where atomic oxygen is predominant, reaction (57) is of primary importance and

$$n^2 (O) = \frac{n (O_2) J_2}{k_1 n (M)}, \tag{61}$$

in which J_2 denotes the dissociation rate coefficient of O_2.

At lower levels ($\sim$70 km), in the mesosphere, in which other recombinations cannot be neglected,

$$n^2 (O) \left[1 + \frac{k_2 k_3 n (O_2)}{k_1 J_3} \right] = \frac{n (O_2) J_2}{k_1 n (M)} . \tag{62}$$

In the stratosphere the following forms can be used accurately because (57) can be neglected:

$$n^2 (O) = \frac{J_2 J_3}{k_2 k_3 n (M)} \tag{63}$$

and

$$n (O_3) = \frac{k_2}{k_3} n (O_2) n (M) \frac{n (O_2) J_2}{n (O_2) J_2 + n (O_3) J_3}, \tag{64}$$

in which $n(O_2) J_2 < n(O_3) J_3$.

Equations (63) and (64) are normally used in studies of the main part of the ozone layer, but it must be pointed out that they become inaccurate above the 60-km level. Rocket data (Fig. 4) obtained by Johnson, Purcell, Tousey, and Watanabe (1952) show the vertical distribution of O_3 up to 70 km and can be compared with the theoretical results.

Now considering equation (64), the conditions which determine the be-

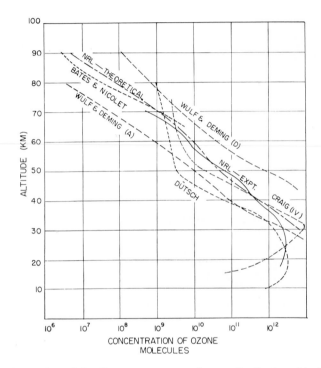

Fig. 4.—Comparison of the direct measurement of ozone distribution with distributions calculated on the basis of photochemical theory; the experimental data are shown by the solid curve (from Johnson, Purcell, Tousey, and Watanabe, 1952).

havior of the stratospheric and tropospheric ozone can be studied in a photochemical equilibrium (cf. Nicolet, 1945):

1. The peak of ozone concentration should be below the absorption maximum of molecular oxygen.

2. The variation of ozone concentration at a definite height depends on the ratio J_2/J_3 and also on the temperature, for k_2/k_3 varies with temperature.

3. When J_2 approaches zero, the ozone concentration should approach zero.

4. During hours of darkness, the equilibrium becomes

$$n(O_3) = \frac{k_2}{k_3} n(O_2) n(M),$$ (65)

in which $k_2/k_3 = 5.5 \times 10^{-25} e^{3070/T}$.

Using the photochemical theory without any atmospheric effect, mesospheric ozone can be explained, and a peak in the vertical distribution may be found. However, it is not possible to explain the behavior of the stratospheric and tropospheric ozone. In other words, if adequate numerical values are chosen for the coefficients, the origin of atmospheric ozone is explained; but its distribution in the lower stratosphere and its presence in the troposphere cannot be justified. Furthermore, instead of the actual trend in the geographical and seasonal amount of O_3, the photochemical theory leads to a decrease from summer to winter and, of course, from equator to pole.

In order to follow the actual ozone distribution, atmospheric motions must be considered. The origin of tropospheric ozone may be found in a mixing due to downward vertical transport of stratospheric ozone. In the stratosphere, where the total amount of ozone is subject to seasonal fluctuations, some atmospheric circulation may be considered.

5.2. DEPARTURE FROM PHOTOCHEMICAL EQUILIBRIUM

If photochemical equilibrium cannot be used to explain the conditions prevailing in the troposphere and in the main part of the stratosphere and if atmospheric transport processes are necessary, then the time required to reach photoequilibrium must be long compared with the time expected for the varying atmospheric conditions.

The time necessary to attain equilibrium between atomic oxygen and ozone is very short at any level in the troposphere or in the stratosphere. The time of dissociation of O_3 subject to solar radiation is less than 1 hour. Furthermore, for any oxygen atom the time of recombination by association with oxygen molecules is very short. This may be shown as follows:

The equation governing the rate of change of $n(O)$ in the stratosphere,

$$\frac{dn(O)}{dt} + n(O)[k_2 n(O_2) n(M) + k_3 n(O_3)] = 2n(O_2) J_2 + n(O_3) J_3,$$ (66)

leads to the solution, when $n(O) \ll n(O_3)$,

$$n(O) = n_0(O) \exp - [k_2 n(O_2) n(M) + k_3 n(O_3)] t$$
$$+ \frac{2n(O_2) J_2 + n(O_3) J_3}{k_2 n(O_2) n(M) + k_3 n(O_3)} \{1 - \exp - [k_2 n(O_2) n(M) + k_3 n(O_3)] t\}$$ (67)

in which $n_0(O) = n(O)$ at $t = 0$.

Because $k_3 = 5 \times 10^{-15}$ to 2×10^{-16} in the troposphere and strato-sphere (≤ 30 km), and $k_2 n(M) = 2 \times 10^{-15}$ to 3×10^{-17} from 2 to 30 km,

$$k_2 n \, (M) \, n \, (O_2) \gg k_3 n \, (O_3) \, ,$$

owing to the atmospheric condition that $n(O_2) \gg n(O_3)$. Thus we can de-fine a time of recombination, $\tau_{recomb}(O)$, for an oxygen atom so that

$$k_2 n \, (O_2) \, n \, (M) \, \tau = 1 \, ,$$

and we find a time less than 1 second below 30 km. The equilibrium be-tween atomic oxygen and ozone is therefore established in minutes or seconds. However, no difference is observed between night and day in the total amount of O_3, because the atomic oxygen concentration is less than the ozone concentration in the main part of the layer.

The production or destruction of odd oxygen atoms (O and O_3) in the stratosphere is given by the following expression:

$$\frac{dn \, (O)}{dt} + \frac{dn \, (O_3)}{dt} = 2 n \, (O_2) \, J_2 - k_3 n \, (O_3) \, n \, (O) \, , \qquad (68)$$

where J_2 denotes the dissociation rate coefficient due to the absorption in the Herzberg continuum at levels below 70 km. Its maximum value at zero optical depth is of the order of 5×10^{-10} sec $^{-1}$. Its variation with height depends mainly on the ozone absorption between 2400 and 1800 A.

Thanks to the fact that $n(O_3) \gg n(O)$, we may assume the following relation for a solution of (68) as a first approximation:

$$n \, (O_3) = n_0 \, (O_3) + 2 n \, (O_2) \, J_2 t \, . \qquad (69)$$

Here $n_0(O_3) = n(O_3)$ at $t = 0$. Using numerical methods, the time re-quired to establish photochemical equilibrium can be determined with the help of (69). Such a computation was made by Wulf and Deming (1937), Nicolet (1945), Dütsch (1946), Craig (1950), and others. Adopting as values of the ozone and molecular oxygen concentrations data which follow from rocket results of the Naval Research Laboratory, we may estimate the time t of recombination by (cf. eq. [69]):

$$n \, (O_3) = 2 n \, (O_2) \, J_2 t \, . \qquad (70)$$

Approximate results derived from the preceding equations exhibit the following features found by various workers:

Altitude (km)......	>50	45	40	30	22.5	20
Time............	1 hr.	Several hr.	1 day	1 mo.	1 yr.	Several yr.

Above 40 km photochemical equilibrium for ozone may be considered as permanent. Departures from equilibrium would persist for several days below 40 km, months below 30 km, and years below 20 km. In treating fluctuations, the fraction situated above 40 km may be neglected, since we know that only one-tenth the total amount of ozone exists above this level. Besides, we must point out again that no clearly detectable fluctuation in the total amount is found between day and night. The variation of solar radiation, therefore, does not affect the major part of the total ozone amount; hence the behavior of atmospheric ozone must be explained by departures from the photochemical equilibrium.

The origin of the seasonal variation is to be found in the main part of the ozone layer. Here, after a departure from photochemical equilibrium, a restoration time of the order of months is required. At the tropopause level and in the troposphere, the photoequilibrium is not effective, and the ozone density is a conservative property of the air mass. Finally, any variation of the vertical distribution in the lower atmosphere depends on the action of atmospheric motions.

5.3. ATMOSPHERIC TRANSPORT PHENOMENA

The atmospheric transport processes leading to the observed vertical distribution and, finally, to the total ozone content may be a priori (1) meridional circulation, in order to explain the peculiar annual variation (maximum in spring and minimum in autumn) and the meridional distribution with maxima occurring mostly between the 50° and 60° latitudes, and (2) a downward vertical transport, introducing ozone into the troposphere.

On the basis of the photochemical theory, the ozone formation is maximum when solar radiation reaches its maximum. Ozone must therefore be transported by a meridional flow from the summer hemisphere toward the winter hemisphere. Furthermore, a meridional circulation should be able to transport ozone coming from the "equatorial" zone down into "polar" regions. Such a view requires, of course, a complete circuit of the circulation over both hemispheres (Dütsch, 1946; Myake and Saruhashi, 1952; Reed and Julius, 1952). When comparison is made with meteorological studies of the general circulation (cf. Byers, chap. 7), it is very difficult to give a consistent picture of the atmospheric behavior. Having found the general character of the ozone transport processes, it should be possible to arrive at a model of atmospheric circulation explaining meteorological phenomena and ozone variations. Thus a circulation pattern cannot be based on the dynamics deduced from meteorological studies of the troposphere, and it is necessary to imagine the dynamics of the stratosphere (Fig. 5) as Kellogg and Schilling (1951) did. Such a flow can explain the meridional circulation of ozone.

Ozone molecules move downward (trying to follow the vertical distribution of other constituents) because of vertical mixing. This explains the presence of ozone down to the ground level. However, the most fundamental features of this continuous downward movement of ozone due to the mass exchange are not yet known. Meteorological investigations of turbulence are still necessary to yield information for the ozone problem. Furthermore, nothing can be said about the part that mixing plays in the seasonal or latitudinal variation. Because of the lack of knowledge concerning the vertical transport in meteorological phenomena, the relative importance of the actions of meridional circulation and vertical exchange is still a matter of debate. These are known to be effective, thanks to the study of the periodic variations of stratospheric ozone and to the existence of tropospheric ozone.

5.4. Ozone Content and Atmospheric Motion Relationships

After assuming meridional circulation and general turbulent exchange related to the photochemistry of ozone to explain the seasonal and latitudinal variation of the total ozone content and also the presence of tropospheric ozone, it remains to study the factors producing the non-periodic variations.

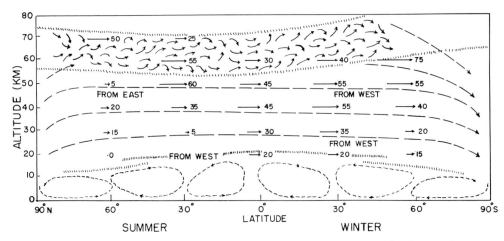

Fig. 5.—Schematic representation of general circulation in meridional cross-section for a northern summer. The heavy vectors represent the mean zonal components of the wind (which are actually normal to the plane), in meters per second. The dashed lines represent the meridional streamlines (from Kellogg and Schilling, 1951).

The day-to-day changes of the total ozone amount have been known since the time of Dobson's early measurements. Significant correlations between total ozone content and various atmospheric quantities were obtained by Meetham (1937). Since an atmospheric transport is responsible for the regular variations which have their origin in the stratosphere, the day-to-day changes must be attributed to the motions related to weather phenomena. Horizontal advection and vertical motions combine in producing a change in the vertical ozone distribution giving the day-to-day variations of the total content (Nicolet, 1945; Dütsch, 1946; Reed, 1950). Horizontal air advection may be expected to produce an increase or decrease of the ozone content according to the origin of the air mass. Vertical motion can produce an increase or decrease according to downward or upward displacement of the air. If no local change of concentration can occur for gases following the atmospheric vertical distribution, the effect of increasing or decreasing the O_3 concentration is important because of its peculiar vertical distribution.

The relative importance of vertical motion and horizontal advection in day-to-day changes is clearly understood by using the ozone mixing ratio (Reed, 1950). The warm and cold areas in the lower stratosphere corresponding, respectively, to pressure troughs and ridges move with the speed of the pressure systems. They are dynamically produced as results of subsidence and lifting, respectively, leading to the increase or decrease of the total content.

If vertical distributions are measured directly, fluctuations of the ozone concentration are to be found at all heights below 40 km. Various interpretations are possible according to the method of analysis of curves which depends on the errors of measurement. Nevertheless, even if features such as maxima, minima, and shoulders in the concentration-curves cannot all be real (cf. Johnson, Purcell, and Tousey, 1951; V. H. Regener, 1951; E. Regener, 1952), widely different vertical distributions below 30 km are due to the atmospheric transport advection and dynamical vertical motions, which change the total ozone content.

5.5. Solar Activity and Atmospheric Ozone

The foregoing analysis can be applied to the problem of the effect of solar activity on atmospheric ozone. Various forms of correlation between ozone and solar activity may be studied. But for this problem we need to call attention to only two possible effects of solar activity, namely, correlation with the relative sunspot number and a direct effect of solar flares on ozone content.

It is apparent from Götz's observations (1949) over a period of 20 years that no general correlation between the 11-year period of solar activity and total ozone content can be found. Even though peaks in the average annual curve of Arosa may exist at the end of April or the end of October, no close relationship is detected in an annual fluctuation of the solar activity. If such maxima are to be associated with some magnetic activity, they should be related to large-scale atmospheric motions playing a role in the magnetic activity.

The effect of a solar flare was checked recently by Fritz (1952) during a sudden ionospheric disturbance. No fluctuation in the total ozone content was found, indicating that an important ionospheric disturbance due to a solar phenomenon has no direct implication for the ozonosphere. The difficulty of measuring solar effects on atmospheric ozone is due to the fact that the most important fraction of its total amount is explained by a complete departure from the photochemical equilibrium. Because no difference appears between day and night, it is not possible to measure a fluctuation of the total amount which would be due to a small variation of solar radiation not yet recognized in the spectral range of wave lengths longer than 2000 A.

In summing up, it seems that ozone behavior suggests that the dynamics of the stratosphere and, a fortiori, of the high atmosphere is entirely different from the dynamics known in meteorological study. At present it is already held to be necessary to consider the dynamical effects in the high atmosphere in terms of laws not yet clarified by conventional meteorological applications for upper-air conditions.

6. MOLECULAR OXYGEN AND ITS DISSOCIATION

6.1. THE PHOTOCHEMICAL EQUILIBRIUM

Dissociation of oxygen has been studied theoretically by assuming a photochemical equilibrium (Chapman, 1930b; Wulf and Deming, 1938; Majumdar, 1938; Rakshit, 1947; Penndorf, 1949; Bates and Nicolet, 1950; Moses and Wu, 1951, 1952). Recent rocket data on the vertical distribution of the solar radiation at 1500 A, obtained by Friedman, Lichtman, and Byram (1951), provide interesting possibilities of testing theories of photochemical equilibrium. The numerical results deduced from photoequilibrium theories depend mainly on values assumed for the molecular coefficients and physical parameters. Neglecting, here, discussions about the accuracy of constants involved in reactions (cf. Penndorf, 1949; Bates and Nicolet, 1950; Moses and Wu, 1951, 1952; Nicolet and Mange,

1954), we will consider times of dissociation of O_2, of recombination of O, and of diffusion and mixing of oxygen.

6.2. RATE AND TIME OF DISSOCIATION OF AN OXYGEN MOLECULE

If the photochemical action is not disturbed in the region where O_2 is only a small fraction of the oxygen content, the general equation can be written, using (57) and (61), as follows:

$$\frac{dn(O_2)}{dt} = -n(O_2) J_2 + a n^2 (O) , \tag{71}$$

where $a \equiv k_1 n(M)$ denotes the recombination coefficient. Because a small variation of $n(O_2)$ does not affect $n(O)$ practically, the solution of (71) may be written as follows:

$$n(O_2) = n_0(O_2) e^{-J_2 t} + \frac{a n^2 (O)}{J_2} [1 - e^{-J_2 t}] , \tag{72}$$

where $n_0(O_2) \equiv n(O_2)$ when $t = 0$.

The time of dissociation, $\tau_{\text{diss}}(O_2)$, will be defined by $J_2 t = 1$, so that $J_2^{-1} = \tau_{\text{diss}}(O_2)$ is the reciprocal of the dissociation-rate coefficient corresponding to the mean lifetime of an O_2 molecule subject to solar radiation.

Numerical values of J_2 have been obtained (Nicolet and Mange, 1954) by using experimental data for the absorption coefficient in the Schumann-Runge continuum and black-body temperatures between $4000°$ and $6000°$ K. From these results one can conclude that the time of dissociation is very sensitive to the assumed temperature. For example,

T(° K).........	6000	5250	5000	4750	4500	4250	4000
$\tau_{\text{diss}}(O_2)$.........	1 hr.	6 hr.	12 hr.	4 days	10 days	1 mo.	4 mo.

Consequently, a permissible application of the photochemical equilibrium depends on the assumed radiation temperature. When temperatures larger than $5000°$ K are used for computation, one may consider that oxygen is maintained by a dissociative equilibrium, for the time of dissociation is less than $\frac{1}{2}$ day. But for lower radiation temperatures, the situation is entirely different, because of the long time required to approach photochemical equilibrium. Wulf and Deming (1938), Spitzer (1949), and Moses and Wu (1951, 1952) have adopted $6000°$ K, while Penndorf (1949) has computed with various values between $6000°$ and $5000°$ K, and Bates and Nicolet (1950) have already used a $5000°$ K black body. With such temperatures it is rather unrealistic to consider a strong departure from the photochemical equilibrium. However, since recent determinations from

rocket data by Friedman, Lichtman, and Byram (1951) indicate that
solar emission in the main part of the Schumann-Runge continuum may
be represented by a 4500° K black body, consideration of the dissociation
of oxygen must take into account a possible departure from the photochemical equilibrium. With such a radiation temperature, the time of dissociation of an O_2 molecule is about 10 days at zero optical depth, or a
time long enough that the possibility of a disturbance due to atmospheric
motion must be considered.

6.3. TIME OF MIXING

Even if theory may be used to predict a time of dissociation, the time
of mixing resulting from large-scale motions, as well as from turbulence or
convection, is unknown. However, the time of diffusion can be estimated
theoretically. If diffusion equilibrium between O_2 and O is assumed, we
can see that, at levels where the optical depth is very small or negligible,
the photochemical equilibrium with two-body recombination shows approximately the same vertical distribution. It would, therefore, be difficult to know, by observational methods, the extent to which atoms and
molecules are sorted in diffusion equilibrium. One might expect that if the
mixing occurs vertically upward within a few days, oxygen molecules
would follow the vertical atmospheric distribution in the region where
they are only a small fraction of the total amount of oxygen.

An analysis of the rocket results on the transmission of the solar radiation at 1500 A (Nicolet and Mange, 1954) leads to the following conclusion: Above 100 km, the vertical distribution of the optical depth at
$\lambda = 1500$ A is followed if the scale height adopted for molecular oxygen
corresponds to the atmospheric scale height deduced from pressure data
(Fig. 6). This result leads to a constant ratio of molecular to atomic oxygen concentrations of not more than $\frac{1}{100}$ and not less than $\frac{1}{50}$. Thus the
time of diffusion and time of dissociation of O_2 cannot be less than the
time of mixing, so that below 115 km $\tau_{mixing}(O_2) < 10$ days. Consequently,
instead of the photochemical expression (71), the more general equation
to be considered is

$$\frac{\partial n\,(O_2)}{\partial t} = \frac{dn\,(O_2)}{dt} - \operatorname{div}\,[n\,(O_2)\,V_M] - \operatorname{div}\,[n\,(O_2)\,V_D]\,, \qquad (73)$$

where $dn(O_2)/dt$ denotes the rate of change of density $n(O_2)$ in a unit volume moving with the air, which is due to physical processes resulting in
photodissociation and recombination; $\operatorname{div}[n(O_2)\,V_M]$ is the term corresponding to the atmospheric transport in the form of large-scale motions

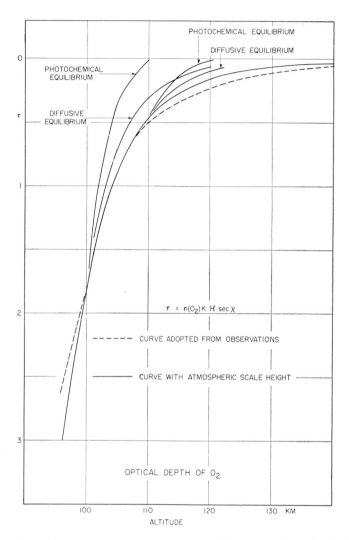

FIG. 6.—Optical depth of molecular oxygen at $\lambda = 1500$ A according to various vertical distributions. *Abscissae,* altitude in kilometers above sea-level; *ordinates,* optical depth at 1500 A of molecular oxygen following various vertical distributions. The variation of the optical depth τ shows that the rocket data cannot be explained by photochemical equilibrium. The vertical distribution depends on atmospheric motions due to diffusion and mixing.

or mass exchange due to turbulence with a velocity vector V_M; and $\text{div}[n(O_2)\,V_D]$ is the term resulting in diffusion with a velocity vector V_D.

It is not yet possible to discuss a general form such as (73), and practical figures may be considered only after assuming simplifications. The air (atomic oxygen and molecular nitrogen) must satisfy the equation of continuity,

$$\frac{\partial n}{\partial t} + \text{div}\,(nV) = 0,\qquad (74)$$

in which V is the velocity vector of the air. Because the variation $\partial n(O_2)/\partial t$ is to be studied, the following simplifications will be made in (74):

1. The local change of air density is negligible; $\partial n/\partial t = 0$, that is to say, the total concentration of $O + N_2$ is considered as constant.

2. The horizontal gradients are also negligible; $\partial n/\partial x = \partial n/\partial y = 0$; i.e., there is a sufficient uniformity in the horizontal distribution of O and N_2.

3. The statical and state equations are, of course, applicable; thus, by (18),

$$\frac{1}{n}\frac{\partial n}{\partial z} = -\frac{1+\beta}{H}.\qquad (75)$$

Under these conditions, (74) may be rewritten in the following form:

$$\text{div}\,V = w\,\frac{1+\beta}{H},\qquad (76)$$

in which w is the vertical velocity component of V.

Since molecular oxygen must follow atmospheric motions, the preceding equation leads to the following expression for the term $\text{div}\,[n(O_2)\,V_M]$:

$$\text{div}\,[n\,(O_2)V_M] = w_M\left[\frac{\partial n\,(O_2)}{\partial z} + \frac{1+\beta}{H}\,n\,(O_2)\right] + u\,\frac{\partial n\,(O_2)}{\partial x} + v\,\frac{\partial n\,(O_2)}{\partial y},\qquad (77)$$

in which u and v denote the horizontal velocity components.

When we neglect $\partial n(O_2)/\partial x$ and $\partial n(O_2)/\partial y$, considering that appreciable horizontal transport in a horizontal layer does not occur before vertical transport, we may assume the approximate equation,

$$\text{div}\,[n\,(O_2)\,V_M] = w_M\left[\frac{\partial n\,(O_2)}{\partial z} + \frac{1+\beta}{H}\,n\,(O_2)\right].\qquad (78)$$

The term $\text{div}\,[n(O_2)\,V_D]$ is already known by (26), when we neglect the horizontal terms.

Since the mixing effect seems to exist above 115 km and perhaps up to 150 km, levels at which the times of diffusion of O_2 are, respectively, 10 days and 1 day (cf. Fig. 7), the time of mixing is not greater than 10 days and might be of the order of 1 day. Because the time of dissociation of O_2 is of the order of 10 days at zero optical depth, we may conclude that in the atmospheric region where $n(O_2) < n(O)$ the mixing processes are strongly effective. In order to have mixing, the following conditions are to be assumed: $\tau_{\text{mixing}}(O_2) < \tau_{\text{dissociation}}(O_2) \geq 10$ days at any height, and $\tau_{\text{mixing}}(O_2) < \tau_{\text{diffusion}}(O_2) = 10$ days or 1 day, according to an efficiency of mixing at 115 and 150 km, respectively.

As we know nothing about large-scale currents which are able to lead to complete mixing above 100 km, no quantitative or even qualitative explanation is possible. The role of the general atmospheric circulation as

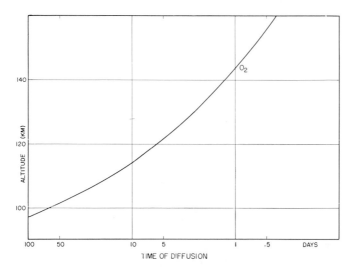

FIG. 7.—Time of diffusion of molecular oxygen. This is the minimum time necessary to reach a vertical distribution following the Dalton law, since the velocity of diffusion is deduced from a vertical distribution gradient derived from a mixed-atmosphere distribution.

an efficient agent in promoting mixing remains to be determined. If the possibility of mixing due to a mass-exchange process, resulting, for example, in turbulence, is accepted, the mechanism must give a velocity between 2 and 20 cm sec^{-1}. As would be expected, the mass-exchange coefficient of the order of 3×10^{-4} gm cm^{-1} sec^{-1} is thus several orders (10^3–10^4) larger than the *relative* mass exchange at 20 km.

It therefore appears necessary to relate these results to the ionospheric winds indicating turbulent velocities and E-layer oscillations. Vertical velocities of the order of 1 m/sec are certainly possible, and it will be interesting to study the mass-exchange process in the atmospheric region between 100 and 150 km in connection with the energy transfer associated with the spectrum of turbulence. However, because the radiation properties are not yet known, it is difficult to discuss a general treatment of the problem. In any case, the vertical distribution of O_2 above 100 km must differ considerably from that of photochemical equilibrium (Nicolet and Mange, 1954); both mixing (Nicolet, 1954a) and diffusion (Nicolet, 1954b) maintain a comparatively high O_2 concentration above the dissociation peak.

6.4. Time of Recombination of an Oxygen Atom

If oxygen molecules can follow a vertical distribution subject to the atmospheric scale height above 100 km, it may be expected that oxygen atoms in the region where O_2 dissociation is not complete are dependent on atmospheric motions.

In a region where O_2 is not dissociated $[n(O_2) \gg n(O)]$, the rate of loss of oxygen atoms is

$$\frac{dn\,(O)}{dt} = - a_1 n^2\,(O) - a_2 n\,(O)\,n\,(X)\,, \tag{79}$$

taking into account direct recombination (coefficient a_1) and association with another molecule (coefficient a_2). The time of recombination is

$$\tau_{\text{recomb}}\,(O) = \frac{1}{a_2 n\,(X)} \tag{80}$$

or

$$\tau_{\text{recomb}}\,(O) = \frac{1}{a_1 n_0\,(O)}\,, \tag{81}$$

if $n_0(O) = n(O)$ when $t = 0$. Results of computations made by Nicolet and Mange (1954) are plotted in Figure 8. Using daytime equilibrium values of the atomic oxygen concentration, we can see that above 85 km the time of recombination is not less than 1 month. In fact, a loss of oxygen atoms has to take place in the process of ozone formation without automatic dissociation, in order to obtain shorter times of dissociation below 85 km. It is reasonable to conclude that one might expect the oxygen atom concentration to increase by means of a downward vertical transport. An increase to one-fiftieth the total concentration at 95 km still indicates a time of recombination of 1 month. In order to obtain a very short time of recombination, namely, of 1 day, the data indicate that O_2 and O concentrations of the same order are necessary at the 90-km level. Consequently, these results prove[3] that the atomic oxygen mixing ratio reaches values greater than the photochemical ratio (Nicolet, 1954b).

3. The uncertainties in the values of coefficients of chemical reactions are stressed, and numerical values used in this chapter may require revision.

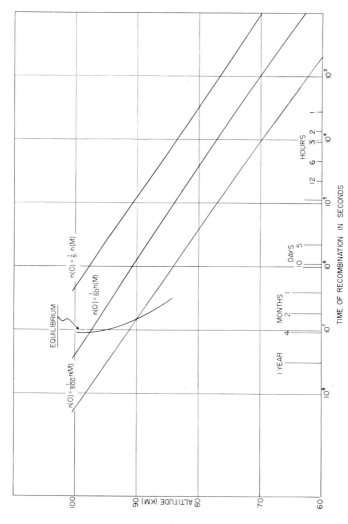

Fig. 8.—Time of recombination of oxygen atoms. By assuming atomic oxygen concentrations which are definite fractions of the total number of particles $n(M)$, namely, $\frac{1}{500}$, $\frac{1}{50}$, and $\frac{1}{5}$, one can determine the mean lifetime of an oxygen atom before recombination. For example, if $\frac{1}{10}$ of the O_2 molecules is dissociated, i.e., $n(O) = \frac{1}{5} n(M)$, the mean lifetime of these atoms is of the order of 10 days at 90 km.

6.5. Atomic Oxygen and the Mesopause

Since oxygen atoms are subject to atmospheric motions before recombining, the rate equation becomes (just as for molecular oxygen)

$$\frac{\partial n\,(\mathrm{O})}{\partial t} = \frac{d n\,(\mathrm{O})}{d t} - w \left[\frac{\partial n\,(\mathrm{O})}{\partial z} + \frac{1+\beta}{H}\, n\,(\mathrm{O}) \right] - \left[u\, \frac{\partial n\,(\mathrm{O})}{\partial x} \right.$$
$$\left. + v\, \frac{\partial n\,(\mathrm{O})}{\partial y} \right] + \frac{1}{m\,(\mathrm{O})}\, \frac{\partial\,(E_z \partial r_1 / \partial z)}{\partial z}, \qquad (82)$$

in which u, v, and w denote the components x, y, and z of the velocity vector due to large-scale currents; E_z denotes the vertical mass-exchange coefficient; and r_1 stands for the atomic oxygen mixing ratio $n(\mathrm{O})m(\mathrm{O})/n(M)m(M)$. By considering the advective mass transport due to large-scale motions as compared with the time of recombination, the lifetime of a disturbance can be obtained. We first confine our attention to low heights, namely, 70–75 km, where the time of recombination is not less than 1 hour if $n(\mathrm{O})$ is larger than the daytime equilibrium concentration, but still is less than $n(M)/50$. Thus a disturbance changing an atomic oxygen mixing ratio from its photochemical value to $\frac{1}{100}$ may have a lifetime of more than 1 hour. Furthermore, the mass exchange below 80 km will be strongly effective in producing fluctuations of the O concentration. From the foregoing discussion it can be concluded with certainty that the O concentration fluctuates and possibly modifies the processes involved in the loss of O_3 in the upper mesosphere.

At 85 km, an approximate half-dissociation of O_2 may be stable for several hours before recombination. Consequently, the atmospheric motions involving mass exchange can transport O from upper levels, thus increasing the oxygen mixing ratio to very great values. Such a dissociation ratio of oxygen affects the mean molecular mass. Consequently, on the basis of a scale-height minimum near 80 km, the conclusion can be reached that the mesopause is related to the dissociation of oxygen.

At 90 km, the time of recombination is further increased, and the former deductions apply even more. Since an O concentration comparable to that of O_2 can be maintained for more than 1 day, it is convenient to postulate a mesopause between 85 and 95 km. In other words, the level of the mesopause is about 10 km above the minimum of the scale height.

Thus the evidence for atmospheric motions in the neighborhood of the mesopause does not favor the existence of a sharp transition region for molecular and atomic oxygen, as is required by the photochemical equilibrium. Since steady atmospheric motions cannot exist, it seems certain that the height of the mesopause is variable. Seasonal and latitudinal variations can occur and also day-to-day changes, for the time of recombination of atomic oxygen varies with height and density.

In summary, it seems quite definitely established that the departure from a photochemical equilibrium must be included in the study of oxygen dissociation; and it seems that the mesopause is the level at which there is a sufficient dissociation of O_2. However, the problem is complicated by the lack of sufficient knowledge about the recombination coefficients.

6.6. Ionospheric Behavior and Vertical Oxygen Transport

The fact that the vertical distribution of oxygen does not correspond to that of a photochemical equilibrium leads to interesting conclusions in ionospheric theory about such questions as the origin of the E layer or charge transfer in the F layer. Since an ultraviolet photoionization has been considered to be the origin of the E layer, namely, ionization in the range of 1000–910 A, O and N_2 are neglected because their photoionization occurs at $\lambda < 910$ A. According to Weissler and Lee's (1952) and Clark's (1952) experimental data, the O_2 absorption coefficient in its first continuum can be estimated to be of the order of $(5 \pm 1) \times 10^{-18}$ cm². Furthermore, many bands whose absorption coefficient is of the order of 10^{-17} cm² are preionized. Since O_2 exists above 100 km and follows the atmospheric vertical distribution with a constant ratio of O_2 to the total concentration of the order of $\frac{1}{100}$, the vertical distribution of electron production is well defined. Since the recombination process is due to a dissociative mechanism (cf. chap. 12, eq. [127]), the normal E layer might be explained by very simple laws as occurring in an atmosphere with varying scale height.

However, there are other factors to be considered. Both N_2 and O are ionized by X-rays, while O_2 is also ionized by $\lambda < 1029$ A (Inn, 1953). The number of X-ray photons with $\lambda \leq 10$ A striking the top of the atmosphere is roughly 5×10^4/cm² sec (Byram, Chubb, and Friedman, 1954a), while, at these wave lengths and for an overhead sun, unit optical depth is reached near the 100-km level. The ionization rate is thus found to be about 0.02 electrons/cm³ sec. At somewhat higher levels, 110–115 km, unit optical depth occurs for $\lambda \simeq 60$ A, for which the number of photons is between 3×10^8 and 3×10^9/cm² sec (Byram, Chubb, and Friedman, 1954a). Here we have an ionization rate of 10^2–10^3 electrons/cm³ sec, about 30 per cent of which is due to oxygen. Solar radiation with $\lambda < 1029$ A appears to contribute about 20 electrons/cm³ sec, since the free-free coronal radiation can give 10^7 to 5×10^7 photons/cm² sec between 910 and 1030 A.

In the F layer, where free electrons are produced by the photoionization of atomic oxygen, charge transfer of the type $O^+ + O_2 \rightarrow O + O_2^+$ should be necessary, according to the Bates and Massey process. Thus the mechanism by which electron recombination occurs, such as $O_2^+ + e \rightarrow O + O$, involves a continuous dissociation. Consequently, charge transfer on O_2 (or another molecule) with the subsequent dissociation requires a continuous upward transport of molecules in order to replenish the F layer with sufficient rapidity. Because of the diffusion above 160 km, an upward vertical transport is possible if the time of diffusion is less than the time of dissociation. The entire question needs more complete investigation, which is possible if the following items are kept in mind: possible values of the charge-transport coefficient, the extent of photodissociation of O_2, and the existence of NO.

7. MOLECULAR NITROGEN AND ITS DISSOCIATION

7.1. Decomposition of Nitrogen

We now proceed to state the facts concerning nitrogen decomposition and give an explanation in terms of the mechanism of dissociative recombination. Dissociation of nitrogen has been studied theoretically, assuming a photochemical equilibrium, by Bates (chap. 12). The dissociation-rate coefficient $J_{N_2} = 10^{-12}$ sec^{-1} (Bates, 1952) in the mesosphere, according to a Herzberg mechanism, which leads to predissociation at about 1240 A. However, another process is operative in the F_1 layer. Molecular nitrogen is ionized by radiation of $\lambda < 796$ A and, at shorter wave lengths, $\lambda < 661$ A. Its absorption coefficient is of the order of 2.2×10^{-17} cm^2 (Weissler, Lee, and Mohr, 1952; cf. also Goldberg, chap. 9, Fig. 4). The number of photons available at the top of the earth's atmosphere is not less than 2×10^9 photons cm^{-2} sec^{-1} (Nicolet, 1952). The ionization-rate coefficient at zero optical depth is therefore not less than 4.4×10^{-8} sec^{-1}.

Ionization of molecular nitrogen followed by dissociative recombination (Bates and Massey, 1947) is a source of nitrogen atoms according to

$$N_2^+ + e \rightarrow 2N , \tag{83}$$

a process whose rate coefficient $a(N_2^+)$ exceeds 10^{-7} cm^{-3} sec^{-1} and is probably near 10^{-6} cm^{-3} sec^{-1} (Biondi, 1951). In any case, the lifetime $\tau(N_2^+)$ of an N_2^+ ion is very short, namely,

$$\tau (N_2^+) = \frac{1}{a n_e} < 100 \text{ seconds} \tag{84}$$

in the F layer. Consequently, the photoionization of N_2 followed by dissociative recombination is an important process for the production of N.

If it is postulated that nitrogen atoms cannot lead to an immediate reformation of N_2 in the F layers, they may fall downward before recombination. It is therefore necessary to discuss the extent to which the yield of atoms by atmospheric transport is a primary process compared with the Herzberg mechanism.

The maximum rate $\mathfrak{N}_M^*(N)$ of N production, which is given by (39), occurs at a height, deduced from the following expression, for which (38) has been used,

$$(1 + \beta) \sec \chi = n(O) K(O) H + n(N_2) K(N_2) H . \tag{85}$$

Using absorption coefficients for O (Bates and Seaton, 1950) and for N_2 (Weissler, Lee, and Mohr, 1952) and $\beta = 0.2$ (cf. Table 4), the height of the maximum rate of atomic nitrogen can be obtained. From Table 4 and $\chi = 0$, we obtain

$$\mathfrak{N}_M^*(N) \geq 8 \times 10^2 \text{ cm}^{-3} \text{ sec}^{-1} \text{ at } 160 \text{ km} . \tag{86}$$

From the data on photoequilibrium (Bates, 1952), it may be seen that, approximately,

$$\frac{n(N)}{n(N_2)} = \frac{J_2}{a_0 n(M) n(O)} , \tag{87}$$

in which $a_0 = 1.5 \times 10^{-32}$ cm^6 sec^{-1} denotes the recombination coefficient and $n(M)$ the three-body concentration.

At 160 km, $J_2 \geq 2.6 \times 10^{-8}$ sec^{-1}, and, by (87),

$$\frac{n(N)}{n(N_2)} \geq 3.8 \times 10^3 . \tag{88}$$

Thus, if a photoequilibrium exists, it implies that the number of atoms is greater than the number of molecules. But, as suggested by Spitzer (1949), diffusion of nitrogen atoms must exist, and their vertical distribution cannot follow the distribution as deduced by Deb (1952).

Ionization by X-rays will produce about 1000 N atoms/cm^3 sec as low as 110 km, and this production may correspond to the excess observed in the X-ray spectrum by Byram, Chubb, and Friedman (1954a). In that region atmospheric mixing and diffusion must be operative.

7.2. The Downward Velocity of Nitrogen Atoms

A further insight into the behavior of nitrogen is furnished by the study of the time of recombination. Considering an atmospheric region where nitrogen is almost entirely dissociated $[n(N_2) < n(N)]$ and where there is maximum probability of loss, the time of recombination, $\tau_{\text{loss}}(\text{N})$, should be

$$\tau_{\text{loss}}(\text{N}) = \frac{1}{a_0 n(\text{M}) \, n(\text{N})} \leq \frac{1}{a n(\text{M}) \, n(\text{O})}, \tag{89}$$

or a time certainly not less than 1 year above 120 km. Thus it can be stated that, above 100 km, atomic nitrogen formed by the absorption of solar radiation at $\lambda < 800$ A does not recombine before a very long period of time has elapsed. Since molecules are not formed sufficiently rapidly, we are now in position to state much concerning diffusion.

Assuming, now, an N_2 atmosphere, the yield of nitrogen atoms is given by (41), and its vertical distribution is shown graphically in Figure 9. The velocity of diffusion is found from an equation of type (54), and, computing for an overhead sun, it is, at the production peak, by (55),

$$w^*_{\text{diff}}(\text{N}) = -130 \text{ cm sec}^{-1}, \tag{90}$$

which is a downward velocity of the order of 1m/sec.

The numerical results for the vertical distribution of the diffusion velocity, as obtained for the atmosphere of Table 1 and an N_2 atmosphere, assuming no N at the start, are shown in Figure 10. Considering, first, the upward velocities, for they seem to indicate a very rapid diffusion equilibrium above 200 km, we may conclude without doubt that there is a real vertical distribution of N, following Dalton's law, from 200 km up to the exosphere. Below 200 km (round figures) N moves downward, before a regeneration process leading to N_2 is able to act. The downward velocity should be approximately constant and of the order of 1 m/sec. Considering a constant zenith distance, this fall may be regarded as a downward displacement of the curve $\chi = 0$ below 160 km by about 5 km/hour. Even if this indication may be considered as only a first step because of the continuous change of $\partial n(\text{N})/\partial z$, it nevertheless predicts that, after production, N necessarily extends into the region of atmospheric mixing. It is obvious that this conclusion is compatible with much of the earlier oxygen evidence. Finally, the stationary N concentration will be in agreement both with a diffusion equilibrium, where it is effective in the atmosphere, namely, above 160–200 km, and with an atmospheric mixing distribution below 150 km and above 100 km. On the basis of this evidence, it is interesting to compute the time of diffusion of N in a mixed atmosphere. Results, which are shown in Figure 11, indicate the nature of the atmospheric effects. The time of diffusion would be less than 1 hour above 200 km and less than 1 day above 140 km. But at 100 km, where the time of diffusion

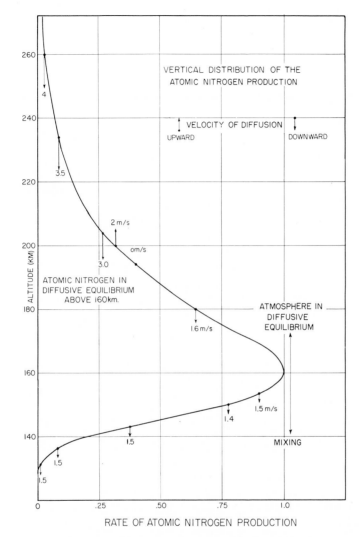

FIG. 9.—Production of nitrogen atoms in the thermosphere and instantaneous velocities of diffusion. The scale of the rate of atomic nitrogen production is normalized to unity at the peak (overhead sun) at 160 km. Below the peak, the diffusion velocities are almost constant and of the order of 1.5 m/sec, due to the form of the vertical distribution of the atomic production. Above the peak, the downward velocity decreases to zero at about 190 km, if no nitrogen exists in the atmosphere. If atomic nitrogen was already in diffusive equilibrium above 160 km, all the velocities will be downward, and their values will increase with altitude.

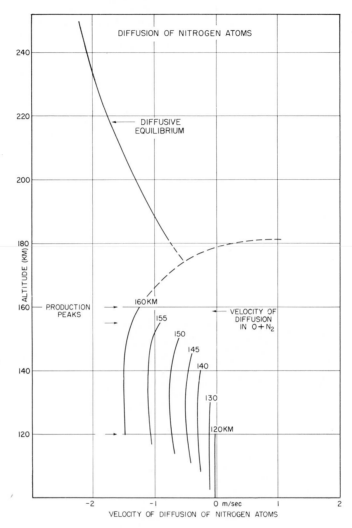

Fig. 10.—Velocity of diffusion of a nitrogen atom after photoproduction in a mixed atmosphere or an atomic nitrogen atmosphere. Below 160 km, diffusion velocities which are computed according to vertical distributions having production peaks at 160, 155, 150, 145, 140, 130, and 120 km, respectively, are almost constant over a range of heights of about 20 km, and therefore the vertical distribution does not change. However, the velocity, which is about −1.5 m/sec for a peak at 160 km, is almost zero for a peak at 120 km. This means that a production peak below 120 km is practically not affected by diffusion, but only by mixing.

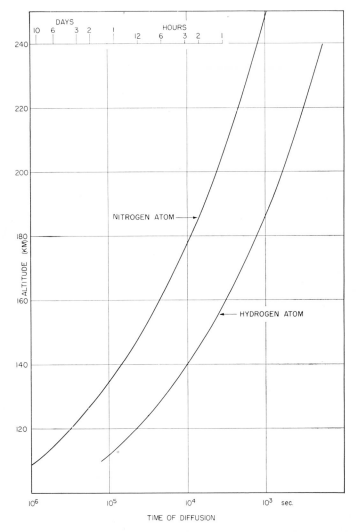

FIG. 11.—Comparison between times of diffusion of nitrogen and hydrogen atoms in an atmosphere in which the vertical distribution gradient is given by mixing. Hydrogen atoms reach diffusive equilibrium almost ten times faster than nitrogen atoms.

is more than 1 month, we have to consider mixing. It should be noted again that both mechanisms discussed—which lead to a downward transport—require that a competing process, such as recombination, play a minor role. Theoretical data permit such a possibility and thus the task remains of obtaining details of the various steps with respect to recombination into molecular nitrogen.

7.3. Nitrogen Recombination

The yield by the Herzberg mechanism is of the order of 1 nitrogen atom cm^{-3} sec^{-1} at about 120 km (Bates, 1952), but the transport from the sources situated above is more important. This continuous increase of N will be balanced by recombination. As we know from the N_2-N photoequilibrium studied by Bates (1952), the recombination of N is not necessarily direct but may occur through a preliminary step $O + N \rightarrow NO$, which prevents the diffusion of the atoms down to lower heights. A subsequent process like the following:

$$NO + N \rightarrow N_2 + O , \qquad (91)$$

leads to the final recombination. According to Bates's equations (cf. chap. 12), it may be seen that various times are

$$\tau_{loss}(N) = \frac{1}{a_0 n(M) n(O) + b n(NO)} , \qquad (92)$$

$$\tau_{recomb}(N) = \frac{1}{a_0 n(M) n(N) + b n(NO)} , \qquad (93)$$

and

$$\tau_{diss}(NO) = \frac{1}{J_{NO} + b n(N)} , \qquad (94)$$

in which $a_0 = 1.5 \times 10^{-32}$ cm^6 sec^{-1}, b is the rate coefficient of (91), and $J_{NO} = 10^{-7}$ sec^{-1}, the dissociation-rate coefficient of NO.

Detailed analysis of the times (92), (93), and (94) cannot yet be made, for the entire picture (chemical reactions and transport processes) is very complex. However, if it is assumed that the ratio $n(N)/n(N_2)$ is of the order of $\frac{1}{1000}$ at 100 km and $\frac{1}{10,000}$ at 180 km, then $b n(N) < J_{NO}$, so that the time of dissociation of NO would be of the order of 6 months. With a ratio of $n(N)/n(N_2) = \frac{1}{100}$, the time of dissociation of NO is given by the competing reaction (91). On this basis, it still may be concluded that diffusion will be efficient at 150 km. It seems that it is necessary for the ratio $n(N)/n(N_2)$ to attain about 0.1 in order to maintain photoequilibrium. It is evident, therefore, that NO formed by a secondary reaction, for which the equilibrium value would be $n(NO) = an(M)n(O)/b$, will follow the Dalton law in the atmospheric region where diffusion is generally operative.

In the region where atmospheric mixing is important, there will be various competing processes, so that the primary step will be difficult to establish. The data on atomic and molecular coefficients associated with atmospheric motions are so poor that further evidence for the simultaneous occurrence of both photochemical and atmospheric processes cannot be obtained. Further observations and experiments are necessary before the time of recombination of N below 100 km can be found.

7.4. Ratio of Concentrations of Atomic to Molecular Nitrogen

Excellent reasons have been given for believing that it is not possible to obtain a precise ratio of the concentrations of N and N_2. The role of NO as an efficient body for promoting the loss of N is predicted from Bates's results (1952), and it cannot be neglected in the final dissipation by N_2 recombination. Because the atmospheric motions lead to a departure from photoequilibrium, it is not possible to plot $n(N)/n(N_2)$ against height. However, a redistribution in height through the agency of atmospheric motions apparently occurs, and therefore it is possible to talk about the total number of nitrogen atoms in vertical columns above z-levels in the simple way called for by a normal distribution.

If the ratio $n(N)/n(N_2) = \frac{1}{100}$, the time for complete recovery of N_2 at 100 km would be of the order of 1 year. Since the yield of N is about 4×10^9 atoms cm^{-2} sec^{-1}, and the vertical transport leads to a column of $n(N)H$ atoms cm^{-2} (H, the scale height), we may expect a total production of atoms in 1 year of not less than 6×10^{16} atoms cm^{-2}, which corresponds to $n(N)/n(N_2) \simeq \frac{1}{100}$. Thus this ratio may be considered to be the maximum compatible with the adopted number of photons. The ratio would remain constant up to the diffusion region, where it would increase with height. However, a secular equilibrium cannot be accepted, and the preceding ratio is not precise, for the vertical transport does not cease at 100 km. If 90 km is used instead, the ratio $n(N)/n(N_2)$ becomes of the order of $\frac{1}{1000}$. Tentatively it seems best to adopt, in the region where mixing is operative, a ratio between $\frac{1}{1000}$ and $\frac{1}{100}$.

However, it is even doubtful whether the ratio can be constant. The ultraviolet radiation, which dissociates nitrogen produced by the action of primary processes like photoionization and dissociative recombination, depends strongly on solar activity. The production of nitrogen atoms will be variable, and the ratio of N to N_2 will also depend on solar activity.

7.5. The Airglow and Atomic Nitrogen

Since the discovery by Courtès (1950) of [N I] λ 5199 A in the airglow and especially in the twilight, observations by Dufay (1951, 1952) and by Nicolet and Pastiels (1952) (Fig. 12) indicate that a theoretical explanation of the line is very difficult (Bates, 1952). Because of diffusion, nitrogen atoms are only a small fraction ($\leq \frac{1}{100}$) of the molecules and are distributed throughout the whole thermosphere. The rate of formation of the

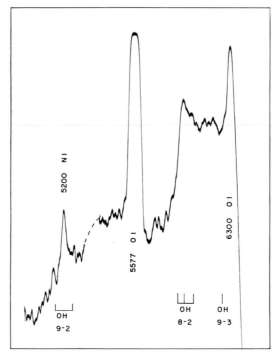

Fig. 12.—Airglow spectrum (twilight sun above 290–295 km) at Arosa, Switzerland, June 11–12, 1951. The characteristic twilight sodium line is not present, but the atomic nitrogen line is present, corresponding to an origin probably due to a dissociative recombination process of N_2^+.

excited atoms by solar radiation would perhaps provide an explanation if there were no deactivation process and if $n(N)/n(N_2) = \frac{1}{100}$. However, the [N I] line seems more easily observed during summer nights, and it is therefore uncertain that the preceding process of excitation may be used to account for its presence. If the dissociative process $N_2^+ + e \rightarrow N + N(^2D)$ suggested by Bates (1952) is really the primary mechanism, it will be interesting to take into account the downward transport of the excited atoms, since they can diffuse out of the volume element considered. The twilight and dawn airglow spectra should then be different, as they actually are.

Finally, the variation of N_2^+ bands due to some auroral activity when twilight airglow spectra are obtained (Fig. 13) appears to be correlated with the intensity of $\lambda\, 5199$ A. Judged by the N_2^+ twilight spectrum and by the dissociative process, the emission layer situated below 150 km is sufficiently well understood (Bates, 1949b). Since N_2^+ will persist only in an atmospheric region where the electron concentration is relatively small, it has a short lifetime in the F layer. But an increase of N_2^+ in a region of low electron density may lead to excited nitrogen atoms, an appreciable fraction of which could emit before suffering deactivation. Thus a careful and continuous investigation of N_2^+ and N airglow spectra might permit one to draw interesting conclusions on the dynamics of nitrogen in the thermosphere.

8. NITROGEN OXIDES

8.1. NITRIC OXIDE IN THE D LAYER

Nitric oxide was considered to be an important constituent of the atmosphere when Nicolet (1945) found the possibility that this gas might be abundant below the $O_2 \rightarrow O$ transition region. He noted also that the presence of this molecule is able to explain the ionization below 100 km; he considered that "the essential phenomenon in the D layer results from NO photoionization." This molecule, whose ionization potential is of the order of 9.5 eV, is able to absorb solar radiation of $\lambda < 1300$ A, for which atmospheric windows exist. In particular, it absorbs Lyman-α radiation at $\lambda = 1215.7$ A, which is very strong in solar flares.

Since this mechanism was proposed, Bates and Seaton (1951) have presented reasons showing that it is difficult to consider any acceptable alternative. From recent rocket observations Byram, Chubb, Friedman, and Lichtman (1952), show the importance of the Lyman-α emission in an atmospheric window. Because the emission in Lyman-α is not less than 6×10^9 photons cm^{-2} sec^{-1}, the rate of ionization of NO must be, after considering $K \sim 2 \times 10^{-18}$ cm^2 (Sun and Weissler, 1952), not less than 1×10^{-8} sec^{-1}. As we know that O_2 has an absorption coefficient at this wave length of about 2.3×10^{-21} cm^2 (Preston, 1940), we see that a ratio $n(\mathrm{NO})/n(O_2) = \frac{1}{1000}$ leads to an absorption of Lyman-α which is approximately the same for each molecule. If this ratio is less than $\frac{1}{1000}$, the vertical distribution of Lyman-α absorption will be governed by O_2. However, $n(\mathrm{NO})/n(O_2) > \frac{1}{1000}$ will yield the same vertical distribution of the absorption if $n(\mathrm{NO})$ follows the atmospheric distribution. Thus it seems that

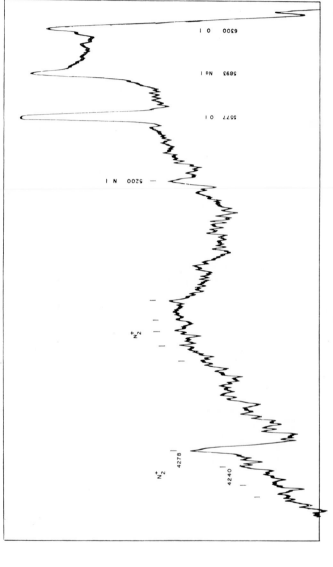

FIG. 13.—Twilight airglow spectrum (twilight sun at 70 km) at Arosa, Switzerland, April 13, 1951. The presence of a strong sodium radiation is the usual feature of a twilight spectrum at this altitude. However, the simultaneous presence of very strong N_2^+ bands and of atomic nitrogen lines indicates an auroral effect. An increase of N_2^+ ions leads to a dissociation of nitrogen molecules, yielding excited nitrogen atoms, able to emit the observed forbidden transition.

it is possible, using precise values of the NO and O_2 absorption coefficients, to find the ratio $n(NO)/n(O_2)$ by rocket measurements.

Much empirical evidence has recently accumulated, showing that the abundance of NO is low. At first it seemed that rocket spectra of the sun confirmed the presence of NO (Durand, Oberly, and Tousey, 1949); but the identification was later withdrawn (Johnson, Purcell, Tousey, and Wilson, 1954). Migeotte and Neven (1952) could not detect telluric NO in the infrared solar spectrum observed at the Jungfraujoch; this sets an upper limit at 5×10^{17} molecules/cm². Petrie and Small (1953) found no evidence of NO in auroral spectra. The absorptions shown in rocket spectra just below 2000 A (cf. **1**, 672) were shown not to be due to telluric NO (Johnson, Purcell, Tousey, and Wilson, 1954), which puts the upper limit as about 10^{11} molecules/cm³. Further, no influence of NO on solar Lyman-α can be detected: the level to which Lyman-α penetrates in the atmosphere appears unaffected by NO (Byram, Chubb, and Friedman, 1954*b*). Since the absorption cross-section of NO near Lyman-α 2.4 $\times$ 10^{-18} cm² and the ionization cross-section 2.1×10^{-18} cm² (Watanabe, 1954), something can be said about the possible NO concentration in the mesosphere. A value of 10^8 molecules/cm³ near 80 km or 10^9 near 65 km appears to account for the ionization rates required in the D layer, both in the presence and in the absence of solar flares. The fractional NO concentration of the atmosphere is then between 2×10^{-7} and 10^{-6}.

8.2. NITRIC OXIDE IN DAYTIME PHOTOEQUILIBRIUM AND ITS TIME OF DISSOCIATION

The recent analysis by Bates (1952) of the photochemical equilibrium of N and NO is important because it demonstrates the role played by the *oxides* of nitrogen in the physics of the high atmosphere. In the following discussion, Bates's results (cf. chap. 12) will be used without reference.

The general equation is, in photoequilibrium,

$$n(NO)\, n(N) = \frac{n(N_2)\, J_2}{b_1},$$ (95)

in which the rate coefficient b_1 is of the order of 10^{-17} cm³ sec⁻¹ at 200° K. Since $n(NO) > n(N)$ in the main part of the D layer, one may discuss the general behavior of NO, neglecting the slowest reactions.

The differential equation for NO may be written

$$\frac{dn(NO)}{dt} = -n(NO)\, J_{NO} - b_1 n(NO)\, n(N) - b_2 n(NO_2)\, n(O)$$
$$+ a_0 n(M)\, n(N)\, n(O) + n(NO_2)\, J_{NO_2},$$ (96)

where the rate coefficients are associated with the following reactions:

$$NO + h\nu \rightarrow N + O ; \qquad J_{NO} = 10^{-7} \text{ sec}^{-1} ; \qquad (97)$$

$$NO_2 + h\nu \rightarrow NO + O ; \quad J_{NO_2} = 5 \times 10^{-3} \text{ sec}^{-1} ; \qquad (98)$$

$$NO + N \rightarrow N_2 + O ; \qquad b_1 = 10^{-17} \text{ cm}^3 \text{ sec}^{-1} \text{ at } 200° \text{ K} ; \qquad (99)$$

$$NO_2 + O \rightarrow NO + O_2 ; \qquad b_2 = 10^{-17} \text{ cm}^3 \text{ sec}^{-1} \text{ at } 200° \text{ K} ; \qquad (100)$$

$$O + N + M \rightarrow NO + M ; \qquad a_0 = 1.5 \times 10^{-32} \text{ cm}^6 \text{ sec}^{-1} . \qquad (101)$$

The time of dissociation of NO (during the day), which may be written

$$\tau_{\text{diss}} (NO) = \frac{1}{J_{NO} + b_1 n (N)} ,$$

is of the order of 10^7 seconds in the region where the N concentration becomes small enough, namely, below the transition region in which the ratio $n(N)/n(NO)$ changes from a value exceeding unity to a fractional value. Thus it becomes clear that atmospheric mixing, as Bates (1952) has mentioned, prevents the full equilibrium of NO from being reached. In other words, NO in the D layer tends to follow the atmospheric vertical distribution, while N, moving downward, recombines. An estimate of the product $n(N)n(NO)$ based on equation (95) in full equilibrium will be changed, for the vertical downward transport of N affects the yield obtained from the Herzberg dissociation process.

8.3. NITROGEN PEROXIDE

As may readily be verified from Bates's equations (chap. 12) and values of rate coefficients (98) and (100), the photodissociation of NO_2 is so rapid during the daytime that its effect on the NO concentration can be neglected. The differential equation may be written, to a first approximation,

$$\frac{dn (NO_2)}{dt} = b_3 n (NO) n (O) - b_2 n (NO_2) n (O) - n (NO_2) J_{NO_2}, \quad (102)$$

in which $b_3 \simeq 10^{-17} \text{ cm}^3 \text{ sec}^{-1}$ denotes the rate coefficient of the association process,

$$NO + O \rightarrow NO_2 + h\nu . \qquad (103)$$

The time of dissociation of NO_2 during the daytime may be written

$$\tau_{\text{diss}} (NO_2) = \frac{1}{J_{NO_2} + b_2 n (O)} = 200 \text{ seconds} , \qquad (104)$$

because $J_{NO_2} > b_2 n(O)$. This is very short, and photoequilibrium will exist.

But during hours of darkness the ratio $n(NO_2)/n(NO)$ increases and tends to reach the equilibrium value,

$$\frac{n(NO_2)}{n(NO)} = \frac{b_3}{b_2}. \qquad (105)$$

The time to reach equilibrium, $\tau_{eq}(NO_2)$, defined by

$$\tau_{eq}(NO_2) = \frac{1}{b_2 n(O)}, \qquad (106)$$

indicates the extent to which the ratio $n(NO_2)/n(NO)$ can increase after sunset. In fact, $n(NO_2)$ approximately increases as

$$\frac{b_3}{b_2} n(NO)[1 - e^{-b_2 n(O)t}]. \qquad (107)$$

Thus the formation of NO_2 during dark hours depends primarily on the concentration of O.

From the spectroscopic studies of NO_2 (Norrish, 1929; Baxter, 1930), it has been found that fluorescence occurs in two bands between 6200–6400 A and 5600–6050 A. As the absorption coefficient of NO_2 is maximum near 4000 A (Hall and Blacett, 1952), Noyes and Henriques (1939) consider that the laboratory fluorescence occurs after a redistribution of energy in the vibrational levels through the agency of collisions. As fluorescence studies have been performed at low pressures (Baxter, 1930), corresponding to heights of 80–90 km, atmospheric fluorescence may also exist. Thus, when NO_2 is formed by a mechanism like (103), even if it is rapidly dissociated (within $\sim$200 seconds), it may be excited (cf. absorption coefficients as measured by Hall and Blacett, 1952), and fluorescence is possible. The two fluorescent bands just mentioned are in the spectral range of the sodium green line and the oxygen red line, which show twilight enhancement; thus there may be NO_2 fluorescence. This is true even if the process suggested by Noyes and Henriques (1939) is not accepted.

During the association process (103), a daytime airglow due to NO_2 should be intense near the mesopause level, where the O concentration is large and NO is abundant. The vertical distribution will be a function of the distribution of the product $n(O)n(NO)$ and will be subject to fluctuations and variations related to atmospheric dynamics affecting the concentration of O. Thus the whole problem of day, twilight, and night airglow depends on reactions involving O, N, NO, and NO_2.

In laboratory experiments, excited NO_2, produced by absorption of $\lambda > 3700$ A, can be expected to dissociate by the acquisition of thermal energy (Noyes and Leighton, 1941). In the upper mesosphere, it seems that dissociation of such excited molecules is very unlikely because of the low temperature. Thus it seems that the normal process of photodissociation occurs only at $\lambda < 3700$ A, while fluorescence occurs for wave lengths which are longer.

Finally, with a possible value of $n(O)n(NO) = 10^{21}$ cm^{-6} and a rate coefficient for (103) of 10^{-17} cm^3 sec^{-1}, a very high emission rate (10^4 cm^{-3} sec^{-1}) would be obtained for an airglow spectrum. Of course, there remains the whole problem of a transfer of radiation involving absorption of solar radiation, fluorescence or dissociation, and radiative formation with subsequent absorption.

8.4. Processes in an Oxygen-Nitrogen Atmosphere

8.41. *Atomic oxygen and ozone loss.*—At night, O can enter into various reactions which ultimately lead to O_2. Oxygen atoms will be removed by the following principal reactions:[4]

$$O+O+M \rightarrow O_2+M \qquad (k_1) ; \tag{108}$$

$$O+O_2+M \rightarrow O_3+M \qquad (k_2) ; \tag{109}$$

$$O+OH \rightarrow H+O_2 \qquad (a_1) ; \tag{110}$$

$$O+NO \rightarrow NO_2+h\nu \qquad (b_3) . \tag{111}$$

Thereafter, they enter into reactions with O_3 and NO_2,

$$O+O_3 \rightarrow O_2+O_2 \qquad (k_3) , \tag{112}$$

$$O+NO_2 \rightarrow NO+O_2 \qquad (b_2) , \tag{113}$$

while the O_3 and NO_2 concentrations are themselves governed by

$$O_3+H \rightarrow O_2+OH \qquad (a_2) ; \tag{114}$$

$$NO_2+H \rightarrow NO+OH . \tag{115}$$

In a pure oxygen atmosphere, the losses of O are due to O_3 formation (109) and O_2 association (108). Thus the O_3 concentration increases during hours of darkness (Bates and Nicolet, 1950), seeking to attain the equilibrium value,

$$n (O_3) = \frac{k_2}{k_3} n (O_2) n (M) , \tag{116}$$

but never exceeding the combined initial concentration of odd oxygen alone. When the free O concentration exceeds the O_3 concentration in the mesosphere, we may conclude that there is an increase of the mesospheric

---

4. For example, we do not consider processes involving HO_2 and other reactions which, though not negligible, require more activation energy.

O_3 during hours of darkness. This effect would be amplified by dynamic motions, which tend to increase the O concentration downward.

In the true atmosphere in which H, for example, affects the O_3 concentration by its catalytic action (Bates and Nicolet, 1950) O and O_3 diminish faster because of reactions such as (110) and (114).

8.42. *Hydrogen-oxygen and OH variations in the airglow.*—The mechanisms given in the preceding paragraph account for the limiting concentration of ozone, whenever the action of hydrogen (110) is considered. Equation (116) is now replaced by

$$n\,(O_3) = \frac{n\,(O)}{n\,(H)}\,\frac{k_2 n\,(O_2)\,n\,(M)}{a_2}, \qquad (117)$$

in which a_2 is of the order of $1.5 \times 10^{-11}\,T^{1/2}\,e^{-3/RT}$ (Bates and Nicolet, 1950) and equals 10^{-13} cm^3 sec^{-1} at $200°$ K and 5×10^{-13} cm^3 sec^{-1} at $250°$ K. It must be pointed out that k_3 values are, respectively, of the order of 3×10^{-17} cm^3 sec^{-1} and 7×10^{-16} cm^3 sec^{-1} and that $a_1 n(H) > k_3 n(O)$ when $n(H) > n(O_2)/1000$. Thus the total increase of $n(O_3)$ at night is not expected to be so great as in a pure oxygen atmosphere, because ozone is destroyed by the process (114), thus exciting the OH bands in the airglow.

Furthermore, assuming an equilibrium (Bates and Nicolet, 1950) between OH, H, O, and O_3, one may write the following equation:

$$\frac{n\,(H)}{n\,(OH)} = \frac{a_1 n\,(O)}{a_2 n\,(O_3) + k_4 n\,(O_2)\,n\,(M) + k_5 n\,(O)\,n\,(M)}, \qquad (118)$$

in which k_4 and k_5 denote the rate coefficients of the reactions

$$H + O_2 + M \rightarrow HO_2 + M \qquad (k_4)\,; \qquad (119)$$

$$H + O + M \rightarrow OH + M \qquad (k_5)\,. \qquad (120)$$

A general indication of the situation may be obtained from (118) if the estimates of the coefficients are not too far wrong; that is, if it be assumed that there is no difference between the day and night equilibria. Considering $a_2 n(O_3)$ to be the most important term in the denominator of (118), one obtains the following approximate equilibrium equation ($a_1 \simeq a_2 = a$):

$$\frac{n\,(H)}{n\,(OH)} = \frac{n\,(O)}{n\,(O_3)}\,. \qquad (121)$$

The relevant differential equation for hydrogen is

$$\frac{dn\,(OH)}{dt} = -\frac{dn\,(H)}{dt} = [\,n\,(O_3)\,n\,(H) - n\,(O)\,n\,(OH)\,]\,a\,. \qquad (122)$$

The catalytic action of hydrogen, which is now clearly evident, transforms oxygen atoms into molecules. It is as rapid as the airglow emission of OH bands. The relation

$$\frac{dn\ (OH^*)}{dt} = n\ (O_3)\ n\ (H)\ a_2,\qquad(123)$$

with $a_2 = 4 \times 10^{-13}$ cm^3 sec^{-1}, indicates, for an emission layer centered near the 65-km level $[n(H) = n(O_3) = 2 \times 10^9$ cm$^{-3}]$, some 10^6 photons cm^{-3} sec^{-1}, or 10^4 times more than the oxygen green-line emission.

The behavior of the OH emission is extremely complicated when all the equations are used, for it is difficult to be sufficiently realistic in the determination of the coefficients and, hence, in the discussion of time variations. It appears that the mechanisms of equations (117) and (121) show lifetimes between $\frac{1}{2}$ hour and 1 hour. Thus the concentration of O changes according to

$$n\ (O) = n_0\ (O)\ e^{-k_2 n(O_2) n(M) t}.\qquad(124)$$

One may say that during hours of darkness O diminishes to the initial concentration of O_3—$\frac{1}{50}$ to $\frac{1}{100}$ of $n_0(O)$—in 3–10 hours. Downward transport is probably not able to furnish a replenishment, and it would seem that photodissociation of O_2 is the primary source of O. As the dissociation rate of O_2 is of the order of 5×10^{-10} sec^{-1}, the yield is approximately 5×10^5 cm^3 sec^{-1}, or about 2×10^{10} cm^3/12 hours, enough to replace the needed supply. If a diurnal variation occurs in the OH emission, one would expect an intensity decrease at the end of the nighttime hours, particularly in winter. Actually, the principal variations should be seasonal and with latitude. Strong differences in intensity seem to dissipate rapidly, for not more than 1 hour is required to establish the dynamical equilibrium (121). However, fluctuations of less than 1 hour in the OH intensities can occur because of convection, which may result from the strong negative temperature gradient in the mesosphere below 75 km. Finally, temperature effects might be expected because of the importance of temperature on bimolecular reactions and because the OH bands will follow diurnal and seasonal variations of the mesospheric temperature.

8.43. *Oxygen and nitrogen oxides.*—Although theory and the constants employed suggest a slow variation for the OH emission, the atmospheric phenomena associated with the bands of O_2 seem to behave differently.

The airglow O_2 bands (Meinel, 1950) are similar to the O_2 bands obtained by Kaplan (1947) in laboratory afterglow spectra, and this fact has suggested that a common mechanism is affecting both excitations. Some oxygen molecules would be formed in the excited a $^1\Delta$, b $^1\Sigma$, and A $^3\Sigma$ states by three-body association. Further, because the observed bands of the Atmospheric system originate from the zero*th* vibration level only, an interchange of electronic energy would be necessary (Bates, chap. 12) as follows:

$$O_2\,(b\ ^1\Sigma, v' > 0)\ +O_2\,(X\ ^3\Sigma, v'' = 0)\ \rightarrow O_2\,(X\ ^3\Sigma, v'' > 0)$$
$$+O_2\,(b\ ^1\Sigma, v' = 0)\,. \qquad (125)$$

At first glance, bimolecular processes occuring in the chemosphere may play an important role, and one might question the existence of a common mechanism for laboratory and airglow spectra.

Among the processes already discussed, we may consider as a source for the excitation of the Atmospheric system the two-body process (113),

$$O + NO_2 \rightarrow NO + O_2\,(b\ ^1\Sigma)\,, \qquad (113)$$

which, in conjunction with (111),

$$NO + O \rightarrow NO_2 + h\nu\,, \qquad (111)$$

is very attractive, since NO has a catalytic action. Using Gaydon's (1942) data, the dissociation energy is $D(O_2) = 117.2$ kcal and $D(NO_2) = 77$ kcal, and reaction (113) leads to an excitation of 40 kcal. Since the excitation energy of $O_2(b\ ^1\Sigma, v' = 0)$ is 37.7 kcal and $O_2(^1\Sigma, v' = 1) = 41.7$ kcal, the process of excitation of Atmospheric bands of oxygen in the airglow would be explained by (113). An objection may be made if the dissociation energy of NO_2 is not 77 kcal but 71–73 kcal, as indicated in thermochemical studies. It is sufficient to mention here that 77 kcal corresponds to a photodissociation obtained with $\lambda < 3700$ A. According to Noyes and Leighton (1941), the type of predissociation at $\lambda < 3700$ A corresponds to a redistribution of vibrational energy without change of electronic state. Dissociation at $\lambda > 3700$ A is due to a few molecules having acquired large thermal energies. Furthermore, fluorescence of NO_2 may be interpreted according to the same ideas. Even if this interpretation should not be correct, the exchange mechanism (125), could be used for $^1\Sigma, v' = 1$ and 2. In any case, the role played by NO_2 in the excitation of Atmospheric bands of O_2 cannot be denied, for this reaction has a probability of 10^{-5} per collision at $40°$ C (Spealman and Rodebush, 1935); and (113) and (111) are related to the oxygen afterglow. Moreover, the conclusion just reached receives support from the fact that the behavior of the Atmospheric bands is predicted to be different from other airglow bands.

The concentration of NO_2, which is very small during the day, will increase at sunset according to the rate

$$\frac{dn\,(NO_2)}{dt} = b_3 n\,(NO)\,n\,(O)\,. \tag{126}$$

Thus, since $n(O)$ is maximum near the mesopause level, the yield of NO_2 immediately becomes appreciable. Furthermore, just below the mesopause, the concentration of O is larger than the photochemical value while $n(NO)$ is still increasing. Therefore, reaction (113), or the production of photons $\lambda\lambda$ 7600–8600, can begin. But, before reaching an equilibrium given by (105), $n(NO_2)$ must increase according to the relevant solution of the differential equation (102) in which $J_{NO_2} = 0$. Consequently,

$$n\,(NO_2) = n_0\,(NO_2)\,e^{-b_2 n(O)t} + \frac{b_3}{b_2}\,n\,(NO)\,[1 - e^{-b_2 n(O)t}]\,, \tag{127}$$

provided that $n(NO)$ and $n(O)$ do not vary appreciably. If a temperature of about 150° K is accepted, b_2 may be of the order of 10^{-18} cm^3 sec^{-1}. Such a value would require a concentration of O as large as 10^{14} cm^{-3} in order to reach an equilibrium during the hours of darkness. It seems, therefore, that the concentration of NO_2 must grow at a rapid rate in order to explain the airglow. Considering equation (126), we see that, 100 seconds after sunset,

$$n\,(NO_2) = \frac{n\,(NO)}{100}\,, \qquad \text{if} \qquad n\,(O) = 10^{13}\ \text{cm}^{-3}$$

$$= \frac{n\,(NO)}{1000}\,, \qquad \text{if} \qquad n\,(O) = 10^{12}\ \text{cm}^{-3}\,.$$

As such O concentrations are certainly of the correct order at the mesopause level, the NO_2 concentration becomes an important fraction of the NO concentration. Furthermore, the coefficient b_2 has been chosen with its minimum value and is sensitive to temperature; for example, $b_2 = 5 \times 10^{-17}$ at 200° K. The rate at which the equilibrium is approached also depends strongly upon the atmospheric region. Above and below the mesopause a temperature gradient is present, so that b_2 will vary.

When the presence of NO is considered in the ozone layer, the following reaction cannot be neglected:

$$NO + O_3 \rightarrow NO_2 + O_2\,, \tag{128}$$

in addition to (112) and (114).

The activation energy of (128) is only 2.5 kcal (Johnston and Crosby, 1952), so that this reaction is very rapid and competes with (111) in the atmospheric region where $n(O)/n(O_3) \leq 100$. At 200° K, the rate coefficient of (128) is of the order of 3×10^{-15} cm^3 sec^{-1}. Thus below 70 km, reaction (128) introduces an excitation of NO_2 leading to an airglow spectrum beginning at 5300 or 5900 A, depending on the adopted value of $D(NO_2)$. In addition, (128) should be added to (114), where this reaction becomes unimportant.

Finally, the presence of N and O leads to a formation of NO by a three-body association, the rate coefficient being of the order of 1.5×10^{-32} cm^6 sec^{-1}, according to Bates (1952). Because normal nitrogen and oxygen atoms cannot approach each other along an appropriate attractive potential curve, the available energy may be used to excite the third body. Since the third body is either O or N_2, the following mechanism:

$$\{O+N\}\,(Y) + N_2\,(X\ ^1\Sigma_g^+) \rightarrow NO\,(X\ ^2\Pi) + N_2\,(A\ ^3\Sigma_u^+) \quad (129)$$

is of interest, instead of a reaction usually invoked, such as

$$N + N + N_2 \rightarrow N_2\,(^1\Sigma) + N_2\,(^3\Sigma)\,. \quad (130)$$

Bates (1952) has discussed the type of process of which (130) is an example and has shown that it does not yield an observable intensity of the Vegard-Kaplan band system unless the N concentration is considerable. With mechanism (129) the process rate is increased, for it involves O. Nevertheless, other objections can be made, as Bates (1952) has indicated. If effort is made to find a possible mechanism for the excitation of Vegard-Kaplan bands in the airglow, attention may be drawn to the fact that (129) is energetically possible if $D(NO) = 149.6$ kcal (Gaydon and Penney, 1945). According to Herzberg (1950), the excitation energies of $N_2(A\ ^3\Sigma_u^+)$ are: $v = 0$, $v' = 0$, 142.2 kcal; $v' = 1$, 146.3 kcal; $v' = 2$, 150.3 kcal; and $v = 1$, $v' = 3$, 147.6 kcal. However, deactivation processes must be studied before determining the exact rate of emission of the Vegard-Kaplan bands.

Thus we suggest that the association $N + O$ be considered as the first process which may lead to an excitation of Vegard-Kaplan bands in the airglow, for it cannot be dismissed without careful investigation. With a rate coefficient for (129) of about 10^{-34} cm^6 sec^{-1}, $n(N_2)$ of the order of 10^{11} cm^{-3} or 10^{12} cm^{-3} would be sufficient.

On account of the approximate character of various laboratory data, the importance of NO_2 and NO is perhaps not so clearly indicated as could be desired. But the preceding analysis shows their leading role in the mesosphere and in the lower thermosphere, so that the importance of atmospheric transport phenomena leading to departures from photochemical equilibrium is plain.

9. ATMOSPHERIC MOTIONS

9.1. Introduction

By studying departures from photoequilibrium of ozone, oxygen, and nitrogen, some indication of vertical motions has been obtained. In the troposphere, the ozone content is primarily due to a mixing effect, and in the stratosphere ozone variations indicate that large-scale motions are responsible for the seasonal and latitudinal distributions. In the mesosphere, and particularly just above the mesopause level, rocket data on solar radiation cannot be explained by an oxygen photoequilibrium but indicate a departure suggesting vertical motions leading to mixing. At higher altitudes, in the thermosphere, where N_2 is continually dissociated, an effect such as diffusion transport explains the existence of N_2 up to the critical level. The loss of N and the formation of NO depend on the rate at which the photoequilibrium is reached, that is, on the importance of vertical motions in the lower thermosphere.

The onset of these motions above the mesopause level has not yet been described by a consistent picture. The motions in the high atmosphere cannot be studied as in meteorology, where the Coriolis force is dominant. In the high atmosphere one must consider not only motions as excited, e.g., by the actions of sun and moon, but also the effects of viscosity and thermal conduction. Also one expects heat transport to depend on various combinations of the three modes—convection, radiation, and conduction —according to the heights involved. Finally, it is necessary to postulate the presence of wave motions. Thus the dynamics of the high atmosphere requires an approach quite different from the theory applied to the meteorological atmosphere (cf. Chandrasekhar, 1952; Martyn, 1950; Little, 1951; Hewish, 1951; Yerg, 1951; Kellogg, 1952; Booker, Ratcliffe, and Shinn, 1950; Brewer, 1949; Goldie, 1950; Wulf, 1945; Wilkes, 1952; Jacchia and Kopal, 1952).

9.2. Photographic and Spectroscopic Methods

9.21. *Noctilucent clouds.*—Noctilucent clouds have remarkable characteristics (Vestine, 1933). Their mean velocity is of the order of 50 m/sec, and they attain 100 m/sec (Störmer, 1933, 1935). Their height is, on the average, very close to 82 km, and their drift shows a movement toward southwest and west. Their form changes rapidly and continuously, indicating nonuniformity of wind motions (Störmer, 1933). Occasionally, wavelike crests occur in the clouds about 10 km apart, indicating cellular convection regions near the top of the mesosphere.

The origin of these clouds is still being debated. Humphreys' hypothesis

(1933) of clouds of ice crystals formed around 160° K remains the most likely explanation. The coloration of the clouds suggests particle sizes of about 1 μ. This could mean either small ice crystals, of the type occurring in the Mars atmosphere in regions of similar temperature and humidity (Kuiper, 1952), or dust of meteoric origin. However, there is no apparent reason why the dust should occur very near the 82-km level or why it should form and re-form as do the observed clouds, or even occur in parallel wave crests. The temperature minimum now known to exist at the mesopause level gives a natural explanation of the clouds, although there is still some discrepancy in the measured and required temperatures at the mesopause. The clouds have been reported between latitudes 45° and 60°, which must correspond to some peculiarity in the general circulation and the upward flux of water vapor.

9.22. *Meteors.*—The visual or photographic observation of meteors and particularly the progressive distortion of glowing meteor trains show that the drifts are due to superimposed currents of various velocities and directions (Olivier, 1942, 1947). At intervals, vertical movements can be recognized in the atmospheric region between 80 and 100 km. Störmer's results (1939) on the meteor train of March 24, 1935, show the nonuniformity in the wind motions without doubt. A recent investigation by de Jager (1952) of the persistent train of Tchoucotte (October 15, 1941) indicates that, turbulent velocities having been deduced with a reasonable approximation, the spectrum of turbulence is followed in the Kolmogoroff region for large wave numbers and that, when deviations occur, they are in agreement with von Karman's predictions for smaller wave numbers.

Visual observations of distortions in the long-duration meteor trails indicate motions of irregularities which imply bodily movements of the air due to horizontal and vertical winds. One must note, however, that the light emitted by meteors as analyzed by their spectrum (Millman, 1935, 1949) consists mostly of the lines of atoms known in meteorites. The continuous spectrum is, in any case, relatively faint compared to the line spectrum. When lines of ionized atoms such as Ca II, Mg II, and Si II dominate the spectrum, they are due to the basic column of the meteor. But the spectrum of persistent train luminosity (Millman, 1950) shows low-excitation lines of neutral atoms, such as Na I, Mg I, Ca I, and Fe I corresponding to a recombination spectrum. These results indicate that the light of meteor trains is due to a spectrum of radiation produced by ions formed by the dissipation of the original kinetic energy of the meteor. Visual or photographic observation of distortions, therefore, must be associated with the lifetimes of ions.

9.23. *Aurorae.*—Störmer (1942) in his study of remarkable auroral forms from southern Norway has deduced motions in aurorae which perhaps correspond to horizontal drifts up to 200 m/sec. In a cloudlike aurora on March 24–25, 1933, situated between 80 and 125 km, the steady structure was moving with a velocity of the order of 200 m/sec over a distance of about 2°. Another cloudlike aurora on January 23–24, 1940, situated at 106 km, with a thickness of about 15 km, exhibited one motion in a westerly direction of about 700 m/sec over a distance of about 7°. At the same time a certain deformation of the outline of the aurora was found which indicates that the whole aurora had moved westward with velocities between 200 and 800 m/sec. Other measurements of motion have been made; e.g., a red patch situated at about 700 km during the aurora of January 25–26, 1930 was observed to be moving eastward over the Atlantic with a velocity of about 1700 m/sec.

These velocities deduced from drifts of auroral forms do not necessarily represent bodily displacements but may be thought of as a displacement of the aurora-producing agent associated with the lifetime of the excitation. Thus it is very difficult to separate the electrodynamic interactions by the auroral agent, the lifetime of the excitation and atmospheric motions.

9.24. *The airglow.*—When observations of airglow radiations like [O] λ 5577 A are made in order to study intensity changes of various parts of the sky, the isophotal plots show the presence of patterns (Roach and Pettit, 1951, 1952, 1953). Diurnal variations are marked by deviations in both time and place. Since there are different causes of excitation for airglow radiations, the emission layers have various heights, and it is not possible to investigate dynamical effects without complete observational data. For example, Huruhata (1952), studying variations in the infrared emissions between 8500 and 11,000 A (OH bands), assumed a height of about 300 km for the emitting layer. Taking 70 km instead, one finds that his estimated velocity must be reduced to less than 100 km/hour.

If the heights of emitting layers were known precisely, it would be interesting to compare the variations of the OH and O_2 emissions with atomic emissions. Atmospheric motions are important for OH and O_2, and this problem should be examined for atomic radiations. Much depends upon the, as yet unknown, excitation processes of airglow emission lines. Pure time variations may be assumed with no special motion or motion of the excitation patterns. In any case, the lifetimes of the "excitation clouds" must be known.

9.3. IONOSPHERIC METHODS

9.31. *Introduction.*—Space does not permit a description of all iono-spheric data relevant to the dynamics of the high atmosphere. Further-more, this task would involve a repetition of such recent publications as *Tidal Phenomena in the Ionosphere*, published by a subcommission (Mar-tyn, chairman) of the International Scientific Union (1952). Reference is made also to articles by Chapman (1951) and Wilkes (1952), who include atmospheric oscillations. The study of ionospheric winds and their dynam-ical explanation are still in their infancy, and a description of the mere facts would not be of general interest. Finally, the earth's magnetic field becomes of importance in the upper ionosphere because it constrains the motions of electrons and ions around lines of magnetic force; therefore, an electrodynamic interaction is to be included in the dynamics of neutral particles, along with the variation of viscosity and conduction effects.

9.32. *Tidal phenomena.*—The earliest attempt to find lunar oscillations in the high atmosphere from aurorae and meteors (Egedal, 1933) was fol-lowed by a conclusive analysis of reliable measurements of variations of *E*-layer heights made by Appleton and Weekes (1939). They found a lunar semidiurnal variation amounting to about 1 km above and below the mean equivalent height. If this oscillation corresponds to a movement of isobars (Wilkes, 1952), it implies a pressure-variation amplitude about 100 times as great as at the ground, if expressed as a fraction of the static pressure (cf. Wilkes, 1952, resonance theory).

Martyn (1947, 1948), McNish and Gautier (1949), and others also find lunar variations in both height and electron concentrations in the *F* layer. Because these variations concern electrons and ions, and not necessarily neutral particles, a dynamical theory involves electrodynamic forces. According to Martyn (1947), an interpretation should be possible, even if the air does not move at all, by assuming that electrons and ions are trans-ported as a result of electrodynamic forces. In any case, vertical electron motions depend on the electron lifetime, which will increase in an upward motion and will decrease in a downward drift. In so far as neutral particles are concerned, effects due to properties such as kinetic viscosity and ther-mal conduction are to be compared with those of eddy viscosity and thermal convection.

Even though lunar tidal variations may be isolated more or less easily, the solar tidal variations are intermingled with other solar variations, such as photoionization. Thus the equation of continuity is

$$\frac{\partial n_e}{\partial t} = \frac{d n_e}{d t} - \operatorname{div}(n_e V),$$

in which *V* denotes the electronic velocity. Computations have been made by Martyn (1947), Kirkpatrick (1948), Mitra (1951), and Weiss (1953) by considering various possibilities dependent upon the lifetime of an electron and the vertical distribution of the recombination coefficient.

There remains much work to be done, for a complete study of the ionosphere requires consideration of electrodynamic and hydrodynamic forces whose ratio depends on the altitude.

9.33. *Ionospheric winds.*—Evidence of the presence of movements in the *F* layer was reported by Beynon (1948), who found that, during the winters of 1942 and 1943, small changes occurring near the mid-point of a base line of about 1000 km were later repeated overhead. An average westward velocity of 120 m/sec seemed to explain the observations. Munro (1950), employing ordinary ionospheric sounding equipment at points separated by tens of kilometers, identified certain large-scale phenomena as irregularities in the horizontal distribution of the ionosphere. The average speeds of moving disturbances were found to be 130 m/sec in the *F* layer and about 60 m/sec in the *E* layer. In addition, reference must be made to Findlay's determinations (1953) of velocities of clouds of ionization in the lower part of the *E* layer. Most of these clouds are observed between 95 and 110 km. Velocities between 20 and 150 m/sec and the duration of the cloud echoes suggest average horizontal dimensions of roughly 700 m. Sporadic *E*-layer ionization also shows movements (cf. Gerson, 1951), which lead to drift velocities of the same order. In particular, observations made by Wells (1952) indicate velocities of 30–50 m/sec for cloud patches with dimensions of some 40 or 50 km.

Salzberg and Greenstone (1951), Phillips (1951), and others[5] have studied the magnitude and the direction (Mitra method, 1949) of the movement of the diffraction pattern produced by the reflection of waves of about 2.4 Mc/sec. The results show that reflection always comes from the *E* layer in the daytime. The distribution of velocities indicates wind speeds up to 300 m/sec, but generally in the range 50–100 m/sec. The winds seem to flow west in winter and east in summer. But there is a need for a world-wide program before one can obtain a complete picture of the diurnal, seasonal, and latitudinal variations. It seems, however, that vertical turbulence does exist and may be of the order of 1 m/sec. Such a value is interesting because it may be correlated with vertical velocities associated with tidal forces and explain phenomena such as departure from photochemical equilibrium by mixing, instead of diffusion, at 120 km. Using the same method, Wells (1952) found values of apparent drift

5. References in Salzberg and Greenstone (1951), Phillips (1951), and Millman (1952).

velocities between 160 and 320 m/sec for the F-layer irregularities, with size varying between 100 and 300 km.

At lower heights, namely, in the D layer, ionospheric investigation is possible only with a low frequency. Millman (1952) has studied the structure of winds with 150 Kc/sec equipment. His observations and an analysis of the D-layer data (Jones, Millman, and Nertney, 1953) indicate that the winds observed at 150 Kc/sec flow at about 75 km in the daytime and at 85–100 km at night. By considering changes in amplitude, Millman (1952) found that there is vertical motion which may be due to turbulence. Furthermore, even though the average wind speed presents little correlation with geomagnetic activity, the turbulence might be a function of magnetic activity. Finally, the fact that the measured winds flow at different levels during the day and at night suggest variations in behavior according to their location with respect to the mesopause level.

It is not intended to synthesize here all data on atmospheric winds and oscillations. If the movement of clouds of ionization implies a transport of ionized gas, it is necessary that the dynamical problem be related to the lifetime of an electron and to its mean free path. But it is also clear that (particularly in the lower ionosphere) ionospheric drifts, which are deduced from movements of inhomogeneities, must be studied with respect to the air motions.

9.4. THE RADIO ASTRONOMY METHOD

9.41. *Radio sources.*—A new attempt to investigate movements in the ionosphere employs the extra-terrestrial radiation from radio sources. It has been found (Smith, 1950; Little and Maxwell, 1951; Ryle and Hewish, 1950) that the fluctuations occur in these sources which are due to irregularities in the F layer. When measurements are made with similar recording instruments, spaced over a base line of a few kilometers, the time displacements of individual fluctuations recorded at each station are explained by the movement of electron clouds in the F layer.

The theory of the scintillation (Little, 1951; Hewish, 1951) shows that ionospheric irregularities produce a nonuniform distribution of radio intensity over the ground, and the analysis of the diffraction pattern allows the ionospheric behavior to be determined. The fluctuations are essentially a nighttime phenomenon, and the *fluctuation index*, which represents the degree of variability of the signal, is maximum around 01 hours. Its diurnal variation is remarkable: a start or an increase from 18–20 hours to the maximum and subsequently a decay to a small value at about noon. The "period" of the fluctuations varies by a considerable factor, but the average duration of an individual fluctuation is about 30 seconds. The "period" or rate of fluctuation seems to be associated with the magnetic activity, while the fluctuation index is not (Hewish, 1952; Maxwell and Little, 1952).

If the amplitude of fluctuations is unaffected by geomagnetic activity or the presence of aurorae (Little and Maxwell, 1952) and the fluctuation rate increases during strong magnetic disturbances, the interpretation of the phenomenon requires careful consideration. The observational data suggest that a change of the diffraction pattern cannot be responsible for the increase of the scintillation rate. Also a change in the average dimensions, which are about 5 ± 2 km, should not be thought of as the cause for the increased rate. There remains an explanation in which the velocity of the wind increases with the geomagnetic activity. Such a conclusion is not unreasonable when one considers that magnetic activity corresponds to a departure from atmospheric equilibrium. Before understanding the mechanism of increase of the wind velocity, one must know the origin of this irregular ionization distribution. In particular, it is not yet possible to explain by turbulence (Mills and Thomas, 1951) ionospheric irregularities which are largest around midnight, if a damping effect of solar origin is not introduced. Prompt reversal of winds still remains a difficulty when the general circulation is examined. However, because the physical properties of the upper ionosphere are not yet well known, it appears that world-wide observations of radio-source fluctuations (cf. Burrows and Little's results, 1952) will lead to knowledge which the usual ionospheric methods cannot provide.

9.42. *Meteors.*—From radio observations of ionization trails produced by meteors, a certain amount of information on wind velocities can be obtained for altitudes of 80–90 km, near the mesopause level, where non-uniform wind velocities must exist.

The trail of a meteor corresponds to a long, narrow column of ionization which may reflect energy from an incident radio wave. The theory (Kaiser and Closs, 1952) predicts two different types of meteor echoes, depending on the electron line density. There are *short-duration echoes* due to a small electronic concentration, which show a regular decay in amplitude due to the diffusion of a uniform column of electrons and ions. The *long-duration echoes* are due to total reflection from trails with very high electron concentrations, and they show fluctuations in their amplitude. The kinetic energy of a meteor is divided between heat, light, and ionization in the ratios $10^4 : 10^2 : 10$ (Greenhow and Hawkins, 1952). The ionization derives from both atmospheric and meteoric constituents. Since dissociative recombination plays the leading role for atmospheric constituents, it is effective before diffusion can act. But dissociative recombination and charge transfer cannot be operative for meteor atoms which have ionization potentials lower than those of molecules (NO, O_2, N_2). As a consequence, the effective recombination coefficient of meteor atoms depends on radiative recombination or attachment, and expansion of the trail is possible before recombination is effective (Kaiser and Greenhow, 1953).

The amplitude fluctuations which are observed in the long-duration echoes are caused by distortion of the column of ionization resulting from relative motion of various reflecting centers due to atmospheric winds, which cause the changing interference conditions (Greenhow, 1952).

Whenever the drifts can be accepted as a steady motion, it is possible to find directions and velocities of winds in the meteor region, at 80–90 km. Greenhow (1952) found winds similar in magnitude and direction to those deduced from measurements made by Manning, Villard, and Peterson (1950), but opposite in direction to those obtained by Mitra (1949), Salzberg and Greenstone (1951), and Phillips (1952). This difference is explained as an altitude effect. While ionospheric results apply to the E layer, meteor observations refer to altitudes of 80–90 km. In other words, the ionospheric measurements are made in the thermosphere, while the meteor data correspond to the neighborhood of the mesopause. Thus, since the trail distortion in radio echoes is not due to a uniform translation but to the degree of nonuniformity of the winds, the existence of turbulence is confirmed. The rapid changes in the speeds and direction of the uniform winds measured by Manning, Villard, and Peterson (1949) and deduced by Greenhow (1952) illustrate the extent of the nonuniformity of the winds at heights near the mesopause. For example, Greenhow (1952) found that wind velocities differed by more than 50 m/sec at points separated by 5–10 km.

In conclusion, at the mesopause level, meteors, ionospheric behavior, and airglow data indicate the leading role played by dynamic effects. It would be interesting to have simultaneous observations of meteor trails, of winds from long-wave radio observations, and of OH and O_2 emissions, in order to study the nature of the rapid changes occurring between the mesosphere and thermosphere.

REFERENCES

Appleton, E. V., and		
Weekes, K.	1939	*Proc. R. Soc. London*, **171**, 171.
Bates, D. R.	1949*a*	*Proc. R. Soc. London*, **196**, 217.
	1949*b*	*Ibid.*, p. 562.
	1952	*Ann. géophys.*, **8**, 194.

BATES, D. R., and
   MASSEY, H. S. W.   1947   *Proc. R. Soc. London*, **192**, 1.
BATES, D. R., and
   NICOLET, M.   1950   *J. Geophys. Res.*, **55**, 301.
BATES, D. R., and
   SEATON, M. J.   1950   *Proc. Phys. Soc. B*, **63**, 129.
BAXTER, W. P.   1930   *J. Amer. Chem. Soc.*, **52**, 3920.
BEYNON, W. J. G.   1948   *Nature*, **162**, 887.
BIONDI, M. A.   1951   *Phys. Rev.*, **83**, 1078.
BOOKER, H. G.;
   RATCLIFFE, J. A.; and
   SHINN, D. H.   1950   *Phil. Trans. R. Soc. London, A*, **242**, 75.
BREWER, A. W.   1949   *Quart. J. R. Meteorol. Soc.*, **75**, 351.
BURROWS, K., and
   LITTLE, C. G.   1952   *Jodrell Bank Am.*, **1**, 29.
BYRAM, E. T.; CHUBB, T.;
   and FRIEDMAN, H.   1954a   *Rocket Exploration of the Upper Atmosphere*, ed.
                              R. L. F. BOYD and M. J. SEATON (London:
                              Pergamon Press), p. 274.
               1954b   *Ibid.*, p. 276.
BYRAM, E. T.; CHUBB,
   T.; FRIEDMAN, H.;
   and LICHTMAN, S. W.   1952   *J. Opt. Soc. Amer.*, **42**, 876.
CHANDRASEKHAR, S.   1952   *M.N.*, **112**, 475.
CHAPMAN, S.   1930a   *Mem. R. Meteorol. Soc.*, **3**, 103.
               1930b   *Phil. Mag.*, **10**, 369.
               1950a   *J. Atm. Terr. Phys.*, **1**, 121.
               1950b   *J. Geophys. Res.*, **55**, 395.
               1951   "Atmospheric Tides and Oscillations" in *Compen-*
                              dium of Meteorology (Boston: American Meteor-
                              ological Society), p. 510.
CHAPMAN, S., and
   COWLING, T. G.   1939   *The Mathematical Theory of Non-uniform Gases*
                              (Cambridge: At the University Press).
CLARK, K. C.   1952   *Phys. Rev.*, **87**, 271.
COURTÈS, G.   1950   *C.R. Acad. Sci., Paris*, **231**, 62.
CRAIG, R. A.   1950   *Met. Mono., Amer. Met. Soc.*, Vol. **1**, No. 2.
DEBB, S.   1952   *J. Atm. Terr. Phys.*, **2**, 309.
DE JAGER, C.   1952   *The Optical Study of the Earth's Atmosphere;* re-
                              printed from *Mém. Soc. R. Sci., Liége*, **12**, 223.
DÜTSCH, H.-U.   1946   Thesis, Zurich (Zurich: Leeman & Co.).
DUFAY, M.   1951   *C.R. Acad. Sci., Paris*, **233**, 419.
               1952   *The Optical Study of the Earth's Atmosphere;* re-
                              printed from *Mém. Soc. R. Sci., Liége*, **12**, 141.
DURAND, E.; OBERLY,
   J. J.; and TOUSEY, R.   1949   *Ap. J.*, **109**, 1.
EGEDAL, J.   1930   *Inst. météorol. danois*, Com. No. 10.

FINDLAY, J. W.   1953   *J. Atm. Terr. Phys.*, **3**, 73.
FRIEDMAN, H.;
  LICHTMAN, S. W.; and
  BYRAM, E. T.   1951   *Phys. Rev.*, **83**, 1025.
FRITZ, S.   1951   *Arch. Met. Geophys. Biokl. A*, **4**, 343.
GAYDON, A. G.   1942   *Spectroscopic and Combustion Theory* (London: Chapman & Hall).

GAYDON, A. G., and
  PENNEY, W. G.   1945   *Proc. R. Soc. London*, **183**, 374.
GERSON, N. C.   1951   *Canadian J. Phys.*, **29**, 251.
GÖTZ, F. W. P.   1947   *Relations entre les phénomènes solaires et géophysiques* (Paris: Centre nationale Recherches scientifiques, 13 Quai Anatole France), p. 287.

GOLDIE, A. H. R.   1950   *R. Meteorol. Soc. Centenary Proc.*, p. 175.
GREENHOW, J. S.   1952   *J. Atm. Terr. Phys.*, **2**, 282.
GREENHOW, J. S., and
  HAWKINS, G. S.   1952   *Nature*, **170**, 355.
HALL, T. C., and
  BLACETT, F. E.   1952   *J. Chem. Phys.*, **20**, 1745.
HAVENS, R. J.;
  KOLL, R. T.; and
  LAGOW, H. E.   1951   *J. Geophys. Res.*, **57**, 59.
HERZBERG, G.   1950   *Molecular Spectra and Molecular Structure* (New York: D. Van Nostrand Co.).

HEWISH, A.   1952   *Proc. R. Soc. London*, **214**, 494.
HULBURT, E. O.   1952   *Physics and Medicine of the Upper Atmosphere* (Albuquerque: University of New Mexico Press), chap. iii.

HUMPHREYS, W. J.   1933   *Month. Weather Rev.*, **61**, 228.
HURUHATA, M.   1952   *Rept. Ionos. Res. Japan*, **6**, 31.
INN, E. C. Y.   1953   *Phys Rev.*, **91**, 1194.
INTERNATIONAL SCIEN-
  TIFIC RADIO UNION   1952   *Tidal Phenomena in the Ionosphere* ("Special Reports," No. 2 [Brussels: Secretariat of URSI]).

JACCHIA, L G., and
  KOPAL, Z.   1952   *J. Meteorol.*, **9**, 13.
JOHNSON, F. S.;
  PURCELL, J. D.; and
  TOUSEY, R.   1951   *J. Geophys. Res.*, **56**, 583.
JOHNSON, F. S.;
  PURCELL, J. D.;
  TOUSEY, R.; and
  WATANABE, K.   1952   *J. Geophys. Res.*, **57**, 157.
JOHNSON, F. S.; PURCELL,
  J. D.; TOUSEY, R.; and
  WILSON, N.   1954   *Rocket Exploration of the Upper Atmosphere*, ed. R. L. F. BOYD and M. J. SEATON (London: Pergamon Press), p. 279.

JOHNSTON, H. S., and
  CROSBY, H.   1951   *J. Chem. Phys.*, **19**, 799.
JONES, R. E.;
  MILLMAN, G. H.; and
  NERTNEY, R. J.   1953   *J. Atm. Terr. Phys.*, **3**, 79.
KAISER, T. R., and
  CLOSS, R. L.   1952   *Phil. Mag.* **43**, 1.
KAISER, T. R., and
  GREENHOW, J. S.   1953   *Proc. Phys. Soc. London*, *B*, **66**, 150.
KAPLAN, J.   1947   *Nature*, **159**, 673.
                        1953   *Amer. Scientist*, **41**, 49.
KELLOGG, W. W.   1952   *Physics and Medicine of the Upper Atmosphere* (Albuquerque: University of New Mexico Press), chap. iv.

KELLOGG, W. W., and
  SCHILLING, G. F.   1951   *J. Meteorol.*, **8**, 222.
KIRKPATRICK, C. B.   1948   *Australian J. Sci. Res.*, **1**, 423.
KUIPER, G. P.   1952   *The Atmospheres of the Earth and Planets* (2d ed.; Chicago: University of Chicago Press), pp. 388–94, 417–18.

LITTLE, C. G.   1951   *M.N.*, **111**, 289.
LITTLE, C. G., and
  LOVELL, A. C. B.   1950   *Nature*, **165**, 423.
LITTLE, C. G., and
  MAXWELL, A.   1951   *Phil. Mag.*, **42**, 267.
                        1952   *J. Atm. Terr. Phys.*, **2**, 356.

McNISH, A. G., and
  GAUTIER, T. N.   1949   *J. Geophys. Res.*, **54**, 181 and 303.
MAJUMDAR, R. C.   1938   *Indian J. Phys.*, **12**, 75.
MANNING, L. A.;
  VILLARD, O. G.; and
  PETERSON, A. M.   1950   *Proc. Inst. Radio Eng.*, **38**, 887.
MARTYN, D. F.   1947   *Proc. R. Soc. London*, **189**, 241, and **190**, 273.
                        1948   *Ibid.*, **194**, 429 and 445.
                        1950   *Ibid.*, **201**, 216.

MAXWELL, A., and
  LITTLE, C. G.   1952   *Nature*, **169**, 746.
MEETHAM, A. R.   1937   *Quart. J. R. Meteorol. Soc.*, **63**, 289.
MEINEL, A. B.   1950   *Ap. J.*, **112**, 464.
MIGEOTTE, M., and
  NEVEN, L.   1952   *Mém. Soc. R. Sci., Liége*, **12**, 165.
MILLMAN, G. H.   1952   *Ann. géophys.*, **8**, 365.
MILLMAN, P. M.   1935   *Harvard Ann.*, **82**, 149.
                        1949   *Astronomy*, **54**, 177.
                        1950   *Nature*, **165**, 1013.

MILLS, B. Y., and
  THOMAS, A. B.   1951   *Australian J. Sci. Res.*, **4**, 158.
MITRA, A. P.   1951   *J. Atm. Terr. Phys.*, **1**, 286.

MITRA, S. K., and
 RAKSHIT, H.   1938   *Indian J. Phys.*, **12**, 47.
MITRA, S. N.   1949   *Proc. Inst. Elect. Eng., London*, **96**, 441.
MOSES, H. E., and
 WU, T.-Y.   1951   *Phys. Rev.*, **83**, 109.
        1952   *Ibid.*, **87**, 628.
MUNRO, G. H.   1950   *Proc. R. Soc. London*, **202**, 208.
MYAKE, Y., and
 SARUHASHI, K.   1951   *J. Meteorol. Soc. Japan*, **29**, 347.
NICOLET, M.   1945*a*   *Inst. R. météorol. Belgique, Misc.*, No. 19.
        1945*b*   "Contribution à l'étude de la structure de l'ionos-
            phère," *Mém. Inst. R. météorol. Belgique,* Vol. **19.**
        1947   *Relations entre les phénomènes solaires et géo-*
            physiques (Paris: Centre nationale Recherche
            Scientifique), p. 35.
        1948   *The Emission Spectra of the Night Sky and Aurora*
            (London: Phys. Soc.), p. 105.
        1950*a*   *J. Atm. Terr. Phys.*, **1**, 141.
        1950*b*   *Ann. géophys.*, **6**, 318.
        1952*a*   *Ibid.*, **8**, 141.
        1952*b*   *Physics and Medicine of the Upper Atmosphere*
            (Albuquerque: University of New Mexico Press),
            chap. xii.
        1954*a*   *Rocket Exploration of the Upper Atmosphere*, ed.
            R. L. F. BOYD and M. J. SEATON (London:
            Pergamon Press), pp. 357 and 361.
        1954*b*   *J. Atm. Terr. Phys.*, **5**, 132.
NICOLET, M., and
 BOSSY, L.,   1949   *Ann. géophys.*, **5**, 275.
NICOLET, M., and
 MANGE, P.   1954   *J. Geophys. Res.*, **59**, 15.
NICOLET, M., and
 PASTIELS, R.   1952   *The Optical Study of the Earth's Atmosphere;* re-
            printed from *Mém. Soc. R. Sci., Liége*, **12**, 47.
NORRISH, R. W.,   1929   *J. Chem. Soc.*, p. 1611.
NOYES, W. A., and
 HENRIQUES, F. C.   1939   *J. Chem. Phys.*, **7**, 767.
NOYES, W. A., and
 LEIGHTON, P. A.   1941   *The Photochemistry of Gases* (New York: Reinhold
            Publishing Corp.).
OLIVIER, C. P.   1942   *Proc. Amer. Phil. Soc.*, **85**, 93.
        1947   *Ibid.*, **91**, 315.
PENNDORF, R.   1949   *J. Geophys. Res.*, **54**, 7.
PETRIE, W., and
 SMALL, R.   1953   *Canadian J. Phys.*, **31**, 911.
PHILLIPS, G. J.   1952   *J. Atm. Terr. Phys.*, **2**, 141.
PRESTON, W. M.   1940   *Phys. Rev.*, **57**, 887.
RAKSHIT, H.   1947   *Indian J. Phys.*, **21**, 57.

REED, R. J.   1950   *J. Meteorol.*, **7**, 263.

REED, R. J., and
   JULIUS, A. L.   1951   *J. Meteorol.*, **8**, 321.

REGENER, E.   1952   *J. Atm. Terr. Phys.*, **2**, 173.

REGENER, V. H.   1952   *Physics and Medicine of the Upper Atmosphere* (Albuquerque: University of New Mexico Press), chap. viii.

ROACH, F. E., and
   PETTIT, H. B.   1951   *J. Geophys. Res.*, **56**, 325.

                          1952   *The Optical Study of the Earth's Atmosphere;* reprinted from *Mém. Soc. R. Sci., Liége*, **12**, 13.

                          1953   *J. Geophys. Res.*, **58**, 73.

RYLE, M., and
   HEWISH, A.   1950   *M.N.*, **110**, 381.

SALZBERG, C. D., and
   GREENSTONE, R.   1951   *J. Geophys. Res.*, **56**, 521.

SMITH, F. G.   1950   *Nature*, **165**, 422.

                          1952   *J. Atm. Terr. Phys.*, **2**, 350.

SPEALMAN, M. L., and
   RODEBUSH, W. H.   1935   *J. Amer. Chem. Soc.*, **57**, 1474.

SPITZER, L.   1949   *The Atmospheres of the Earth and Planets*, ed. G. P. KUIPER (Chicago: University of Chicago Press), p. 213.

STÖRMER, C.   1933   *Pub. Univ. Obs. Oslo*, No. 6.

                          1935   *Astrophysica Norveg.*, Vol. **1**, No. 3.

                          1939   *Ibid.*, Vol. **3**, No. 5.

                          1942   *Geofys. Pub.*, Vol. **13**, No. 7.

TOWNSEND, J. W., JR.;
   MEADOWS, E. B.; and
   PRESSLY, E. C.   1954   *Rocket Exploration of the Upper Atmosphere*, ed. R. L. F. BOYD and M. J. SEATON (London, Pergamon Press), p. 169.

VESTINE, E. H.   1934   *J.R. Astr. Soc. Canada*, **28**, 249.

WATANABE, K.   1954   Private communication.

WEISS, A. A.   1953   *J. Atm. Terr. Phys.*, **3**, 30.

WEISSLER, G. L., and
   LEE, PO   1952   *J. Opt. Soc. Amer.*, **42**, 200.

WEISSLER, G. L.; LEE,
   PO; and MOHR, E. I.   1952   *J. Opt. Soc. Amer.*, **42**, 84.

WELLS, H. W.   1952   *Carnegie Inst. Washington Year Book*, No. 51, p. 78.

WILKES, M. V.   1952   *Quart. J. R. Meteorol. Soc.*, **78**, 321.

WULF, O. R.   1945   *Terr. Mag.*, **50**, 185.

WULF, O. R., and
   DEMING, L. S.   1936a   *Terr. Mag.*, **41**, 299.

                          1936b   *Ibid.*, p. 375.

                          1937   *Ibid.*, **42**, 195.

                          1938   *Ibid.*, **43**, 283.

YERG, D. G.   1951   *J. Meteorol.*, **8**, 244.

CHAPTER 14

The Earth as Seen from Outside
the Atmosphere

By CLYDE T. HOLLIDAY

Applied Physics Laboratory, The Johns Hopkins University[1]

1. INTRODUCTION

As a result of the many upper-atmosphere research programs (Smith, Rosen, and Bridger, 1947; Van Allen, 1948) that have originated since the end of World War II, man has for the first time been able to observe photographically (Holliday, 1950a) and by means of television (Moore, 1950), the surface of the earth from an altitude where the pressure is so low (Warfield, 1947) that, for all practical purposes, it may be considered outside the earth's atmosphere.

It is impossible to establish the date when man first began to wonder just how the earth might appear from above the heights to which he could ascend; this, no doubt, predates recorded history. However, we do know that some of the theories that underlie the use of metric photography today were investigated over two hundred years ago (Church and Quinn, 1948). There seems to be no detailed account of the first attempt to make photographs from the air. However, there is evidence that many different devices, such as kites, balloons, and rockets, were used to carry the cameras aloft, and one experimenter actually obtained a few successful photographs from a small camera carried by a pigeon (Reeves, 1927).

The crude rockets that were produced in the 1850's could reach an altitude of only a few hundred meters. But they were among the first devices used by the early experimenters, and today rockets are still among the most successful vehicles in high-altitude research. The rockets themselves differ only in detail, not in principle.

1. Work supported by the Navy Bureau of Ordnance, under Contract NOrd. 7385.

713

The first successful aerial photographs were made by M. Nadar from a captive balloon over Paris in 1856, and the earliest record of the application of aerial photography to military operations was the photographing of enemy fortifications from a balloon by Colonel Rénard of the French Army during the 1900 China campaign (Clerc, 1920). The first photographic record from an airplane was apparently made from a biplane, piloted by Wilbur Wright at Centrocellia, Italy, in 1909 (Reeves, 1927). Although aerial photography received its greatest impetus during World War I, it was not until the middle 1930's, when photographs were made from the stratosphere balloons "Explorer" (Stevens, 1934) and "Explorer II" (Stevens, 1935), that man was approaching an altitude that could be considered to be *outside* the earth's atmosphere. One of these photographs, made on infrared film from an altitude of 22.066 km, revealed for the first time the curvature of the earth on a photograph.

2. THE HIGH-ALTITUDE PHOTOGRAPHIC PROJECT

As the upper-atmosphere research project at the Applied Physics Laboratory (Fraser, 1951) made progress, it became apparent that a satisfactory method for determining missile orientation throughout its flight had to be found. The high-altitude photographic project was the result of this need for accurate missile-aspect data.

On October 24, 1946, V-2 No. 13 was launched at the White Sands Proving Ground near Las Cruces, New Mexico. This rocket carried a 35-mm motion-picture camera and made the first successful photographs at an altitude that gave a fairly true concept of the appearance of the earth from outside the atmosphere. From these photographs it was possible to deduce missile-orientation data of such accuracy (Fraser and Ostrander, 1950) that a high-altitude photographic project was proposed with the following objectives: (1) to determine missile orientations; (2) to make meteorological studies from the upper atmosphere; and (3) to investigate the possibilities of photographic reconnaissance from guided missiles.

During the next four years cameras were placed in German V-2 and Aerobee[2] rockets and in other missiles of various kinds. Many different cameras were used; however, the three basic types were 16-mm motion-picture, 35-mm motion-picture, and 10.16 × 12.7-cm aerial reconnaissance cameras. The choice depended upon the rocket and the type of informa-

2. The Aerobee rocket was developed for the Navy, under the technical supervision of the Applied Physics Laboratory.

tion that was needed. Recovery was made on 96 per cent of all cameras installed, and satisfactory data could be obtained from 98 per cent of the recovered films. Well over a thousand successful photographs were taken.

3. APPEARANCE OF THE EARTH FROM OUTSIDE THE ATMOSPHERE

It is difficult to visualize the appearance of the earth from outer space. Even after extensive travel over its surface, one would not possess a clear picture of the earth in its entirety. The rocket photographs show that the most striking impression of an outside observer would be the flatness of the earth's surface. The color would be very delicate pastels, predominantly blue-green and red-brown. However, the shifting clouds would indicate the presence of an atmosphere that would obscure some of the surface detail. The highest mountain peak and the deepest canyon would be but minor irregularities on the relatively smooth surface of the earth.

The greatest change in the appearance of the earth would nearly always be the result of *changes in the climatic conditions* (see Figs. 1, 2, 3, and 4). These four photographs, showing approximately the same area as seen from nearly the same altitude, were made at different seasons of the year and over different weather conditions.

Photographs such as these have been under study by the United States Weather Bureau. Composite photographs, made from a single rocket flight, offer the meteorologist a chance, for the first time, to study simultaneous cloud formations that cover at least 10^6 square miles (2.5×10^6 km²) of the earth's surface (Holliday, 1950b).

The photographs show how cumulus clouds often form over mountain tops, where the warm air, moving up the slopes, has carried moisture aloft, which then condenses around or above the colder peaks (see Figs. 4 and 5). Cloud "streets," long lines of clouds with clear gaps between, can be seen streaming across vast areas (see Figs. 4, 5, and 6). They move in the direction of the wind and may be caused by topographic features. Inhabited areas are clearly visible, especially in vertical and low oblique photographs such as Figures 6 and 7. Table 1 lists the technical data pertaining to the illustrations, while the legends identify the principal features.

Figure 8 shows an interesting profile of the terrestrial atmosphere. Since in the infrared the reflection by water is quite low, the light in front of the ocean just below the horizon is largely contributed by the atmosphere. Just above the horizon the path length in the atmosphere suddenly doubles, and the intensity will double also if the atmosphere in the line

FIG. 1.—Elevation 122 km; winter. The dark prominence in the right foreground is an ancient lava bed called "Mal Pais." Just above it are the snow-covered Jicarilla Mountains, with Carizzo Peak (9656 ft. = 2.94 km); and to the right the Sierra Blanca Mountains with Nogal Peak (9983 ft. = 3.04 km); Sierra Blanca itself is just off the photograph. Near the upper right corner are the Capitan Mountains (10,205 ft. = 3.11 km). Between the lava beds and the mountains is a railroad (Southern Pacific). The Sierra Oscura (up to 8732 ft. = 2.66 km) are center foreground.

Fig. 2.—Elevation 120 km; spring. Approximately same area as Fig. 1, but extending to horizon. Surface almost obscured by cirrus and cirrocumulus clouds. Note different cloud strata and formations.

FIG. 3.—Elevation 115 km; summer. Approximately same area as Figs. 1 and 2. Forest areas, covering high mountains, now are dark. Center right is the Lincoln National Forest; center and left edge (below center) the Cibola National Forest. Left, above center, the Santa Fe National Forest and beyond, into Colorado. Cumulus clouds are forming over the Sangre de Cristo Mountains (*top*) in northern New Mexico and southern Colorado. Note cloud masses trailing off toward east (*right*) from mountain peaks. Hazy horizon 750 miles (1200 km) away.

FIG. 4.—Elevation 112 km; fall. Approximately same area as Figs. 1–3. At lower right is Tularosa, 12 miles north of Alamogordo. The fine black line running upward from it is the Southern Pacific Railroad. Vegetation in the Sierra Oscura is still black.

719

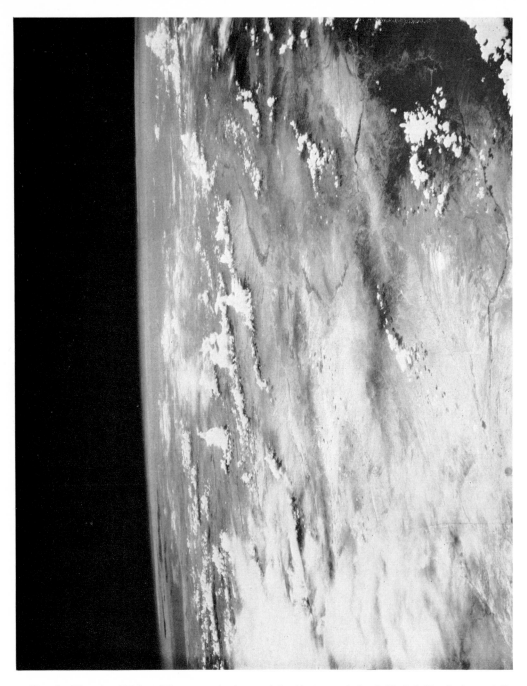

FIG. 5.—Elevation 104 km. (Please turn horizon up.) Looking toward the Gulf of California (*upper left*) and the Pacific Ocean. Note shadows of cirrus clouds on Pacific sea fog. Nearer, thunderheads are forming over mountain ranges, with cloud streets prominent near all mountains. The Gila River (*right of center*) flows from the Mogollon Mountains (*center foreground;* elevation up to 10,890 ft. = 3.32 km) to the Gulf of California.

FIG. 6.—Elevation 112 km. Looking east, from above Alamogordo (*below center, on the railroad*); Tularosa (*left center*); Holloman Air Base (*bottom center*); White Sands (*lower left*). Upper half shows Lincoln National Forest and the Sacramento Mountains near Cloudcroft. Sierra Blanca, 12,000 ft. (3.66 km), at upper left, below cumulus formation; mountaintop is above timberline.

FIG. 7.—Elevation 99 km. Upper Mesilla Valley along Rio Grande, with southwest up. Dark area along river is irrigated farm land. Las Cruces, New Mexico, is near center, in irrigated strip. Remainder is mostly desert land. Fine dark line, one-fourth from upper edge, is El Paso–Deming railroad. Numerous extinct volcanoes and several lava beds in upper quarter. Organ Mountains (up to 9012 ft.=2.75 km) capped by stray cumulus clouds in lower left; Florida Mountains (up to 7400 ft.=2.25 km) in upper right.

FIG. 8.—Elevation 125 km. (Please turn horizon up.) Looking southwest, toward the Gulf of California (*dark*), the Lower California peninsula, and the Pacific Ocean. In the Gulf one sees the islands Tiburón, San Esteban, San Lorenzo, and Angel de la Guarda. Punta Eugenia projects into the Pacific Ocean, with Cedros Island just to the north. A fog bank and a few cirrus clouds may be seen many miles out to sea. Snow-covered mountains in New Mexico, Arizona, and Mexico are prominent in the foreground. Earth's curvature visible on horizon over 800 miles away.

of sight is clear everywhere, because the phase angle of illumination is the same all along the line. This intensity jump is clearly shown in Figure 8. Above the horizon the intensity is expected to fall off according to the barometric formula.

Readers may wish to consult a map of New Mexico and adjacent areas for the identification and study of additional features. The *Official Road Map of New Mexico*, issued annually by the New Mexico State Highway Department, shows towns, roads, railroads, national forests, and principal mountain peaks. Elevation contours are found on the scale 1:1,000,000 *World Aeronautical Chart*, No. 406, and adjacent sheets, obtainable from

TABLE 1*

TECHNICAL DATA ON THE FIGURES

Fig. No.	Camera	Film	Rocket	Fig. No.	Camera	Film	Rocket
1.......	35	IN	A	5.......	F	P	V₂
2.......	F	P	V₂	6.......	F	P	A
3.......	F	P	V₂	7.......	F	P	V₂
4.......	F	P	A	8.......	35	IN*	A

* The letters in columns of this table have the following meanings:
35 = 35-mm motion picture, 50 frames/sec; focal length 50 mm; exposure 1/500 sec.
F = 4×5 inch (10.2×12.7-cm) film, 2 frames/sec; focal length 161 mm, used at F:8; exposure 1/500 sec.
IN = Eastman IN spectroscopic film and Wratten 29A filter.
IN* = same film, but Wratten 89A filter.
P = (Panchromatic) Aerographic Super XX film; Wratten 25A filter.
A = U.S. Navy Aerobee.

the United States Coast and Geodetic Survey. More detail is given on the *Sectional Aeronautical Charts*, scale 1:500,000, also issued by the Coast and Geodetic Survey, of which the Roswell chart Q-4 is of greatest interest here, and on the very detailed topographic maps.

REFERENCES

CHURCH, E., and
  QUINN, A. O.   1948   *Elements of Photogrammetry* (Syracuse, N.Y.: Syracuse University Press).

CLARK, W.   1946   *Photography by Infrared* (New York: John Wiley & Sons, Inc.).

CLERC, L. P.   1920   *Application de la photographie aérienne* (Paris: Octave Doin et Fils), p. 1.

FRASER, L. W.   1951   *High Altitude Research at the Applied Physics Laboratory* ("Johns Hopkins University Applied Physics Laboratory Bumblebee Ser.," Rept. No. 153).

FRASER, L. W., and
  OSTRANDER, R. S.   1950   *Photographic Engineering*, **1**, No. 4, 105.

HOLLIDAY, C. T.   1950a   *Photographic Engineering*, **1**, No. 1, 16.
                      1950b   *National Geographic Magazine*, **98**, 511.
MOORE, W. C.   1950   *Rocket-borne Television Camera* (Technical Note
                              No. 7) (Boston: Upper Atmosphere Research
                              Laboratory, Boston University), Part II.
REEVES, D. M.   1927   *Aerial Photographs, Characteristics and Military
                              Applications* (New York: Ronald Press), p. 3.
SMITH, C. H., JR.;
  ROSEN, M. W.; and
  BRIDGER, J. M.   1947   *Aviation*, **46**, No. 6, 40.
STEVENS, A. W.   1934   *The National Geographic Society–U.S. Army Air
                              Corps Stratosphere Flight of 1934 in the Balloon
                              "Explorer"* ("National Geographic Society Con-
                              tributed Technical Papers, Stratosphere Ser.,"
                              No. 1).
                      1935   *The National Geographic Society–U.S. Army Air
                              Corps Stratosphere Flight of 1935 in the Balloon
                              "Explorer II"* ("National Geographic Society
                              Contributed Technical Papers, Stratosphere
                              Ser.," No. 2).
VAN ALLEN, J. A.   1948   *Sky and Telescope*, **7**, 7.
WARFIELD, C. N.   1947   *Tentative Tables for the Properties of the Upper At-
                              mosphere* (N.A.C.A. Technical Notes," No.
                              1200).

CHAPTER **15**

Albedo, Color, and Polarization
of the Earth

By ANDRÉ DANJON
Director, Observatoire de Paris

1. THE EARTHLIGHT ON THE MOON

THE part of the moon's surface which is not directly illuminated by the sun is nevertheless visible during most of the lunar month. Its light is feeble, and observers have called it either grayish, bluish, or greenish. This faint light is the *earthshine* or *earthlight*.[1] Among the ancients some considered the moon as being phosphorescent, others supposed it to be translucent. Following Kepler (1604), the earthlight is now explained as being the second reflection of sunlight, the first reflection being by the earth.

The earthlight is easily observable between new moon and first quarter. Thereafter, its visibility rapidly diminishes, and a few days before full moon it can no longer be seen. A few days later it reappears, and it becomes increasingly visible toward new moon. By using Lyot's coronograph on the Pic du Midi, Dollfus has been able to see the earthlight closer than 38 hours before full moon (Lyot and Dollfus, 1949). He has been able to photograph it in yellow and red light when the phase angle was only 20°.

Since the earthlight comes from light first reflected by the earth, its study will enable us to obtain photometric, colorimetric, and spectroscopic data concerning the earth, which can then be compared with the other planets; even the polarization of the earth's light may be deduced.

1. The French term is *lumière cendrée* or *ashen light*. In this translation of the French original the word *earthlight* has been used in analogy with *moonlight*, caused entirely similarly. *Earthshine* might suggest something rather brighter than the at times extremely dim source here described. — *Editor.*

Some useful meteorological information on the cloud cover of the earth can also be obtained in this manner. Thus the study of the earthlight is important; but its difficulty is such that few investigations have been made so far. The part of the moon illuminated by the earthlight is very faint compared with the sunlit part. Some of the light of the sunlit crescent is scattered by our atmosphere or diffracted in the telescope. The photometer or the spectrograph receives both light from the earthlight and scattered and diffracted light coming from the crescent. This is the main difficulty in the study of the earthlight, a difficulty which is also encountered in studies of the partially eclipsed moon.

The following remarks show how the visibility of the earthlight varies in the course of a synodic month. Let λ be the phase angle of the moon as seen from the center of the earth and τ the phase angle of the earth as seen from the center of the moon. If σ is the heliocentric angle between earth and moon, then τ is found from the equation

$$\tau = 180° - (\lambda + \sigma) \ .$$

Since σ never exceeds 9 minutes of arc, the selenocentric phase angle of the earth is always nearly equal to the supplement of the geocentric phase angle of the moon. The earthlight is therefore at its maximum at new moon. Soon thereafter the lunar crescent is narrow and faint, and the scattered and diffracted light is weak. The earthlight is then strongly visible. A little before or after full moon, on the other hand, the earthlight results from a very narrow earth crescent, while the scattered and diffracted light is very strong. The earthlight is then as difficult to observe as the corona outside eclipse, and the use of the coronograph becomes necessary. For these observations one needs, besides, a very clear sky, even at new moon, while a high altitude of the observatory is a great advantage.

2. PHOTOMETRY OF THE EARTHLIGHT

Three principal methods have been used: the brightness of the earthlight is compared with that of (a) an adjustable artificial light-source; (b) the crescent, by means of a photometer with two separated fields; (c) the crescent, but with a double-image photometer with superimposed fields.

a) Comparison with an artificial source has the advantage that one does not need to know the light-curve of the moon. There is the disadvantage that a large correction for atmospheric absorption is required when the moon is at low altitude. Furthermore, the measures give the sum of the earthlight and the illuminated sky superimposed on it. As has been stated, this excess illumination is due to scattering and diffraction of the crescent's light by our atmosphere and in the observing instrument, respectively. In Very's (1912, 1913) observations (see also Russell, 1916) the sky brightness was, on the average, 1.3 times, and once even 10 times, as bright as the earthlight. It is therefore essential that the brightness of the sky be measured and applied as a correction to the observations. However, such a measure cannot be made on the moon's disk itself. The brightness of the scattered and diffracted light varies with the location of the point of observation on the crescent. The law of this variation is complicated, since diffraction causes luminous rings around the crescent. However, continuity requires the sky brightness to be nearly the same at two points close together, one inside and the other outside the disk. Only at the rim of the disk is it therefore possible to determine the correction with precision.

b) Comparison of the earthlight with the sunlit crescent requires only differential atmospheric correction, which is always very small and may be made zero, even near the horizon, if portions of the moon at the same altitude are compared. But the light-curve of the moon has to be known before the measures can be reduced to a definite system.

If this comparison is made with a photometer with separated fields, one illuminated by the earthlight and the other by the crescent, further measures of the sky background are necessary in order to correct for it, as under method a. The same correction has to be applied if the photometry is done photographically. E. S. King's (1924) photographic measures appear to be strongly affected by the light of the crescent, since they would indicate that the earthlight intensities increase as the lunar phase angle, λ, decreases, which is not possible.

c) The correction for sky background can be eliminated through the use of the double-image photometer in which the fields are superimposed. In this type of photometer one sees in the same field two images of the moon, one of controllable intensity. If the images are arranged in such a manner that, as indicated in Figure 1, region B of the crescent of one image touches region A of the earthlight of the other image, the scattered or diffracted light affects both regions A and B identically. If the intensity of B is reduced to that of A, the equality thus obtained is not affected by the superimposed light. Atmospheric effects of scattering and extinction are also eliminated.

Regions A and B have to be chosen on the moon's limb so as to be on the same diameter, and they should, as far as possible, have the same physical appearance. In view of the libration, it would be more advantageous to choose spots in the center of the disk, which would present them-

selves nearly the same way at each lunation. But the necessity for eliminating the sky background requires the use of regions near the limb.

Method c was used the first time in 1850 by Arago (1856) and Laugier
with a double-image Arago photometer in which the fields were superimposed. It consisted of an objective and an eyepiece, a double refracting
Rochon prism, and a rotating Nicol polarizer. It operated like the photometer later used by E. C. Pickering in stellar photometry.

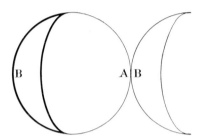

FIG. 1.—Juxtaposition of two images

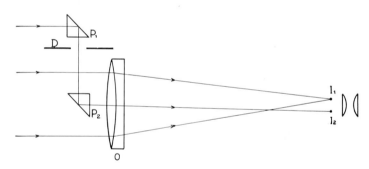

FIG. 2.—Schematic diagram of the cat-eye photometer

During the years 1926–1935, Danjon (1928, 1936) secured 207 photometric measures of the earthlight by this method, but he used his "cat-
eye" photometer (see Fig. 2). Image I_1 of A comes directly from the
objective O, while the reduced image I_2 of B comes in after two reflections
by right-angle prisms, P_1 and P_2, between which is located a square
adjustable diaphragm D, the "cat eye." One can also turn one or both of
the prisms by 180° and thereby replace total reflection by reflection on the
glass surface. The photometer is calibrated by a rotating sector in front of
a constant light-source. One of the lunar spots A and B is located between Mare Crisium and Mare Fecunditatis, the other between Oceanus

Procellarum and Mare Orientalis. These two regions have the same appearance at full moon.

The cat-eye photometer gives the ratio E/C of the regions A and B, E corresponding to the earthlight and C to the crescent. This ratio is expressed in stellar magnitudes, $M = 2.5 \log C/E$, and reduced to the mean distance of the moon. It does not depend on the distance of the

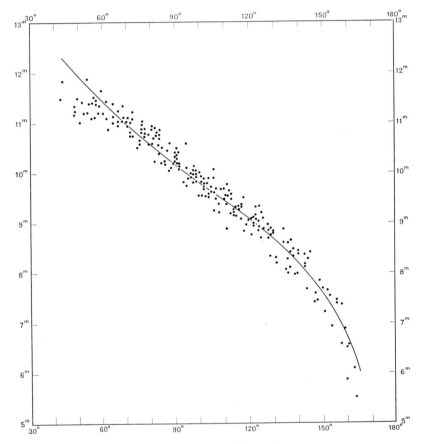

FIG. 3.—*Abscissae*, phase angle λ of the moon; *ordinates*, brightness ratio, expressed in magnitudes, of regions A (earthlight) and B (sunlit crescent). Uncorrected results.

sun. Figure 3 shows the values of M not corrected for distance as a function of the moon's phase angle. After the distance correction is applied, the mean residual of the points from the average curve is found to be ± 0.15 mag.

The brightness C varies with the phase angle λ. Before the earth's light-curve can be found, the variation of C must be determined. For this Danjon used a second double-image photometer, by which the brightness of region B of the crescent was compared to that of the sun. The sun's image was cut down by a photometric wedge. Sixty measures were made between 1930 and 1934 for values of λ ranging from $11°$ to $156°$, partly before and partly after full moon. The brightness S for the full moon was obtained by extrapolation. Thus was found the ratio C/S of the region utilized for phase angles λ and zero respectively. Finally, the product of

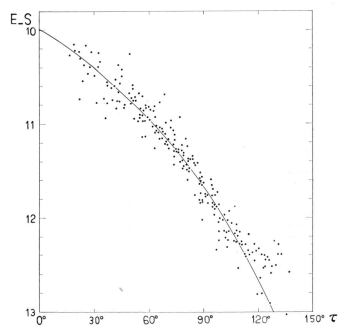

Fig. 4.—*Abscissae*, phase angle τ of the earth; *ordinates*, magnitude difference (as seen from the moon) between earth and sun. Corrected to mean distances and for seasonal variations.

the ratios E/C and C/S, expressed in magnitudes, gave the difference $E-S$ of the selenocentric magnitudes of the sun and the earth, the phase angle of the earth being $\tau = 180° - \lambda$. The results are shown in Figure 4. The measures, averaged in $10°$ intervals, give the results found in Table 1. In this table morning and evening observations have been combined. Galileo, Hevelius, and others thought that the morning earthlight was brighter than the evening one. This is an illusion resulting from the unequal distribution of bright and dark markings on the moon. There are indications of seasonal changes, but none is permanent.

3. THE ALBEDO OF THE EARTH AND ITS
SEASONAL CHANGES

The following formula gives a good approximation of the difference $E-S$ as a function of the earth's phase angle, τ, expressed in degrees:

$$E - S = 9.99 + 1.30 \left(\frac{\tau}{100}\right) + 0.19 \left(\frac{\tau}{100}\right)^2 + 0.48 \left(\frac{\tau}{100}\right)^3. \quad (1)$$

However, the last two values in Table 1 give large residuals, -0.52 and -0.65. Also, Figure 4 shows that, for $\tau > 110°$, most of the observed points lie above the computed curve. For such phase angles, the earth as seen from the moon appears as a narrow crescent. The corresponding region of the earth's surface is a spindle less than $50°$ wide. It should be noted, however, that measures at that time are very difficult to make,

TABLE 1

PHASE-CURVE OF THE EARTH

τ	$E-S$	n	τ	$E-S$	n
18.6......	10.21	3	85.5....	11.55	29
25.6......	10.35	9	95.7....	11.85	21
35.6......	10.59	8	105.2....	12.14	20
44.3......	10.65	15	115.0....	12.36	14
54.9......	10.85	23	123.3....	12.78	3
65.2......	11.06	21	125.2*...	12.45*	12
75.0......	11.27	24	133.4*...	12.54*	5

* See text.

owing to the faintness of the earthlight, and they might be affected by systematic errors. The measures of Table 1, as well as those of Dubois (1942, 1943, 1944, 1947), which confirm and supplement this table, were obtained in France. Fritz (1949) remarks rightly that these data do not necessarily apply to the earth as a whole. New measures made at very different longitudes are therefore necessary.

With this reservation, the data of Table 1 can be used for computing the mean visual albedo of the earth. This albedo, following Bond, is defined as follows. Let a sphere be exposed to parallel light. Then its albedo, A, is the ratio of the whole amount of light reflected by the sphere to the whole amount incident upon it. The brightness of a planet at a given phase angle, τ, is given by an expression of the form (1). The frequency of occurrence of τ in a uniform spherical distribution is $\sin \tau \, d\tau$. Therefore, the total brightness, found by integration over all values of τ, is an integral composed of two parts: one over the constant part of (1) and one over the part containing powers of τ, both with the weight factor $\sin \tau \, d\tau$. The second part is called the *phase integral*. For the earth the phase integral is 1.095, as derived from (1).

The magnitude difference of earth and sun at unit distance is $9.99 +$ $12.95 = 22.94$, if $8''.80$ is used for the solar parallax. Hence,

Visual albedo of earth, $A_{\text{vis}} = 0.40$.

This value is independent of the magnitude adopted for the sun. It is slightly different from the value of 0.39 given by the author in 1936, because the phase function was then taken to be uneven, while there is no reason to make this hypothesis. The phase function used here is the result of a new reduction.

The question remains whether the coefficients of the phase function represented by equation (1) vary in the course of a year. The measures by

TABLE 2

MONTHLY AVERAGES OF THE MAGNITUDE OF FULL EARTH

Month	Moon Increasing	Moon Decreasing	Month	Moon Increasing	Moon Decreasing
January.....	10.00	9.84	July.......	10.24	10.16
February....	9.89	....	August.....	10.24	10.16
March.......	9.94	....	September..	10.14	10.15
April........	9.97	....	October....	9.73	10.07
May........	9.98	....	November..	9.80	10.13
June........	9.99	9.92	December..	9.96	9.89

Danjon and Dubois are not sufficient to decide this matter. If the coefficients are assumed to be constant, each observation gives a value of the magnitude of the full earth ($\tau = 0$). When these values are examined, they show seasonal variations from the mean of 9.99. Arranged by months, the averages, according to Danjon's measures, are those found in Table 2.

The earthlight varies in the opposite sense as the numbers in Table 2. The earth therefore shows maximum intensity from March to June, minimum for July to September, and another maximum in October and November. The observations by Dubois made in France from 1940 to 1945 confirm these results and supplement them for the decreasing moon.

It is very probable that these seasonal changes are accompanied by changes in the coefficients of the phase function, which, in turn, should cause a change in the phase integral itself. However, since we have no precise information on this point, the best we can do is to suppose that the integral is constant at the value of 1.095. The extreme values in

Table 2, namely, 9.73 and 10.24, will then give 0.52 and 0.32 as the limits between which the earth's visual albedo varies. The first value then occurs in October, the second in July.

The variations of the albedo are unquestionably related to meteorological phenomena. Fritz (1949) made an interesting study in an effort to evaluate the mean albedo for the entire earth. According to this author, the mean albedo would be 0.04 less than the value deduced from observations made in France. The new reduction by Danjon would then make the *mean albedo* 0.36. It would be of great interest to verify this result by observations in other regions. Fritz correctly states: "Since Danjon's measurements were made in France, the Pacific Ocean area would not contribute to his measurements. Secondly, the latitudinal variation of cloudiness and of land and water surface might affect the calculations somewhat. This would also be true of the fact that the projected area of clouds as seen from the sun would not be exactly the same as the cloudiness reported by an observer on the earth's surface in regions of high airmass."

Fritz tries to establish how the light of the earth is derived from the various scattering layers. He examines various hypotheses, one of which gives the following distribution: light scattered by the ground contributes about 2.3 per cent; the atmosphere above the ground or above clouds, about 9 per cent; and the clouds themselves, a little over 23 per cent. Other hypotheses lead to slightly different values. It is noted that scattering by the ground is only a small part of the total. For an outside observer the details on the surface of the earth in visual light would show very little contrast (cf. also chap. 14). On the other hand, Fritz estimates that the albedo of clouds alone is about 0.5. Since we have found a maximum of 0.52 for the earth's albedo, this appears to confirm Fritz's result. Compare also chapter 7, Section 1.2, for a fuller discussion of the terrestrial observations of scattering and reflection; the mean albedo there derived is also 0.36.

4. COLORIMETRY OF THE EARTHLIGHT AND THE EARTH

Some observers call the earthlight bluish-green, others olive-green (Arago, 1856). The measures with the cat-eye photometer give more precise information. When the brightness of spots A and B is made equal, it becomes easy to compare the colors (Danjon, 1936, p. 171): *the earthlight then appears bluish*, while the crescent looks reddish. If the images are examined through color filters it appears that the visibility of the earthlight remains good in blue light, although the light scattered by the atmosphere is then quite strong. Hence it is relatively easy to photograph the earthlight, even when it is faint (Janssen, 1881). At the Flammarion Observatory (Juvisy, France; altitude 92 m), Quénisset has obtained very good negatives of the earthlight for phase angles of the earth up to 138° (Danjon, 1936).

The color of the earthlight undergoes *seasonal* and *random* variations, and these changes accompany those in intensity. For the seasonal changes there is the simple law that the brighter the earthlight, the bluer it is. The opposite seems to be true for the random changes.

Let Δ be the seasonal fluctuation of the earthlight, being the excess of the difference $E-S$ over its mean value of the corresponding phase; Δ is negative when the earthlight is brighter than its mean value and positive in the opposite case. A new reduction of Danjon's (1936, p. 171) measures gives the following results for $E-S$:

$$\text{Red} - \text{visual} = 0.26 - 0.27\Delta ,$$

$$\text{Visual} - \text{blue} = 0.31 - 0.7\Delta .$$

This gives the correlation between the color of the earthlight and its seasonal fluctuations in brightness. By a slight extrapolation, we may reduce these values of $E-S$ to the standard color-index interval of wave length:

$$\text{Visual} - \text{photographic} = 0.42 - 1.2\Delta \qquad (E - S) .$$

According to Rougier (1937) the color index of the moon is 1.10 in a system in which the color index of the sun is 0.79. We then find, for the earthlight,

$$\text{C.I.} = + 0.68 + 1.2\Delta \qquad \text{(earthlight)} .$$

In October, when $\Delta = -0.26$, the color index comes out only $+0.37$. In July–August, when $\Delta = 0.25$, it reaches $+0.98$.

The color index of the earth itself is obtained from the difference $E-S$ combined with the index of the sun. If we again adopt 0.79 for the latter, we have for the earth:

$$\text{C.I.} = + 0.37 + 1.2\Delta \qquad \text{(earth)} .$$

This index varies between $+0.06$ (October) and $+0.67$ (July–August). These values apply to regions of the earth which illuminate the moon during observations made from France.

Random changes in the earthlight are seen in France generally a few days before full moon, when the section of the earth illuminating the moon is reduced to a spindle that includes the Atlantic Ocean. Appreciable increases in the brightness of the earthlight are often seen then, probably because of clouds; but these increases do not reduce the color index— quite the opposite. This is well shown by Danjon's observation of February 24, 1931 (Danjon, 1936, p. 177). One might account for these results by assuming that the random changes are due to increases in the reflection by clouds over the North Atlantic Ocean and that the seasonal variations are due to fluctuations in the scattering by very small particles suspended in the atmosphere. The color effects of these two mechanisms would then be different.

This problem should be studied by spectroscopic methods. If the altitude of the scattering layer varies, there will be corresponding variations in the strength of the telluric lines of the earthlight. Such observations have never been made, despite their meteorological interest.

5. POLARIZATION

Lyot and Dollfus (1949) have studied the polarization of the earthlight by means of the coronograph of the Pic du Midi in conjunction with a new polariscope. They concluded that there is strong polarization, 1.2 times as much over the dark "seas" as over the brighter regions; it reaches maximum when the moon's phase angle is near 80° and then exceeds 10 per cent for the "seas"; the plane of polarization is parallel to the plane passing through the sun. The authors explain these results as follows: light scattered by the earth will be strongly polarized; scattering by the moon's surface will reduce this polarization, since it will be multiplied by a coefficient of depolarization which varies inversely as the albedo. Such a depolarization is found for volcanic ashes, and the coefficient may be estimated to amount to about 0.3. The polarization-curve of the earth will therefore have a high maximum for the phase angle 100°, amounting to perhaps 30 per cent, which is interpreted as due principally to scattering by the atmosphere.

More recently, Dollfus (1952) has obtained numerous additional measures of the earthlight. With the aid of a small portable polarimeter, he has studied from the ground the polarization of light reflected by various types of terrains; and from mountains, that of clouds. Further, on free balloon flights he has been able to measure polarization of light returned by the ground; this was done at different altitudes and hence through different thicknesses of atmosphere. From the combined measures obtained, Dollfus found that the atmospheric polarization is by far the largest; but for an extra-terrestrial observer it would be diluted by the intense, but little-polarized, light from the background formed by the ground, the sea, and the clouds. The resulting polarization for the combined terrestrial light may be roughly calculated; for phase angle 90° it is as high as 36 per cent. The amount varies with phase similar to the polarization of the earthlight.

6. INTERCOMPARISON OF THE EARTH, THE TERRESTRIAL PLANETS, AND THE MOON

The photometric, colorimetric, and polarimetric observations of the earthlight indicate large differences between the earth and those other bodies of the solar system which one can observe at all phases: Mercury, Venus, and the moon (cf. Danjon, 1949, 1950). This is seen from the following table:

Planet	Magnitude at Unit Distance from Sun and Observer	Phase Integral	Visual Albedo	C.I.
Mercury...	$-0.21 + 3.80(\tau/100)$ $-2.73(\tau/100)^2 + 2.00(\tau/100)^3$	0.563	0.055	$+1.00$
Venus.....	$-4.14 + 0.09(\tau/100)$ $+2.39(\tau/100)^2 - 0.65(\tau/100)^3$	1.296	.64	$+1.00$
Earth.....	$-3.92 + 1.30(\tau/100)$ $+0.19(\tau/100)^2 + 0.48(\tau/100)^3$	1.095	.40	$+0.37$
Moon.....	$+0.21 + 2.98(\tau/100)$ $-0.78(\tau/100)^2 + 0.90(\tau/100)^3$	0.584	0.073	$+1.10$

The left-hand section contains the phase functions of the four bodies. As has been stated, the terms containing τ, multiplied by $2 \sin \tau \, d\tau$ and integrated from 0 to π, yield the phase integrals. They are tabulated in the next column; they measure the relative importance of the larger phase angles in the total light scattered. By comparison, the value of the phase integral is $\frac{3}{2}$ for a sphere diffusing according to Lambert's law (Russell, 1916, p. 178).

The phase integrals are large for Venus and the earth, which is attributed to the presence of atmospheres on these bodies. They are small for the moon and Mercury, apparently owing to the roughness of their surfaces. The albedos vary in the same direction as the phase integrals.

The earth has the greatest analogy with Venus, although there are notable differences. The albedo of Venus is higher than that of the earth, even when the latter is entirely covered with clouds. Furthermore, the Venus albedo does not show measurable fluctuations, while that of the earth oscillates in a few months between 0.32 and 0.52. On the other hand, the polarization of the total scattered light is much higher for the earth than for Venus. Finally, the earth's color index is much lower than that of Venus, and it changes from $+0.06$ to $+0.67$, while the latter seems constant at $+1.00$. These differences point to very different properties of the two atmospheres. The atmosphere of Venus is always laden with scattering particles spread through a layer of great thickness, while that of the earth can be transparent, hazy, or cloudy, according to the meteorological situation. From this point of view the earth is unique in the solar system.

In summary, the appearance of the earth as a planet is mainly determined by its meteorology. Changes of the surface and its vegetation are probably not conspicuous, at least in visible or ultraviolet light, and much less striking than the seasonal changes of the Martian surface. Since the optical properties of the earth as a whole can be revealed only through the earthlight, it is to be hoped that astronomers and meteorologists will in the future devote more attention to its study.

REFERENCES

ARAGO, F.	1856	*Astr. pop.*, **3**, 480.
DANJON, A.	1928	*Ann. Obs. Strasbourg*, **2**, 165.
	1936	*Ibid.*, **3**, 139.
	1949	*Bull. astr.*, **14**, 315.
	1950	*Ibid.*, **15**, 105.
	1954	*Ibid.*, **17**, 363.
DOLLFUS, A.	1952	*C. R. Acad. Sci., Paris.*, **235**, 1013.
DUBOIS, J.	1942	*Ciel et terre*, **58**, 350.
	1943	*Ibid.*, **59**, 375.
	1944	*L'Astronomie*, **58**, 136.
	1947	*Bull. astr.*, **13**, 193.
FRITZ, S.	1949	*J. Meteorol.*, Vol. **6**, No. 4.
JANSSEN, J.	1881	*C.R. Acad. Sci., Paris*, **92**, 496.
KEPLER, J.	1604	*Astronomiae*, pars optica.
KING, E. S.	1924	*Harvard Circ.*, No. 267.
LYOT, B., and		
DOLLFUS, A.	1949	*C.R. Acad. Sci., Paris*, **228**, 1773.
ÖPIK, E.	1924	*Pub. Obs. Tartu*, Vol. **26**, No. 1.
ORLAWA, N. S.	1941	*Pub. U. Leningrad*, Nos. 82 and 86 (in Russian).
PENNDORF, R.	1937	*Meteorol. Zs.*, **54**, 348.
ROUGIER, G.	1937	*Ann. Obs. Strasbourg*, **3**, 257.
RUSSELL, H. N.	1916	*Ap. J.*, **43**, 180.
VERY, F. W.	1912	*A.N.*, **196**, 269.
	1915	*Ibid.*, **201**, 353.

Subject Index

*Gutenberg's estimates now reduced by factor 100.

Index of Definitions